Body shape	Mass, and x, y, z coordinates of CM	

Ellipsoid:

$$m = \frac{1}{6}\rho\pi abc$$

$$I_{0x} = \frac{1}{20}m(b^2 + c^2)$$

$$I_{0y} = \frac{1}{20}m(a^2 + c^2)$$

$$I_{0z} = \frac{1}{20}m(a^2 + b^2)$$

$$I_{x_1} = \frac{1}{20}m(b^2 + 6c^2)$$

$$I_{y_1} = \frac{1}{20}m(c^2 + 6a^2)$$

$$I_{z_1} = \frac{1}{20}m(b^2 + 6a^2)$$

Paraboloid of revolution:

$$m = \frac{1}{8}\rho\pi d^2 h$$

$$x_c = \frac{2}{3}h$$

$$y_c = z_c = 0$$

$$I_{0x} = I_x = \frac{1}{12}md^2$$

$$I_{0y} = I_{0z} = \frac{1}{72}m(3d^2 + 4h^2)$$

$$I_y = I_z = \frac{1}{24}m(d^2 + 12h^2)$$

$$I_{y_1} = I_{z_1} = \frac{3}{72}m(d^2 + 12h^2)$$

$$I_{x_1} = \frac{1}{3}md^2$$

Rectangular parallelepiped:

$$m = \rho abc$$

$$x_c = \frac{1}{2}a$$

$$y_c = \frac{1}{2}b$$

$$z_c = \frac{1}{2}c$$

$$I_{0x} = \frac{1}{12}m(b^2 + c^2)$$

$$I_{0y} = \frac{1}{12}m(a^2 + c^2)$$

$$I_{0z} = \frac{1}{12}m(a^2 + b^2)$$

$$I_x = \frac{1}{3}m(b^2 + c^2)$$

$$I_y = \frac{1}{3}m(a^2 + c^2)$$

$$I_z = \frac{1}{3}m(a^2 + b^2)$$

$$I_{z_1} = \frac{1}{12}m(4b^2 + c^2)$$

Engineering
Mechanics
Dynamics

Engineering Mechanics
Dynamics

Joseph F. Shelley

Trenton State College at Hillwood Lakes

McGRAW-HILL BOOK COMPANY

New York   St. Louis   San Francisco   Auckland   Bogotá
Hamburg   Johannesburg   London   Madrid
Mexico   Montreal   New Delhi   Panama   Paris
São Paulo   Singapore   Sydney   Tokyo   Toronto

ENGINEERING MECHANICS: DYNAMICS

1 2 3 4 5 6 7 8 9 0   DODO   8 9 8 7 6 5 4 3 2 1 0

Library of Congress Cataloging in Publication Data

Shelley, Joseph F
   Engineering mechanics, dynamics.

   Includes index.
   1. Dynamics. I. Title.
TA352.S53   620.1′04   79-22908
ISBN 0-07-056553-8

This book was set in Times Roman by York Graphic Services, Inc. The editors were Julienne V. Brown and J. W. Maisel; the designer was Albert M. Cetta; the production supervisor was Dominick Petrellese. The drawings were done by Felix Cooper.
R. R. Donnelley & Sons Company was printer and binder.

To
Gabrielle
and
Stefanie, Suzanne,
Matthew, and Meredith

Your sweet love
such wealth brings,
I scorn to change
my state with kings.

and
in memory of
Dr. Hanns Guenther Reissner

Contents

Preface

Engineering mechanics is the study of the effects that forces produce on bodies. It has two major subdivisions: statics, in which the bodies are at rest or are moving with constant velocity; and dynamics, in which the bodies move with varying velocity—so that acceleration becomes a necessary part of the description of dynamics problems. As a general concept, acceleration, which is a vector quantity, is the time rate of change of velocity. The absence of acceleration effects distinguishes statics from dynamics. Dynamics is the first engineering course in the fields of aeronautical, civil, and mechanical engineering and technology. A thorough understanding of the basic principles of this body of knowledge is a necessary prerequisite to further study in mechanical design and analysis, vibrations, control systems, and fluid dynamics.

The subject of dynamics rests upon a very limited number of simply stated physical laws—notably Newton's second law and the law of conservation of energy. Despite this apparent simplicity, dynamics is an inherently complex subject. The central objective is to identify from the physical problem the type of force-motion relation that exists, and then to use the appropriate techniques to obtain the final solution.

In preparing this work, I have attempted the following:

1. To present the basic theory in a straightforward manner.
2. To point out, and emphasize, the potential pitfalls that exist in certain areas of the subject matter.
3. To illustrate the particular theory with one or more example problems.

4. To present a summary section, at the end of each chapter, on the major concepts in the chapter.
5. To provide with each chapter a set of problem assignments, of varying degrees of complexity, that illustrates the different aspects of the theory.

An attempt has been made, wherever possible, to give a physical, or "hardware," flavor to the example problems and problem assignments, with major emphasis on obtaining useful technical solutions. In many cases, the effect on the solution of varying one, or more, of the initial conditions of the problem is shown and discussed. In the more difficult areas of the subject matter, every attempt has been made to anticipate the reader's questions. Throughout the text, the units are equally divided between the U. S. Customary System (USCS) and the International System (SI). Answers to odd-numbered problem assignments are provided at the end of the text.

The general organization of the text is as follows. Chapter 15 considers the motion of particles without regard for the forces that produce these motions, referred to as the subject of kinematics. Chapter 16 introduces particle dynamics, where the relation between the force that acts on a particle and the resulting motion is obtained. Chapter 17 presents the kinematics of plane motion of a rigid body. Chapter 18 digresses from the main stream of dynamics to introduce centroids and mass moments of inertia of rigid bodies. The results from Chapters 17 and 18 are then used in Chapter 19, the dynamics of rigid bodies in plane motion, where the relation between the forces and moments that act on a body and the resulting translational and angular motions are obtained. Chapter 20 considers the use of work-energy methods to obtain solutions to problems in particle and rigid-body dynamics.

Chapter 21 considers the highly significant technical problem of impact of bodies, and impulse-momentum solutions. Chapter 22 covers three-dimensional dynamic motion of rigid body with emphasis on rotating unbalance, dynamic balancing, and gyroscopic moments. Chapter 23 is a treatment of damped and undamped free and forced vibration of a single degree of freedom mechanical systems. Chapter 24, the final chapter, considers the motion of a body subjected to viscous, or quadratic resistance, drag forces. Chapters 15 through 21 contain the material usually found in a first course in dynamics. The remaining chapters may be studied in any order, depending on the emphasis desired.

The mathematics used in this text includes trigonometry, algebra, and elementary differential and integral calculus. The derivative is used principally in the definitions of velocity and acceleration; and the integral is used primarily to interpret the area under displacement, velocity and acceleration curves. A very limited number of problems require formal differentiation or integration techniques for their solution.

It is difficult to acknowledge formally all the people who have offered comments and suggestions, and who have influenced this work. The following individuals, however, deserve special mention. Professor Kenneth Schneider, California State Polytechnic University at Pomona, served as consulting editor on this project from its inception. The barriers of distance between Pomona and the author's home in Princeton, New Jersey did not prevent the editor and the author from having numerous discussions and meetings at all stages of the work. Professor Schneider's constructive suggestions and insights are woven throughout the entire fabric of this book. Professors Peter Basch, Pratt Institute, Brooklyn, New York; John Pautz, Middlesex County College, Edison, New Jersey; Emil Yanchula, George Brown University, Canada; and Dean Gerald Seeley, Tri-State University, Angola, Indiana formally served as reviewers. The work was also reviewed by Professors Chia- Ching Feng and Clay Carlisle of Trenton State College. Invaluable comments, from the point of view of the student, were offered by Kenneth Lore and David Davidson, undergraduates at Trenton State College. The opinion of colleagues in the profession was also sought, and comments on the manuscript were offered by Dr. Frederick Tepper, team leader, Mechanical Analysis Staff, U. S. Army Research and Development Command, Dover, New Jersey, and Dr. Donald Mack, Program Manager for Technical Education, General Electric Company, Fairfield, Connecticut. James Scullin, a friend and consulting engineer, performed invaluable service in working out all the problem assignments as a check on the author's computations. Finally, the manuscript was typed completely, correctly, and cheerfully by Anna Waite.

The author also wishes to express his appreciation to the McGraw-Hill Book Company for their high level of enthusiasm and support for the project. B. J. Clark served as Editor-in-Chief and Julienne V. Brown as editor. Felix Cooper fashioned the illustrations with fertile imagination and deft fingers. Jack Maisel, as editing supervisor, attended to the details both large and small required to transform the author's manuscript to its final book form, and his accomplishment was to make the whole greater than the sum of its parts.

Preparation of a work such as this, and its companion volume *Engineering Mechanics: Statics,* is a very subjective exercise in creation. It reflects many judgments on the part of the author with respect to organization of material and emphasis of topics. As with any other textbook, it receives its ultimate review by the readership only after publication. This author welcomes comments of any kind from the readers, and an attempt will be made in all cases to acknowledge such communications.

Joseph F. Shelley

15

Kinetics and Particles

15.1 INTRODUCTION

Kinematics is the science which studies the motions of particles and bodies, *without concern for the forces which produce these motions*. A particle is a physical body which has mass and whose physical dimensions are assumed to be vanishingly small. The consequence of this assumption is that all rotation effects, of the body which is represented as a particle, about any axis through the body may be neglected. The particle may thus be thought of as a *point* in space.

If a physical element is not assumed to be a particle, it is referred to as a *body*. All the bodies considered in this text are assumed to be rigid. In a rigid body, the distance between any two points is always the same, no matter what type of force system acts on the body. Thus a *rigid body* may be viewed as a body with unchanging dimensions. It is left as an exercise for the reader to show why the assumption of rigidity has no meaning when applied to a particle.

Kinetics studies the relationships between the forces which act on a particle, or a rigid body, and the motions of the particle or rigid body. It is apparent that *a necessary prerequisite for the study of kinetics is the study of kinematics*. *Dynamics* includes both kinematics and kinetics.

In view of the above discussion, a more specific description of the subject matter of this text would be "particle and rigid body dynamics."

Two general types of particle motion may be identified. The first type is referred to as rectilinear translation, and this type of

motion is straight-line motion. In Fig. 15.1 a particle, shown
by the dark circle, is constrained to move along the straight line
ab. The motion of the particle in this case is described as
rectilinear translation.

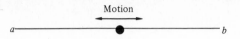

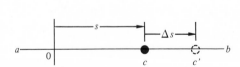

Fig. 15.1

The second general type of particle motion is called curvilinear translation. In Fig. 15.2, the particle is constrained to move
along the curved path *ab*. For this case, the motion of the
particle is described as curvilinear translation. It is emphasized that, in *both* of the above definitions, the term *translation*
implies that no rotation, or angular motion, effects are required
for the complete kinematic description of the motion of the
particle. The reason for this, from the definition of a particle,
is that all dimensions of the particle are effectively zero.

There are two general types of problems in dynamics. In the
first type, the motion of the particle or body is known and the
forces or moments which produce this motion are to be found.
In the second general class of problems in dynamics, the forces
or moments which act on the particle or body are known and it
is desired to find the motions which result from the application
of these force effects. This latter type of problem is the one
usually encountered in the solution of engineering problems in
dynamics.

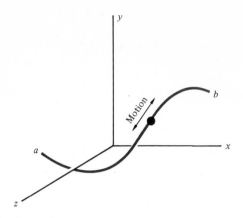

Fig. 15.2

15.2 GENERAL RECTILINEAR MOTION

Figure 15.3 shows a particle which is constrained to move along
the straight line *ab*. The *displacement,* or position, of the
particle is the location of the particle with respect to a fixed
reference point. For the situation shown in Fig. 15.3, the fixed
reference point is 0. The coordinate *s* describes the displacement of the particle with respect to this point. The positive
sense of the coordinate *s* is the sense of increasing *s*, or to the
right in the figure. If a value of *s* is positive, the particle is
located to the right of the origin. If this coordinate has a
negative value, the particle is located to the left of the origin.

From the above description, it follows that the displacement
is a vector quantity. The *magnitude* of the displacement is the
magnitude of the value of the *s* coordinate. The *direction* of
the displacement is along the line *ab*. Finally, the *sense* of the
displacement is determined by the sign of the value of *s*. There
is a single, known direction in rectilinear translation problems.
Thus, vector quantities in these types of problems will *not* be
indicated in boldface type.

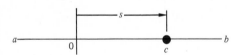

Fig. 15.3

The *velocity v* of a particle is defined to be the first time
derivative of the displacement. The velocity may be thought
of as the time rate of change of displacement.

In Fig. 15.4, the particle moves from *c* to *c'* during the time
interval Δt. The average velocity v_{avg} is defined to be

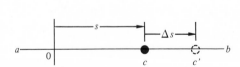

Fig. 15.4

474

$$v_{\text{avg}} = \frac{\Delta s}{\Delta t} \tag{15.1}$$

The time interval Δt is now allowed to decrease without limit. The formal definition of the velocity v of the particle is then

$$v = \lim_{\Delta t \to 0} \frac{\Delta s}{\Delta t} = \frac{ds}{dt} \tag{15.2}$$

Throughout this text, a dot over a quantity will indicate the first time derivative of this quantity, and two dots will represent a second time derivative. Thus,

$$v = \frac{ds}{dt} = \dot{s} \tag{15.3}$$

A very important observation will now be made about the relationship between the positive sense of the velocity and the positive sense of the coordinate s. The term Δs, by definition, is

$$\Delta s = s_{c'} - s_c \tag{15.4}$$

Since $s_{c'} > s_c$, Δs *is positive* in the same sense as s. Δt is always positive, since time may only increase. From consideration of Eq. (15.2), it then follows that *the velocity is positive in the same sense as the displacement coordinate.* Thus, the choice of a positive sense for the displacement automatically establishes the positive sense of the velocity.

If the velocity of the particle in Fig. 15.4 is positive, then the particle moves to the right. If this velocity is negative, the particle moves to the left. These conclusions are independent of the position of the particle along line ab.

The units of velocity are length divided by time. Typical U.S. Customary System (USCS) units for velocity are feet per second or inches per second. In SI units, the velocity is expressed in meters per second.

The term *speed* is a *scalar* quantity used to describe the *magnitude* of the velocity.

Figure 15.5 shows the two velocities of the particle at the locations c and c'. The *acceleration a* of the particle is defined to be the first time derivative of the velocity. The acceleration may thus be thought of as describing the time rate of change of velocity. The formal definition of the acceleration of the particle is

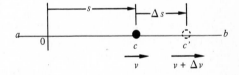

Fig. 15.5

$$a = \lim_{\Delta t \to 0} \frac{\Delta v}{\Delta t} = \frac{dv}{dt} \tag{15.5}$$

The above results may be expanded further as

$$a = \frac{dv}{dt} = \frac{d}{dt}(v) = \frac{d}{dt}\left(\frac{ds}{dt}\right) = \frac{d^2s}{dt^2} = \ddot{s} \tag{15.6}$$

where two dots over a variable represent the second time derivative of the quantity. The fundamental units of acceleration, from Eq. (15.5), are velocity divided by time, or length divided by time squared. In the U.S. Customary System, typical acceleration units are feet per second squared or inches per second squared. The SI units for acceleration are meters per second squared.

From Eq. (15.5) it may be seen that the positive senses of a and v are the same. As was shown earlier, the positive senses of v and s are the same. Thus, *the positive sense of the acceleration is always the same as the positive sense of the coordinate s.* It follows from the discussion that the choice of a positive sense for the displacement coordinate automatically establishes the *same* positive senses for the velocity and the acceleration. The term *deceleration* is commonly used to describe an acceleration of negative sense. The average value a_{avg} of the acceleration in the region of motion between c and c' in Fig. 15.5 is

$$a_{avg} = \frac{\Delta v}{\Delta t} \tag{15.7}$$

Example 15.1 A particle moves with rectilinear translation. From a prior calculation, the displacement of the particle is known to be

$$s = (100 - 4t^2) \tag{15.8}$$

where t is in seconds and s is in meters.

a Find the general forms of the velocity and acceleration of the particle.

b Find the values of the displacement, velocity, and acceleration when $t = 0$. Show these results on the axis of motion.

c Do the same as in part b for the time when the particle passes through the origin.

d Find the value of the average velocity for the interval between $t = 0$ and the time found in part c.

e Where is the particle when $t = 10s$? What are the values of the velocity and acceleration at this time? Sketch these results on the axis of motion.

Solution

a The general forms of the velocity and acceleration are

$$v = \dot{s} = \frac{ds}{dt} = \frac{d}{dt}(100 - 4t^2) = -8t \text{ m/s} \tag{15.9}$$

$$a = \ddot{s} = \frac{d}{dt}(\dot{s}) = \frac{d}{dt}(-8t) = -8 \text{ m/s}^2 \tag{15.10}$$

b When $t = 0$,

$$s = 100 - 4(0) = 100 \text{ m} \tag{15.11}$$

$$v = \dot{s} = -8(0) = 0 \tag{15.12}$$

$$a = \ddot{s} = \dot{v} = -8 \text{ m/s}^2 \tag{15.13}$$

The results are shown in Fig. 15.6.

#15.3 $s = 2t^2 + 9t + 10$

a) $v = \frac{ds}{dt} = 4t + 9 = \dot{s}$

$a = \frac{dv}{dt} = 4 \text{ ft/s}^2 = \dot{v} = \ddot{s}$

b) $t = 0$ & $t = 4$

$v|_{t=0} = 0 + 9 = 9 \text{ ft/s}$ $v|_{t=4} = (4)(4) + 9 = 25 \text{ ft/s}$

$a|_{t=0} = a|_{t=4} = 4 \text{ ft/s}^2$

$s|_{t=0} = 10 \text{ ft}$ $s|_{t=4} = (2)(16) + 36 + 10 = 78 \text{ ft}$

c) $v_{avg} = \frac{\Delta s}{\Delta t} = \frac{s_f - s_i}{T_f - T_i} = \frac{78 - 10}{4 - 0} = 17 \text{ ft/sec}$

$a_{avg} = \frac{\Delta v}{\Delta t} = \frac{v_f - v_i}{T_f - T_i} = \frac{25 - 9}{4 - 0} = 4 \text{ ft/s}^2$

d) $0 \le t \le 4$ sec ; is $v = 0$ ever?

$v = 4t + 9 = 0$

$t = -\frac{9}{4}$ can't be neg.; vel. is

o better. $0 \to 4$ sec

e) $s = 2t^2 + 9t + 10 = 0$

$t = -\frac{9}{2}, -2.6$

can't be neg, ; never passes through o

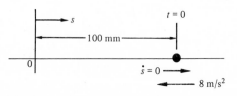

Fig. 15.6

c When the particle passes through the origin, $s = 0$. From Eqs. (15.8) through (15.10),

$$0 = 100 - 4t^2 \qquad t = 5\text{ s} \qquad (15.14)$$

$$v = -8t = -8(5) = -40\text{ m/s} \qquad (15.15)$$

$$a = -8\text{ m/s}^2 \qquad (15.16)$$

These results are shown in Fig. 15.7.

d The average velocity between $t = 0$ and $t = 5$ s is

$$v_{\text{avg}} = \frac{\Delta s}{\Delta t} = \frac{s|_{t=5} - s|_{t=0}}{5 - 0} = \frac{0 - 100}{5} = -20\text{ m/s} \quad (15.17)$$

At the beginning of this interval the velocity is zero. At the end of the interval, when $t = 5$ s, the velocity has a magnitude of 40 m/s. It may be seen that the average value of the velocity is representative of *neither* of these two endpoints. This example illustrates that *caution must be exercised in using average values to describe a problem.* The average value of velocity will more closely approach the true value of the velocity as the time interval Δt decreases and approaches zero.

e When $t = 10$ s,

$$s = 100 - 4t^2 = 100 - 4(10)^2 = -300\text{ m} \qquad (15.18)$$

$$v = -8(10) = -80\text{ m/s} \qquad (15.19)$$

$$a = -8\text{ m/s}^2 \qquad (15.20)$$

These values are shown in Fig. 15.8.

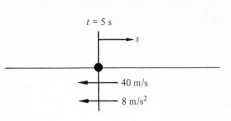

Fig. 15.7

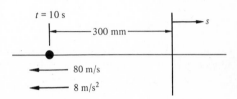

Fig. 15.8

15.3 GRAPHICAL INTERPRETATION OF DISPLACEMENT, VELOCITY, AND ACCELERATION DIAGRAMS FOR RECTILINEAR MOTION

The relationships among displacement, velocity, acceleration, and time, for a particle in rectilinear translation, may be plotted to show graphically the variations in these quantities. These curves are referred to as *motion diagrams*. The fundamental definition of velocity, from Eq. (15.2), is

$$v = \frac{ds}{dt} \qquad (15.21)$$

It follows from the above equation that the *velocity is equal to the slope of the displacement-time curve.* Equation (15.21) may be written in the form

$$ds = v\,dt \qquad (15.22)$$

$$\int_{s_1}^{s_2} ds = \int_{t_1}^{t_2} v\,dt \qquad (15.23)$$

$$s_2 - s_1 = \int_{t_1}^{t_2} v\,dt \qquad (15.24)$$

477

where 1 and 2 represent the endpoints of a particular interval of interest along the axis of motion. The term on the right side of Eq. (15.24) may be recognized as the area under the velocity curve between points 1 and 2. Furthermore, this area is equal to the *change, $s_2 - s_1$, in the displacement s* over this interval. The graphical interpretation of these results is shown in Fig. 15.9.

The fundamental definition of the acceleration, for the case of rectilinear translation, is

$$a = \frac{dv}{dt} \tag{15.25}$$

It may be seen from the above equation that the *acceleration is equal to the slope of the velocity–time curve.* This equation may be written in the form

$$dv = a\,dt \tag{15.26}$$

$$\int_{v_1}^{v_2} dv = \int_{t_1}^{t_2} a\,dt \tag{15.27}$$

$$v_2 - v_1 = \int_{t_1}^{t_2} a\,dt \tag{15.28}$$

The limits of integration indicated by the numbers 1 and 2 have the same interpretation as before, as the endpoints of the interval of interest along the axis of motion. The term on the right

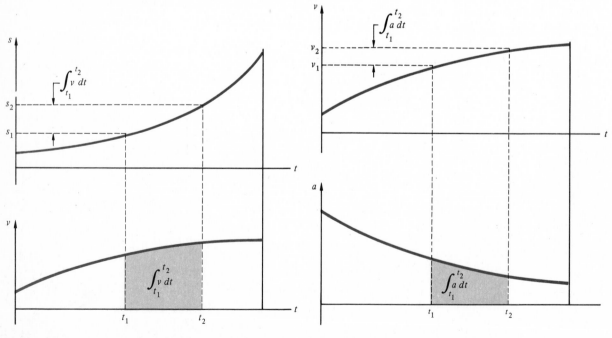

Fig. 15.9   Fig. 15.10

side of Eq. (15.28) is the area under the acceleration-time curve between locations 1 and 2. It may thus be concluded that the area under the acceleration-vs.-time curve between two points 1 and 2 is equal to the change, $v_2 - v_1$, in the velocity of the particle as it moves from the first to the second point. The above effect is shown graphically in Fig. 15.10.

Before the above results are used to solve problems, positive and negative slopes of plane curves will be reviewed briefly. Figure 15.11a shows a plane curve referenced to a set of xy coordinates. The slope of the curve at a given point is found by using the tangent of a typical triangle, such as triangle abc in the figure. In order to move from point a to point b, one could follow path ac and then path cb. For this case both Δx and Δy are positive, since the sense of the travel along both legs of the triangle is in the two positive coordinate senses. The slope of the curve shown in Fig. 15.11b has the form

$$\frac{dy}{dx} = \lim_{\Delta x \to 0} \frac{\Delta y}{\Delta x} = \frac{+}{+} = + \tag{15.29}$$

It follows that the slope of the curve in Fig. 15.11 is *positive*. It may also be seen that the slope *decreases in magnitude* as one advances along the curve in the positive x coordinate sense. If the curve were traversed from b to a, along the two legs of the triangle, then both Δx and Δy are negative, since the travel is in the negative coordinate senses. Equation (15.29) would then be the quotient of two negative values; and it would again be concluded that the slope is positive.

Figure 15.12 shows another shape of curve which has a positive slope. In this case, however, it may be concluded that *the magnitude of the slope increases* as one moves along the curve in the positive x coordinate sense.

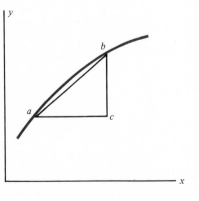

(a)

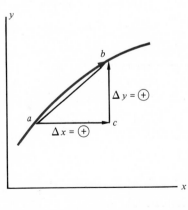

(b)

Fig. 15.11

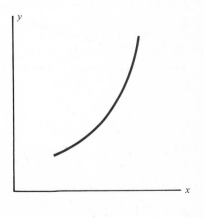

Fig. 15.12

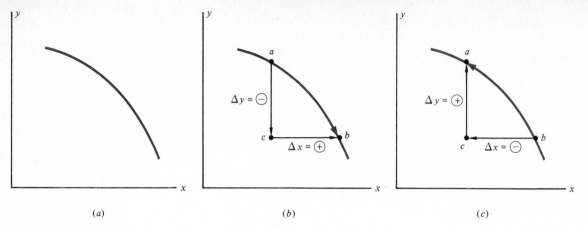

Fig. 15.13

Figure 15.13a shows a curve and orientation which are unlike the previous two curves. If the curve is traversed in the sense *a* to *b*, the slope has the form

$$\frac{dy}{dx} = \lim_{\Delta x \to 0} \frac{\Delta y}{\Delta x} = \frac{-}{+} = -$$ (15.30)

The alternate sense of movement along the curve is from *b* to *a*. For this case,

$$\frac{dy}{dx} = \lim_{\Delta x \to 0} \frac{\Delta y}{\Delta x} = \frac{+}{-} = -$$ (15.31)

It follows that the slope of the curve shown in Fig. 15.13 is negative. It may also be seen from this figure that the magnitude of the slope increases as one moves along the curve in the positive *x* coordinate sense. A rigorous mathematical description says that *the slope of the curve is decreasing,* since the change in the slope is from one negative quantity to a negative quantity of larger magnitude.

A fourth possible curve is shown in Fig. 15.14, and it may be concluded that this curve has a negative slope. As one advances in the positive *x* coordinate sense, the value of the slope goes from one negative quantity to a negative quantity of smaller magnitude. Such a change in a negative slope is an *increase.*

These results may be conveniently summarized in the diagram shown in Fig. 15.15. The four quadrants of the circle represent the four general shapes of a plane curve.

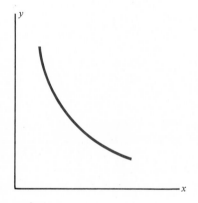

Fig. 15.14

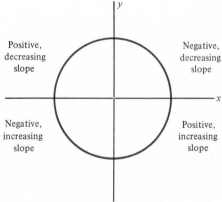

Fig. 15.15

Example 15.2 Using graphical methods, find the solution to parts *c* and *e* of Example 15.1.

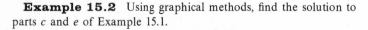

480

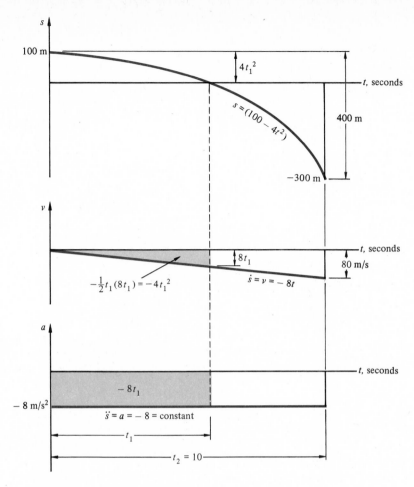

Fig. 15.16

Solution The displacement, velocity, and acceleration functions were found in Example 15.1 to be

$$s = (100 - 4t^2) \text{ m} \qquad (15.32)$$

$$v = -8t \text{ m/s} \qquad (15.33)$$

$$a = -8 \text{ m/s}^2 \qquad (15.34)$$

These three functions are plotted in Fig. 15.16.

When the particle passes through the origin, $s = 0$ and the corresponding time is designated t_1. A dashed line, corresponding to $t = t_1$, is drawn through the motion diagrams of Fig. 15.16. The area under the acceleration curve, over the interval 0 to t_1, is $-8t_1$. This area is equal to the change in the velocity over the same interval. The area under the velocity diagram over the same interval is $-4t_1^2$, as shown in the figure. When this area is added to the displacement value at $t = 0$, the result is zero, so that

$$100 - 4t_1^2 = 0 \qquad t_1 = 5 \text{ s} \qquad (15.35)$$

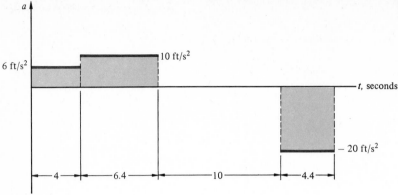

Fig. 15.17

For the interval from 0 to 10 s, the area under the acceleration curve is $-8(10) = -80$ m/s. This value is equal to the change in velocity over the same interval. The area under the triangular velocity diagram is then $\frac{1}{2}(10)(-80) = -400$ m. When this value is added to the initial displacement value of 100 m, the final result for the displacement at 10 s is -300 m.

Example 15.3 A vehicle starts from zero velocity and moves along a straight, horizontal roadway. The rectilinear acceleration of the vehicle is shown in Fig. 15.17.

a Using graphical methods, construct the velocity and displacement diagrams for the motion of the vehicle.

b What is the maximum value of the velocity attained by the vehicle?

c How far has the vehicle traveled by the time it comes to rest?

d Find the average velocity of the vehicle over the entire interval of motion.

Solution

a The acceleration diagram is redrawn in Fig. 15.18. Since this diagram consists of constant values of acceleration, the velocity diagram must consist of curves of constant slope, or straight-line elements. The areas under the three distinct portions of the acceleration diagram are shown in the figure. These values, then, are the changes in velocity over the corresponding time intervals.

The velocity diagram construction, if one observes that the vehicle starts at zero initial velocity, is shown in Fig. 15.18. Since the values of acceleration are positive constants in the first two intervals, the corresponding velocity diagram has positive slopes in these intervals. It also follows that the slope of the velocity diagram in the second interval is steeper than that in the first interval.

Since the last acceleration value is a negative constant, the corresponding velocity diagram for this interval is a straight line with a negative slope.

The areas under the velocity diagram are computed next, and they are the change in the displacements over the corresponding intervals.

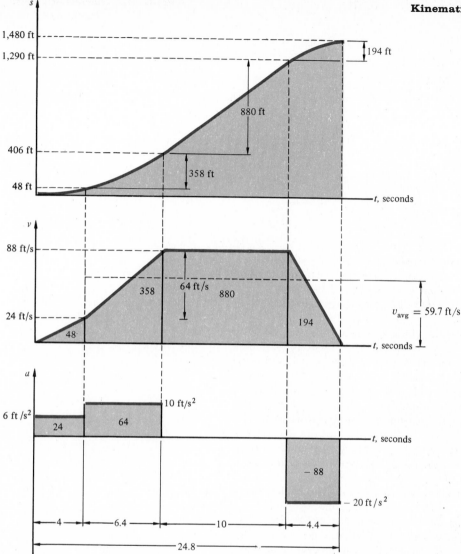

Fig. 15.18

Then the slopes of the displacement curve are determined from the magnitudes of the velocities and from whether these magnitudes are increasing or decreasing.

b The maximum value of the velocity attained by the vehicle is 88 ft/s.

c The total distance traveled by the vehicle is 1,480 ft.

d The average velocity v_{avg} of the vehicle over the entire interval of motion is a constant value shown as the dashed line in the velocity diagram of Fig. 15.18,

$$v_{avg} = \frac{1,480}{24.8} = 59.7 \text{ ft/s} \qquad (15.36)$$

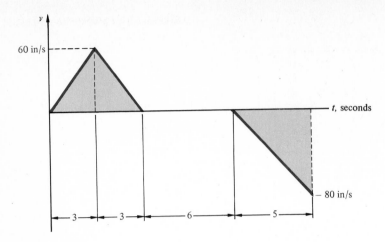

Fig. 15.19

Example 15.4 An experimental vehicle moves along a straight
track with the velocity diagram shown in Fig. 15.19.
  a Sketch the acceleration and displacement diagrams.
  b Discuss the location of the vehicle when $6 \text{ s} \leq t \leq 12 \text{ s}$.
  c Find the position and acceleration of the vehicle when $t = 17 \text{ s}$.

Solution
  a The velocity diagram is redrawn in Fig. 15.20. The acceleration
diagram is constructed first. Since the velocity diagram consists of
straight-line elements, the corresponding acceleration values must be
constant over the intervals. The slope of the velocity diagram in the
first interval is $60/3 = 20 \text{ in/s}^2$, and this is the value of the acceleration. In the second interval, the slope of the velocity diagram is
$-60/3 = -20 \text{ in/s}^2$. The minus sign is written to recognize that this
portion of the velocity diagram has a negative slope. In the last
portion of the velocity diagram the slope, which is the acceleration, is
$-80/5 = -16 \text{ in/s}^2$. The areas under the velocity diagram are
computed next, and they are used to sketch the displacement curve.
  b During $6 \text{ s} \leq t \leq 12 \text{ s}$, the vehicle is at the fixed location
$s = 180 \text{ in}$. The velocity and acceleration are zero during this time.
  c At $t = 17 \text{ s}$, the displacement of the vehicle is given by
$s \doteq -20 \text{ in}$. The corresponding value of the acceleration is
-16 in/s^2. Thus, the value of the deceleration is 16 in/s^2.

15.4 RECTILINEAR MOTION WITH
CONSTANT ACCELERATION

A very important type of motion is rectilinear translation with
constant acceleration. This type of motion describes the case
of a freely falling body in the earth's gravitational field, in the
absence of any frictional retarding effects. It also describes the
motion of a particle which is acted upon by *a resultant force
which has a constant value.*

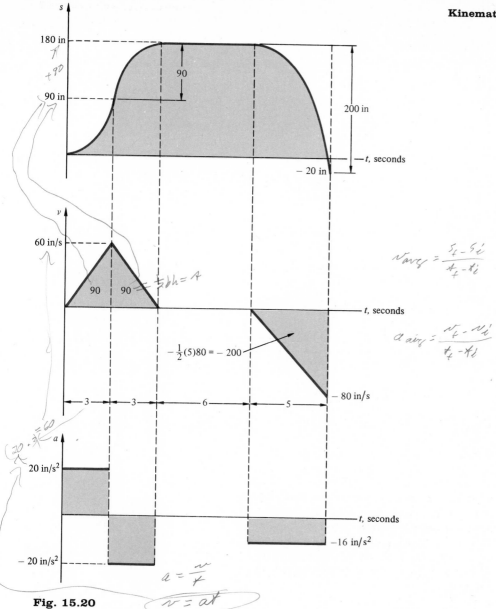

Fig. 15.20

The *constant* magnitude of the acceleration will be designated a, so that

$$a = \frac{dv}{dt} = \text{constant} \qquad (15.37)$$

The integral form of the above equation is

$$\int_{v_1}^{v_2} dv = \int_{t_1}^{t_2} a \, dt \qquad (15.38)$$

As before, the numbers 1 and 2 represent the endpoints of the time interval under consideration. Since a is a constant, it may be moved outside the integral sign:

$$\int_{v_1}^{v_2} dv = a \int_{t_1}^{t_2} dt \qquad (15.39)$$

This equation is integrated, and

$$v \Big|_{v_1}^{v_2} = at \Big|_{t_1}^{t_2} \qquad (15.40)$$

$$v_2 - v_1 = a(t_2 - t_1) \qquad (15.41)$$

Equation (15.41) is a perfectly general relationship among the velocity, acceleration, and times of the problem. This result will now be put into a more convenient form. The initial time of the problem is t_1, with the value

$$t_1 = 0 \qquad (15.42)$$

The corresponding velocity v_1 will be defined to be the *initial velocity,* designated by v_0, so that

$$v_1 = v_0 \qquad (15.43)$$

The velocity and time v_2 and t_2 at the end of the interval of consideration will be written as

$$v_2 = v \qquad (15.44)$$

$$t_2 = t \qquad (15.45)$$

With the above changes in notation, Eq. (15.41) appears as

$$v = v_0 + at \qquad (15.46)$$

Equation (15.46) is the first of three basic equations used to characterize the problem of rectilinear motion with constant acceleration. v_0 is the initial velocity at $t = 0$, and v is the velocity at a later time t. v_0, v, and a may have positive or negative values. If v and a are assumed to be positive, the corresponding velocity and acceleration diagrams would have the forms shown in Fig. 15.21.

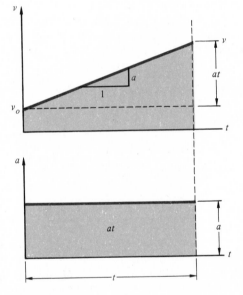

Fig. 15.21

The displacement and velocity are related by

$$v = \frac{ds}{dt} \qquad (15.47)$$

The integral form of this equation is

$$\int_{s_1}^{s_2} ds = \int_{t_1}^{t_2} v \, dt \qquad (15.48)$$

The displacement s_1, corresponding to $t_1 = 0$, is the initial displacement, designated by the term s_0. The terms s_2 and t_2 will be taken as

$$s_2 = s \tag{15.49}$$

$$t_2 = t \tag{15.50}$$

Equation (15.46) is substituted into Eq. (15.48), with the result

$$\int_{s_0}^{s} ds = \int_{0}^{t} (v_0 + at)\, dt \tag{15.51}$$

$$s \Big|_{s_0}^{s} = (v_0 t + \tfrac{1}{2}at^2) \Big|_{0}^{t} \tag{15.52}$$

$$s - s_0 = v_0 t + \tfrac{1}{2}at^2 \tag{15.53}$$

$$s = s_0 + v_0 t + \tfrac{1}{2}at^2 \tag{15.54}$$

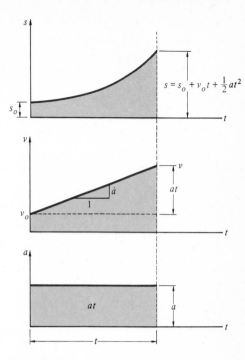

Fig. 15.22

This result is the *second* basic equation for the solution of rectilinear motion problems with constant acceleration. s_0 is the initial displacement at time $t = 0$, and s is the displacement at a later time t. All the terms in this equation, except t, may have positive or negative values. In many problems the reference point of the coordinate s may be chosen to make $s_0 = 0$.

If s_0, v_0, and a are assumed to be positive, the displacement, velocity, and acceleration diagrams would have the forms shown in Fig. 15.22.

If t is eliminated from Eqs. (15.46) and (15.54), the result is

$$v^2 = v_0^2 + 2a(s - s_0) \tag{15.55}$$

Equations (15.46), (15.54), and (15.55) are the *three basic equations* used in the solution of all problems in rectilinear translation with constant acceleration. These three equations are repeated below.

$$v = v_0 + at \tag{15.56}$$

$$s = s_0 + v_0 t + \tfrac{1}{2}at^2 \tag{15.57}$$

$$v^2 = v_0^2 + 2a(s - s_0) \tag{15.58}$$

The only requirement for using the above equations is that *the acceleration must have a constant value.*

For the case of a freely falling body, *the magnitude of the acceleration a is equal to the magnitude g of the acceleration of the gravitational field.* If the coordinate axis has a sense which is upward with respect to the surface of the earth, then

$$a = -g \tag{15.59}$$

The three equations above then have the forms

$$v = v_0 - gt \tag{15.60}$$

$$s = s_0 + v_0 t - \tfrac{1}{2}gt^2 \tag{15.61}$$

$$v^2 = v_0^2 - 2g(s - s_0) \tag{15.62}$$

487

The value of g in USCS units is 32.2 ft/s², or 386 in/s². In SI units, the value of g is 9.81 m/s².

In the following examples, all frictional resistance effects of air on the particles are neglected.

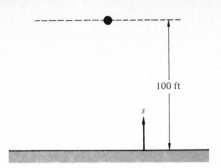

Fig. 15.23

Example 15.5 A particle initially at rest is dropped from a height of 100 ft. Find the velocity with which it strikes the ground and the time of flight.

Solution The definition of the coordinate system is shown in Fig. 15.23. The initial conditions of the problem are described by

$$s_0 = 100 \text{ ft} \qquad v_0 = 0 \qquad t = 0 \tag{15.63}$$

When the particle strikes the ground, $s = 0$. Using Eq. (15.62), we get

$$v^2 = v_0^2 - 2g(s - s_0) \tag{15.64}$$
$$= -2g(-s_0) \tag{15.65}$$
$$= -2(32.2)(-100) \qquad v = \pm 80.2 \text{ ft/s} \tag{15.66}$$

From physical considerations, the minus sign is used in Eq. (15.66). The formal solution for the velocity with which the particle strikes the ground is

$$v = -80.2 \text{ ft/s} \tag{15.67}$$

The time of flight is found from Eq. (15.60) as

$$v = v_0 - gt \qquad -80.2 = 0 - 32.2t \qquad t = 2.49 \text{ s} \tag{15.68}$$

An alternate way of solving for the time of flight is to use Eq. (15.61):

$$s = s_0 + v_0 t - \tfrac{1}{2}gt^2 \tag{15.69}$$
$$0 = 100 + 0 - \tfrac{1}{2}(32.2)t^2 \qquad t = 2.49 \text{ s} \tag{15.70}$$

This result serves as a check on the value obtained in Eq. (15.68).

Example 15.6 With what minimum value of initial velocity v_0 must the particle in Example 15.5 be projected downward if the total time of flight is not to exceed 2 s?

Solution The conditions are

$$s_0 = 100 \text{ ft} \qquad s = 0 \qquad t = 2 \text{ s} \tag{15.71}$$

Using Eq. (15.61), we have

$$s = s_0 + v_0 t - \tfrac{1}{2}gt^2 \tag{15.72}$$
$$0 = 100 + v_0(2) - \tfrac{1}{2}(32.2)(2^2) \qquad v_0 = -17.8 \text{ ft/s} \tag{15.73}$$

The negative sign in Eq. (15.73) is consistent with the physical problem, since the particle must be projected *downward,* in the negative coordinate sense.

Example 15.7 It is desired to have the particle in Example 15.5 be in flight for exactly 3 s. What is the required initial velocity of the particle, if it is launched from the height of 100 ft?

Solution The conditions are

$$s_0 = 100 \text{ ft} \qquad s = 0 \qquad t = 3 \text{ s} \qquad (15.74)$$

Using Eq. (15.61), we find

$$s = s_0 + v_0 t - \tfrac{1}{2}gt^2 \qquad (15.75)$$

$$0 = 100 + v_0(3) - \tfrac{1}{2}(32.2)(3^2) \qquad v_0 = 15.0 \text{ ft/s} \qquad (15.76)$$

In this case, the particle would have to be projected *upward* in order to gain the extra time in flight.

Example 15.8 A person stands on a balcony, as shown in Fig. 15.24, and throws a ball vertically upward with an initial velocity of 8 m/s. At the instant the ball leaves the person's hand, it is 18 m above the ground.
  a Find the maximum height reached by the ball during its flight.
  b At what time is this maximum height reached?
  c Find the velocity when the ball passes a point 18 m above the ground.
  d With what velocity does the ball strike the ground?
  e What is the total time of flight?

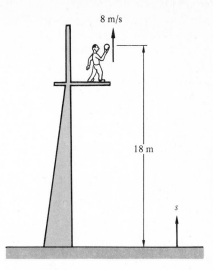

Fig. 15.24

Solution The initial conditions of the ball are

$$s_0 = 18 \text{ m} \qquad v_0 = 8 \text{ m/s} \qquad (15.77)$$

a When the maximum height is reached, $v = 0$.

$$v^2 = v_0^2 - 2g(s - s_0) \qquad (15.78)$$
$$0 = 8^2 - 2(9.81)(s - 18) \qquad s = 21.3 \text{ m} \qquad (15.79)$$

b The time at which the maximum height is reached is found from

$$v = v_0 - gt \qquad (15.80)$$

$$0 = 8 - 9.81t \qquad t = 0.815 \text{ s} \qquad (15.81)$$

c When the ball passes a point 18 m above the ground, $s = s_0 = 18$ m. Thus,

$$v^2 = v_0^2 - 2g(s - s_0) \qquad (15.82)$$

$$= v_0^2 - 2g(0) \qquad v = \pm v_0 = \pm 8 \text{ m/s} \qquad (15.83)$$

The positive value of v corresponds to the initial upward velocity of the ball. When the ball passes the 18-m height again, on its way down, its velocity is

$$v = -8 \text{ m/s} \qquad (15.84)$$

The minus sign is consistent with the fact that the ball is moving downward.

d When the ball strikes the ground, $s = 0$.

$$v^2 = v_0^2 - 2g(s - s_0) \qquad (15.85)$$

$$= 8^2 - 2(9.81)(0 - 18) \qquad v = \pm 20.4 \text{ m/s} \qquad (15.86)$$

The positive answer above is an extraneous root, and the velocity with which the ball strikes the ground is

$$v = -20.4 \text{ m/s} \qquad (15.87)$$

489

e The total time of flight may be found by using the result for part *d*. The time for the ball to fall from the maximum height to the ground, using $v_0 = 0$ as the initial condition for this part of the example, is found from

$$v = v_0 - gt \tag{15.88}$$

$$-20.4 = 0 - 9.81t \qquad t = 2.08 \text{ s} \tag{15.89}$$

The time to reach the maximum height was given in Eq. (15.81) as 0.815 s. The time t_T for the entire flight is then

$$t_T = 2.08 + 0.815 = 2.90 \text{ s} \tag{15.90}$$

An alternate way of solving for the total time of flight is to use Eq. (15.61):

$$s = s_0 + v_0 t - \tfrac{1}{2}gt^2 \tag{15.91}$$

$$0 = 18 + 8t - \tfrac{1}{2}(9.81t^2) \tag{15.92}$$

$$4.91t^2 - 8t - 18 = 0 \tag{15.93}$$

The two roots of Eq. (15.93) are

$$t = 2.90 \text{ s}, \ -1.27 \text{ s} \tag{15.94}$$

The negative root is discarded, so the total flight time is 2.90 s. It may be observed that the first solution in part *e* yields more information about the problem than Eq. (15.94).

15.5 PLANE CURVILINEAR MOTION— NORMAL AND TANGENTIAL COMPONENTS

Figure 15.25 shows a particle which experiences curvilinear translation, in the sense of *a* to *b*, along a plane curve. The coordinate of length along the curve is *s*. At time *t*, the particle is assumed to be at location *a*. The *displacement,* or *position,* of the particle at this time is given by the position vector $\mathbf{r}(t)$. This position vector is referenced to the origin of the coordinate system. At a later time $t + \Delta t$ the particle is at the position *b* on the curve. The displacement of the particle at this new location is given by the position vector $\mathbf{r}(t + \Delta t)$. The *change* in the position, or displacement, of the particle as it goes from *a* to *b* is given by the vector $\Delta\mathbf{r}$. From the triangle law of vector addition,

$$\mathbf{r}(t) + \Delta\mathbf{r} = \mathbf{r}(t + \Delta t) \tag{15.95}$$

The equation may be written as

$$\Delta\mathbf{r} = \mathbf{r}(t + \Delta t) - \mathbf{r}(t) \tag{15.96}$$

The form of Eq. (15.96) emphasizes the fact that the change in the displacement of the particle is the *difference* between the position at the *later* time and the position at the *earlier* time.

From the fundamental definition of the velocity $\mathbf{v}$, as the time rate of change of displacement, it follows that

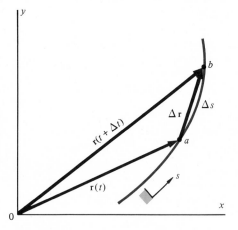

Fig. 15.25

$$v = \lim_{\Delta t \to 0} \frac{\Delta r}{\Delta t} \qquad (15.97)$$

As $\Delta t \to 0$, the point b approaches the point a, and the *chord length ab* approaches the *arc length ab*. In the limit, the *magnitude* of Δr is equal to Δs, and the *direction* of Δr is the direction of a line tangent to the curve at the point a. It follows from the discussion that the magnitude v of the velocity along the curve is

$$v = \lim_{\Delta t \to 0} \frac{\Delta s}{\Delta t} = \frac{ds}{dt} \qquad (15.98)$$

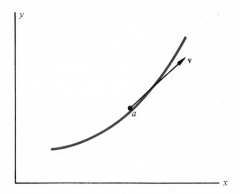

Fig. 15.26

In summary, when a particle moves along a plane curve, the direction of the velocity is tangent to the curve. The magnitude of this velocity is equal to the speed with which the particle moves along the curve. Figure 15.26 shows the typical appearance of the graphical representation of the velocity of the particle at point a.

The acceleration of a particle in curvilinear translation will be found next. Figure 15.27 shows the velocities of the particles at points a and b on the curved path of motion. ρ_a and ρ_b are the two radii of curvature of the plane curvilinear path at these points, with the centers 0_a and 0_b. $\Delta \theta$ is the included angle between ρ_a and ρ_b, and Δs is the corresponding arc length. The time interval which corresponds to movement of the particle from a to b is Δt. The magnitude of v_b in the figure is greater than the magnitude of v_a, to show an increase in this quantity as the particle moves in the positive sense of the coordinate s.

The velocity v_b is now redrawn at point a, as shown in Fig. 15.28. Δv is the *vector difference* between v_a and v_b, and $\Delta \theta$ is

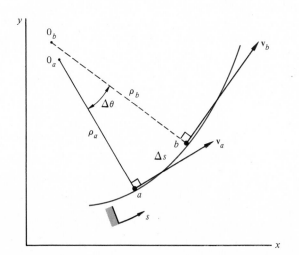

Fig. 15.27

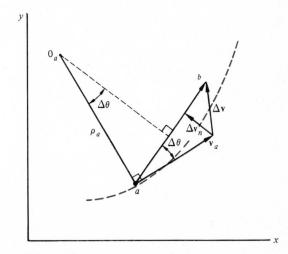

Fig. 15.28

the included angle between these two quantities. The velocity triangle is shown in Fig. 15.29.

The velocity difference Δv is now represented as the sum of two rectangular components. Δv_n will be referred to as the *normal* component of the velocity change, and Δv_t is called the *tangential* component of this velocity change. The term *normal* will mean a direction normal to a line which is tangent to the curve. Thus, this direction is that of the radius of curvature of the curve at the point of interest. The term *tangential* will mean the direction of the line which is tangent to the curve.

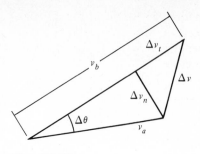

Fig. 15.29

The acceleration of a particle is defined to be the time rate of change, or the first time derivative, of the velocity. From consideration of Fig. 15.29, it may be seen that two distinct components of acceleration of the particle along the curve may be identified. The first component is called the *normal acceleration* a_n. The direction of this component of acceleration is normal to the line which is tangent to the curve. If the fundamental definition of acceleration is used, the quantity may be expressed as

$$a_n = \lim_{\Delta t \to 0} \frac{\Delta v_n}{\Delta t} \qquad (15.99)$$

The positive sense of a_n must be the same as the positive sense of v_n. From Fig. 15.28, it follows that the normal acceleration a_n is always directed toward the center of curvature of the plane curve. As $\Delta t \to 0$, the corresponding limiting value of the magnitude of Δv_n is equal to the product $v_a(\Delta \theta)$. Equation (15.99) then appears as

$$a_n = \lim_{\Delta t \to 0} \frac{\Delta v_n}{\Delta t} = \lim_{\Delta t \to 0} \frac{v_a \, \Delta \theta}{\Delta t} \qquad (15.100)$$

As the limit is approached, the value ρ_a of the radius of curvature at point a approaches the general value ρ, the term v_a approaches the general term v, and $\Delta s \to \rho \, \Delta \theta$. The normal acceleration then has the form

$$a_n = \lim_{\Delta t \to 0} \frac{v \, \Delta \theta}{\Delta t} = \lim_{\Delta t \to 0} \frac{v}{\Delta t} \frac{\Delta s}{\rho} = \lim_{\Delta t \to 0} \frac{v}{\rho} \frac{\Delta s}{\Delta t} \qquad (15.101)$$

The term $\lim_{\Delta t \to 0} (\Delta s / \Delta t)$ in Eq. (15.101) is equal to the magnitude v of the velocity, or the speed with which the particle moves along the curve, given by

$$\lim_{\Delta t \to 0} \frac{\Delta s}{\Delta t} = \frac{ds}{dt} = \dot{s} = v \qquad (15.102)$$

The final form of the Eq. (15.101) is then

$$a_n = \frac{v^2}{\rho} \qquad (15.103)$$

Equation (15.103) is of fundamental importance in dynamics. It states that a particle moving with curvilinear motion will experience a component of acceleration in a direction which is normal to the direction of motion. In addition, the sense of this acceleration will always be from the particle toward the center of curvature of the curve. An alternate term which is used for the normal acceleration is centripetal acceleration.

It may finally be observed that the normal component of acceleration of a particle in curvilinear translation arises solely from changes in the direction of the velocity vector as the particle travels along the curve. It is a function of velocity *only* and in no way is related to the acceleration of the particle in the direction tangent to the curve. Thus, the normal acceleration of a particle that moves in curvilinear translation is never zero. It may be observed that the only way for a_n to be zero is for v to be zero, which means that there is no motion of the particle, or for $\rho \to \infty$. This latter condition implies that the curve is a straight line, so that the motion is rectilinear translation.

The second component of the acceleration of the particle is called the tangential acceleration a_t. The direction of this quantity is along a line tangent to the curve. From Fig. 15.29, and using the basic definition of acceleration, we have

$$a_t = \lim_{\Delta t \to 0} \frac{\Delta v_t}{\Delta t} = \frac{dv_t}{dt} \qquad (15.104)$$

The positive sense of a_t is the same as the positive sense of Δv_t. The last term in Eq. (15.104) may be recognized as the time rate of change of the speed v with which the particle moves along the curve.

Using

$$\frac{dv_t}{dt} = \frac{dv}{dt} = \dot{v} \qquad (15.105)$$

the tangential component of acceleration in curvilinear translation has the final form

$$a_t = \dot{v} \qquad (15.106)$$

It may be observed from Eq. (15.106) that if the particle moves along the curved path with constant speed, the tangential acceleration is identically zero. Since s is the coordinate of length along the curve, the velocity v may be written as

$$v = \frac{ds}{dt} = \dot{s} \qquad (15.107)$$

The component of tangential acceleration may then be written as

$$a_t = \dot{v} = \ddot{s} \qquad (15.108)$$

In summary, the acceleration of a particle in curvilinear motion may be described by two components. The first component, the *normal, or centripetal, acceleration,* is given by

$$a_n = \frac{v^2}{\rho} \qquad (15.109)$$

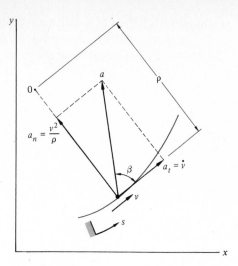

Fig. 15.30

The direction of this vector is along the radius of curvature ρ of the curve, and the sense is *always* toward the center of curvature.

The second component of acceleration of a particle in curvilinear motion is called the *tangential acceleration,* given by

$$a_t = \dot{v} \qquad (15.110)$$

The direction of this vector is along a line tangent to the curve, and the positive sense of a_t is the same as the positive sense of s, the displacement along the curve.

The two components of acceleration for a particle in plane curvilinear translation are shown in Fig. 15.30. The resultant acceleration a is then

$$a = \sqrt{a_n^2 + a_t^2} \qquad (15.111)$$

The direction β of this acceleration, with respect to the tangent line to the curve, may be found from

$$\tan \beta = \frac{a_n}{a_t} = \frac{v^2}{\rho \dot{v}} \qquad (15.112)$$

A very important difference between the visualization of the velocity and acceleration of a particle in plane curvilinear translation may be noted. The velocity of the particle is *always* tangent to the curve, and thus a mental picture of this motion may be formed readily. The direction of the total acceleration of a particle moving along a curved path is *never* tangent to the curve, except for the trivial case where $v = 0$ and there is no motion. The effects of acceleration of the particle, therefore, cannot be visualized readily. The consequence is that problems involving the acceleration of a particle are inherently more difficult than those involving only the velocity.

Figure 15.31 shows a plane curve with a shape defined by $y = f(x)$. It is shown in texts on analytic geometry and calculus that the radius of curvature ρ of a plane curve is given by

$$\frac{1}{\rho} = \frac{\pm d^2y/dx^2}{[1 + (dy/dx)^2]^{3/2}} \qquad (15.113)$$

The terms dy/dx and d^2y/dx^2 are the first two derivatives of the known function $y = f(x)$. If Eq. (15.113) is written without the plus or minus sign, the result for ρ will be positive or negative, depending on whether the general orientation of the radius of

494

curvature is that shown in the figure as ρ_a or ρ_b. Thus, in using this equation, *the proper sign is chosen to make the radius of curvature a positive value.* The point c in Fig. 15.31 is referred to as a point of inflection. At this location on the curve, $\rho \to \infty$.

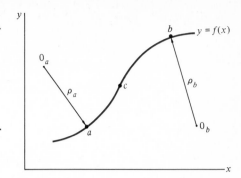

Fig. 15.31

15.6 PLANE CURVILINEAR TRANSLATION— RECTANGULAR COMPONENTS

The last section developed the general forms of the normal and tangential components of the acceleration of a particle in curvilinear translation. Now this acceleration will be expressed in terms of rectangular components.

Figure 15.32 shows the velocity of a particle moving along a plane curve. Since the velocity is a vector quantity, it may be expressed in terms of two rectangular components. The directions of these components will be taken to be the directions of the coordinate axes. The two components v_x and v_y of the velocity v are shown in the figure.

Angle θ is related to the slope of the curve by

$$\tan \theta = \frac{dy}{dx} \tag{15.114}$$

The relationships among the velocity and its components are

$$v_x = v \cos \theta \qquad v_y = v \sin \theta \tag{15.115}$$

Elimination of θ from Eq. (15.115) results in

$$v = \sqrt{v_x^2 + v_y^2} \tag{15.116}$$

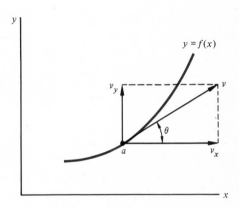

Fig. 15.32

Figure 15.33 shows normal and tangential components of the acceleration of the particle. These components are projected onto the x and y axes, with the results

$$a_x = a_t \cos \theta - a_n \sin \theta \tag{15.117}$$

$$a_y = a_t \sin \theta + a_n \cos \theta \tag{15.118}$$

a_x and a_y are the x and y components of the total acceleration of the particle. θ is defined by Eq. (15.114). The quantities a_x and a_y are positive in the positive coordinate senses. The magnitude of the acceleration is given by

$$a = \sqrt{a_x^2 + a_y^2} = \sqrt{a_n^2 + a_t^2} \tag{15.119}$$

This equation illustrates that the acceleration may be expressed in terms of two *different* pairs of rectangular coordinates. The direction of the total acceleration with respect to the positive x axis is then given by the angle $\theta + \beta$, where θ is given by Eq. (15.114) and β is given by Eq. (15.112).

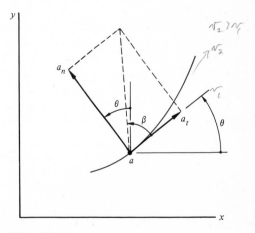

Fig. 15.33

495

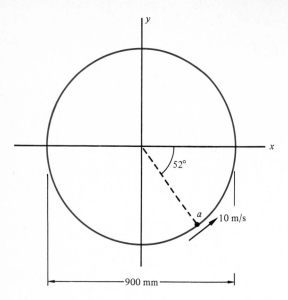

Fig. 15.34

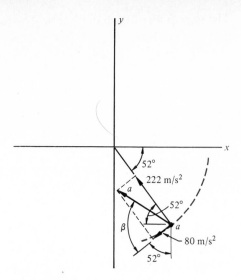

Fig. 15.35

The operations presented above are referred to as the description of the velocity and acceleration, in curvilinear translation, in terms of rectangular components. These equations will be used subsequently in this chapter to characterize the very important problem of projectile motion in a gravitational field.

Example 15.9 A particle moves around a circular track with constant velocity, as shown in Fig. 15.34. At the instant that the particle is at point a, it has a tangential deceleration of 80 m/s².

a Find the normal acceleration and the magnitude and direction of the total acceleration at point a.

b Find the x and y components of the velocity and acceleration at point a.

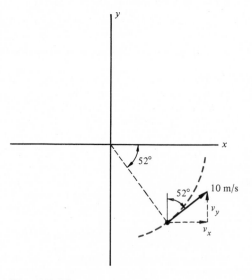

Fig. 15.36

Solution a The normal acceleration is

$$a_n = \frac{v^2}{\rho} = \frac{10^2}{0.5(900 \text{ mm})(1 \text{ m}/1{,}000 \text{ mm})} = 222 \text{ m/s}^2 \quad (15.120)$$

The sense of this normal acceleration component is from a to the center of the track. Since the particle is described as decelerating at point a, the sense of the tangential acceleration at this point must be opposite to the sense of the velocity.

The two acceleration components are shown in Fig. 15.35. The magnitude of the total acceleration at a is

$$a = \sqrt{a_n^2 + a_t^2} = \sqrt{222^2 + (-80)^2} = 236 \text{ m/s}^2 \quad (15.121)$$

The orientation of angle β is defined in Fig. 15.35, and

$$\tan \beta = \frac{222}{80} = 2.78 \qquad \beta = 70.2° \qquad (15.122)$$

b From Fig. 15.36, the x and y components of the velocity are

$$v_x = 10 \sin 52° = 7.88 \text{ m/s} \qquad (15.123)$$

$$v_y = 10 \cos 52° = 6.16 \text{ m/s} \qquad (15.124)$$

Using these results, we find that the magnitude of the total velocity is

$$v = \sqrt{v_x^2 + v_y^2} = \sqrt{7.88^2 + 6.16^2} = 10.0 \text{ m/s} \qquad (15.125)$$

This calculation confirms the data given originally.

From Fig. 15.35, the x and y components of the acceleration are

$$a_x = -222 \cos 52° - 80 \sin 52° = -200 \text{ m/s}^2 \qquad (15.126)$$

$$a_y = 222 \sin 52° - 80 \cos 52° = 126 \text{ m/s}^2 \qquad (15.127)$$

These two components are shown in Fig. 15.37.

An alternate method for finding the x and y components of the acceleration is shown in Fig. 15.38. The magnitude and direction of the resultant acceleration are known from Eqs. (15.121) and (15.122). The components of this vector are then found directly as

$$a_x = -236 \cos 32.2° = -200 \text{ m/s}^2 \qquad (15.128)$$

$$a_y = 236 \sin 32.2° = 126 \text{ m/s}^2 \qquad (15.129a)$$

As a check on the equations above

$$a = \sqrt{a_x^2 + a_y^2} = \sqrt{(-200)^2 + 126^2} = 236 \text{ m/s}^2 \qquad (15.129b)$$

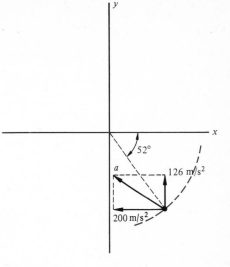

Fig. 15.37

Example 15.10 A particle moves along a track which has the shape of a parabola, as shown in Fig. 15.39. The speed of the particle along the track has the constant value 100 in/s. The shape of the parabola is given by $y = 5 + 0.3x^2$, where x and y are in inches.

a Find the x and y components of the velocity at points a and b.

b Find the magnitude and direction of the normal acceleration of the particle at a and b.

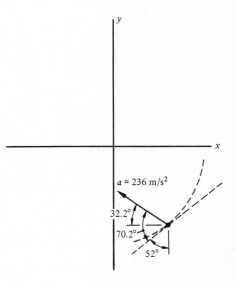

Solution

a At point a, from inspection of the figure,

$$v_x = 100 \text{ in/s} \qquad v_y = 0 \qquad (15.130)$$

Fig. 15.38

The slope of the curve is

$$\frac{dy}{dx} = \frac{d}{dx}(5 + 0.3x^2) = 0.6x \qquad (15.131)$$

At point b,

$$\left.\frac{dy}{dx}\right|_{x=2} = 0.6x \bigg|_{x=2} = 0.6(2) = 1.2 = \tan \theta \qquad \theta = 50.2° \qquad (15.132)$$

497

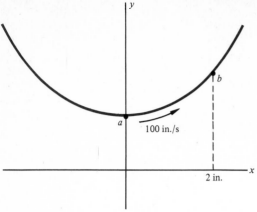

Fig. 15.39

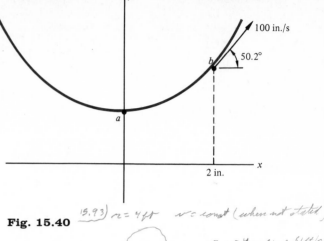

Fig. 15.40

The orientation of the velocity at point b is shown in Fig. 15.40. The x and y components of the velocity are

$$v_x = 100 \cos 50.2° = 64.0 \text{ in/s} \qquad (15.133)$$

$$v_y = 100 \sin 50.2° = 76.8 \text{ in/s} \qquad (15.134)$$

b The first derivative of the curve is given by Eq. (15.131). The second derivative is

$$\frac{d^2y}{dx^2} = 0.6 \qquad (15.135)$$

The radius of curvature at point a is then

$$\frac{1}{\rho_a} = \frac{\pm d^2y/dx^2}{[1 + (dy/dx)^2]^{3/2}} \bigg|_{x=0} \qquad (15.136)$$

$$\frac{1}{\rho_a} = \frac{\pm 0.6}{\{1 + [0.6(0)]^2\}^{3/2}} \qquad \rho_a = 1.67 \text{ in} \qquad (15.137)$$

The normal component of acceleration of the particle at point a is

$$a_{n,a} = \frac{v^2}{\rho_a} = \frac{100^2}{1.67} = 5{,}990 \text{ in/s}^2 \qquad (15.138)$$

This acceleration acts upward along the y axis. At point b,

$$\frac{1}{\rho_b} = \frac{\pm d^2y/dx^2}{[1 + (dy/dx)^2]^{3/2}} \bigg|_{x=2} \qquad (15.139)$$

$$\frac{1}{\rho_b} = \frac{\pm 0.6}{\{1 + [0.6(2)]^2\}^{3/2}} \qquad \rho_b = 6.35 \text{ in} \qquad (15.140)$$

The normal acceleration at point b is then

$$a_{n,b} = \frac{v^2}{\rho_b} = \frac{100^2}{6.35} = 1{,}570 \text{ in/s}^2 \qquad (15.141)$$

Using Eq. (15.132), we find that the direction of the normal acceleration at b is at 50.2° from the y axis, as shown in Fig. 15.41.

15.93) $r = 4 ft$ $v = const$ (when not stated)

$v_x = 2.4 \cos 51 = 1.51 ft/s$
$v_y = -2.4 \sin 51 = -1.8$
$v = 2.4$

a) $t = 9 \sec$
$s = vt = 2.4(9) = 21.6 ft$
circumference $= 2\pi r = 25.1 ft$
avg. displacement $= \frac{21.6}{25.1} \times 360 = 309°$

$360 - 309 = 51°$

b) at $t=0$
$a_n = \frac{v^2}{9} = \frac{v^2}{r} = \frac{(2.4)^2}{4} = 1.44 ft/s^2$

c) $a_x = a_n \sin 51° = 1.12 ft/s^2$
$a_y = a_n \cos 51° = .906 ft/s^2$

to use formulas, take $90 - 51 =$
because of how θ was defined

$a_x = a_n \cos(90 - 51) = 1.12$
$a_y = a_n \sin(39) = .906$

498

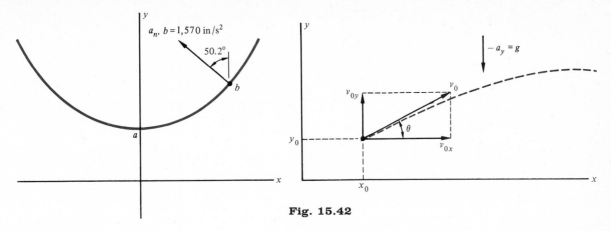

Fig. 15.42

Fig. 15.41

15.7 PLANE PROJECTILE MOTION IN TERMS OF COMPONENT MOTIONS

Figure 15.42 shows the motion when a particle is launched with initial velocity in a vertical plane. Typical physical situations which would be represented by Fig. 15.42 are a cannon firing a projectile, a player hitting a baseball with a bat, or a pebble being thrown from an automobile tire. The path traced out by the particle is referred to as the *trajectory* of the particle.

The curvilinear translational motion of the particle will be expressed now in terms of *component motions* in the x and y directions. In this model of the actual motion, all air resistance effects will be neglected.

The motion of the particle in the y direction is a case of the freely falling motion of a body in a gravitational field. The initial velocity of the particle in this direction is v_{0y}. Equations (15.60) through (15.62) apply directly, and for this case these equations have the forms

$$v_y = v_{0y} - gt \qquad (15.142)$$

$$y = y_0 + v_{0y}t - \tfrac{1}{2}gt^2 \qquad (15.143)$$

$$v_y^2 = v_{0y}^2 - 2g(y - y_0) \qquad (15.144)$$

From consideration of Fig. 15.42, it follows that the component of the gravitational acceleration in the x direction is zero. Thus,

$$v_x = \text{constant} \qquad (15.145)$$

The constant value of the x component of velocity in Eq. (15.145) must be the same as v_{0x}, the x component of the initial velocity v_0. Equation (15.145) now appears as

$$v_x = v_{0x} = \text{constant} \qquad (15.146)$$

499

This equation is integrated, with the result

$$x = v_{0x}t + \text{constant} \qquad (15.147)$$

The problem commences at $t = 0$ when the particle is launched from the position $x = x_0$, $y = y_0$. Thus, the constant in Eq. (15.147) must be equal to x_0. The final forms of the equations for the component motion of the particle in the x direction are

$$v_x = v_{0x} = \text{constant} \qquad (15.148)$$

$$x = x_0 + v_{0x}t \qquad (15.149)$$

It follows from Fig. 15.42, that

$$v_{0x} = v_0 \cos \theta \qquad v_{0y} = v_0 \sin \theta \qquad (15.150)$$

For brevity, the components of the initial velocity have been written in the above equations as v_{0x} and v_{0y}, rather than as the right sides of Eqs. (15.150).

The case of projectile motion in a vertical plane exhibits the interesting characteristic that one component of the total motion is rectilinear motion with *constant velocity,* while the other component is rectilinear motion with *constant acceleration.*

Example 15.11 Figure 15.43 shows a shell being fired from an artillery weapon. The muzzle velocity of the shell upon exit from the gun tube is 1,000 ft/s.

a Find the maximum height reached by the shell and the time to reach this height.

b Find the duration of the flight and the distance from the gun at which the shell strikes the ground.

c Find the velocity with which the shell strikes the ground.

Solution Since the origin of coordinates is placed at the muzzle,

$$x_0 = y_0 = 0 \qquad (15.151)$$

The initial conditions are

$$v_0 = 1,000 \text{ ft/s} \qquad (15.152)$$

$$v_{0x} = 1,000 \cos 20° = 940 \text{ ft/s} \qquad (15.153)$$

$$v_{0y} = 1,000 \sin 20° = 342 \text{ ft/s} \qquad (15.154)$$

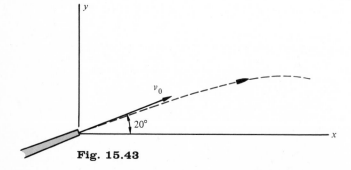

Fig. 15.43

a When the maximum height is reached,

$$v_y = 0 \tag{15.155}$$

$$0 = v_{0y} - gt \tag{15.156}$$

$$0 = 342 - 32.2t \qquad t = 10.6 \text{ s} \tag{15.157}$$

The magnitude of the maximum height is found from

$$y = y_0 + v_{0y}t - \tfrac{1}{2}gt^2 \tag{15.158}$$

$$y_{max} = 0 + 342(10.6) - \tfrac{1}{2}(32.2)(10.6^2) = 1,820 \text{ ft} \tag{15.159}$$

Equation (15.159) may be checked by using

$$v_y^2 = v_{0y}^2 - 2g(y - y_0) \tag{15.160}$$

$$0 = 342^2 - 2(32.2)(y_{max} - 0) \qquad y_{max} = 1,820 \text{ ft} \tag{15.161}$$

b When the shell strikes the ground, $y = 0$. From Eq. (15.143),

$$y = y_0 + v_{0y}t - \tfrac{1}{2}gt^2 \tag{15.162}$$

$$0 = 0 + 342t - \tfrac{1}{2}(32.2t^2) \tag{15.163}$$

$$t(16.1t - 342) = 0 \qquad t = 0, 21.2 \text{ s} \tag{15.164}$$

The first value corresponds to the initial time. The shell strikes the ground 21.2 s after launch. From Eq. (15.149)

$$x = x_0 + v_{0x}t \tag{15.165}$$

$$x_{max} = 0 + 940(21.2) = 19,900 \text{ ft} \tag{15.166}$$

The shell strikes the ground at 19,900 ft, or 3.77 mi, from the gun.
c When the shell strikes the ground, $t = 21.2$ s. From Eq. (15.142),

$$v_y = v_{0y} - gt \tag{15.167}$$

$$v_y = 342 - 32.2(21.2) = -342 \text{ ft/s} \tag{15.168}$$

The velocity component has the same magnitude as the initial y component of velocity, but is of opposite sense. The x component of the striking velocity is the same as v_{0x}, given by Eq. (15.153) as 940 ft/s. The magnitude of the striking velocity is

$$v = \sqrt{v_x^2 + v_y^2} = \sqrt{940^2 + (-341)^2} = 1,000 \text{ ft/s} \tag{15.169}$$

This value is the same as the magnitude of the initial velocity, an expected result, since there are no air-resistance losses.

Example 15.12 Figure 15.44 shows a projectile which is launched with initial velocity v_0. The range is the distance from the gun to where the projectile strikes the ground. For what angle of launch will the range be maximum?

Solution For this example

$$x_0 = y_0 = 0 \tag{15.170}$$

The x displacement is

$$x = v_{0x}t = (v_0 \cos \theta)(t) \tag{15.171}$$

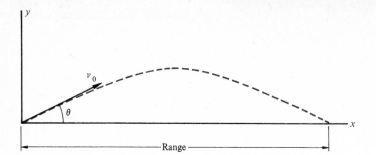

Fig. 15.44

and the y displacement is

$$y = v_{0y}t - \tfrac{1}{2}gt^2 \tag{15.172}$$

When the projectile strikes the ground, $y = 0$, so that

$$0 = (v_0 \sin \theta)t - \tfrac{1}{2}gt^2 \tag{15.173}$$

$$t(v_0 \sin \theta - \tfrac{1}{2}gt) = 0 \tag{15.174}$$

The root $t = 0$ is discarded, since this time corresponds to the initial time of the problem. Thus,

$$v_0 \sin \theta - \tfrac{1}{2}gt = 0 \qquad t = \frac{2v_0 \sin \theta}{g} \tag{15.175}$$

This value of t is substituted into Eq. (15.171), with the result

$$x = (v_0 \cos \theta)\left(\frac{2v_0 \sin \theta}{g}\right) \tag{15.176}$$

$$x = \frac{v_0^2}{g}(2 \sin \theta \cos \theta) = \frac{v_0^2}{g} \sin 2\theta \tag{15.177}$$

The sine function has its maximum positive value at 90°. The value θ_m of launch angle for maximum range is then

$$2\theta_m = 90° \tag{15.178}$$

$$\theta_m = 45° \tag{15.179}$$

Example 15.13 A person holds a garden hose, as shown in Fig. 15.45. The velocity of the water leaving the nozzle is 50 ft/s. For what range of values of x_1 will the stream of water clear the vertical wall? The stream of water may be imagined to be a succession of particles, each of which has the same initial conditions of velocity.

Solution From the figure,

$$x_0 = 8 \text{ ft} \qquad y_0 = 4 \text{ ft} \tag{15.180}$$

$$v_{0x} = 50 \cos 36° = 40.5 \text{ ft/s} \tag{15.181}$$

$$v_{0y} = 50 \sin 36° = 29.4 \text{ ft/s} \tag{15.182}$$

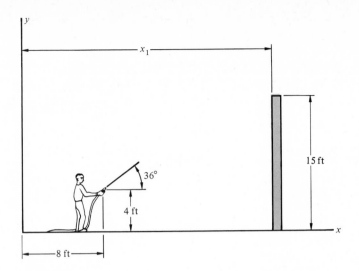

Fig. 15.45

The time t when the fluid stream is at the height of the wall will be found first. Using

$$y = y_0 + v_{0y}t - \tfrac{1}{2}gt^2 \qquad (15.183)$$

$$15 = 4 + 29.4t - \tfrac{1}{2}(32.2t^2) \qquad (15.184)$$

$$16.1t^2 - 29.4t + 11 = 0 \qquad (15.185)$$

The solution to this quadratic equation is

$$t = \frac{29.4 \pm \sqrt{(-29.4)^2 - 4(16.1)(11)}}{2(16.1)} \qquad (15.186)$$

$$= 0.525,\ 1.30\ \text{s} \qquad (15.187)$$

The distances x which correspond to the above two times are

$$x = x_0 + v_{0x}t \qquad (15.188)$$

$$x_{min} = 8 + 40.5(0.525) = 29.3\ \text{ft} \qquad (15.189)$$

$$x_{max} = 8 + 40.5(1.30) = 60.7\ \text{ft} \qquad (15.190)$$

The stream will theoretically clear the wall if $29.3\ \text{ft} \le x_1 \le 60.7\ \text{ft}$.

15.8 RELATIVE DISPLACEMENT, VELOCITY, AND ACCELERATION

A situation that occurs frequently in problems in dynamics is when one particle moves relative to a second particle that is also in motion. This section develops equations that describe the displacement, velocity, and acceleration of the particles with respect to each other. As a preliminary consideration, we will discuss concepts of absolute displacement, velocity, and acceleration.

Figure 15.46 shows an *xyz* coordinate system imagined to be affixed to a distant star. A coordinate system such as this is referred to as an *absolute,* or *inertial,* coordinate reference system. An inertial coordinate system may also be described as a coordinate system within which Newton's laws of motion are valid. The particle *P* may be referenced to the inertial coordinate system by the *absolute displacement, or position, vector* **s**. If velocity **v** and acceleration **a** of the particle are measured in the inertial coordinate system, then these quantities are referred to as *absolute velocity and absolute acceleration.* In the majority of engineering problems in dynamics, a set of axes that are imagined to be attached to the earth may be considered as absolute coordinates. Expressions will now be developed for the relationships among the absolute displacements, velocities, and accelerations of particles in motion, and the values of these quantities measured relative to the particles. Results will be obtained only for plane motion of the particles. The techniques used, however, may readily be extended to the case where the particles move with general three-dimensional motion.

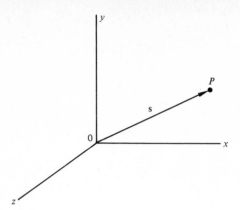

Fig. 15.46

Figure 15.47 shows two particles, *a* and *b*, which are constrained to move in the *xy* plane. These axes are assumed to be absolute coordinates. At the instant of observation shown in the figure, the two particles *a* and *b* have the displacements $\mathbf{s}_a$ and $\mathbf{s}_b$, and the absolute velocities $\mathbf{v}_a$ and $\mathbf{v}_b$.

The *relative displacement* $\mathbf{s}_{ab}$ is defined to be

$$\mathbf{s}_{ab} = \mathbf{s}_a - \mathbf{s}_b \qquad (15.191)$$

The term $\mathbf{s}_{ab}$ is read as "the displacement of *a* relative to *b*." Note that Eq. (15.191) represents a *vector* subtraction. The equation may be written as

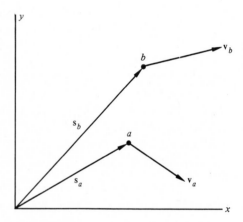

Fig. 15.47

$$\mathbf{s}_{ab} = \mathbf{s}_a + (-\mathbf{s}_b) \qquad (15.192)$$

The construction is shown in Fig. 15.48. It may be seen that for the situation in Fig. 15.47, particle *a* is located *relative* to particle *b* in a direction and sense that is generally down and to the left of particle *b*.

The subscripting convention that will be used is that a single subscript on a displacement, velocity, or acceleration term represents an *absolute quantity.* Thus, $\mathbf{s}_a$ and $\mathbf{s}_b$ are absolute displacements. A double subscript on a term represents a *relative quantity.* The second subscript indicates the particle that is the reference point, while the first subscript identifies the particle whose relative motion quantity is being measured. Thus, the term $\mathbf{s}_{ab}$ is the relative displacement of particle *a* with respect to particle *b*, while the term $\mathbf{s}_{ba}$ represents the relative

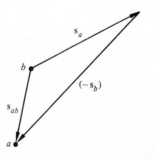

Fig. 15.48

504

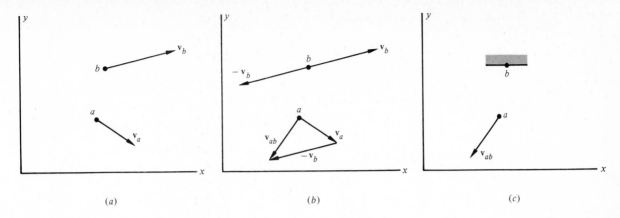

(a)   (b)   (c)

Fig. 15.49

displacement of particle b with respect to particle a. It is left as an exercise for the reader to show that

$$\mathbf{s}_{ab} = -\mathbf{s}_{ba} \qquad (15.193)$$

The relative velocity of particle a with respect to particle b is defined to be

$$\mathbf{v}_{ab} = \mathbf{v}_a - \mathbf{v}_b \qquad (15.194)$$

Equation (15.194) is a vector subtraction. The concept of relative velocity may have either of the following two physical interpretations:

1. The relative velocity of a with respect to b is the velocity which an observer, who is imagined to travel with the motion of particle b, would perceive the velocity of particle a to be.
2. If the velocity $-\mathbf{v}_b$ were added to both of the original velocities $\mathbf{v}_a$ and $\mathbf{v}_b$, then particle b would have zero absolute velocity and the relative velocity $\mathbf{v}_{ab}$ would then be the absolute velocity of particle a. This effect is shown in Fig. 15.49.

Equation (15.194) may be written as

$$\mathbf{v}_a = \mathbf{v}_b + \mathbf{v}_{ab} \qquad (15.195)$$

The interpretation of this equation is that the *absolute velocity* of particle a is the vector sum of

1. The *absolute velocity* of particle b
2. The *relative velocity* of particle a with respect to particle b

The graphical construction used to find the relative velocity from Eq. (15.195) is shown in Fig. 15.50. $\mathbf{v}_a$ and $\mathbf{v}_b$ are first drawn from a common point. The direction of $\mathbf{v}_{ab}$ is along a line joining the tip ends of $\mathbf{v}_a$ and $\mathbf{v}_b$. The sense of $\mathbf{v}_{ab}$ is determined by placing the tip, on the line segment which rep-

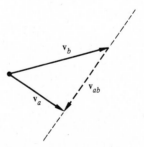

Fig. 15.50

resents $\mathbf{v}_{ab}$, in such a way that the vector equality in Eq. (15.195) is satisfied.

The techniques presented above for the determination of the relative velocity may also be used to find the relative acceleration. If the absolute accelerations of the particles are $\mathbf{a}_a$ and $\mathbf{a}_b$, then the relative acceleration $\mathbf{a}_{ab}$ is defined to be

$$\mathbf{a}_{ab} = \mathbf{a}_a - \mathbf{a}_b \qquad (15.196)$$

It is left as an exercise for the reader to show that

$$\mathbf{v}_{ab} = -\mathbf{v}_{ba} \qquad (15.197)$$

$$\mathbf{a}_{ab} = -\mathbf{a}_{ba} \qquad (15.198)$$

The concepts of relative displacement, velocity, and acceleration find widespread application in the kinematic analysis of linkages, cams, and gears. The study of these elements is included in the subject usually referred to as the kinematic analysis of mechanisms.

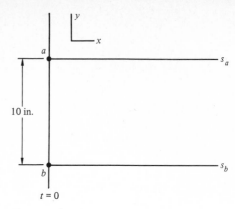

Fig. 15.51

Example 15.14 Two particles move along parallel rectilinear paths, as shown in Fig. 15.51. At time $t = 0$, both particles are in the positions shown in the figure. The motion of particle a is given by

$$s_a = 12t^2 - 4t^3 \qquad (15.199)$$

where s_a is in inches and t is in seconds.

Particle b moves with a constant velocity of

$$v_b = 12 \text{ in/s} \qquad (15.200)$$

a Find the relative displacement of particle a with respect to particle b at $t = 1$ s.

b Find the relative velocity of particle a with respect to particle b at times $t = 1$, 2, and 3 s.

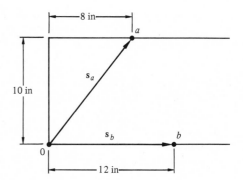

Fig. 15.52

Solution

a The velocity of particle a is

$$v_a = \dot{s}_a = \frac{d}{dt}(12t^2 - 4t^3) = 24t - 12t^2 \qquad (15.201)$$

When $t = 1$ s,

$$s_a = (12t^2 - 4t^3)|_{t=1} = 12(1)^2 - 4(1)^3 = 8 \text{ in} \qquad (15.202)$$

and

$$s_b = v_b t = 12(1) = 12 \text{ in} \qquad (15.203)$$

The positions of the particles are shown in Fig. 15.52, and point O is arbitrarily chosen as the reference point for the displacement vectors s_a and s_b. The construction for the relative displacement is shown in Fig. 15.53. From the right triangle in Fig. 15.53,

$$s_{ab} = \sqrt{10^2 + 4^2} = 10.8 \text{ in} \qquad (15.204)$$

$$\theta = \tan^{-1}\left(\frac{10}{4}\right) = 68.2° \qquad (15.205)$$

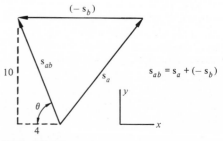

$$s_{ab} = s_a + (-s_b)$$

Fig. 15.53

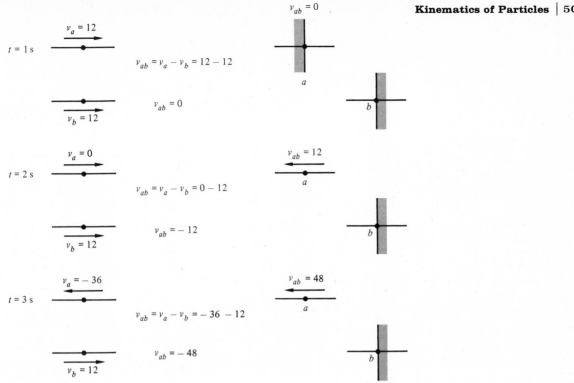

Fig. 15.54

The relative displacement of a with respect to b is seen to be "up and to the left" of particle b. This quantity may also be described in terms of components. Thus, from Fig. 15.53,

$$x_{ab} = -4 \text{ in} \qquad y_{ab} = 10 \text{ in} \qquad (15.206)$$

The physical interpretation of these results is that particle a is 4 in to the left of, and 10 in above, particle b.

The results obtained in Eq. (15.206) are independent of the location of the arbitrary reference point O in Fig. 15.52, and the proof of this is left as an exercise for the reader.

b The absolute and relative velocities of the two particles at $t = 1$, 2, and 3 s are shown in Fig. 15.54, together with a pictorial description of how an observer sitting on particle b would see the motion of particle a. It may be observed that the separation distance between the paths of the two particles does *not* enter into the calculations for the relative velocities.

Example 15.15 Two vehicles move with constant velocity along straight roadways, as shown in Fig. 15.55. At $t = 0$, vehicle a crosses roadway b. At this time, vehicle b has the position shown in Fig. 15.55.

a Find the relative velocity, at time $t = 0$, of vehicle b with respect to vehicle a.

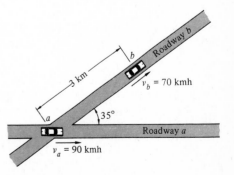

Fig. 15.55

b Do the same as in part *a*, for $t = 2$ s.

c Find the magnitude of the relative displacement of vehicle *b* with respect to vehicle *a*, when the direction of this quantity is normal to roadway *a*, and the corresponding time.

The two vehicles may be treated as particles, since there are no rotation effects of these elements in the plane of motion.

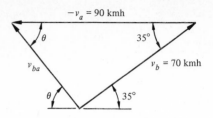

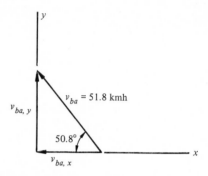

Fig. 15.56

Solution

a The equation of relative velocity is

$$v_{ba} = v_b - v_a \qquad (15.207)$$

The equation is shown in Fig. 15.56.

Using the law of cosines, we find that

$$v_{ba}^2 = 90^2 + 70^2 - (2)(90)(70) \cos 35° \qquad v_{ba} = 51.8 \text{ kmh} \quad (15.208)$$

From the law of sines, we find that

$$\frac{v_{ba}}{\sin 35°} = \frac{v_b}{\sin \theta} \qquad (15.209)$$

$$\frac{51.8}{\sin 35°} = \frac{70}{\sin \theta} \qquad \theta = 50.8° \qquad (15.210)$$

The components of the relative velocity may be found from Fig. 15.57 as

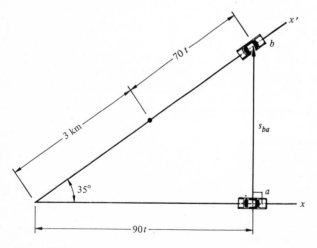

Fig. 15.57

$$v_{ba,x} = -51.8 \cos 50.8° = -32.7 \text{ kmh} \qquad (15.211)$$

$$v_{ba,y} = 51.8 \sin 50.8° = 40.1 \text{ kmh} \qquad (15.212)$$

An observer sitting in vehicle *a* would see vehicle *b* receding with a direction and sense which is generally up and to the left of vehicle *a*.

b The relative velocity of vehicle *b* with respect to vehicle *a* is the same for all times in the problem, since the absolute velocities of the two vehicles have constant magnitudes, directions, and senses.

c Figure 15.58 shows the configuration when the relative displace-

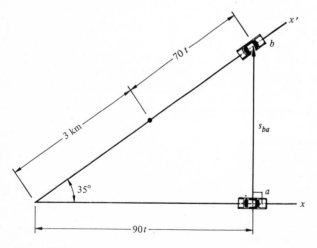

Fig. 15.58

The corresponding time is *t*, with the units hours.

From Fig. 15.58,

$$\cos 35° = \frac{90t}{3 + 70t} \qquad t = 0.0752 \text{ h} = 4.51 \text{ min} \qquad (15.213)$$

The displacements at this time are

$$s_a = 90(0.0752) = 6.77 \text{ km} \qquad (15.214)$$

$$s_b = 3 + 70(0.0752) = 8.26 \text{ km} \qquad (15.215)$$

The magnitude of the relative displacement of vehicle *b* with respect to vehicle *a* is then

$$s_{ba} = \sqrt{s_b^2 - s_a^2} \qquad (15.216)$$

$$= \sqrt{8.26^2 - 6.77^2} = 4.73 \text{ km} \qquad (15.217)$$

15.9 SUMMARY

A particle is a physical body whose dimensions are assumed to be vanishingly small. Thus, a particle cannot experience rotation effects.

Kinematics is the science that studies the motion of particles and bodies, without regard for the forces that produce these motions. The motion of a particle along a straight path is referred to as rectilinear translation. The particle motion is referred to as curvilinear translation if the motion is along a curved path.

The displacement of a particle is the position, or location, of the particle with respect to a given reference point. The velocity of a particle is given by the first time derivative of the displacement. The acceleration of a particle is given by the first time derivative of velocity, or by the second time derivative of displacement. Fundamentally, velocity is the time rate of change of displacement, and acceleration is the time rate of change of velocity. Displacement, velocity, and acceleration are vector quantities. The choice of the positive sense of a displacement coordinate automatically establishes the same positive sense for the velocity and acceleration. The magnitude of the velocity is called speed. Deceleration refers to an acceleration that acts in the negative coordinate sense.

Graphical displays of the variation of displacement, velocity, and acceleration with respect to time are called motion diagrams. The magnitude of the velocity is equal to the slope of the displacement-time curve, and the magnitude of the acceleration is equal to the slope of the velocity-time curve. The area under the curve between two times on the velocity-time curve is equal to the change in displacement of the particle between these two times. The area under the acceleration curve between two times is equal to the change in the velocity between these two times.

The equations that relate the displacement, velocity, acceleration, and time of a particle which moves in rectilinear translation with constant acceleration a are given by

$$v = v_0 + at \tag{15.218}$$

$$s = s_0 + v_0 t + \tfrac{1}{2} a t^2 \tag{15.219}$$

$$v^2 = v_0^2 + 2a(s - s_0) \tag{15.220}$$

where s_0 and v_0 are the initial displacement and velocity, respectively, at $t = 0$, and x and v are the displacement and velocity at time t. For the case of a freely falling particle in the absence of air resistance, the above three equations have the forms

$$v = v_0 - gt \tag{15.221}$$

$$s = s_0 + v_0 t - \tfrac{1}{2} g t^2 \tag{15.222}$$

$$v^2 = v_0^2 - 2g(s - s_0) \tag{15.223}$$

where g is the acceleration of the gravitational field and the positive sense of s is upward from the surface of the earth.

The velocity of a particle that moves in plane curvilinear translation is always tangent to the path of motion. The acceleration of the particle has two distinct components. The magnitude of the normal component a_n is expressed by

$$a_n = \frac{v^2}{\rho} \tag{15.224}$$

where v is the speed of the particle and ρ is the radius of curvature at the point where a_n acts. The direction of a_n is normal to the tangent line to the curved path at the point of interest, or along the radius of curvature. The sense of a_n is always directed toward the center of curvature. The normal acceleration arises because of changes in the direction of the velocity of the particle as it travels along the curve. The normal acceleration is never zero for a particle that moves in curvilinear motion. The normal acceleration is also referred to as the centripetal acceleration.

The magnitude of the tangential component a_t of acceleration is given by

$$a_t = \dot{v} \tag{15.225}$$

where $\dot{v}$ is the time rate of change of velocity along the curved path. The direction of the tangential acceleration is along a line tangent to the curve at the point of interest. The positive sense of a_t is the same as the positive sense of s, the displacement along the curve.

The motion of a particle launched with initial velocity in a vertical plane may be expressed in terms of component motions. If the x axis is horizontal and the y axis is vertical, the component equations of motion are

$$v_x = v_{0x} = \text{constant} \qquad (15.226)$$

$$x = x_0 + v_{0x}t \qquad (15.227)$$

$$v_y = v_{0y} - gt \qquad (15.228)$$

$$y = y_0 + v_{0y}t - \tfrac{1}{2}gt^2 \qquad (15.229)$$

$$v_y^2 = v_{0y}^2 - 2g(y - y_0) \qquad (15.230)$$

$$v_{0x} = v_0 \cos\theta \qquad v_{0y} = v\sin\theta \qquad (15.231)$$

where v_0 is the magnitude of the initial launch velocity, at the direction θ with the x axis.

An absolute, or inertial, coordinate system is imagined to be fixed with respect to a distant star. Such a coordinate system may also be defined as a reference system in which Newton's laws of motion are valid. For most problems in engineering dynamics, the earth may be considered to be an inertial reference system. If the displacement, velocity, or acceleration of a particle is measured in an absolute coordinate system, these terms are referred to as absolute. An absolute quantity has a single subscript to indicate the particle under consideration. Thus, s_a, v_a, and a_a are the absolute displacement, velocity, and acceleration, respectively, of particle a. A relative quantity is indicated by a double subscript, so that s_{ab}, v_{ab}, and a_{ab} are the relative velocity, displacement, and acceleration, respectively, of particle a with respect to particle b. A physical interpretation of a relative motion quantity is that it is that motion effect which a person would observe if he moved with the motion of the reference particle. The relative motion terms are defined by

$$s_{ab} = s_a - s_b \qquad (15.232)$$

$$v_{ab} = v_a - b_b \qquad (15.233)$$

$$a_{ab} = a_a - a_b \qquad (15.234)$$

It should be noted that Eqs. (15.232) through (15.234) are vector operations.

PROBLEMS

15.1 through 15.6 A particle moves in rectilinear translation with the displacement-time function given.

(*a*) Find the general functional forms of the velocity and acceleration of the particle.

(*b*) Find the displacement, velocity and acceleration when $t = 0$ and when $t = 4\,\text{s}$. Show these values on the axis of motion.

(c) Find the average values of the velocity and acceleration in the time interval between $t = 0$ and $t = 4$ s.

(d) At what times, if any, during the time interval $0 \leq t \leq 4$ s does the particle have zero velocity?

(e) If the particle passes through the point $s = 0$ in the time interval between $t = 0$ and $t = 4$ s, find the corresponding values of the velocity and acceleration.

15.1 $s = 32t - 50$, where s is in meters and t is in seconds.

15.2 $s = 50 - 32t$, where s is in meters and t is in seconds.

15.3 $s = 2t^2 + 9t + 10$, where s is in feet and t is in seconds.

15.4 $s = 2t^2 - 9t + 10$, where s is in feet and t is in seconds.

15.5 $s = 1 - e^{-2t}$, where s is in meters and t is in seconds.

15.6 $s = 25 \sin \pi t/2$, where s is in inches and t is in seconds.

15.7 The displacement of a particle which moves with rectilinear translation is known to have the functional form $s = at^2 + bt + 8$, where s is in feet and t is in seconds, and a and b are constants to be chosen.

(a) Find the required values of a and b, if $s = 100$ ft and $\dot{s} = -10$ ft/s when $t = 9.5$ s.

(b) What are the units of a and b?

(c) Find the functional form of the acceleration.

(d) Find the average value of the velocity in the time interval between 9 and 10 s. Would you consider this value to be representative of the velocity in this time interval?

(e) Are there any times in the interval $9 \leq t \leq 10$ s when the displacement and velocity are zero?

15.8 Do the same as in Prob. 15.7, if $s = 100$ ft and $\dot{s} = 10$ ft/s when $t = 9.5$ s.

15.9 Do the same as in Prob. 15.7, if $s = 0$ and $\dot{s} = 100$ ft/s when $t = 2$ s, for the time interval $1.5 \leq t \leq 2.5$ s.

15.10 Do the same as in Prob. 15.7, if $s = 0$ and $\dot{s} = 0$ when $t = 5$ s, for the time interval $4.5 \leq t \leq 5.5$ s. s is in meters.

15.11 through 15.19 The acceleration of a particle which moves with rectilinear translation is given by the function shown. At $t = 0$, the displacement and velocity are zero.

(a) Use graphical methods to find the velocity and displacement when $t = 2$ s and when $t = 4$ s.

(b) Find the average values of the velocity and the acceleration in the intervals $0 \leq t \leq 2$ s, $2 \leq t \leq 4$ s, and $0 \leq t \leq 4$ s, and discuss the results.

(c) Find any times in the interval $0 \leq t \leq 4$ s when the displacement is zero, and the corresponding values of the velocity and acceleration.

15.11 $a = 12 \text{ m/s}^2$.

15.12 $a = -4 \text{ in/s}^2$.

15.13 $a = 0.2t \text{ m/s}^2$.

15.14 $a = (t - 2) \text{ m/s}^2$.

15.15 $a = (2 - t) \text{ ft/s}^2$.

15.16 $a = (4 - t) \text{ ft/s}^2$.

15.17 $a = (-3t - 20) \text{ m/s}^2$.

15.18 $a = 0; \ 0 \leq t < 2$ s.
$a = 8 \text{ m/s}^2; \ 2 \leq t \leq 4$ s.

15.19 $a = -4.8t; \ 0 \leq t \leq 2$ s.
$a = -9.6 \text{ in/s}^2; \ 2 \leq t \leq 4$ s.

15.20 through 15.25 The velocity-time diagram of a particle that starts from rest and moves in rectilinear translation is shown in the figure, and all times are in seconds.

(a) Sketch the displacement and acceleration diagrams for the total time interval shown in the figure.

(b) Find the extreme value(s) of the acceleration.

(c) Find the total distance through which the particle travels during the time interval.

(d) Find the displacement, at the end of the time interval, of the particle from its starting position.

(e) Sketch the average values of the velocity and the acceleration on the respective motion diagrams.

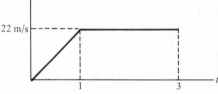

Fig. P15.20

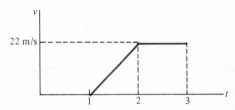

Fig. P15.21

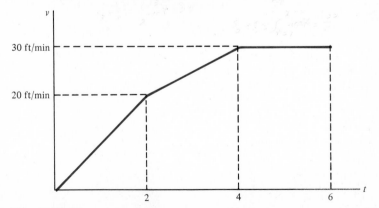

Fig. P15.22

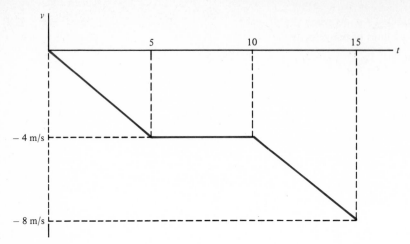

Fig. P15.23

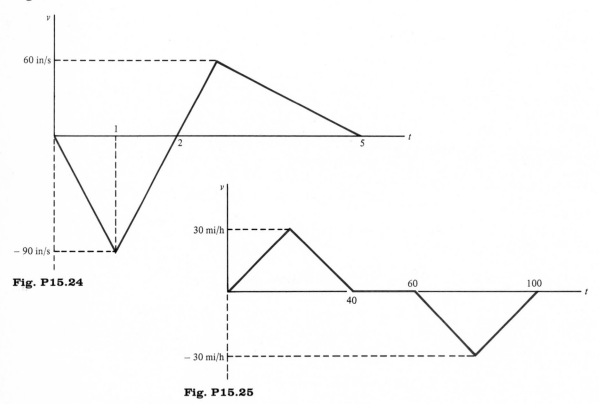

Fig. P15.24

Fig. P15.25

15.26 through 15.37 A particle moves in rectilinear translation with the acceleration-time diagrams shown, and with the initial velocity given. All times are in seconds.

(a) Sketch the velocity and displacement diagrams.

(b) Identify the extreme values of velocity and displacement.

(c) Sketch the average velocity and acceleration on the respective motion diagrams.

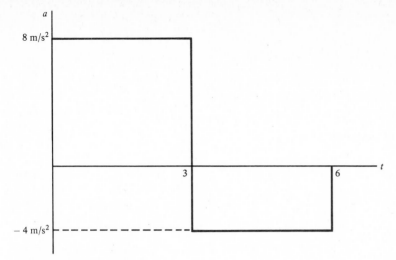

Figs. P15.26, 27.28

15.26 Initial velocity = 0.

15.27 Initial velocity = 10 m/s.

15.28 Initial velocity = −15 m/s.

15.29 Initial velocity = 0.

15.30 Initial velocity = 20 in/s.

15.31 Initial velocity = −72 in/s.

15.32 Initial velocity = 0.

15.33 Initial velocity = 1.8 m/s.

15.34 Initial velocity = −3 m/s.

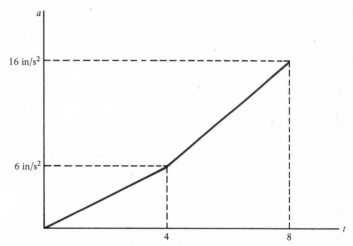

Figs. P15.29, 15.30, 15.31

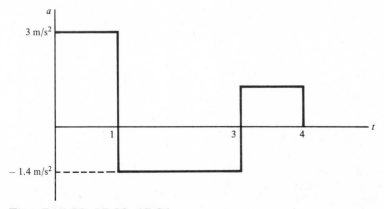

Figs. P15.32, 15.33, 15.34

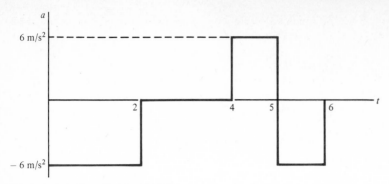

Figs. P15.35, 15.36, 15.37

15.35 Initial velocity $= 0$.

15.36 Initial velocity $= 10 \text{ m/s}$.

15.37 Initial velocity $= -10 \text{ m/s}$.

15.38 The velocity diagram of a particle in rectilinear translation is shown in Fig. P15.38.
(a) Find the required value of the time t_1 if the final displacement
of the particle from its starting position is 80 in.
(b) Find the extreme value of the acceleration of the particle.

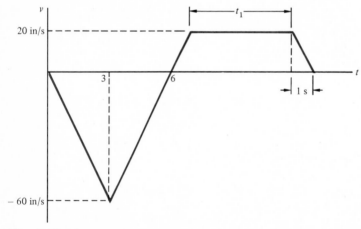

Fig. P15.38

15.39 Do the same as in Prob. 15.38, if the final displacement of
the particle is zero.

15.40 The velocity diagram of a particle which moves in rectilinear translation is shown in Fig. P15.40. The maximum value of the
acceleration which the particle may be subjected to is 0.8 m/s^2.
(a) Find the minimum time t_1 required for the particle to move
through a distance of 3 m.
(b) Find the average values of the velocity and acceleration during
the time interval $0 \le t \le t_1$.

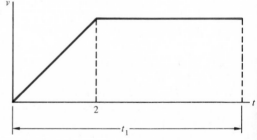

Fig. P15.40

15.41 Do the same as in Prob. 15.40, if the maximum allowable value of the acceleration is 1.3 m/s², and the distance is 3.8 m.

15.42 The acceleration diagram of a particle which moves in rectilinear translation is shown in Fig. P15.42. The particle starts with an initial velocity of 100 in/s.
(a) Find the time t_1 at which the velocity of the particle is zero.
(b) Find the displacement of the particle at $t = t_1$.
(c) Find the total distance through which the particle travels during the time interval $0 \leq t \leq t_1$.

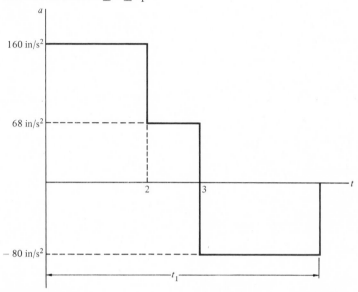

Fig. P15.42

15.43 Do the same as in Prob. 15.42, if the initial velocity is $= -100$ in/s.

15.44 The acceleration diagram of a particle in rectilinear translation is shown in Fig. P15.44. The initial velocity is 12 m/s.
(a) Find the value of a_1 if the particle comes to rest in 4 s.
(b) Find the maximum value of the magnitude of the velocity of the particle.

15.45 Do the same as in Prob. 15.44, if the initial velocity is 20 m/s and the vehicle comes to rest in 3.5 s.

15.46 A particle slides along a straight track with a speed of 6.5 m/s, as shown in Fig. P15.46. At $t = 0$ a force, shown as the dashed arrow in the figure, is applied to the particle and the resulting deceleration is 1.6 m/s².
(a) Find the time when the velocity of the particle is reduced to 50 percent of its initial value and the corresponding distance traveled by the particle.
(b) Find the time when the particle comes to rest and the corresponding total distance through which the particle travels.

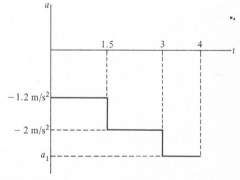

Fig. P15.44

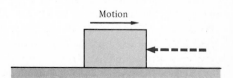

Fig. P15.46

15.47 Do the same as in Prob. 15.46, if the applied force causes a deceleration of 3 m/s².

15.48 An automobile moves along a straight roadway with a constant speed of 40 mi/h.
(*a*) Find the increase in speed if the automobile accelerates at 5 ft/s² for 5 s.
(*b*) Find the distance traveled by the automobile during the motion described in part *a*.
(*c*) At a later time the brakes are applied, causing a deceleration of 10 ft/s². Find the stopping time and distance of the automobile.

15.49 Do the same as in Prob. 15.48 if the automobile accelerates at 3 ft/s² for 9 s.

15.50 Do the same as in Prob. 15.48 if the maximum available braking deceleration of 18 ft/s² is used.

15.51 Two vehicles approach each other in opposite lanes of a straight horizontal roadway, as shown in Fig. P15.51. At time $t = 0$ the vehicles have the speeds and positions shown in the figure.
(*a*) Find the time and positions at which the vehicles meet if both continue to move with constant speed.
(*b*) Find the speed of each vehicle and relative velocity of vehicle A with respect to vehicle B as they pass each other.

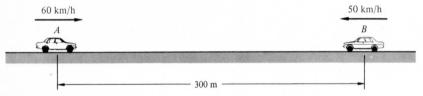

60 km/h   50 km/h

A B

|— 300 m —|

Fig. P15.51

15.52 Do the same as in Prob. 15.51 if at $t = 0$ vehicle A continues to move with constant speed and vehicle B starts to accelerate at 1.6 m/s².

15.53 Do the same as in Prob. 15.51 if at $t = 0$ both vehicles start to accelerate at 1.6 m/s².

15.54 Do the same as in Prob. 15.51 if at $t = 0$ vehicle A continues to move with constant speed and vehicle B starts to decelerate at 0.6 m/s².

15.55 Do the same as in Prob. 15.51 if at $t = 0$ both vehicles start to decelerate at 0.6 m/s².

15.56 If vehicle A in Fig. P15.51 continues to move at constant speed, find the required value of constant acceleration of vehicle B so that the vehicles pass each other at the midpoint of their initial separation distance.

15.57 If vehicle B in Fig. P15.51 continues to move at constant speed, find the required value of constant deceleration of vehicle A if the vehicles are to pass each other at the midpoint of their initial separation distance.

15.58 An automobile travels along a straight road at 35 mi/h through a 25-mi/h speed zone. A police car observes the automobile approaching. At the instant that the two vehicles are abreast of each other, the police car starts to pursue the automobile and overtakes it 16 s later. For the purposes of this problem, the police car is assumed to move with constant acceleration.

(*a*) Find the acceleration of the police car.

(*b*) Find the total distance traveled by the police car while overtaking the automobile.

(*c*) Find the speed of the police car at the time that it overtakes the automobile.

15.59 The motorist in Prob. 15.58 observes the police car in his rear view mirror 12 s after the police car started the pursuit. He applies his brakes and decelerates at 10 ft/s^2.

(*a*) Find the total time required for the police car to overtake the automobile.

(*b*) Find the total distance traveled by the police car while overtaking the automobile.

(*c*) Find the speed of the police car at the time it overtakes the automobile.

15.60 At $t = 0$, vehicle A, traveling at a speed of 60 km/h, passes a road marker on a straight horizontal roadway. Vehicle B, traveling with a speed of 90 km/h, passes the marker 2 s later. Find the time when vehicle B overtakes vehicle A, and the corresponding distance from the road marker.

15.61 Do the same as in Prob. 15.60 if vehicle B starts to accelerate at the rate of 2 m/s^2 at the instant that it passes the road marker.

15.62 Vehicle A in Prob. 15.60 starts to accelerate at the rate of 0.5 m/s^2 at the instant that vehicle B passes the road marker. Will vehicle B overtake vehicle A?

15.63 Vehicle B is stopped at a traffic light, as shown in Fig. P15.63. At the instant that the light turns green, vehicle B starts to accelerate at 3 ft/s^2. At this time vehicle A is 300 ft behind vehicle B, traveling at a speed of 30 mi/h.

(*a*) At what distance past the light will A overtake B?

(*b*) At what distance past the light will vehicle B overtake vehicle A?

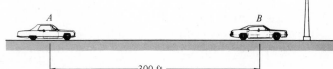

Fig. P15.63   300 ft

15.64 For what range of values of constant acceleration of vehicle B in Prob. 15.63 could vehicle A not overtake this vehicle?

15.65 An automobile travels along a straight roadway at a speed of 55 mi/h. The driver sees a disabled vehicle blocking the road ahead and applies the brakes. The resulting deceleration of the car is 18 ft/s². If the driver's visual reaction time is 0.75 s, how far has the automobile traveled between the time the driver first sees the disabled vehicle and the time that the vehicle comes to rest?

15.66 Do the same as in Prob. 15.65, if the initial speed of the automobile is 70 mi/h.

15.67 Do the same as in Prob. 15.65 if, because of some preoccupation, the driver's visual reaction time is 1.5 s.

15.68 Do the same as in Prob. 15.65, if the initial speed is 70 mi/h and the driver's visual reaction time is 1.5 s.

15.69 An archer shoots an arrow vertically upward.
(*a*) If the arrow ascends to a maximum height of 90 ft, find the required value of the initial velocity of the arrow.
(*b*) Find the time for the arrow to attain the maximum height.
(*c*) Find the total time that the arrow is in flight.

15.70 A ball is dropped from a roof, as shown in Fig. P15.70. A second ball is dropped from the roof 1 s after the first ball is dropped. Find the position and velocity of the second ball when the first ball strikes the ground.

15.71 At the instant that the ball is dropped from the roof of the building in Fig. P15.70 a second ball is projected upward, from a window at a height of 13 m above the ground, with a velocity of 2 m/s.
(*a*) Which ball strikes the ground first?
(*b*) Find the elapsed time between the impacts of the two balls with the ground.

15.72 A child drops a stone into a well shaft, as shown in Fig. P15.72. Three seconds after the child drops the stone, he hears the sound of the stone hitting the bottom of the well shaft. Find the depth, in feet, of the well. Assume that a sound wave travels with a constant velocity of 1,120 ft/s.

15.73 Figure P15.73 shows an elevator at a construction site. The elevator moves upward with a velocity of 6 ft/s. At the instant that the elevator is at a height of 120 ft above the ground, a pebble is dislodged from the bottom of the elevator cage. Find the position of the elevator when the pebble strikes the ground.

15.74 Do the same as in Prob. 15.73 if the elevator moves downward at 6 ft/s and the pebble is dislodged when the cage is 120 ft above the ground.

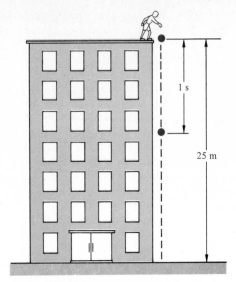

Fig. P15.70

Fig. P15.72

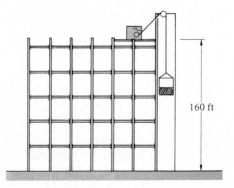

Fig. P15.73

15.75 Do the same as in Prob. 15.73 if the elevator decelerates at 0.5 ft/s². At the instant that the pebble is dislodged, the elevator velocity is 6 ft/s upward and the cage is at a height of 120 ft above the ground.

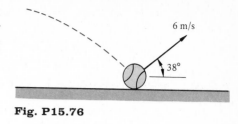

Fig. P15.76

15.76 Figure P15.76 shows a ball rebounding from a pavement.
(a) Find the maximum height to which the ball will rise.
(b) Find the distance from the initial position at which the ball strikes the pavement again.

15.77 Figure P15.77 shows a conveyor belt system for moving metal castings. The castings are assumed to leave the upper conveyor belt at point *a* and strike the lower conveyor belt at point *b*. Find the maximum permissible value of the spacing dimension *x*.

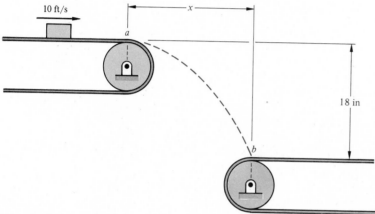

Fig. P15.77

15.78 Figure P15.78 shows the observed motion of a cricket. The distances *a* and *b* are estimated to be 1.5 m and 400 mm, respectively. Find the corresponding values of the magnitude v_0 and direction θ of the initial velocity of the cricket.

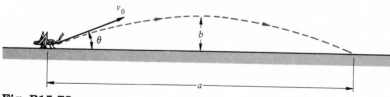

Fig. P15.78

15.79 A ball is struck by a paddle and has the initial velocity shown in Fig. P15.79.
(a) Find the maximum height to which the ball will rise, and the time to reach this height.
(b) How far does the ball travel from the initial position before it strikes the ground?
(c) Find the velocity with which the ball strikes the ground.
(d) Find the total time that the ball is in flight.

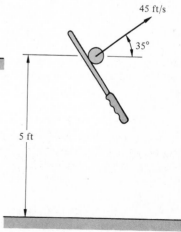

Fig. P15.79

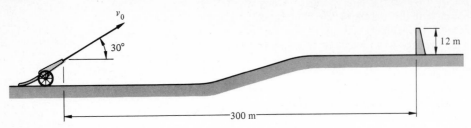

Fig. P15.80

15.80 Find the range of values of v_0 for which the cannon projectile in Fig. P15.80 will clear the top edge of the vertical wall.

15.81 Find the radius of curvature of the trajectory of the shell in Example 15.11 when the shell is at its maximum height above the ground.

15.82 A bomber flies in a horizontal direction with a speed of 400 mi/h, as shown in Fig. P15.82. The bombardier wishes to hit a target at b.

(a) How many seconds before the plane is directly over the target should the bomb be relased from the plane?

(b) Find the distance x_1 which corresponds to the solution to part a.

(c) Find the magnitude and direcion of the velocity with which the bomb strikes the target.

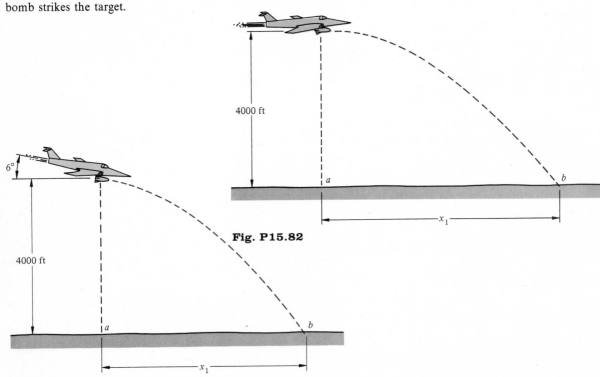

Fig. P15.82

Fig. P15.83

15.83 Do the same as in Prob. 15.82 if the plane is in a glide of constant direction, with a speed of 400 mi/h, as shown in Fig. P15.83.

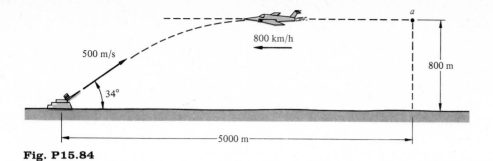

Fig. P15.84

15.84 Figure P15.84 shows an antiaircraft gun emplacement. At $t = 0$ a plane passes point a, traveling in a horizontal direction at constant velocity.
(a) At what time of firing will the gun shell hit the plane?
(b) How far is the plane from the gun emplacement when it is hit?

15.85 Figure P15.85 shows a gun emplacement. Find the minimum value of θ if the shell is to clear point a.

15.86 Figure P15.86 shows a gun emplacement.
(a) For which distance x will the shell hit the stationary tank?
(b) How long is the shell in flight?
(c) With what velocity does the shell hit the tank?

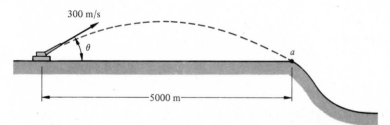

Fig. P15.85

15.87 Figure P15.87 shows two tanks on horizontal ground. Find the value of the distance x, if the shell fired from tank A is to hit tank B.

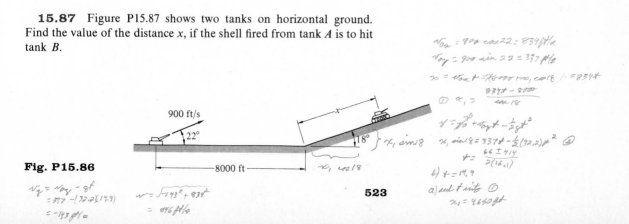

Fig. P15.86

$v_y = v_{0y} - gt$
$\quad = 337 - (32.2)(17.9)$
$\quad = -143 \, ft/s$

$v = \sqrt{143^2 + 834^2}$
$\quad = 846 \, ft/s$

$v_{0x} = 900 \cos 22 = 834 \, ft/s$

$v_{0y} = 900 \sin 22 = 337 \, ft/s$

$x_1 = v_{0x} t = (8000 + x_1 \cos 18) \quad t = 834 t$

① $x_1 = \dfrac{834t - 8000}{\cos 18}$

$y = y_0 + v_{0y} t - \frac{1}{2} g t^2$

$x_1 \sin 18 = 337t - \frac{1}{2}(32.2) t^2$ ②

$t = \dfrac{66 \pm 4.14}{2(16.1)}$

b) $t = 19.9$

a) and t into ①

$x_1 = 4650 \, ft$

135 m/s

A

25°

B

x

Fig. P15.87

15.88 Tank A in Fig. P15.87 is stationary, and tank B advances toward tank A at a speed of 72 km/h. At $t = 0$ the gunner in tank A fires his gun. At this instant, the separation distance of the two tanks is x. Find the value of x if the shell is to hit tank B.

15.89 Do the same as in Prob. 15.88, if tank B is stationary and tank A advances toward tank B at a speed of 72 km/h.

15.90 Do the same as in Prob. 15.90, if both tanks approach each other with speeds of 72 km/h each.

15.91 Show that the trajectory of a particle which moves in a vertical plane without air resistance is a plane parabolic curve.

15.92 Figure P15.92 shows the vertical wall of a tank that contains water. Fluid flows through two small orifices in the wall. If all friction losses are neglected, it can be shown that the velocity of the fluid jet is

$$v = \sqrt{2gh}$$

where h is the vertical distance between the orifice and the surface of the liquid. Find the locations x and y at which the centerlines of the two fluid streams intersect.

15.93 A particle travels around a circular track, as shown in Fig. P15.93. The speed of the particle is 2.4 ft/s and at $t = 0$, the particle is at position a.
(a) Find the position of the particle, and the x and y components of the velocity, when $t = 9$ s.
(b) Find the normal and tangential components of the acceleration when $t = 9$ s.
(c) Find the x and y components of the acceleration when $t = 9$ s.

15.94 A particle moves along a circular track, shown in Fig. P15.94, with constant tangential acceleration $a_t = 0.28$ m/s². The particle starts from rest at point a.
(a) Find the x and y components of the velocity when the particle first reaches point b.
(b) Find the magnitude and direction of the acceleration when the particle first reaches point b.

15.95 Do the same as in Prob. 15.94, if $a_t = -0.28$ m/s².

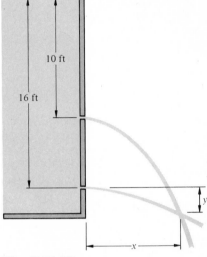

10 ft

16 ft

y

x

Fig. P15.92

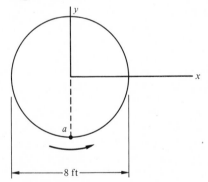

y

x

a

8 ft

Fig. P15.93

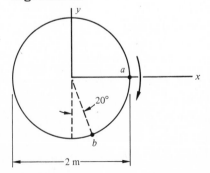

y

x

a

20°

b

2 m

Fig. P15.94

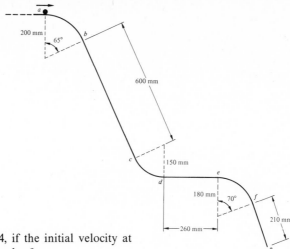

Fig. P15.98

15.96 Do the same as in Prob. 15.94, if the initial velocity at point *a* is 1.5 m/s, in a downward sense in the figure.

15.97 Do the same as in Prob. 15.94, for the case where the particle is at point *b* the second time.

15.98 A particle moves along a curved track that lies in a horizontal plane, as shown in Fig. P15.98. The speed of the particle has a constant value of 0.15 m/s. (*a*) Find the maximum value of acceleration which the particle experiences as it moves from *a* to *g*. (*b*) Where along the path does this acceleration occur?

15.99 A particle moves with constant speed of 22 ft/s along a path of parabolic shape that passes through the points *a*, *b*, and the origin, as shown in Fig. P15.99. Find the magnitude, direction, and sense of the acceleration at the origin, and at points *a* and *b*. (*Hint:* The general equation of a plane parabolic curve is $y = ax^2 + bx + c$, where *a*, *b*, and *c* are constants.)

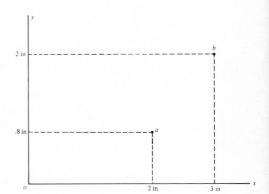

Fig. P15.99

15.100 Two particles move along straight parallel paths, as shown in Fig. P15.100. Particle *a* moves with a velocity of 1.6 m/s. Particle *b* accelerates a 0.4 m/s². At time zero the particles have the positions shown, and $v_b = 0.5$ m/s.
(*a*) At what time is the direction of the relative displacement of *b* with respect to *a* normal to the path of motion?
(*b*) Find the corresponding values of the relative velocity and acceleration of particle *a* with respect to particle *b*.

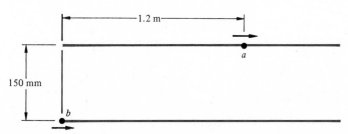

Fig. P15.100

15.101 Figure P15.101 shows two vehicles on intersecting roads. At the instant shown, $v_A = 60$ km/h and $v_B = 45$ km/h. Vehicle B accelerates at 2 m/s² and vehicle A decelerates at 3.8 m/s². Find the relative displacement, velocity, and acceleration of vehicle A with respect to vehicle B at the instant shown.

15.102 Do the same as in Prob. 15.101, if vehicle A accelerates at 2.9 m/s².

15.103 At $t = 0$ vehicle B just passes beneath the overpass and vehicle A is 1,000 ft from this structure. At this instant, $v_A = 35$ mi/h and vehicle A starts to accelerate at 4 ft/s², while vehicle B continues at a constant speed of 55 mi/h.

(a) Find the relative displacement, velocity, and acceleration of vehicle A with respect to vehicle B at the time that vehicle A crosses the overpass.

(b) Find the x and y components of the relative displacement, velocity and acceleration of vehicle B with respect to vehicle A at the time that vehicle A crosses the overpass.

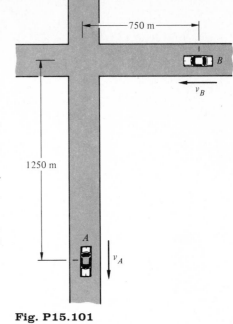

Fig. P15.101

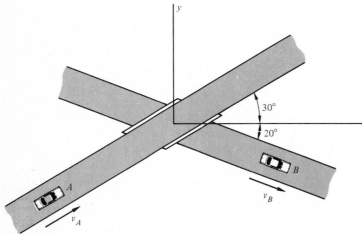
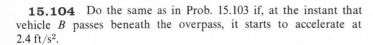
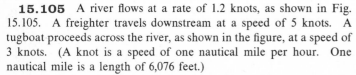

Fig. P15.103

15.104 Do the same as in Prob. 15.103 if, at the instant that vehicle B passes beneath the overpass, it starts to accelerate at 2.4 ft/s².

15.105 A river flows at a rate of 1.2 knots, as shown in Fig. 15.105. A freighter travels downstream at a speed of 5 knots. A tugboat proceeds across the river, as shown in the figure, at a speed of 3 knots. (A knot is a speed of one nautical mile per hour. One nautical mile is a length of 6,076 feet.)

(a) Find the relative velocity of the tugboat with respect to the freighter.

(b) For what value of the distance x would the two vessels collide?

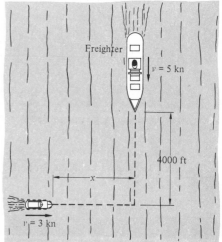

Fig. P15.105

526

15.106 Do the same as in Prob. 15.105, if the position of the tugboat with respect to the freighter is as shown in Fig. 15.106.

15.107 Figure P15.107 shows two concentric circular tracks that lie in a horizontal plane. Particle a travels in a counterclockwise sense with a velocity of 10 m/s, and particle b travels in a clockwise sense with a velocity of 26 m/s. Find the magnitude and direction of the relative displacement and velocity of particle a with respect to particle b for the following positions.
(a) $\theta_a = \theta_b = 0$
(b) $\theta_a = 0 \qquad \theta_b = 180°$
(c) $\theta_a = 250° \qquad \theta_b = 130°$
(d) $\theta_a = -40° \qquad \theta_b = 90°$

15.108 Figure P15.108 shows a Ferris wheel in an amusement park. The wheel has eight equally spaced cars. The velocity of each car is 14 ft/s, with a direction which is tangent to the rim of the ferris wheel. When the wheel is in the position shown in the figure, a passenger in car A looks out and observes a friend who is in car B. Find the magnitude, direction, and sense of the velocity with which the friend in car B moves with respect to the passenger in car A.

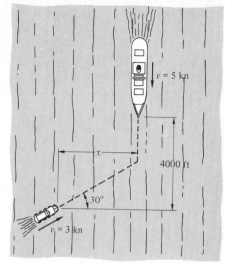

Fig. P15.106

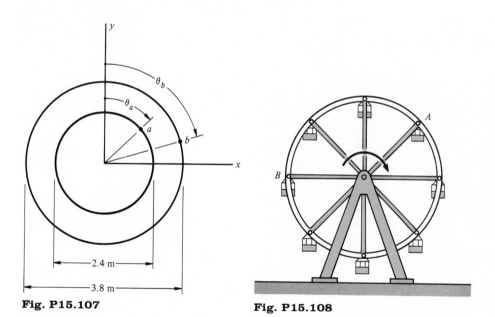

Fig. P15.107

Fig. P15.108

15.109 Do the same as in Prob. 15.108, when car A is in its lowest possible position.

16
Dynamics of Particles

16.1 INTRODUCTION—NEWTON'S SECOND LAW

In Chap. 1 a particle was defined to be a physical element, with mass, whose dimensions are all vanishingly small. Consequently, no rotation effects need be considered when the motion of the particle is described. It follows, then, that the motion of a particle is completely defined by describing its *translational* motion.

The motion of a particle may be one of two general types. The first kind occurs when the particle moves along a straight line. This type of motion is described as *rectilinear translation*. The second type occurs when the particle moves along a curved path. This type of motion is called curvilinear translation. This curved path may lie in either a two- or a three-dimensional space. The former motion is described as *plane curvilinear motion*, while the latter is referred to as *general curvilinear motion*.

In this chapter, we will study the relation between the force that acts on a particle and the resulting motion. The fundamental basis of all engineering dynamics is Newton's second law, which states that a particle which is acted on by a resultant force will experience an acceleration which is directly proportional to this force and in the direction of the force. In equation form, Newton's second law for a particle appears as

$$\mathbf{F} = m\mathbf{a} \qquad (16.1)$$

where m = mass of particle
$\mathbf{a}$ = acceleration of particle
$\mathbf{F}$ = resultant force acting on the particle

This resultant force is expressed by

$$F = \sum_{i=1}^{i=n} F_i \qquad (16.2)$$

where n is the number of forces F_i which act on the particle and the summation operation is understood to be a vector summation. The acceleration $\mathbf{a}$ in Newton's second law must be expressed in terms of an absolute inertial coordinate system.

It may be seen from Eq. (16.2) that $\mathbf{F}$ and $\mathbf{a}$ are two vector quantities related by the scalar multiplier m. It follows that $\mathbf{F}$ and $\mathbf{a}$ have the *same direction and sense* and differ only in *magnitude* by the positive factor m. Equation (16.2), which expresses Newton's second law, is an example of the multiplication† of a vector quantity by a scalar quantity.

The physical interpretation of Newton's second law is that if a *resultant* force $\mathbf{F}$ acts on a particle of mass m, then the particle will experience an acceleration which has the direction and sense of the resultant force. The magnitude of the acceleration is then given by

$$a = \frac{1}{m}F \qquad (16.3)$$

where F and a are the magnitudes of the resultant force and the acceleration. The effect described above is shown in Fig. 16.1a, where a particle is acted on by the three forces $\mathbf{F}_1$, $\mathbf{F}_2$, and $\mathbf{F}_3$. The resultant force $\mathbf{F}$ is shown in Fig. 16.1b. From the definition of Newton's second law, it follows that the direction of the acceleration is along line ab, with a sense from a to b. The reader is urged to master this fundamental concept and interpretation of Newton's second law, because the relationship is used repeatedly throughout the study of engineering dynamics.

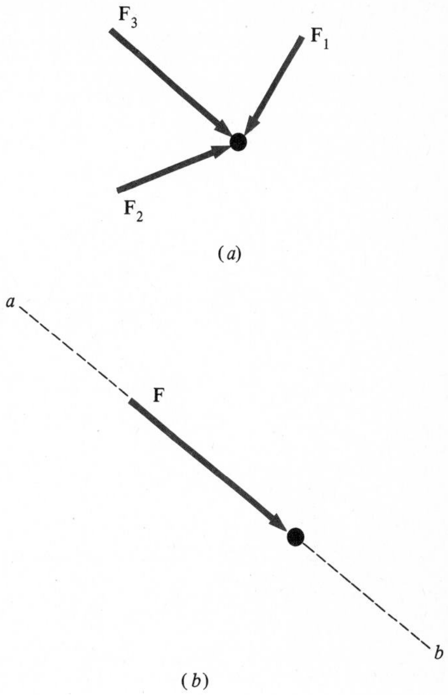

If the resultant force which acts on a particle is zero, Newton's second law has the form

$$0 = m\mathbf{a} \qquad \mathbf{a} = 0 \qquad (16.4)$$

The components of the vector $\mathbf{a}$ along the three coordinate directions are a_x, a_y, and a_z. A necessary condition for Eq. (16.4) to be true is

$$a_x = \ddot{x} = 0 \qquad a_y = \ddot{y} = 0 \qquad a_z = \ddot{z} = 0 \qquad (16.5)$$

$$v_x = \dot{x} = \text{constant} \qquad v_y = \dot{y} = \text{constant} \qquad (16.6)$$

$$v_z = \dot{z} = \text{constant}$$

If these equations are satisfied, it follows that the resultant force

(a)

(b)

Fig. 16.1

---

†See the author's *Engineering Mechanics: Statics,* McGraw-Hill, New York, 1980, sec. 2.4, for a discussion of this operation.

which acts on the particle is zero. It also follows that the particle is at rest, or moving with constant velocity. The above conditions of motion and resultant force are the necessary conditions for the *static* equilibrium of a particle.

In the examples in this chapter, bodies will be considered that have finite dimensions. It may be recalled that a particle is defined as a physical body with mass and vanishingly small dimensions. Thus, the bodies used in the Examples do not fit the strict definition of a particle. It will be shown in Chap. 19, however, that the equations of particle dynamics accurately describe the translational motion of a body if all rotation effects are considered to be negligible. The distinguishing characteristic of particle motion is therefore the absence of all rotation effects.

16.2 UNITS

In the U.S. Customary System (USCS) of units, length, time, and force are chosen to be fundamental units. The length unit is the foot, the force unit is the pound, and the time unit is the second. The symbols used to represent these quantities are

Foot, ft

Pound, lb

Second, s

The value of the gravitational acceleration g in USCS units is 32.17 ft/s². (Throughout the text, a rounded-off value of 32.2 ft/s² will be used.) A multiple of the fundamental length unit commonly used in dynamics problems is the mile, and

$$1 \text{ mi} = 5{,}280 \text{ ft} \tag{16.7}$$

The mass unit is the slug. A *slug* is that mass which, when acted on by a force of one pound, will experience an acceleration of one foot per second squared. Using Newton's second law, we have

$$F = ma \tag{16.8}$$

$$1 \text{ lb} = 1 \text{ slug}\left(1 \ \frac{\text{ft}}{\text{s}^2}\right) \tag{16.9}$$

$$1 \text{ slug} = 1 \ \frac{\text{lb} \cdot \text{s}^2}{\text{ft}} \tag{16.10}$$

The unit of angular measurement is the degree, with the symbol °, defined by

$$1 \text{ revolution} = 1 \text{ r} = 360° = 2\pi \text{ radians} = 2\pi \text{ rad} \tag{16.11}$$

$$1 \text{ rad} = 57.3° \tag{16.12}$$

In SI units, length, time, and mass are chosen to be fundamental units. The length unit is the meter, the mass unit is the
kilogram, and the time unit is the second. The symbols used to
represent these quantities are

Meter, m

Kilogram, kg

Second, s

The value of the gravitational acceleration g in SI units is 9.807
m/s^2. (Throughout the text, a rounded-off value of 9.81 m/s^2
will be used.)

The derived unit of force is the *newton*, with the symbol N.
A force of one newton will give a mass of one kilogram an
acceleration of one meter per second squared. Using Newton's
second law, we get

$$F = ma \qquad (16.13)$$

$$1\ \text{N} = 1\ \text{kg}\left(1\ \frac{\text{m}}{\text{s}^2}\right) = 1\ \frac{\text{kg}\cdot\text{m}}{\text{s}^2} \qquad (16.14)$$

The factors for conversion between the USCS and SI units are

$$
\begin{aligned}
1\ \text{ft} &= 0.3048\ \text{m} \approx 0.305\ \text{m} \\
1\ \text{m} &= 3.281\ \text{ft} \approx 3.28\ \text{ft}
\end{aligned}
\qquad (16.15)
$$

$$
\begin{aligned}
1\ \text{lb} &= 4.448\ \text{N} \approx 4.45\ \text{N} \\
1\ \text{N} &= 0.2248\ \text{lb} \approx 0.225\ \text{lb}
\end{aligned}
\qquad (16.16)
$$

$$
\begin{aligned}
1\ \text{slug} &= 14.59\ \text{kg} \approx 14.6\ \text{kg} \\
1\ \text{kg} &= 0.06854\ \text{slug} \approx 0.0685\ \text{slug}
\end{aligned}
\qquad (16.17)
$$

As an estimate of the relative sizes of the above length and
force units, it may be noted that 1 m is approximately 3 ft,
while 1 N is approximately 0.25 lb.

The units of angular measurement in SI units are the same as
in USCS units.

16.3 DYNAMICS OF A PARTICLE IN RECTILINEAR TRANSLATION

The case will now be considered where the particle is acted on
by an applied force and moves with rectilinear translation.
Figure 16.2 shows the typical appearance of this situation. The
x axis is the axis of motion. A very important conclusion may
be drawn from this figure. Since the particle is constrained to
move in the x direction *only*, the y component of displacement
and velocity of the particle must be zero. The consequence of
this is that the y component of the resultant of the applied and
reaction forces which act on the particle must be zero. Thus, it
is only the x component of the resultant force which produces

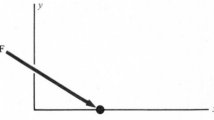

Fig. 16.2

acceleration along the axis of translation. Moreover, the particle must be in static equilibrium in the y direction.

A set of general rules for the solution of dynamics problems
in rectilinear translation is as follows:

1. A coordinate is chosen to represent the displacement of
   the mass particle from some reference point. From the
   discussion in Chap. 15, *this definition of the positive sense
   of displacement automatically establishes the positive senses
   of the velocity and acceleration.*
2. A free-body diagram of the particle is drawn, and all the
   forces acting on the particle are shown. These forces will
   include both the known applied forces acting on the particle, and the unknown reaction forces exerted on the particle by the immediate supporting foundation which is
   imagined to be removed.
3. The components of the resultant force in the direction of
   the axis of motion, and normal to this direction, are computed. A force component is considered positive if it has
   the sense of a positive coordinate axis.
4. The component of the resultant force which is normal to
   the direction of motion is set to equal to zero, to satisfy the
   static equilibrium requirements in this direction.
5. The component of the resultant force in the direction of
   motion is then used in Newton's second law. Since the
   directions of the force and the acceleration are known, the
   equation will be in terms of the scalar magnitudes of the
   latter two quantities.

The basic steps in solving for the acceleration of a mass
particle in rectilinear translation are summarized below.

1. Choose the displacement coordinate of the particle.
2. Draw the free-body diagram of the particle.
3. Find the components of the resultant force in the direction
   parallel to, and normal to, the direction of motion.
4. Set the normal component of the resultant force equal to
   zero.
5. Use the parallel component of the resultant force in Newton's second law, to find the acceleration of the particle.

If the component of the resultant force in the direction of
motion has a constant value, it follows that the *acceleration of
the particle is constant.* The case of rectilinear translation with
constant acceleration was presented in Sec. 15.4. The kinematic equations which describe this type of motion are

$$v = v_0 + at \qquad (16.18)$$

$$s = s_0 + v_0 t + \tfrac{1}{2}at^2 \qquad (16.19)$$

$$v^2 = v_0^2 + 2a(s - s_0) \qquad (16.20)$$

where s is a symbolic displacement coordinate. If the particle moves along the x axis, for example, then s is defined to be x. At $t = 0$, the initial displacement and velocity of the particle are s_0 and v_0, respectively. To solve a problem of particle dynamics in rectilinear translation, in which the force in the direction of motion is constant, first this force is used to find the *constant* value of the acceleration of the particle. Then this acceleration is used with Eqs. (16.18) to (16.20) to obtain a complete description of the motion of the particle.

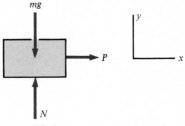

Fig. 16.3

Example 16.1 A block of mass m rests on a smooth, horizontal surface, as shown in Fig. 16.3. A horizontal force of constant magnitude P is applied to the block. Find the resulting acceleration of this element.

Solution This is a problem where the force is known and the resulting motion is to be found.

The free-body diagram of the block is shown in Fig. 16.4, together with an arbitrarily assumed positive sense for the displacement x. The known applied forces which act on the block are the weight force mg and the applied force P. The unknown reaction force is designated as N. For equilibrium in the y direction,

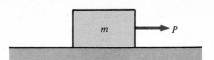

Fig. 16.4

$$\sum F_y = 0 \qquad -mg + N = 0 \qquad N = mg \qquad (16.21)$$

This result has no further use at present. The equation of motion in the x direction is

$$\sum F_x = ma \qquad P = ma \qquad a = \frac{P}{m} = \text{const.} \qquad (16.22)$$

Example 16.2 A 130-lb block slides along a smooth, horizontal track with a velocity of 50 ft/s as shown in Fig. 16.5. At a certain point the smooth track joins a section of rough, horizontal track. The coefficient of kinetic friction between the block and the rough track is 0.24.

a How long will it take for the block to come to rest?

b How far along the rough track will the block slide before coming to rest?

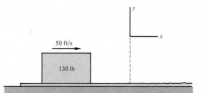

Fig. 16.5

Solution The displacement coordinate x is measured from the beginning of the rough track. The free-body diagram of the block, when sliding on the rough track, is shown in Fig. 16.6.

For equilibrium in the y direction,

$$\sum F_y = 0 \qquad -130 + N = 0 \qquad N = 130 \text{ lb} \qquad (16.23)$$

The equation of motion in the x direction is

$$\sum F_x = ma \qquad -\mu_k N = ma \qquad (16.24)$$

$$-0.24(130) = \frac{130}{32.2}a$$

$$a = -7.73 \text{ ft/s}^2 \qquad (16.25)$$

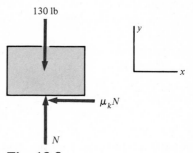

Fig. 16.6

The friction force in Eq. (16.25) is written with a minus sign, since this force acts in the opposite sense of the positive displacement coordinate x. The negative value obtained in Eq. (16.25) indicates that the sense of the acceleration is opposite to that of the velocity, so that the block is slowing down. Thus, the formal statement of the solution is that the deceleration of the block is 7.73 ft/s².

a The time to come to rest is found from

$$v = v_0 + at \qquad (16.26)$$

$$0 = 50 + (-7.73)t \qquad t = 6.47 \text{ s} \qquad (16.27)$$

b The distance traveled by the block before it comes to rest is given by

$$v^2 = v_0^2 + 2a(x - x_0) \qquad (16.28)$$

With $x_0 = 0$,

$$0 = 50^2 + 2(-7.73)(x - 0) \qquad x = 162 \text{ ft} \qquad (16.29)$$

This result may be checked by using the equation

$$x = x_0 + v_0 t + \tfrac{1}{2}at^2 \qquad (16.30)$$

$$x = 0 + 50(6.47) + \tfrac{1}{2}(-7.73)(6.47^2) = 162 \text{ ft} \qquad (16.31)$$

The tacit assumption is made in this problem that the length of the roughened section of the track is at least 162 ft.

Example 16.3 A person stands in an elevator, as shown in Fig. 16.7. The person's weight is 180 lb.

a The elevator accelerates upward with a constant value of 8 ft/s². What is the apparent weight of the person during this period of acceleration?

b Do the same as in part *a* for a constant downward acceleration of the elevator of 8 ft/s².

c If the elevator cage weighs 1,450 lb, find the cable tensile force T which corresponds to the acceleration of part *a*.

d For what value of acceleration of the elevator would the person appear to be weightless?

Fig. 16.7

Solution This is an example where the acceleration is known and the value of the force is to be obtained.

a The free-body diagram of the person is shown in Fig. 16.8. The equation of motion in the y direction is

$$\sum F_y = ma \qquad N - 180 = \frac{180}{g}a = \frac{180}{32.2}(8) = 44.7 \text{ lb}$$

$$N = 225 \text{ lb} \qquad (16.32)$$

N is the force exerted by the elevator floor on the person. From Newton's third law, the force exerted by the person on the elevator floor is *equal and opposite* to the force N shown in Fig. 16.8. This latter force is the "weight" of the person. It may be seen that, for upward acceleration of the elevator, the person appears to weigh *more* than he or she actually does.

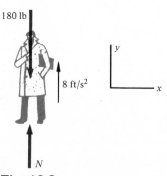

Fig. 16.8

b The free-body diagram of the person for downward acceleration of the elevator is shown in Fig. 16.9. The equation of motion is

$$\sum F_y = ma \qquad N - 180 = \frac{180}{g}a = \frac{180}{32.2}(-8) = -44.7 \text{ lb}$$
$$N = 135 \text{ lb} \qquad\qquad (16.33)$$

For downward acceleration of the elevator, the person appears to weigh *less* than she or he actually does.

c The free-body diagram of the elevator is shown in Fig. 16.10, and T is the tensile force in the elevator cable. The equation of motion is

$$\sum F_y = ma \qquad T - 1{,}630 = \frac{1{,}630}{g}a = \frac{1{,}630}{32.2}(8)\,T = 2{,}030 \text{ lb}$$
$$(16.34)$$

It may be observed that the normal force between the person and the elevator floor does *not* enter into this problem. The reason is that this force is an *internal* force when the free-body diagram of the system (the elevator cage and the man) is considered.

d The free-body diagram for general motion of the person is shown in Fig. 16.11. In order for the person to appear weightless, he or she must exert no force on the floor of the elevator, or $N = 0$. The equation of motion, in the negative y coordinate sense, is then

$$\sum F_y = ma \qquad -180 = \frac{180}{g}a \qquad a = -g \qquad (16.35)$$

For this case the elevator is in free fall, as if the cable had been cut.

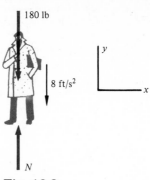

Fig. 16.9

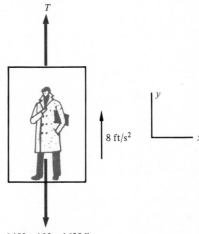

1450 + 180 = 1630 lb

Fig. 16.10

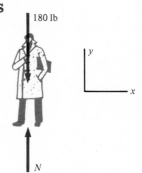

Fig. 16.11

16.4 DYNAMICS OF CONNECTED PARTICLES IN RECTILINEAR TRANSLATION

In certain problems the motion of two or more particles connected by cables or links is desired. For this case, the assumptions are made that the cable or link is inextensible, the mass of the cable or link is negligible compared with the masses of the particles, and the cable cannot transmit a compressive force.

The technique for solving for the motion of two connected particles is to draw individual free-body diagrams and write the equation of motion for each mass particle. The cable, or link, force will appear in these free-body diagrams as a single unknown force. Since the cable or link is assumed to be inextensible and the particle moves in rectilinear translation, it follows that the acceleration of both the connected bodies must be the same.

There are thus two equations of motion of the particle, in terms of the unknown cable force and acceleration. These two equations may then be solved simultaneously to obtain the final solution.

Example 16.4 The system of two blocks in Fig. 16.12 is released from rest at $t = 0$.

a Find the acceleration of the two blocks and the cable tensile force.

b At what time will the two blocks pass each other?

c What are the velocities of the blocks when they pass each other?

d If block B were suddenly brought to rest 1.6 s after the onset of motion, describe the ensuing motion of block A.

The pulley is massless, and the pulley bearings are frictionless.

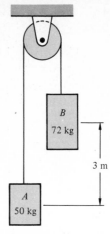

Fig. 16.12

Solution From physical considerations, it may be concluded that block A moves upward and block B moves downward. The free-body diagrams of the two blocks are shown in Fig. 16.13, and T is the unknown magnitude of the cable tensile force.

a The equations of motion are

Block A $\sum F_y = ma$ $T - 491 = 50a$ (16.36)

Block B $\sum F_y = ma$ $706 - T = 72a$ (16.37)

The solutions to Eqs. (16.36) and (16.37) are

$$a = 1.77 \text{ m/s}^2 \qquad T = 579 \text{ N} \qquad (16.38)$$

b Both blocks start from rest with the *same* acceleration. The time t for the two centerlines to be at the same horizontal level is found from

$$y = y_0 + v_0 t + \tfrac{1}{2}at^2 \qquad (16.39)$$

$$\tfrac{1}{2}(3) = 0 + 0(t) + \tfrac{1}{2}(1.77)t^2 \qquad t = 1.30 \text{ s} \qquad (16.40)$$

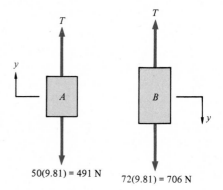

Fig. 16.13

c The velocity of each block when they pass each other is obtained from

$$v = v_0 + at \qquad (16.41)$$

$$= 0 + 1.77(1.30) = 2.30 \text{ m/s} \qquad (16.42)$$

d The velocity of block A at $t = 1.6$ s is

$$v = v_0 + at \qquad (16.43)$$

$$= 0 + 1.77(1.6) = 2.83 \text{ m/s} \qquad (16.44)$$

At the instant that block B comes to rest, the value of the cable force T drops to zero. Thereafter, block A behaves as a particle with an initial upward velocity in a gravitational field. The maximum *additional* height y which it will attain is found from the equation

$$v^2 = v_0^2 + 2a(y - y_0) \qquad (16.45)$$

With $y_0 = 0$ and $a = -g = -9.81$ m/s^2, Eq. (16.45) has the form

$$0 = 2.83^2 + 2(-9.81)y \qquad y = 0.408 \text{ m} \qquad (16.46)$$

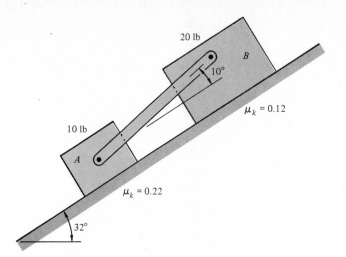

Fig. 16.14

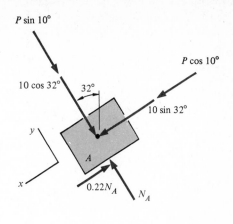

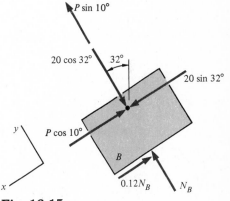

Fig. 16.15

The time to reach this height is found from

$$v = v_0 + at \qquad (16.47)$$

$$0 = 2.83 + (-9.81)t \qquad (16.48)$$

$$t = 0.288 \text{ s} \qquad (16.49)$$

Example 16.5 The two blocks in Fig. 16.14 are connected by a massless link.
a Find the acceleration of the system and the force in the link.
b Would the answer to part *a* be different if the positions of the two blocks on the plane were interchanged?

Solution
a The link may be recognized as being a two-force, or truss, member since the forces acting on this element are applied at its ends only. Thus, the directions of these forces are collinear with the axis of the link. The free-body diagrams of the two blocks are shown in Fig. 16.15, where P is the compressive force in the link.
The equilibrium and motion requirements of the two blocks are

Block A
$$\sum F_y = 0 \qquad -P \sin 10° - 10 \cos 32° + N_A = 0 \qquad (16.50)$$

$$\sum F_x = ma \qquad P \cos 10° + 10 \sin 32° - 0.22 N_A = \frac{10}{32.2}a \qquad (16.51)$$

Block B
$$\sum F_y = 0 \qquad -20 \cos 32° + P \sin 10° + N_B = 0 \qquad (16.52)$$

$$\sum F_x = ma \qquad 20 \sin 32° - P \cos 10° - 0.12 N_B = \frac{20}{32.2}a \qquad (16.53)$$

N_A is eliminated between Eqs. (16.50) and (16.51), to obtain

$$0.947P + 3.43 = 0.310a \qquad (16.54)$$

537

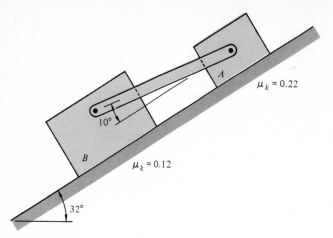

Fig. 16.16

Elimination of N_B between Eqs. (16.52) and (16.53) results in

$$8.56 - 0.964P = 0.621a \qquad (16.55)$$

Equations (16.54) and (16.55) are solved simultaneously, and the final results are

$$a = 12.9 \text{ ft/s}^2 \qquad P = 0.598 \text{ lb} \qquad (16.56)$$

b Figure 16.16 shows the configuration when the positions of the two blocks are interchanged. It is left as an exercise for the reader to show, from a sketch of the free-body diagrams of the two blocks, that this is a different problem from that of part *a*. This problem is to be solved as Prob. 16.48.

16.5 DYNAMICS OF A PARTICLE IN PLANE CURVILINEAR MOTION—NORMAL AND TANGENTIAL COMPONENTS

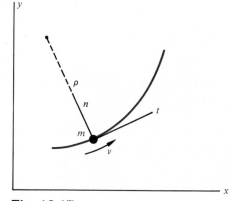

Fig. 16.17

Figure 16.17 shows a mass particle which moves along a plane curve. A set of *nt* axes are positioned on the curve, so that the *t* axis is tangent to the curve and the *n* axis is normal to this direction. It was shown in Chap. 15 that the particle traveling on the plane curve experiences two distinct acceleration effects. These two effects are related to the normal and tangential components of the *total* acceleration of the particle.

The first effect is called the normal, or centripetal, acceleration a_n. This quantity is given by

$$a_n = \frac{v^2}{\rho} \qquad (16.57)$$

where v is the magnitude of the velocity, or the speed, along the curve and ρ is the local radius of curvature. The direction of a_n is along the radius of curvature. Its sense is always from the particle toward the center of curvature.

The second acceleration effect is referred to as the tangential acceleration a_t. It is defined as

$$a_t = \dot{v} = \ddot{s} \qquad (16.58)$$

where s is the length coordinate along the curve. The direction of a_t is tangent to the curve, and $\dot{v}$ is the time rate of change of the magnitude of velocity, or of the speed, along the curve. Figure 16.18 shows the positive senses of a_n and a_t.

Newton's second law may be written for a particle which moves along a plane curvilinear path. Figure 16.19 shows the general appearance of a particle acted on by a resultant force **F**. This force may be resolved into normal and tangential components, as shown in the figure. Newton's second law in the component directions of the particle is then

$$F_n = ma_n = \frac{mv^2}{\rho} \qquad (16.59)$$

$$F_t = ma_t = m\dot{v} = m\ddot{s} \qquad (16.60)$$

These two equations reveal a very significant characteristic of plane curvilinear motion. From consideration of Eq. (16.59), it may be concluded that F_n will be zero *only* if $v = 0$ or $\rho \rightarrow \infty$. The former condition is the trivial case of no motion of the particle, while the latter implies that the curvilinear path is a straight-line path. The above observations now lead to a very important conclusion: *if a mass particle moves with plane curvilinear motion, the normal component of the resultant force which acts on the particle is never zero.* This component of force is required to make the particle *continually* chnge the *direction* of its velocity vector, in order to follow the curvature of the curved path. The results of the above case may be compared with the requirements for rectilinear translation of a particle. In this latter problem, the particle is always in static equilibrium in the direction normal to the motion.

The effects described above may be illustrated with the system shown in Fig. 16.20. The particle is assumed to rest on a frictionless horizontal plane and move along the curved path *abc*. The normal force F_n which acts on the particle is the force which is required to make the particle follow the curved path. This normal force is now imagined to be suddenly removed when the particle reaches point *b*. At the instant that the force is removed, Newton's second law in the normal direction has the form

$$F_n = 0 = \frac{v^2}{\rho} \qquad (16.61)$$

When the particle reaches point *b*, it has a nonzero speed v. The only way that Eq. (16.61) can be satisfied is for $\rho \rightarrow \infty$.

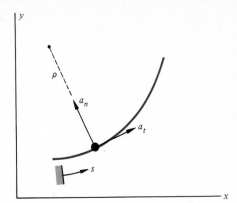

Fig. 16.18

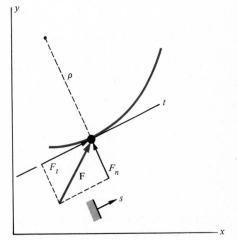

Fig. 16.19

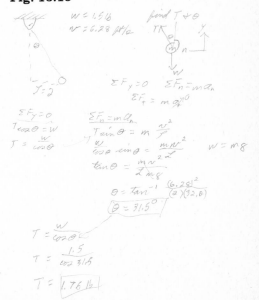

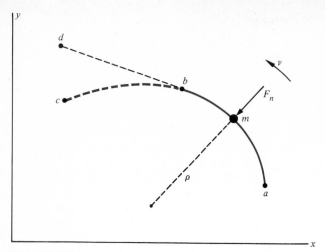

Fig. 16.20

Thus, the subsequent motion of the particle beyond point b is along the straight line bd shown in the figure. It also follows that the particle will move with *constant* speed v along this straight line, since the resultant force that acts on the particle during this time is zero.

A set of general steps, which are similar to the ones listed in Sec. 16.3 for the case of rectilinear translation, for the solution of dynamics problems in plane curvilinear motion are presented below. In all cases, the *normal* direction is along the radius of curvature, with a positive sense which is from the path toward the center of curvature, and the *tangential* direction is along a straight line tangent to the path.

1. Draw a free-body diagram of the particle.
2. Find the normal and tangential components of the resultant force which acts on the particle.
3. Write the two component equations of motion given by Eqs. (16.59) and (16.60).

In certain problems, the normal acceleration a_n may be constant. This motion, however, is *never* referred to as motion with constant acceleration, since the direction of the acceleration of the particle is continually changing.

Example 16.6 A mass particle connected to an inextensible string moves with a constant velocity of 6 m/s in a circular path in a vertical plane, as shown in Fig. 16.21.

 a Find the tensile force in the string when the particle is at point a.
 b Do the same as in part a when the particle is at point b.

Solution

 a Figure 16.22 shows the free-body diagram of the particle at point a, and T is the tensile force in the string. The equation of motion of the particle is

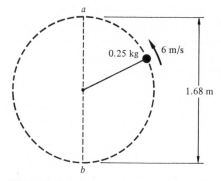

Fig. 16.21

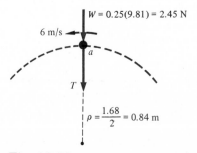

Fig. 16.22

$$\sum F_n = ma_n \qquad W + T = \frac{mv^2}{\rho} \qquad (16.62)$$

$$2.45 + T = \frac{0.25(6^2)}{0.84} \qquad T = 8.26 \text{ N} \quad (16.63)$$

b Figure 16.23 shows the free-body diagram when the particle is at point *b*. Newton's second law is written as

$$\sum F_n = ma_n \qquad T - W = \frac{mv^2}{\rho} \qquad (16.64)$$

$$T - 2.45 = \frac{0.25(6^2)}{0.84} \qquad T = 13.2 \text{ N} \quad (16.65)$$

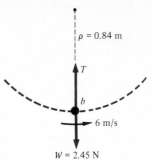

Fig. 16.23

The force *T* in both cases is the force exerted by the string on the mass. By Newton's third law, the force exerted on the string by the mass is equal and opposite to *T*. This latter force is also referred to as a *centrifugal force*.

Example 16.7 The system shown in Fig. 16.24 is a conical pendulum. The mass particle, which is connected to an inextensible string, moves with constant velocity in a circular path in a horizontal plane. The weight of the particle is 4 N, and the maximum permissible value of the cable tensile force is 7 N.

a Find the maximum permissible value of the angle θ between the string and the vertical direction.
b Find the corresponding value of the speed of the particle.

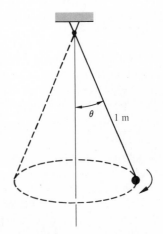

Solution
a The free-body diagram of the particle is shown in Fig. 16.25. For static equilibrium in the *y* direction,

$$\sum F_y = 0 \qquad T \cos \theta - W = 0 \qquad (16.66)$$

$$7 \cos \theta - 4 = 0 \qquad \theta = 55.2° \qquad (16.67)$$

For any value of θ greater than 55.2°, the maximum allowable cable tensile force of 7 N will be exceeded.
b Using the above value of θ, we get

$$\rho = (1)(\sin \theta) = (1)(\sin 55.2°) = 0.821 \text{ m} \qquad (16.68)$$

The equation of motion in the normal direction is

$$\sum F_n = ma_n \qquad T \sin \theta = mv^2/\rho \qquad (16.69)$$

$$7 \sin 55.2° = \frac{4/9.81 \, v^2}{0.821} \qquad v = 3.40 \text{ m/s}$$

Fig. 16.24

Example 16.8 A 3,600-lb automobile is to travel along either of the two road surfaces shown in Fig. 16.26.
a How much would the vehicle appear to weigh if its speed is 60 mi/h at the position shown on road surface *A*?
b Do the same as in part *a* for road surface *B*.

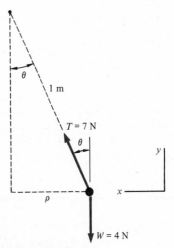

Fig. 16.25

541

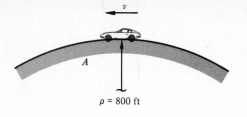

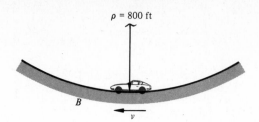

Fig. 16.26

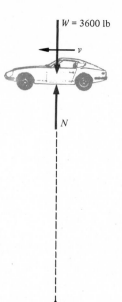

c The brakes are suddenly applied and the wheels locked when the automobile is in either of the two configurations shown in Fig. 16.26. For which road shape would the braking effect be greater? The coefficient of kinetic friction between the tires and the road surface is assumed to be 0.7.

d Find the minimum distance required for the car to come to rest, for cases of rectilinear motion, and motion along road surfaces A and B. (Assume that for motion along the two curved road surfaces, the deceleration values found in part c have constant values.)

e At what speed would the wheels of the automobile traveling on road A lose contact with the road surface?

Fig. 16.27

Solution

a The free-body diagram of the automobile on road surface A is shown in Fig. 16.27. N is the total reaction force of the road on the four wheels of the vehicle.

The speed $v = 60$ mi/h may be expressed as

$$v = \left(60\ \frac{\text{mi}}{\text{h}}\right)\left(\frac{5{,}280\ \text{ft}}{1\ \text{mi}}\right)\left(\frac{1\ \text{h}}{3{,}600\ \text{s}}\right) = 88.0\ \frac{\text{ft}}{\text{s}} \qquad (16.70)$$

The equation of motion is

$$\sum F_n = ma_n \qquad W - N = \frac{W}{g}\frac{v^2}{\rho} \qquad (16.71)$$

$$3{,}600 - N = \frac{3{,}600}{32.2}\frac{88.0^2}{800} \qquad (16.72)$$

$$N = 2{,}520\ \text{lb}$$

The vehicle would appear to weigh 2,520 lb on road surface A, and the percent difference between this value and the actual weight of the car is

$$\%\ \text{D} = \frac{2{,}520 - 3{,}600}{3{,}600}100 = -30\% \qquad (16.73)$$

b The free-body diagram of the automobile on road surface B is shown in Fig. 16.28. The equation of motion is

$$\sum F_n = ma_n \qquad N - W = \frac{W}{g}\frac{v^2}{\rho} \qquad (16.74)$$

$$N - 3{,}600 = \frac{3{,}600}{32.2}\frac{88.0^2}{800} \qquad (16.75)$$

$$N = 4{,}680\ \text{lb}$$

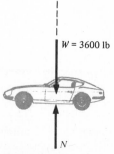

Fig. 16.28

The percent difference between the above value and the actual weight of the car is

$$\% \ D = \frac{4{,}680 - 3{,}600}{3{,}600} \ 100 = +30\% \qquad (16.76)$$

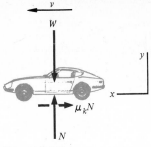

c Figure 16.29 shows the free-body diagram of the car when the brakes are applied and the wheels are locked. μ_k is the coefficient of kinetic friction between the tires and the road surface.

The equation of motion for the sliding car is

$$\sum F = ma \qquad -\mu_k N = \frac{W}{g} a \qquad (16.77)$$

Fig. 16.29

For the case of rectilinear translation, $N = W = $ constant, and Eq. (16.77) appears as

$$-\mu_k W = \frac{W}{g} a \qquad (16.78)$$

$$a = -\mu_k g = -0.7(32.2) = -22.5 \ \text{ft/s}^2 \qquad (16.79)$$

It may be seen that for the case of rectilinear translation of the automobile, the deceleration due to the frictional braking force is *independent* of the weight of the vehicle.

The stopping distance is found from

$$v^2 = v_0^2 + 2a(s - s_0) \qquad (16.80)$$

$$0 = 88.0^2 + 2(-22.5)(s - 0) \qquad s = 172 \ \text{ft} \qquad (16.81)$$

For the case of a vehicle traveling on a curved roadway as shown in Fig. 16.26, the frictional braking force is directly proportional to the normal force exerted by the road on the vehicle. The mass of the car, by comparison, is the *actual* weight of the car divided by g. The equation of motion for the case of the car sliding on roadway A, following Eq. (16.72), is

$$\sum F = ma \qquad -0.7(2{,}520) = \frac{3{,}600}{32.2} a \qquad a = -15.8 \ \text{ft/s}^2$$
$$(16.82)$$

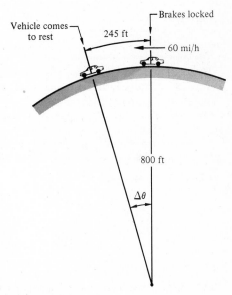

The stopping distance is found from

$$v^2 = v_0^2 + 2a(s - s_0) \qquad (16.83)$$

$$0 = 88.0^2 + 2(-15.8)(s - 0) \qquad s = 245 \ \text{ft} \qquad (16.84)$$

This distance is 42.4 percent greater than the required value of 172 ft for stopping with rectilinear translation. Figure 16.30 shows the stopping configuration for road surface A. The angle $\Delta\theta$ is found from

Fig. 16.30

$$\Delta\theta = \frac{245}{800} = 0.306 \ \text{rad} = 17.5° \qquad (16.85)$$

It is left as an exercise for the reader to decide whether the result above supports the assumption that the *deceleration is constant* over the stopping distance.

For roadway B, Eq. (16.82) has the form

$$\sum F = ma \qquad -0.7(4{,}680) = \frac{3{,}600}{32.2} a \qquad (16.86)$$

$$a = -29.3 \ \text{ft/s}^2 \qquad (16.87)$$

$$v^2 = v_0^2 + 2a(s - s_0) \qquad (16.88)$$

$$0 = 88.0^2 + 2(-29.3)(s - 0) \qquad s = 132 \text{ ft} \qquad (16.89)$$

This value is 23.3 percent less than the required value in the rectilinear case of 172 ft.

The angle $\Delta\theta$ for road surface b, from a sketch similar to Fig. 16.30, is

$$\Delta\theta = \frac{132}{800} = 0.165 \text{ rad} = 9.45° \qquad (16.90)$$

This example illustrates the problems involved in braking on the crest of a hill where, in addition to the reduced visibility, the braking capacity may be substantially reduced.

e From consideration of Fig. 16.27, the wheels of the automobile lose contact with roadway A when $N \to 0$. Using Eq. (16.71), we have

$$\sum F_n = ma_n \qquad W - N = \frac{W}{g}\frac{v^2}{\rho} \qquad (16.91)$$

$$W - 0 = \frac{W}{g}\frac{v^2}{\rho} \qquad (16.92)$$

$$v^2 = g\rho = 32.2(800) \qquad (16.93)$$

$$v = 160 \text{ ft/s} = 109 \text{ mi/h} \qquad (16.94)$$

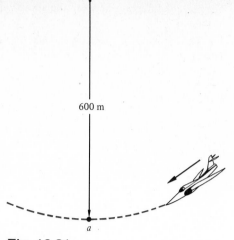

600 m

a

Fig. 16.31

Example 16.9 A fighter pilot is in a power dive, as shown in Fig. 16.31. The speed of the plane is 960 km/h, and the minimum radius of curvature of the flight path occurs at point a, as the pilot is pulling out of the dive. How many g's of acceleration does the pilot experience as the plane passes point a?

Solution The acceleration a_n of the plane at point a is

$$a_n = \frac{v^2}{\rho} \qquad (16.95)$$

Using $v = 960(1,000/3,600) = 267$ m/s and $\rho = 600$ m, we get

$$a_n = \frac{267^2}{600} = 119 \frac{\text{m}}{\text{s}^2} \qquad (16.96)$$

The quantity referred to as a g is a measure of the magnitude of an acceleration. The magnitude of one g is equal to the magnitude of the acceleration of the gravitational field. The number of g's experienced by the pilot is thus $119/9.81 = 12.1$ g's.

Example 16.10 An automobile drives around a horizontal, circular track at constant speed, as shown in Fig. 16.32. The road surface is wet macadam, and the value of the coefficient of static friction between the tires and the road is assumed to be 0.42.

a At what speed will sliding motion of the automobile on the road shown in Fig. 16.32a be impending?

b Do the same as in part a if the road surface is banked as shown in Fig. 16.32b.

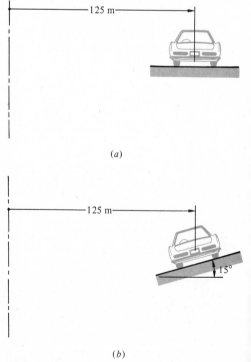

125 m

(a)

125 m

15°

(b)

Fig. 16.32

Solution

a The free-body diagram of the automobile is shown in Fig. 16.33. The direction and sense of the impending sliding motion are radially outward from the center of the track. When this sliding motion is impending, the friction force has its maximum possible value $\mu_s N$. For equilibrium in the y direction,

$$\sum F_y = 0 \qquad -W + N = 0 \qquad N = W \qquad (16.97)$$

The equation of motion is

$$\sum F_n = ma_n \qquad \mu_s N = \frac{W}{g} a_n \qquad (16.98)$$

$$\mu_s W = \frac{W}{g} \frac{v^2}{\rho} \qquad v = \sqrt{\mu_s \rho g} \qquad (16.99)$$

$$= \sqrt{0.42(125)(9.81)} = 22.7 \text{ m/s} \qquad (16.100)$$

$$v = \left(22.7 \, \frac{\text{m}}{\text{s}}\right)\left(\frac{1 \text{ km}}{1,000 \text{ m}}\right)\left(\frac{3,600 \text{ s}}{1 \text{ h}}\right) = 81.7 \, \frac{\text{km}}{\text{h}} \qquad (16.101)$$

It may be seen that the above result is *independent* of the weight of the car.

b Figure 16.34 shows the free-body diagram of the automobile for the case of the banked roadway. As before, the car is considered to be a mass particle in plane curvilinear translation. For static equilibrium in the y direction,

$$\sum F_y = 0 \qquad -W - \mu_s N \sin 15° + N \cos 15° = 0 \qquad (16.102)$$

$$N(\cos 15° - 0.42 \sin 15°) = W \qquad N = 1.17 \, W \qquad (16.103)$$

The equation of motion of the car is

$$\sum F_n = ma_n \qquad N \sin 15° + \mu_s N \cos 15° = \frac{W}{g} a_n$$

$$= \frac{W}{g} \frac{v^2}{\rho} \qquad (16.104)$$

$$N(\sin 15° + \mu_s \cos 15°) = \frac{W}{g} \frac{v^2}{\rho} \qquad (16.105)$$

$$1.17 \, W(\sin 15° + 0.42 \cos 15°) = \frac{W}{9.81} \frac{v^2}{(125)} \qquad (16.106)$$

$$v = 30.9 \text{ m/s} = 111 \text{ km/h} \qquad (16.107)$$

This above result is again independent of the weight of the vehicle.

Example 16.11 Figure 16.35 is a representation of a device seen in amusement parks. A vertical drum in the form of a right circular cylinder is made of heavy steel mesh. People stand around the inside circumference of the drum, and a motor brings the drum up to a constant angular speed. At this time the floor is allowed to lower, as shown by the dashed outline, and the people are held in position by the friction forces exerted by the steel mesh of the drum on their bodies.

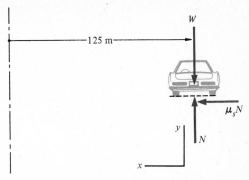

Fig. 16.33

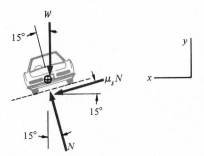

Fig. 16.34

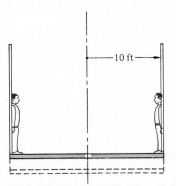

Fig. 16.35

a If the coefficient of static friction between the steel mesh and the person's clothing is estimated to be 0.5, what is the minimum required speed of the person to avoid slipping along the drum?

b What is the corresponding acceleration, in the normal direction, which the person experiences?

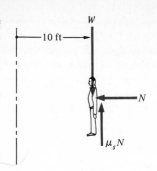

Solution The free-body diagram of the person is shown in Fig. 16.36. The equation of motion is

$$\sum F_n = ma_n \qquad N = \frac{W}{g}a_n = \frac{W}{g}\frac{v^2}{\rho} \qquad (16.108)$$

Fig. 16.36

For vertical equilibrium,

$$\sum F_y = 0 \qquad \mu_s N - W = 0 \qquad (16.109)$$

N is eliminated from Eqs. (16.108) and (16.109), yielding

$$v = \sqrt{\frac{\rho g}{\mu_s}} \qquad (16.110)$$

$$= \sqrt{\frac{10(32.2)}{0.5}} = 25.4 \; \frac{\text{ft}}{\text{s}} \qquad (16.111)$$

b The acceleration experienced by the person is

$$a_n = \frac{v^2}{\rho} = \frac{25.4^2}{10} = 64.5 \; \frac{\text{ft}}{\text{s}^2} \qquad (16.112)$$

This acceleration has a magnitude of $64.5/32.2 = 2.00$ g's.

Example 16.12 A 3,200-lb vehicle drives from a straight road onto a curved road of circular shape, as shown in Fig. 16.37. As the vehicle passes point a, it has a speed of 55 mi/h and is decelerating at a uniform rate of 6 ft/s².

a Find the magnitude, direction, and sense of the acceleration of the vehicle when it passes point b. Point b is 260 ft from point a, measured along the curved roadway.

b Find the horizontal force at point b exerted by the roadway on the vehicle.

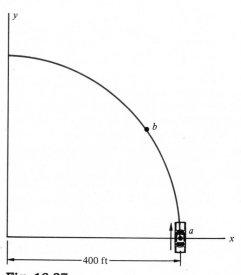

Fig. 16.37

c Find the minimum value of the coefficient of static friction at point b if the vehicle is not to slide off the road.

Solution

a The coordinate of length along the curve is designated s, and $s = 0$ corresponds to point a. The velocity at point b is found from

$$v_b^2 = v_0^2 + 2as \qquad (16.113)$$

Using $v_0 = 55$ mi/h $= 80.7$ ft/s, we get

$$v_b^2 = 80.7^2 + 2(-6)(260) \qquad (16.114)$$

$$v_b = 58.2 \text{ ft/s} \qquad (16.115)$$

The centripetal acceleration at point b is

$$a_n = \frac{v^2}{\rho} = \frac{58.2^2}{400} = 8.47 \; \frac{\text{ft}}{\text{s}^2} \qquad (16.116)$$

546

The tangential acceleration has the constant value $a_t = -6$ ft/s² given in the example statement.

These two components of acceleration are shown in Fig. 16.38. The magnitude of the total acceleration is

$$a = \sqrt{a_n^2 + a_t^2} = \sqrt{8.47^2 + (-6)^2} = 10.4 \text{ ft/s}^2 \quad (16.117)$$

The angles α and β are found as

$$\beta = \frac{260}{400} = 0.650 \text{ rad} = 37.2° \quad (16.118)$$

$$\tan \alpha = \frac{6}{8.47} \qquad \alpha = 35.3° \quad (16.119)$$

The angle ζ between the resultant acceleration vector and the x axis is

$$\zeta = \beta + \alpha = 37.2° + 35.3° = 72.5° \quad (16.120)$$

The x' axis is collinear with the direction of the resultant acceleration of the car, as shown in Fig. 16.38.

b By using Newton's second law, the force F exerted by the roadway on the car is

$$\sum F_{x'} = ma_{x'} \qquad F_{x'} = \frac{3{,}200}{32.2}(10.4) = 1{,}030 \text{ lb} \quad (16.121)$$

This force has the direction ζ shown in Fig. 16.38.

c When sliding motion of the vehicle is impending, the force $F_{x'}$ given above has its maximum value

$$F_{x'} = \mu_s N \quad (16.122)$$

The normal force is equal to the weight of the vehicle. The minimum required value of the coefficient of friction, then, is given by

$$\mu_{s,\min} = \frac{F_{x'}}{N} = \frac{1{,}030}{3{,}200} = 0.322 \quad (16.123)$$

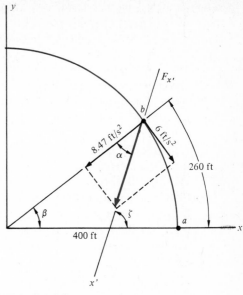

Fig. 16.38

16.6 THE D'ALEMBERT, OR INERTIA, FORCE

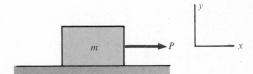

(a)

In this section a technique will be presented which converts the solution of a problem in dynamics to the form of a problem in statics. This is accomplished by the introduction and use of a term referred to as the *D'Alembert, or inertia, force.*

The block on a smooth, horizontal plane of Example 16.1 is shown in Fig. 16.39a, and the free-body diagram of the block is shown in Fig. 16.39b. The equation of motion of the block was shown to be

$$\sum F_x = ma \qquad P = ma \quad (16.124)$$

Equation (16.124) may be written as

$$P - ma = 0 \qquad P + (-ma) = 0 \quad (16.125)$$

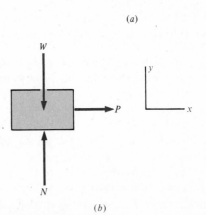

(b)

Fig. 16.39

The quantity $-ma$ is referred to as the *D'Alembert, or inertia, force* which acts on the mass particle m. From consideration of Eq. (16.125) and Fig. 16.39b, the following observations may be made.

1. The magnitude of the inertia force is the product of mass and acceleration.
2. *The inertia force exists only when the particle is accelerating.* Thus, for the cases of a particle at rest or moving with constant velocity, the magnitude of the inertia force is identically zero.
3. Since the inertia force is related to the *mass* of the body, this force is a body force.
4. From the structure of Eq. (16.125), the sense of the inertia force $-ma$ is positive in the same sense as that of force P. It follows then, from Fig. 16.39, that the inertia force, as defined above, is positive in the sense of the positive coordinate axis.
5. Because of the minus sign in the term $-ma$ and the fact that m is always positive, the actual sense of the inertia force is always *opposite* to the actual sense of the acceleration.

If the inertia force were thought of as an *external, applied* force which acts on the mass, the free-body diagram of the block would have the form shown in Fig. 16.40. By including the inertia force in the free-body diagram, the dynamics problem is reduced to a statics problem. The requirement of *static equilibrium* is then

$$\sum F_x = 0 \qquad P + (-ma) = 0 \qquad P = ma \quad (16.126)$$

There are three general rules to follow in using the inertia force in the solution of problems in particle dynamics.

1. Draw an arrow on the free-body diagram of the mass particle which has the direction of the acceleration of the particle and the same sense as the positive sense of this acceleration.
2. Designate the magnitude of the arrow drawn on the free-body diagram by ma, where m is the mass of the particle and a is the acceleration of the particle. In a given problem, either the term a may be known, or it may be the quantity which is to be solved for.
3. Insert a minus sign in front of the quantity ma. The quantity $-ma$ is now the inertia force which acts on the particle. This quantity is considered to be positive if it acts in the positive sense of the acceleration.

The use of the inertia force in the solution of problems in particle dynamics does not offer a significant advantage over the direct use of Newton's second law. The use of this tech-

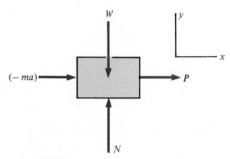

Fig. 16.40

nique, however, finds widespread application in the solution of problems in the dynamics of rigid bodies. This technique is used almost exclusively in the solution of advanced problems in dynamics.

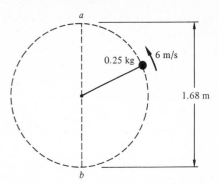

Example 16.13 The system of Example 16.6 is repeated in Fig. 16.41. The mass particle is connected to an inextensible string and moves with a constant velocity of 6 m/s in a circular path in a vertical plane. Use the inertia force technique to find the string tensile force when the particle is at points a and b.

Solution Figure 16.42 shows the free-body diagram when the particle is at point a. T is the cable tensile force. The positive sense of the acceleration a_n is from the particle toward the center of the circular path. The inertia force which acts on the particle is shown in the figure.

Fig. 16.41

For equilibrium of the particle,

$$\sum F_n = 0 \qquad -m\frac{v^2}{\rho} + W + T = 0 \qquad (16.127)$$

$$-0.25\left(\frac{6^2}{0.84}\right) + 2.45 + T = 0 \qquad T = 8.26 \text{ N} \quad (16.128)$$

When the particle is at point b, the free-body diagram has the appearance shown in Fig. 16.43. The equilibrium requirement is

$$\sum F_n = 0 \qquad -m\frac{v^2}{\rho} - W + T = 0 \qquad (16.129)$$

$$-0.25\left(\frac{6^2}{0.84}\right) - 2.45 + T = 0 \qquad T = 13.2 \text{ N} \quad (16.130)$$

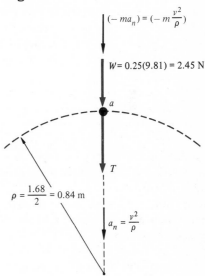

Fig. 16.42

16.7 SUMMARY

The fundamental basis of all of engineering dynamics is Newton's second law, which states that a particle acted upon by a resultant force will experience an acceleration directly proportional to this force, and in the direction of the force. The equation form of Newton's second law for a particle is

$$\mathbf{F} = m\mathbf{a} \qquad (16.131)$$

where $\mathbf{F}$ = resultant force
m = mass of particle
$\mathbf{a}$ = acceleration

This acceleration has the same direction and sense as the resultant force. If a particle is at rest, or moving with constant velocity, the acceleration is zero. From the equation above, it follows that the resultant force is also zero. Thus, a particle at rest, or moving with constant velocity, is in static equilibrium.

In USCS units, length, time, and force are fundamental units and mass is a derived unit. The force unit is the pound and the mass unit is the slug. The value of the gravitational accelera-

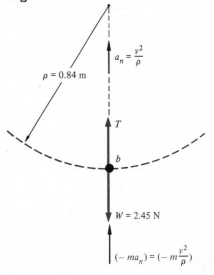

Fig. 16.43

tion g is 32.2 ft/s². In SI units, length, time, and mass are fundamental units and force is the derived unit. The force unit is the newton and the mass unit is the kilogram. The value of the gravitational acceleration g is 9.81 m/s². One meter is approximately three feet in length; and one newton is a force of approximately one-quarter pound.

Newton's second law for a particle in rectilinear translation has the form

$$F = ma \qquad (16.132)$$

where F is the component of force in the direction of motion. The boldface vector notation is not required, since both the force and the acceleration have the known direction of the axis of motion. If the force in the direction of the rectilinear motion is a constant, it follows that the acceleration is a constant. The motion of a particle with constant acceleration is given by

$$v = v_0 + at \qquad (16.133)$$

$$s = s_0 + v_0 t + \tfrac{1}{2}at^2 \qquad (16.134)$$

$$v^2 = v_0^2 + 2a(s - s_0) \qquad (16.135)$$

To solve the problem of motion of two connected particles in rectilinear translation, a free-body diagram of each particle is drawn. Newton's second law is written for each particle, considering the single cable or link force to be an unknown. The two equations obtained may then be solved simultaneously for the force and the common acceleration of the two particles.

When a particle moves in plane curvilinear translation, the normal force F_n which acts on the particle is never zero, since this force is required to cause the particle to follow the curved path. The component equations of Newton's second law for a particle in plane curvilinear motion are

$$\sum F_n = ma_n = m\frac{v^2}{\rho} \qquad (16.136)$$

$$\sum F_t = ma_t = m\dot{v} \qquad (16.137)$$

The use of the D'Alembert, or inertia, force is a technique which converts a dynamics problem to the form of a statics problem. An arrow representing a vector, which acts in the sense of the positive acceleration, is first sketched on the particle. The magnitude of this vector is designated ma, where a is the symbolic positive acceleration, and a minus sign is affixed to this term. The quantity $(-ma)$ is the inertia force. This term is considered to be a force applied to the body, acting in the sense of the positive acceleration. With the inclusion of the inertia force, the dynamic equilibrium requirements of the particle are

$$F = \sum_i F_i = 0 \qquad (16.138)$$

Note that this equation has the form of an equation of static equilibrium.

PROBLEMS

16.1 The particle in Fig. P16.1 is acted on by the system of forces shown, and moves with rectilinear translation in a frictionless guide. At $t = 0$ the particle is at rest.
(a) Find the magnitude of the acceleration.
(b) Find the velocity and displacement when $t = 2$ s.

16.2 Do the same as in Prob. 16.1, if the direction of motion is that shown in Fig. P16.2.

16.3 Do the same as in Prob. 16.1, if the direction of motion is that shown in Fig. P16.3.

16.4 Do the same as in Prob. 16.2, if the applied forces are removed from the particle.

16.5 Do the same as in Prob. 16.3 if the applied forces are removed from the particle.

16.6 Do the same as in Prob. 16.1, if the 3-lb force shown in Fig. P16.6 also acts on the particle.

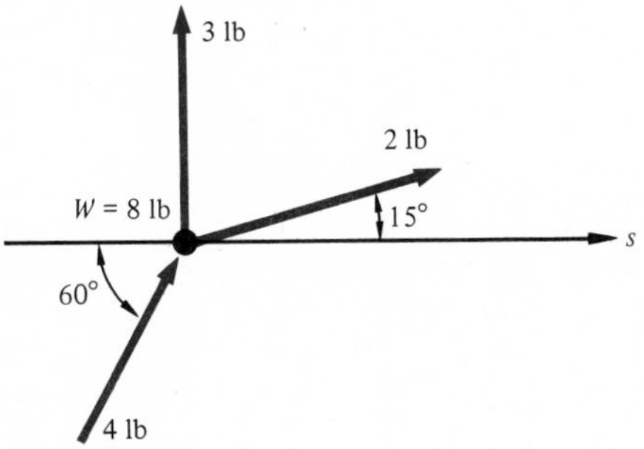

16.7 Do the same as in Prob. 16.1, for the force system shown in Fig. P16.7.

16.8 A particle of mass 4 kg slides along a straight frictionless track with a speed of 6.5 m/s, as shown in Fig. P16.8. At $t = 0$ a force, shown as the dashed arrow in the figure, is applied to the particle and the resulting deceleration is 1.6 m/s². Find the magnitude of the applied force.

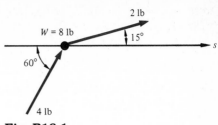
Fig. P16.1

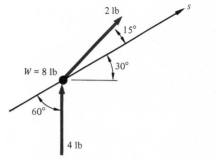
Fig. P16.2

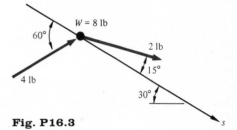
Fig. P16.3

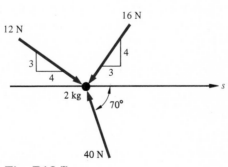
Fig. P16.6

Fig. P16.7

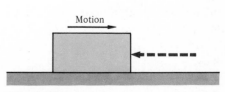
Fig. P16.8

16.9 An automobile moves along a straight roadway with a constant speed of 40 mi/h. The automobile experiences a constant acceleration for 5 s and reaches a speed of 50 mi/h. The weight of the automobile is 3,600 lb.

(a) Find the required value of the resultant force acting on the automobile that will produce this acceleration.

(b) Find the distance covered by the automobile during this period of time.

16.10 Do the same as in Prob. 16.9, if the automobile accelerates for 5 s and changes the speed of the car from 50 to 60 mi/h.

16.11 Do the same as in Prob. 16.9 if at the time that the vehicle is traveling at 40 mi/h, the brakes are applied for a period of 3 s. The speed changes from 40 to 25 mi/h and the braking deceleration may be assumed to be constant.

16.12 Do the same as in Prob. 16.9, if the brakes are applied for a period of 6.5 s, and bring the vehicle to rest from a speed of 40 mi/h.

16.13 A vehicle has a mass of 1,200 kg and moves in rectilinear translation. The vehicle is initially at rest. A resultant force of 120 lb, in the direction of motion, is applied to the vehicle. Find the acceleration of the vehicle, in meters per second squared, and the distance, in feet, covered by the vehicle at the end of 15 s.

16.14 Figure P16.14 shows a simple model of a hoisting device to lift cargo out of the hold of a ship. The ship is anchored in calm water in a harbor. When the load is first raised, the cable accelerates the load at 1.5 ft/s². The total weight of the hoisting motor is 375 lb.

(a) Find the force exerted by the lifting motor on the support beam when the load is first raised.

(b) Find the force exerted by the lifting motor on the support beam at a later time when the load moves at a constant speed of 8.6 ft/s.

16.15 The ship of Prob. 16.14 is at sea in rough water. Do the same as in Prob. 16.14, if a wave causes a constant upward acceleration of the ship of 5 ft/s².

16.16 Figure P16.16 shows a light-weight passenger elevator with a mass of 500 kg. A passenger of mass 70 kg rides in the elevator. When the elevator moves upward with constant acceleration, the cable tensile force is 6,500 N.

(a) Find the value of the acceleration of the elevator.

(b) Find the apparent weight of the passenger as the elevator accelerates.

16.17 Do the same as in Prob. 16.16, if the cable tension is 4,200 N as the elevator accelerates downward with a constant value.

16.18 Do the same as in Prob. 16.16, if a second passenger with a mass of 50 kg joins the first passenger in the elevator.

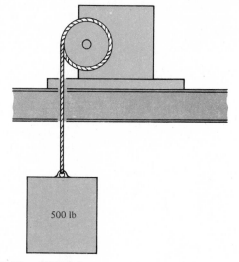

500 lb

Fig. P16.14

T

Fig. P16.16

16.19 Do the same as in Prob. 16.17, for the conditions of Prob. 16.18.

16.20 The acceleration-time variation of a passenger elevator is shown in Fig. P16.20. The weight of the passenger is 165 lb and the weight of the elevator cage is 1,800 lb. When the elevator accelerates upward, the passenger experiences an apparent weight gain of 18 lb. When the elevator decelerates to zero velocity, the passenger experiences an apparent weight loss of 22 lb.
(*a*) Find the magnitudes a_0 and a_1.
(*b*) Find the corresponding values of the elevator cable tensile force T.

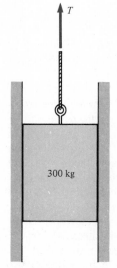

Fig. P16.21

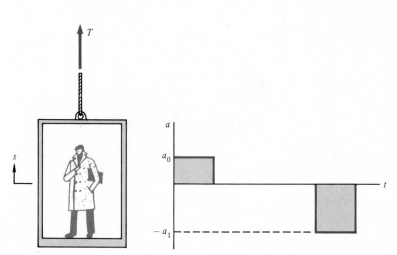

Fig. P16.20

16.21 Figure P16.21 shows a pile-driver weight. The total friction force exerted by the guides on the weight is estimated to be 350 N. Find the value of the constant cable tensile force T that will raise the weight 8 m in 4 s. The weight is initially at rest.

16.22 Do the same as in Prob. 16.21, if the weight is to be raised through the distance 8 m in 2 s.

16.23 When the system of two blocks shown in Fig. P16.23 is released from rest, the force in the cable is 42 lb. Find the acceleration of the blocks, and the mass of block *B*.

16.24 Do the same as in Prob. 16.23, if the force in the cable, after release of the blocks, is 78 lb.

16.25 Do the same as in Prob. 16.23, if the force in the cable, after release of the blocks, is 60 lb.

16.26 At $t = 0$, block *A* in Fig. P16.26 has an upward velocity of 1.85 m/s. Find the time at which block *B* comes to rest.

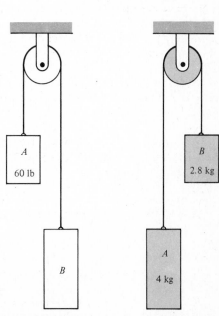

Fig. P16.23   **Fig. P16.26**

16.27 Do the same as in Prob. 16.26, if a mass of 1 kg is added to block *B*.

16.28 Do the same as in Prob. 16.26, if a mass of 1 kg is added to block *A*.

16.29 Figure P16.29 shows an experimental device that may be used to measure the acceleration of a body moving in rectilinear translation. A small mass particle slides in a frictionless path, in a vertical plane, with the form of a quarter circle. The device accelerates to the right in the figure with an acceleration of constant magnitude *a*.
  (*a*) Find the relation between the observed angle θ and the actual acceleration *a* of the device.
  (*b*) Find the magnitude of the normal force between the particle and the track, if the mass of the particle is 30 g and the acceleration of the device is 6 m/s².

16.30 How could the device shown in Prob. 16.29 be used to measure constant deceleration of a body in rectilinear translation?

16.31 A block slides along a horizontal plane with a constant value of deceleration, as shown in Fig. P16.31. The speed of the block decreases from 35 in/s to zero over a length of 100 in.
  (*a*) Find the value of the coefficient of kinetic friction.
  (*b*) If a second block weighing 6 lb is attached to the top of the 14-lb block, find the distance through which the system of blocks will move before coming to rest. The initial velocity is 35 in/s.

16.32 A block slides down an inclined plane with an acceleration of 1.62 m/s², as shown in Fig. P16.32. Find the magnitude of the friction force that acts on the block.

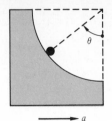

Fig. P16.29

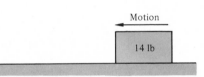

Fig. P16.31

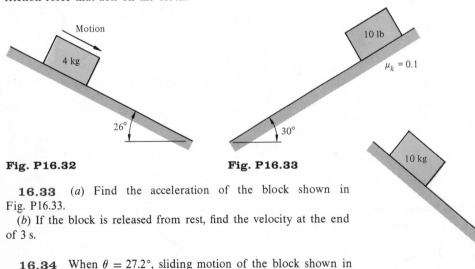

Fig. P16.32   **Fig. P16.33**

16.33 (*a*) Find the acceleration of the block shown in Fig. P16.33.
  (*b*) If the block is released from rest, find the velocity at the end of 3 s.

16.34 When $\theta = 27.2°$, sliding motion of the block shown in Fig. P16.34 is impending. Find the value of the acceleration of the block when $\theta = 40°$.

Fig. P16.34

16.35 A flat crate rests on the bed of a truck, as shown in Fig. P16.35. The coefficient of static friction between the crate and the truck bed is 0.3, and the mass of the crate is 200 kg. Find the magnitude of the friction force exerted by the bed on the crate when the truck decelerates at 1.2 m/s².

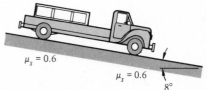

Fig. P16.35

16.36 Do the same as in Prob. 16.35, if the truck decelerates at 3.5 m/s².

16.37 Do the same as in Prob. 16.35 if the truck travels on the downhill grade shown in Fig. P16.37.

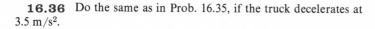

16.38 Do the same as in Prob. 16.37 for the conditions of Prob. 16.36.

Fig. P16.37

16.39 The truck in Fig. P16.35 travels at 30 km/h. The brakes are applied and the vehicle is assumed to decelerate at constant magnitude until it comes to rest. Find the minimum value of the total stopping distance, if the crate is not to slide on the truck bed.

16.40 An approximate value of coefficient of friction of a rubber automobile tire on an ice-covered pavement is 0.05.
(*a*) Using this data, find the minimum time required for an automobile to accelerate from rest to 30 mi/h on a horizontal ice-covered pavement.
(*b*) Find the corresponding distance traveled by the automobile.

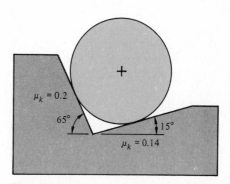

Fig. P16.41

16.41 A cylinder of mass 6 kg rests in a trough, as shown in Fig. P16.41. A force of 30 N is applied along the center axis of the cylinder, normal to the plane of the figure. Find the acceleration of the cylinder.

16.42 Find the magnitude and sense of the acceleration of the two blocks in Fig. P16.42, if $W = 100$ lb. The coefficient of kinetic friction between the block and the plane is 0.3.

16.43 Do the same as in Prob. 16.42, if $W = 300$ lb.

16.44 Find the acceleration of the system of two blocks shown in Fig. P16.44. The mass of block B is 160 kg. Assume that $\mu_k \approx \mu_s$.

16.45 Find the required value of the mass of block B in Fig. P16.44, if the acceleration of the system is to be 2.9 m/s².

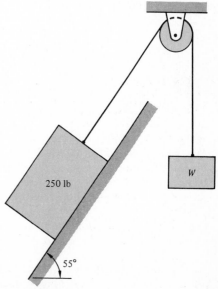

16.46 For what range of values of weight of block A in Fig. P16.46 will the *magnitude* of the acceleration of the blocks be less than, or equal to, 5 ft/s². Assume that $\mu_k \approx \mu_s$.

Fig. P16.42

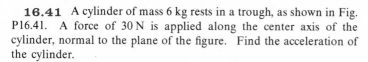

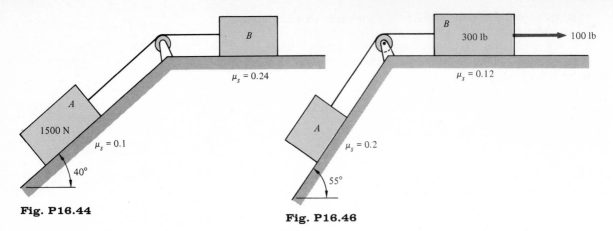

$\mu_s = 0.24$

B

$\mu_s = 0.1$

A

1500 N

40°

Fig. P16.44

B

300 lb

100 lb

$\mu_s = 0.12$

A

$\mu_s = 0.2$

55°

Fig. P16.46

16.47 Block A in Fig. P16.47 weighs 10 lb and block B weighs 40 lb. The link may be assumed to be weightless. The coefficients of kinetic friction between blocks A and B and the plane are 0.12 and 0.18, respectively.
(*a*) Find the acceleration of the system of blocks.
(*b*) Find the force in the connecting link.

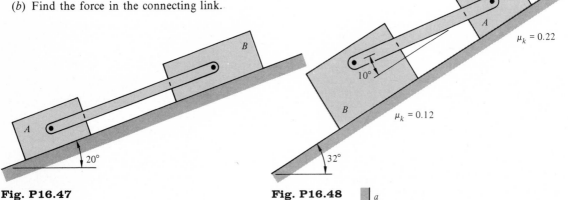

B

A

20°

Fig. P16.47

$\mu_k = 0.22$

A

10°

$\mu_k = 0.12$

B

32°

Fig. P16.48

16.48 Find the acceleration of the system of two blocks shown in Fig. P16.48. Compare this result with the solution to Example 16.5.

16.49 Block A in Fig. P16.49 is connected to the ground by the weightless truss link ab. The masses of blocks A and B are 100 and 150 kg, respectively. The coefficients of kinetic friction between the mating surfaces are $\mu_{AB} = 0.1$ and $\mu_{BC} = 0.14$. Find the required magnitude of the horizontal force acting on block B that will cause this element to accelerate to the left at 2 m/s^2.

16.50 Do the same as in Prob. 16.49, for rightward acceleration of the block of 2 m/s^2.

16.51 (*a*) For what value of acceleration a will sliding motion of block B with respect to block A, Fig. P16.51, be impending?
(*b*) Find the required value of the horizontal force acting on block A to produce the acceleration of part *a*. Assume that $\mu_k \approx \mu_s$.

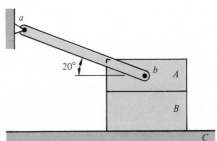

a

20°

b A

B

C

Fig. P16.49

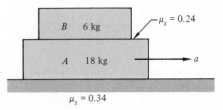

B 6 kg

$\mu_s = 0.24$

A 18 kg

a

$\mu_s = 0.34$

Fig. P16.51

16.52 Do the same as Prob. 16.51, if the blocks are arranged as shown in Fig. P16.52.

16.53 A force of 100 lb, with variable direction θ, acts on the block shown in Fig. P16.53.
(*a*) For what value of θ will the acceleration of the block be maximum?
(*b*) Find the value of this maximum acceleration.

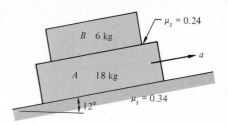

Fig. P16.52

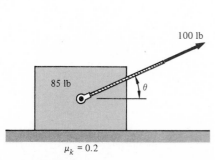

Fig. P16.53

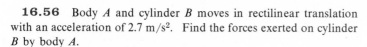

Fig. P16.54

16.54 The links in the plane frame in Fig. P16.54 may be assumed to be weightless, and all friction effects may be neglected. The mass of block A is 4 kg.
(*a*) Find the instanteous value of the acceleration of block A when $\theta = 40°$.
(*b*) Do the same as in part *a*, if $\theta = 30°$.
(*c*) Do the same as in part *a*, if $\theta = 20°$.

16.55 Do the same as in Prob. 16.54, if $\mu_k = 0.1$ at the sliding surface between the block and the guide.

16.56 Body A and cylinder B moves in rectilinear translation with an acceleration of 2.7 m/s². Find the forces exerted on cylinder B by body A.

16.57 The system of blocks in Fig. P16.57 is released from rest at $t = 0$. The coefficient of kinetic friction on all sliding surfaces is 0.08. Find the magnitude, direction, and sense of the relative acceleration of block A with respect to block B.

16.58 A 0.5-kg mass particle connected to an inextensible cable moves with constant velocity in a circular path in a vertical plane, as shown in Fig. P16.58. When the particle is at point a, the tensile force in the string is 10 N.
(*a*) Find the speed v of the particle.
(*b*) Find the cable tensile force when the particle is at position b.

16.59 Find the minimum value of the speed of the particle in Prob. 16.58, if the cable is to always experience a tensile force.

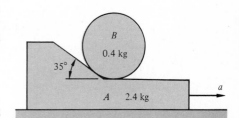

Fig. P16.56

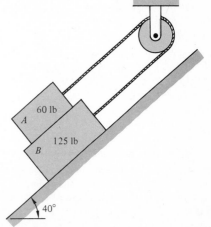

Fig. P16.57

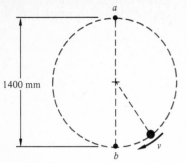

Fig. P16.58

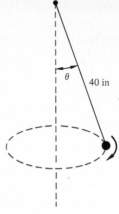

40 in

Fig. P16.60

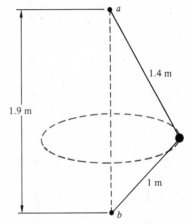

Fig. P16.62

16.60 The mass particle in the conical pendulum in Fig. P16.60 moves with constant speed v, and $\theta = 20°$.

(*a*) Find the speed v of the particle.

(*b*) Find the force in the inextensible string, if the particle has a weight of 0.6 lb.

16.61 Find the factors by which the speed, and string force, in Prob. 16.60 increase when the angle θ is increased by a factor of 2.

16.62 The 0.1-kg mass particle in Fig. P16.62 travels at a speed of 3.2 m/s in a circular path. Find the forces in the two inextensible cables.

16.63 Find the limiting value of speed in Prob. 16.62 at which a cable force just ceases to be tensile force.

16.64 A frictionless particle of weight 2 lb slides down a track in a vertical plane, as shown in Fig. P16.64. At the lowest point in the track, the particle has an apparent weight which is 50 percent greater than its actual weight. Find the velocity of the particle at this point.

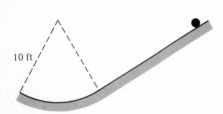

Fig. P16.64

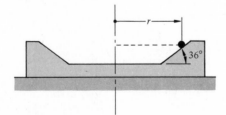

Fig. P16.65

16.65 The 65-mg mass particle shown in Fig. P16.65 travels at a speed of 2.2 m/s around the surface of the stationary drum. All surfaces are assumed to be frictionless.

(*a*) Find the required value of r.

(*b*) Find the normal force exerted by the mass particle on the surface of the drum.

16.66 Figure P16.66 shows an elementary model of one turbine blade on a turbine wheel. The mean diameter of the circular path traveled by the blade is 28 in, and the speed of the blade is 1,260 ft/s. Find the force exerted by the blade on the turbine wheel, if the blade weighs 0.38 lb.

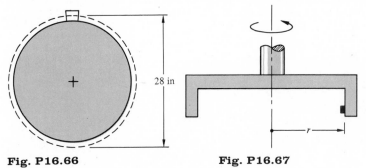

28 in

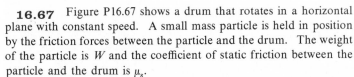

r

Fig. P16.66

Fig. P16.67

16.67 Figure P16.67 shows a drum that rotates in a horizontal plane with constant speed. A small mass particle is held in position by the friction forces between the particle and the drum. The weight of the particle is W and the coefficient of static friction between the particle and the drum is μ_s.

(*a*) Find the general expression for the speed of the particle at which slipping motion is impending.

(*b*) Find the numerical value of the speed if $r = 8$ in and $\mu_s = 0.2$.

16.68 A driver wishes to make a left turn into a street, as shown in Fig. P16.68. Which of the three curves labeled *a*, *b*, and *c* do you think the driver would intuitively follow? Why?

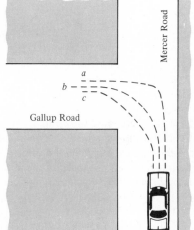

Mercer Road

Gallup Road

a
b
c

Fig. P16.68

16.69 A vehicle moves along a roadway at a constant speed of 60 km/h, as shown in Fig. P16.69.

(*a*) Find the apparent weight of the vehicle at points *a* and *b*.

(*b*) With what maximum value of speed could the vehicle travel along the road and not lose contact with the road surface?

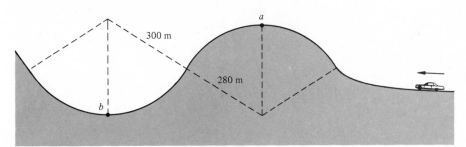

300 m

a

280 m

b

Fig. P16.69

16.70 A test driver drives a car around a horizontal circular track at constant speed v. The coefficient of static friction between the wheels and the track is 0.65, and sliding motion of the vehicle is impending when $v = 86$ mi/h. Find the diameter of the track.

16.71 A horizontal circular curve has the banking shown in Fig. P16.71. The coefficient of static friction between the tires and the road surface is 0.5. At what speed of the automobile will sliding motion be impending?

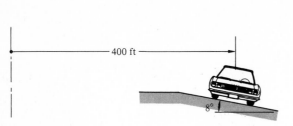

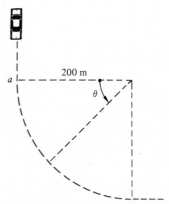

Fig. P16.71

Fig. P16.72

16.72 Figure P16.72 shows an experimental automobile testing track. For the embankment of the track, sliding motion of the automobile is impending when the vehicle is at rest. Find the maximum permissible constant speed of the automobile, if sliding motion is not to occur when the vehicle is in motion. Assume $\mu_k \approx \mu_s = 0.58$.

16.73 A racing car enters a circular track from a straight roadway, as shown in Fig. P16.73. When the car passes point a it has a speed of 68 km/h and starts to accelerate with a constant value of a_t. The car uses a special-design low-profile radial tire, and it may be assumed that $\mu_k \approx \mu_s = 0.7$. When $\theta = 72°$, sliding motion of the car is impending. Find a_t.

16.74 Do the same as in Prob. 16.73, if sliding motion of the car is impending when $\theta = 90°$.

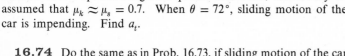

Fig. P16.73

Note: The following problems were first presented in Chap. 15.

16.75 A 300-mg particle moves along a frictionless circular track, shown in Fig. P16.75, with constant tangential acceleration $a_t = 0.28$ m/s². The particle starts from rest at point a. Find the normal force exerted on the particle when it first reaches point b. (See Prob. 15.94.)

16.76 Do the same as in Prob. 16.75, if $a_t = -0.28$ m/s². (See Prob. 15.95.)

16.77 Do the same as in Prob. 16.75, if the initial velocity at point a is 1.5 m/s, in a downward sense in the figure. (See Prob. 15.96.)

16.78 Do the same as in Prob. 16.75, for the case where the particle is at point b the second time. (See Prob. 15.97.)

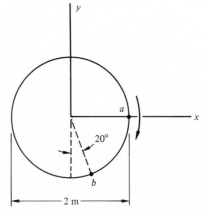

Fig. P16.75

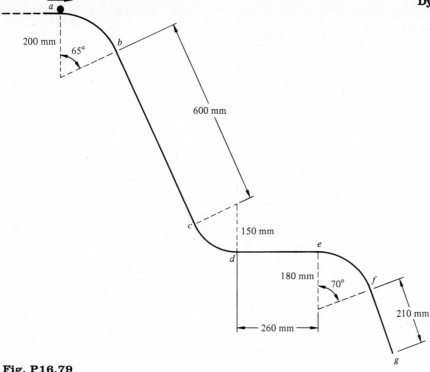

Fig. P16.79

16.79 A particle of mass 0.8 kg moves along a curved track which lies in a horizontal plane, as shown in Fig. 16.79. The speed of the particle has a constant value of 0.15 m/s.

(*a*) Find the maximum value of normal force which the particle experiences as it moves from *a* to *g*.

(*b*) Where along the path does this maximum force occur? (See Prob. 15.98.)

17

Kinetics of Plane Motion of a Rigid Body

Kinematics

17.1 INTRODUCTION

In Chap. 15 the kinematic relationships for the motion of a particle were presented. Only two types of motion of a particle are possible. The first type is rectilinear translation. In this case, the particle moves along a straight-line path. The second general type of particle motion is curvilinear translation. Here the particle is constrained to move along a curved path. The location of the particle is defined by a position, or displacement, vector which locates the particle with respect to a fixed reference point. This point is usually the origin of a set of coordinate axes. The velocity and acceleration of a particle were defined next, and both were shown to be vectors. The velocity of a particle is the first derivative of the displacement with respect to time. An alternate definition is that the velocity is the time rate of change of displacement. The direction of the velocity is always tangent to the path of motion of the particle. The magnitude of the velocity of a particle is also called the speed of the particle. The acceleration is the first derivative of the velocity with respect to time. It follows that the acceleration of a particle is also equal to the second derivative of the displacement with respect to time. An alternate definition is that acceleration is the time rate change of velocity.

For the case of rectilinear translation, the displacement, velocity, and acceleration all have the same direction, and this direction is that of the axis of motion. For the case of plane curvilinear translation of a particle, the acceleration was seen to have two distinct and *independent* components. The first is the normal, or centripetal, acceleration, designated by a_n and defined by

$$a_n = \frac{v^2}{\rho} \qquad (17.1)$$

where v is the magnitude of the velocity and ρ is the radius of curvature of the curved path at the point of interest. The actual sense of the normal acceleration is always *from* the particle *toward* the reference point for measuring ρ. It may be seen that a_n is independent of changes in the magnitude of the velocity, and it is a function of only the magnitudes of the velocity and the radius of curvature. The existence of the normal acceleration is a necessary condition to cause a continuous change in the direction of the velocity as the particle travels along the curved path.

The second component of acceleration of the particle in plane curvilinear translation is the tangential acceleration a_t. The direction of this component of acceleration is always tangent to the path of motion. It may be noted that this direction is the same as the direction of the velocity of the particle. The magnitude of the tangential component of acceleration of the particle in curvilinear translation is equal to the first derivative with respect to time of the magnitude of the velocity. In equation form,

$$a_t = \dot{v} = \ddot{s} \qquad (17.2)$$

where s is the coordinate of length along the curve.

In this chapter the kinematics of plane motion of a rigid body will be studied. The concepts of the velocity and acceleration of a particle in rectilinear or curvilinear translation will be extended to characterize the motion of the rigid body. In a rigid body, the distance between any two points is always the same, no matter what type of force system acts on the body. A rigid body thus may be viewed as having unchanging shape. Since the rigid body has nonzero length dimensions, it may experience rotation. It is the *absence* of any rotation effects which distinguishes the problem in particle kinematics from that in rigid-body kinematics.

17.2 RECTILINEAR, AND PLANE CURVILINEAR, TRANSLATION OF A RIGID BODY

Figure 17.1 shows a plane rigid body which lies in the *xy* plane. If the body moves so that *all* points in the body move along *straight parallel lines,* the motion is described as *rectilinear translation.* An alternate definition of this type of motion is that the body moves in such a way that any line, such as line *ab*

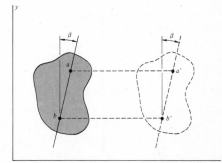

Fig. 17.1

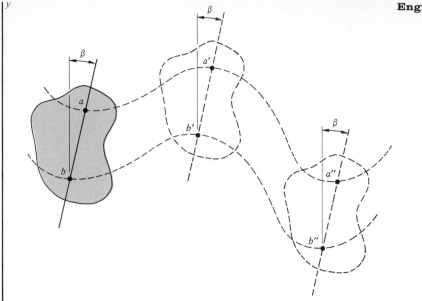

Fig. 17.2

in the figure, always has the same direction with respect to some fixed reference line. For the body in Fig. 17.1, the direction of line *ab* is given by the constant value of the angle β between the line and a vertical axis.

Figure 17.2 shows the situation when the body moves with plane curvilinear motion. For this case, the two arbitrary points *a* and *b* on the body trace out *parallel,* plane curvilinear paths. An alternate interpretation of this type of motion is that, as the body moves in plane curvilinear translation, any arbitrary line on the body is always parallel to its original position. It may be seen from the figure that lines $a'b'$ and $a''b''$ are always parallel to the original position *ab*.

When a body moves with either rectilinear or curvilinear translation, the velocity and acceleration of *all* points on the body have the *same magnitude, direction, and sense.* This effect is shown in Fig. 17.3a, where a body moves with plane curvilinear translation with the known values v_a and a_a at point *a*. The velocity and acceleration at the two arbitrary points *b* and *c* are then as shown in Fig. 17.3b, and

$$v_a = v_b = v_c \qquad a_a = a_b = a_c \qquad (17.3)$$

It follows from the discussion above that rectilinear translation is a special case of plane curvilinear translation, where the plane curved paths of all particles in the body have the limiting configuration of straight lines. It also follows that the distinguishing characteristic of rectilinear or curvilinear translational motion is the complete absence of any rotation effects of the rigid body.

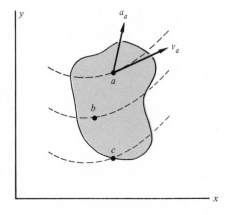

(*a*)

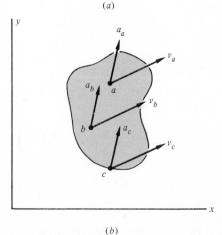

(*b*)

Fig. 17.3

17.3 ROTATION OF A RIGID BODY ABOUT A FIXED AXIS

Figure 17.4 shows a rigid link hinged to an absolute reference point such as the earth. The only possible motion of the link is rotation about the hinge. The axis of rotation is an axis which passes through the center of the hinge pin and is perpendicular to the plane of the figure. This axis is referred to as the *center of rotation,* or the *center of turning.*

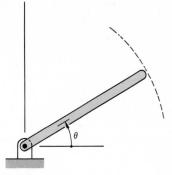

Fig. 17.4

The term *rotation,* in a general sense, is understood to mean motion in which a reference line on the rigid body experiences a *changing* angular position with respect to a fixed reference line in the plane of motion.

The angular displacement of the link is given by angle θ, and this displacement is a vector quantity. The direction of θ may be defined by the plane in which it is measured or by the direction of a line normal to this plane. The basic magnitude of an angle is expressed in radians. The arrow representing θ in the figure indicates that the positive sense of θ is counter-clockwise. The vector description of angular displacement is directly analogous to the vector description of a moment. Since the directions of all angular displacements are the same in plane motion of a rigid body, the boldface vector notation is not necessary when writing these terms.

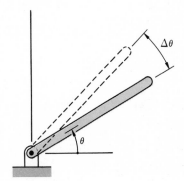

Fig. 17.5

The hinged link is redrawn in Fig. 17.5. The angular displacement θ corresponds to time t. At a later time $t + \Delta t$, the link has rotated to the new position shown by the dashed outline. The *angular velocity* ω of the link is defined to be the time rate of change of angular displacement, or

$$\omega = \lim_{\Delta t \to 0} \frac{\Delta\theta}{\Delta t} = \frac{d\theta}{dt} = \dot{\theta} \qquad (17.4)$$

The basic units of angular velocity are radians per second, written as rad/s. These units are the same in both USCS and SI notation. Since $\Delta\theta$ is positive in the sense of increasing θ and Δt is always positive, it follows that the angular velocity ω is always *positive in the same sense as θ.*

The *angular acceleration* α is defined to be the time rate of change of angular velocity. Thus,

$$\alpha = \frac{d\omega}{dt} = \frac{d}{dt}(\omega) = \frac{d}{dt}\left(\frac{d\theta}{dt}\right) = \frac{d^2\theta}{dt^2} = \ddot{\theta} \qquad (17.5)$$

The basic units of angular acceleration are radians per second squared (rad/s^2). These units are the same in both USCS and SI notation. Following a development similar to that for angular velocity, it can be shown that *the angular acceleration α is always positive in the positive sense of θ.*

Example 17.1 The disk in Fig. 17.6 has an index line marked on it. The angular displacement of the disk, and with it the reference line, is given by

$$\theta = (7.95t - 10.2t^3) \qquad (17.6)$$

where t is in seconds and θ is in radians.

a Find the initial values of the angular displacement, velocity and acceleration at $t = 0$.

b Find the time at which the disk reaches its maximum counter-clockwise angular displacement and the value of this maximum displacement.

c At what time does the disk pass through the initial position again?

d Find the angular velocity and angular acceleration corresponding to the time of part c.

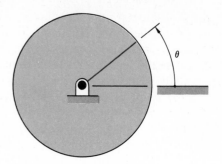

Fig. 17.6

Solution

a The angular displacement of the disk is given by

$$\theta = (7.95t - 10.2t^3) \qquad (17.7)$$

The angular velocity and acceleration are

$$\omega = \dot{\theta} = 7.95 - 3(10.2)t^2 = (7.95 - 30.6t^2) \text{ rad/s} \qquad (17.8)$$

$$\alpha = \ddot{\theta} = -2(30.6t) = -61.2t \text{ rad/s}^2 \qquad (17.9)$$

At $t = 0$ the initial velocity ω_0, from Eq. (17.8), is

$$\omega_0 = 7.95 - 30.6(0) = 7.95 \text{ rad/s} \qquad (17.10)$$

The initial displacement, from Eq. (17.7), is zero and, from Eq. (17.9), the initial acceleration is zero.

b It may be seen from Eq. (17.8) that the angular velocity is initially positive and at later times becomes negative. Thus, when the angular velocity is zero, the disk reaches its position of maximum angular displacement, and

$$0 = 7.95 - 30.6t^2 \qquad t = 0.510 \text{ s} \qquad (17.11)$$

The corresponding angular displacement is

$$\theta = 7.95t - 10.2t^3 = 7.95(0.510) - 10.2(0.510)^3 \qquad (17.12)$$

$$\theta = 2.70 \text{ rad} = 155° \qquad (17.13)$$

The acceleration at this position is

$$\alpha = -61.2t = -61.2(0.510) = -31.2 \text{ rad/s}^2 \qquad (17.14)$$

c When the disk passes through the initial position again, $\theta = 0$. Using Eq. (17.7), we get

$$0 = 7.95t - 10.2t^3 \qquad (17.15)$$

$$0 = t(7.95 - 10.2t^2) \qquad t = 0, 0.883 \text{ s} \qquad (17.16)$$

The time $t = 0$ is the initial time of the problem. At $t = 0.883$ s the disk again passes through the initial position.

d The velocity and acceleration when the disk returns to the initial position are

$$\omega = 7.95 - 30.6t^2 = 7.95 - 30.6(0.883^2) = -15.9 \text{ rad/s} \quad (17.17)$$

$$\alpha = -61.2t = -61.2(0.883) = -54.0 \text{ rad/s}^2 \quad (17.18)$$

These results are displayed in Fig. 17.7.

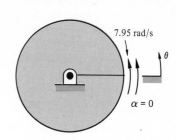

Initial position

17.4 GRAPHICAL INTERPRETATION OF ANGULAR DISPLACEMENT, VELOCITY AND ACCELERATION DIAGRAMS

In Sec. 15.3 it was shown that the displacement, velocity, and acceleration of a particle in rectilinear translation had a very useful graphical interpretation. In this section a similar interpretation will be made for the case of a rigid body rotating about a fixed axis. The similarity is that the displacement, velocity, and acceleration have a common direction. The relationship between the angular velocity and displacement for the rigid body in rotation is

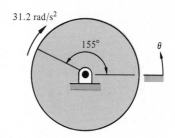

Maximum angular displacement

$$\omega = \frac{d\theta}{dt} \quad (17.19)$$

It may be seen from this equation that the angular velocity is equal to the slope of the angular displacement vs. time curve. Equation (17.19) may be written as

$$d\theta = \omega \, dt \quad (17.20)$$

$$\int_{\theta_1}^{\theta_2} d\theta = \int_{t_1}^{t_2} \omega \, dt \qquad \theta_2 - \theta_1 = \int_{t_1}^{t_2} \omega \, dt \quad (17.21)$$

In these equations 1 and 2 designate the endpoints of a time interval of interest. The term on the right-hand side of Eq. (17.21) is the area under the velocity diagram between times 1 and 2, and this area is equal to the change $\theta_2 - \theta_1$ in angular displacement during the time interval.

The definition of angular acceleration for the rigid body in rotation is

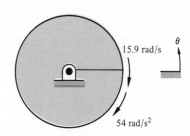

Return through initial position

Fig. 17.7

$$\alpha = \frac{d\omega}{dt} \quad (17.22)$$

It follows from Eq. (17.22) that the angular acceleration is equal to the slope of the angular-velocity-vs.-time curve.

This equation may be written in the form

$$d\omega = \alpha \, dt \quad (17.23)$$

$$\int_{\omega_1}^{\omega_2} d\omega = \int_{t_1}^{t_2} \alpha \, dt \qquad \omega_2 - \omega_1 = \int_{t_1}^{t_2} \alpha \, dt \quad (17.24)$$

Thus the *change* in the angular velocity is equal to the *area* under the angular acceleration-vs.-time curve.

The techniques, presented in Sec. 15.1, for sketching positive or negative increasing or decreasing slopes may be used directly with Eqs. (17.19) and (17.22).

Example 17.2 Figure 17.8 shows a punch press. A heavy steel flywheel rotates at 20 r/min. During the punching operation a clutch engages the flywheel with the punching mechanism, and the corresponding acceleration diagram of the flywheel is shown in Fig. 17.9. The metallic sheet stock to be punched consists of a thin, soft material on top and a thicker, hard material on the bottom, and the total punching operation takes place during the 1.7-s interval shown in the figure. After the punching operation is completed, the flywheel rotates through 0.5 r and engages with a motor which gives the flywheel a constant acceleration of 0.1 rad/s^2. When the flywheel reaches its original angular velocity, the motor is disengaged from the flywheel.

a Draw the motion diagrams for the entire cycle of operation of the punch press.

b Find the time needed for the motor to return the flywheel to its original speed.

c Find the total time for one cycle of operation.

Solution The initial angular velocity of the flywheel is 20 r/min, so that the time t_0 to complete $\frac{1}{2}$ r is

$$t_0 = \frac{1}{2}\left(\frac{1}{20\,\text{r/min}}\right) = \frac{1}{2}\left(0.05\,\frac{\text{min}}{\text{r}}\right)\left(\frac{60\,\text{s}}{1\,\text{min}}\right) = 1.5\,\text{s} \quad (17.25)$$

The complete acceleration diagram is shown in Fig. 17.10, and t_1 is the time interval required for the motor to restore the flywheel to its initial velocity.

The areas of the acceleration diagram are computed first, and these values are the changes in the angular velocity. The initial angular velocity, at $t = 0$, is known to be 20 r/min = 2.09 rad/s.

For the last time interval,

$$\omega_2 - \omega_1 = \int_{t_1}^{t_2} \alpha\,dt \quad (17.26)$$

$$2.09 - 1.56 = 0.1t_1 \qquad t_1 = 5.3\,\text{s} \quad (17.27)$$

The areas of the velocity diagram are computed next, and these values are the changes in the angular displacement. The initial displacement of the flywheel at $t = 0$ is defined to be $\theta_0 = 0$. As the final step in the solution, the displacement diagram is sketched.

The total time t for one cycle of operation is

$$t = 1.7 + 1.5 + 5.3 = 8.5\,\text{s} \quad (17.28)$$

The corresponding total angular displacement θ is

$$\theta = 15.2\,\text{rad} = 2.42\,\text{r} \quad (17.29)$$

An alternate method of solution for t_1 is to apply

$$\omega_2 - \omega_1 = \int_{t_1}^{t_2} \alpha\,dt \quad (17.30)$$

directly to the acceleration diagram. 1 and 2 will be chosen to represent the endpoints of the cycle of the punch press. Since the flywheel is returned to its original velocity,

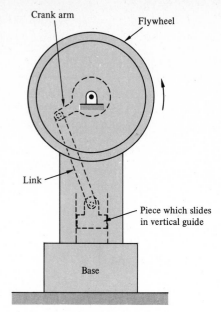

Fig. 17.8

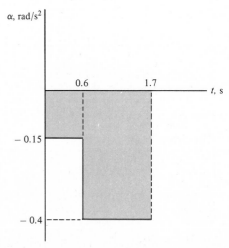

Fig. 17.9

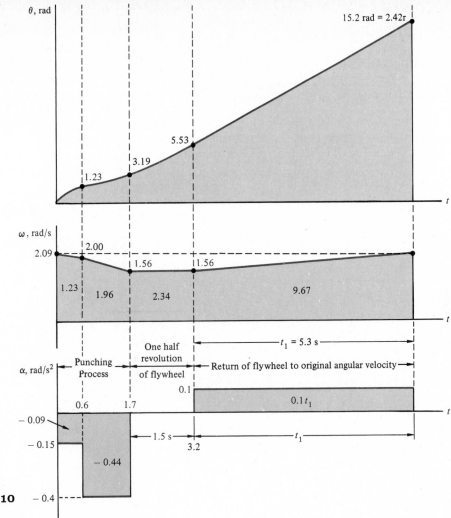

Fig. 17.10

$$\omega_1 = \omega_2 \qquad (17.31)$$

$$\omega_1 - \omega_2 = 0 = \int_{t_1}^{t_2} \alpha \, dt \qquad (17.32)$$

From Eq. (17.32) the *net area* of the acceleration diagram must be zero, or

$$-0.15(0.6) - 0.4(1.7 - 0.6) + 0.1t_1 = 0 \qquad t_1 = 5.3 \text{ s} \quad (17.33)$$

17.5 ROTATION, WITH CONSTANT ACCELERATION, OF A RIGID BODY ABOUT A FIXED AXIS

A situation encountered frequently in problems in dynamics is the case of a rigid body which rotates, with *constant angular acceleration,* about a fixed axis. It will be shown in Chap. 18 that this case occurs when the *resultant moment* acting on the body has a *constant* value.

The magnitude of the angular acceleration is given by

$$\frac{d\omega}{dt} = \alpha = \text{constant} \qquad d\omega = \alpha\,dt \qquad (17.34)$$

The integral form of this equation is

$$\int_{\omega_1}^{\omega_2} d\omega = \int_{t_1}^{t_2} \alpha\,dt \qquad (17.35)$$

The numbers 1 and 2 define the endpoints of the time interval under consideration. Since α is a constant, it may be moved outside the integral sign. The result is

$$\int_{\omega_1}^{\omega_2} d\omega = \alpha \int_{t_1}^{t_2} dt \qquad (17.36)$$

$$\omega \Big|_{\omega_1}^{\omega_2} = \alpha t \Big|_{t_1}^{t_2} \qquad (17.37)$$

$$\omega_2 - \omega_1 = \alpha(t_2 - t_1) \qquad (17.38)$$

Equation (17.38) is a general relationship among angular velocity, acceleration, and time at t_1 and t_2. t_1 is defined to be the initial time of the problem, with the value

$$t_1 = 0 \qquad (17.39)$$

The corresponding angular velocity ω_1 is defined to be the *initial velocity* ω_0, so that

$$\omega_1 = \omega_0 \qquad (17.40)$$

The angular velocity and time, ω_2 and t_2, at the end of the time interval under consideration are written as

$$\omega_2 = \omega \qquad t_2 = t \qquad (17.41)$$

With the above changes in notation, Eq. (17.38) appears as

$$\omega = \omega_0 + \alpha t \qquad (17.42)$$

The angular displacement and angular velocity are related by

$$\omega = \frac{d\theta}{dt} \qquad d\theta = \omega\,dt \qquad (17.43)$$

The integral form of Eq. (17.43) is

$$\int_{\theta_1}^{\theta_2} d\theta = \int_{t_1}^{t_2} \omega\,dt \qquad (17.44)$$

The angular displacement θ corresponding to $t_1 = 0$ is designated the initial displacement θ_0. By using $\theta_2 = \theta$ and $t_2 = t$, Eq. (17.44) appears as

$$\int_{\theta_0}^{\theta} d\theta = \int_0^t \omega\,dt = \int_0^t (\omega_0 + \alpha t)\,dt \qquad (17.45)$$

$$\theta \Big|_{\theta_0}^{\theta} = (\omega_0 t + \tfrac{1}{2}\alpha t^2) \Big|_0^t \qquad (17.46)$$

$$\theta - \theta_0 = \omega_0 t + \tfrac{1}{2}\alpha t^2 \qquad (17.47)$$

$$\theta = \theta_0 + \omega_0 t + \tfrac{1}{2}\alpha t^2 \qquad (17.48)$$

If t is eliminated between Eqs. (17.42) and (17.48), the result is

$$\omega^2 = \omega_0^2 + 2\alpha(\theta - \theta_0) \qquad (17.49)$$

Equations (17.42), (17.48), and (17.49) are the three basic equations that describe the rotation of a rigid body with constant angular acceleration about a fixed axis. These equations are repeated here:

$$\omega = \omega_0 + \alpha t \qquad (17.50)$$

$$\theta = \theta_0 + \omega_0 t + \tfrac{1}{2}\alpha t^2 \qquad (17.51)$$

$$\omega^2 = \omega_0^2 + 2\alpha(\theta - \theta_0) \qquad (17.52)$$

These equations are identical in structure to Eqs. (15.56) through (15.58). These latter equations were used to describe the problem of rectilinear translation of a particle with constant acceleration.

Example 17.3 Figure 17.11 shows a radial-arm wood saw which has an operating speed of 1,500 r/min. When the saw is turned off, a magnetic brake brings the blade to rest in 1 min.

a If the braking deceleration is assumed to be constant, through how many revolutions does the blade rotate before coming to rest?

b In a certain operation the blade jams in a piece of material and comes to rest in $\tfrac{3}{4}$ r. Find the average value of the deceleration and the corresponding time needed for the blade to come to rest.

Solution The initial speed of the saw blade is

$$\omega_0 = 1,500 \,\frac{r}{min}\left(\frac{2\pi \text{ rad}}{1 \text{ r}}\right)\left(\frac{1 \text{ min}}{60 \text{ s}}\right) = 157 \,\frac{rad}{s} \qquad (17.53)$$

a The saw blade comes to rest in 1 min, so that

$$\omega = 0 = \omega_0 + \alpha t \qquad (17.54)$$

$$0 = 157 + \alpha(60 \text{ s}) \qquad \alpha = -2.62 \text{ rad/s}^2 \qquad (17.55)$$

The total number of revolutions of the saw blade is found from

$$\omega^2 = \omega_0^2 + 2\alpha(\theta - \theta_0) \qquad (17.56)$$

$$0 = 157^2 + 2(-2.62)(\theta - 0) \qquad (17.57)$$

$$\theta = 4,700 \text{ rad} = 749 \text{ r} \qquad (17.58)$$

This result may be checked by using

$$\theta = \theta_0 + \omega_0 t + \tfrac{1}{2}\alpha t^2 \qquad (17.59)$$

$$= 0 + 157(60) + \tfrac{1}{2}(-2.62)(60^2) \qquad (17.60)$$

$$= 4,700 \text{ rad} = 749 \text{ r} \qquad (17.61)$$

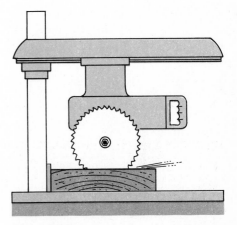

Fig. 17.11

b For the case where the saw blade jams, this element comes to rest in $0.75\,r = 4.71$ rad, and the average value of the acceleration is found from

$$\omega^2 = \omega_0^2 + 2\alpha(\theta - \theta_0) \tag{17.62}$$

$$0 = 157^2 + 2\alpha(4.71 - 0) \qquad \alpha = -2620 \text{ rad/s}^2 \tag{17.63}$$

The corresponding time is found from

$$\omega = \omega_0 + \alpha t \tag{17.64}$$

$$0 = 157 + (-2620)t \tag{17.65}$$

$$t = 0.0599 \text{ s} = 59.9 \text{ ms} \tag{17.66}$$

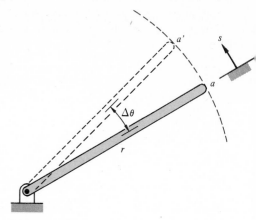

Fig. 17.12

17.6 RELATION BETWEEN TRANS-LATIONAL AND ROTATIONAL MOTION

Figure 17.12 shows a link of length r which rotates about a fixed axis. Point a on the tip of the link may be considered to be a particle in curvilinear translation along the circular path. The relationships between the translational velocity and acceleration of point a and the angular velocity and acceleration of the link will be developed now.

The velocity of point a must be tangent to the path of motion. Thus, the direction of the velocity of point a is normal to the link. The magnitude of this velocity is given by

$$v = \frac{ds}{dt} \tag{17.67}$$

where s is the coordinate of length along the curve. Point a in Fig. 17.12 is assumed now to move to position a' as the link moves through the angle $\Delta\theta$ in time Δt. The arc length from a to a' is

$$\Delta s = r\,\Delta\theta \tag{17.68}$$

Both sides of Eq. (17.68) are divided by Δt, with the result

$$\frac{\Delta s}{\Delta t} = r\frac{\Delta\theta}{\Delta t} \tag{17.69}$$

Δt is now allowed to approach zero and, in the limit,

$$\lim_{\Delta t \to 0}\frac{\Delta s}{\Delta t} = \lim_{\Delta t \to 0} r\frac{\Delta\theta}{\Delta t} \tag{17.70}$$

$$\frac{ds}{dt} = r\frac{d\theta}{dt} = r\dot{\theta} = r\omega \tag{17.71}$$

where ω is the angular velocity. Equations (17.67) and (17.71) are combined to obtain the final result

$$v = r\omega \qquad (17.72)$$

Equation (17.72) is a fundamental relationship between the linear velocity of a point on a rigid link and the angular velocity of the link. This equation may be plotted along the link, and the result is shown in Fig. 17.13. This figure shows the linear variation of velocity along the length of the link.

The normal component of acceleration of point a has the form

$$a_n = \frac{v^2}{\rho} \qquad (17.73)$$

The direction of this term is along the axis of the link, and the sense is from point a toward the center of rotation. By using $v = r\omega$ and $\rho = r$, this equation appears as

$$a_n = \frac{(r\omega)^2}{r} = r\omega^2 \qquad (17.74)$$

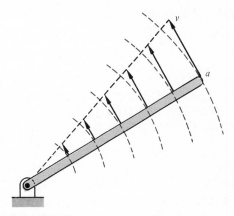

Fig. 17.13

The direction of the tangential component a_t of the acceleration of point a is along the path of motion. The magnitude of this term is equal to the first time derivative of the speed of the particle. Using Eq. (17.72), we get

$$a_t = \frac{dv}{dt} \qquad (17.75)$$

$$= r\frac{d\omega}{dt} = r\alpha \qquad (17.76)$$

where α is the angular acceleration.

Example 17.4 The saw blade of Example 17.3 is 10 in in diameter. Point a is located on the rim of the blade. Find the magnitude of the velocity and acceleration of point a,

a When the blade rotates at 1,500 r/min
b At the instant that the magnetic braking starts
c At the instant that the blade jams, as described in part b of Example 17.3

Solution
a When the blade rotates freely at 1,500 r/min,

$$v = r\omega = 5(157) = 785 \text{ in/s} = 65.4 \text{ ft/s} \qquad (17.77)$$

$$a_n = r\omega^2 = 5(157^2) = 1.23 \times 10^5 \frac{\text{in}}{\text{s}^2} = 1.03 \times 10^4 \frac{\text{ft}}{\text{s}^2} \quad (17.78)$$

$$a_n = 320 \text{ g's} \qquad a_t = 0 \qquad (17.79)$$

b At the instant that the magnetic braking starts,

$$a_t = r\alpha = 5(-2.62) = -13.1 \text{ in/s}^2 = -1.09 \text{ ft/s}^2 \quad (17.80)$$

v and a_n have the same values as in part a. It may be seen that $a_t \ll a_n$.

c When the saw blade jams,

$$a_t = r\alpha = 5(-2,620) =$$
$$-13,100 \text{ in/s}^2 = 1,090 \text{ ft/s}^2 \quad (17.81)$$
$$a_t = 33.9 \text{ g's} \quad (17.82)$$

v and a_n again have the same values as in part a. The magnitude of the total acceleration is

$$a = \sqrt{a_n^2 + a_t^2} = \sqrt{(1.03 \times 10^4)^2 + 1,090^2} \quad (17.83)$$
$$= 1.04 \times 10^4 \text{ ft/s}^2 = 323 \text{ g's} \quad (17.84)$$

17.7 RELATION BETWEEN TRANSLATIONAL AND ROTATIONAL MOTION OF CONNECTED BODIES

Figure 17.14a shows a pulley hinged to the ground. Around the pulley is wrapped an inextensible string which is connected to a weight. It will now be shown that a unique relationship exists between the motions of the pulley and the weight.

The positive senses of the displacement coordinates of the two bodies are shown in Fig. 17.14b. The angular displacement of the pulley is θ, and y is the rectilinear displacement of the weight. The pulley is now imagined to rotate through the angle θ. During this rotation, a length $r\theta$ of string is unwound from the pulley. The string is inextensible, and the force in the string is assumed to be always a tensile force. The displacement y of the weight corresponding to the rotation of the pulley is then

$$y = r\theta \quad (17.85)$$

This equation may be differentiated twice with respect to time, with the results

$$\frac{dy}{dt} = r\frac{d\theta}{dt} \qquad v = r\omega \quad (17.86)$$

$$\frac{d^2y}{dt^2} = r\frac{d^2\theta}{dt^2} \qquad a = r\alpha \quad (17.87)$$

These two equations are very useful relationships among the displacement, velocity, and acceleration of connected bodies.

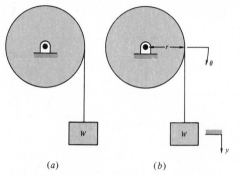

(a)   (b)

Fig. 17.14

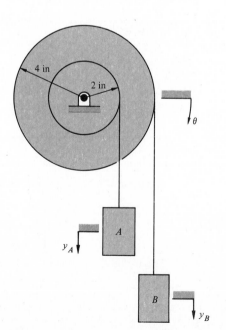

Example 17.5 At a certain instant the pulley in Fig. 17.15 has a counterclockwise angular velocity of 300 r/min and is decelerating at the rate of 8,600 r/min².

a Find the corresponding velocity and acceleration of the weights A and B.

b Find the relative velocity and acceleration of weight A with respect to weight B.

Express the answers in feet and seconds.

Solution The angular velocity of the pulley, with reference to the positive sense of angular displacement shown in the figure, is

Fig. 17.15

$$\omega = -300 \frac{r}{min}\left(\frac{2\pi \text{ rad}}{r}\right)\left(\frac{1 \text{ min}}{60 \text{ s}}\right) = -31.4 \frac{rad}{s} \quad (17.88)$$

Since the pulley is decelerating, the angular acceleration must have a sense opposite that of the angular velocity, so that

$$\alpha = 8{,}600 \frac{r}{min^2}\left(\frac{2\pi \text{ rad}}{r}\right)\left(\frac{1 \text{ min}}{60 \text{ s}}\right)^2 = 15.0 \frac{rad}{s^2} \quad (17.89)$$

The two weights move as particles in rectilinear translation, and the velocities and accelerations are

Block A $\qquad v_A = r_A\omega \qquad\qquad\qquad\qquad\qquad\qquad (17.90)$

$$= 2 \text{ in}\left(-31.4 \frac{rad}{s}\right)\left(\frac{1 \text{ ft}}{12 \text{ in}}\right) = -5.23 \frac{ft}{s}$$

$$a_A = r_A\alpha \qquad\qquad\qquad\qquad\qquad\qquad\qquad (17.91)$$

$$= 2 \text{ in}\left(15.0 \frac{rad}{s^2}\right)\left(\frac{1 \text{ ft}}{12 \text{ in}}\right) = 2.5 \frac{ft}{s^2}$$

Block B $\qquad v_B = r_B\omega \qquad\qquad\qquad\qquad\qquad\qquad (17.92)$

$$= 4(-31.4)(\tfrac{1}{12}) = -10.5 \text{ ft/s}$$

$$a_B = r_B\alpha \qquad\qquad\qquad\qquad\qquad\qquad\qquad (17.93)$$

$$= 4(15.0)(\tfrac{1}{12}) = 5 \text{ ft/s}^2$$

The *relative* velocity and acceleration, v_{AB} and a_{AB}, of weight A with respect to weight B are given by

$$v_{AB} = v_A - v_B = -5.23 - (-10.5) = 5.27 \text{ ft/s} \quad (17.94)$$

$$a_{AB} = a_A - a_B = 2.5 - 5 = -2.5 \text{ ft/s}^2 \quad (17.95)$$

v_{AB} and a_{AB} are both positive in the positive senses of v_A and a_A. To an observer positioned on weight B, weight A would appear to be slowing down as it moves toward her or him. These conclusions are shown in Fig. 17.16.

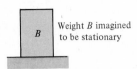

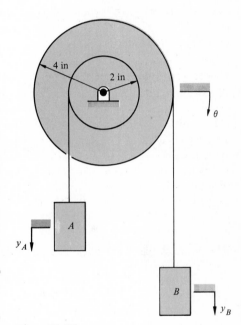

Fig. 17.16

Example 17.6 Do the same as in Example 17.5 if weight A is supported from the left side of the inner pulley.

Solution The system is shown in Fig. 17.17. The velocity and acceleration of weight B are the same as before, with the values

$$v_B = -10.5 \text{ ft/s} \qquad a_B = 5 \text{ ft/s}^2 \quad (17.96)$$

For weight A,

$$v_A = -(r_A\omega) = -[2(-31.4)(\tfrac{1}{12})] = 5.23 \text{ ft/s} \quad (17.97)$$

$$a_A = -(r_A\alpha) = -2(15)(\tfrac{1}{12}) = -2.5 \text{ ft/s}^2 \quad (17.98)$$

The relative velocity and acceleration of A with respect to B are

$$v_{AB} = v_A - v_B = 5.23 - (-10.5) = 15.7 \text{ ft/s} \quad (17.99)$$

$$a_{AB} = a_A - a_B = -2.5 - 5 = -7.5 \text{ ft/s}^2 \quad (17.100)$$

Senses of the relative velocity and acceleration, shown in Fig. 17.18, are the same as in Example 17.5. Magnitudes of both these quantities, however, are greater than those in the latter problem.

Fig. 17.17

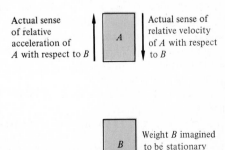

Fig. 17.18

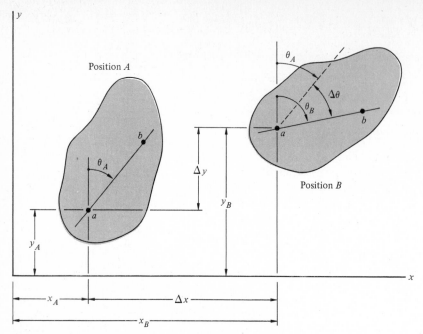

Fig. 17.19

17.8 GENERAL PLANE MOTION OF A RIGID BODY

The most general type of plane motion is a combination of rotation and translation. The body in Fig. 17.19 is initially in position A. This position may be described by specifying the coordinates x_A and y_A of an arbitrary point a on the body, as well as the angular displacement θ_A of the body with respect to an arbitrary reference line.

At a later time, the body is in position B. The total motion which is required for the body to move from the initial position A to the final position B may be envisioned to be the sum of the following two distinct motions:

1. *Translation* of the body until point a has the position defined by $x = x_B$ and $y = y_B$.
2. *Rotation* of the body, about the final position of a, until the angle θ_B is obtained.

The initial description of the position of the body is given by x_A, y_A, and θ_A, and the final position is defined by x_B, y_B, and θ_B. The *change* in the position may be found from the general equation which defines change, given by

Change in condition =
$$\text{(final condition)} - \text{(initial condition)} \quad (17.101)$$

The change in position of the body in Fig. 17.19 is found to be

$$\Delta x = x_B - x_A \quad (17.102)$$

$$\Delta y = y_B - y_A \tag{17.103}$$

$$\Delta \theta = \theta_B - \theta_A \tag{17.104}$$

Kinematics of Plane Motion | 577
of a Rigid Body

These results are for the change in displacement, or position, of the body in general plane motion. These results can be generalized readily to the case of the velocity or acceleration of the body. It can be shown that the velocity or acceleration of the rigid body in general plane motion is the sum of the translational velocity or acceleration of any arbitrary point on the body and the rotational velocity or acceleration with respect to this point.

The concept of viewing the general plane motion of a rigid body as a combination of translational and rotational motion finds very useful application in the solution of problems in rigid-body dynamics. This technique also is applied in describing a quantity which is referred to as the kinetic energy of the body. Here, one part of the total energy due to motion is related to the translational velocity of the body, while the remaining part of this energy is related to the angular velocity of the body with respect to a certain point on the body. This topic is studied in detail in Chap. 20.

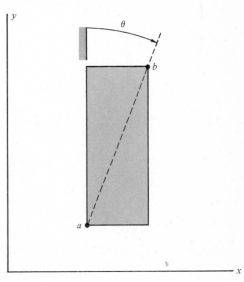

Fig. 17.20

Example 17.7 At $t = 0$ a flat, rigid plate has the position shown in Fig. 17.20. The displacement of corner a is given by

$$x = (3.94 + 4.82t) \tag{17.105}$$

$$y = (2.26 - 9.64t + 5t^2) \tag{17.106}$$

where t is in seconds and x and y are in inches. The angular position of the line ab is expressed by

$$\theta = (1.98t^3 + 0.38) \tag{17.107}$$

where t is in seconds and θ is in radians.

a Sketch the position of the plate when $t = 1$ s.

b Describe the change in position of the plate during the time interval from 0 to 1 s.

c Find the magnitude, direction, and sense of the velocity at point a when $t = 1$ s.

d Describe the change in velocity of corner a of the plate during the time interval from 0 to 1 s.

e Find the change in the angular velocity during the time interval from 0 to 1 s.

Solution

a The plate is redrawn in Fig. 17.21. The initial position of the plate is defined by

$$t = 0 \qquad x = 3.94 + 4.82(0) = 3.94 \text{ in} \tag{17.108}$$

$$y = 2.26 - 9.64(0) + 5(0)^2 = 2.26 \text{ in} \tag{17.109}$$

$$\theta = 1.98(0)^3 + 0.38 = 0.38 \text{ rad} = 21.8° \tag{17.110}$$

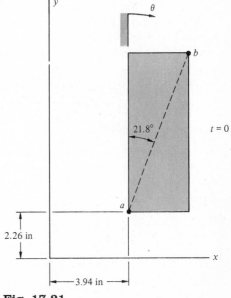

Fig. 17.21

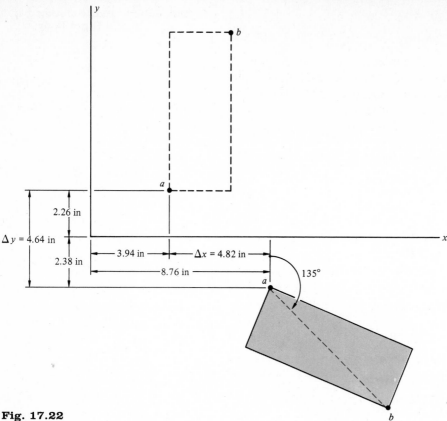

Fig. 17.22

At the end of 1 s, the position of the plate is given by

$$x = 3.94 + 4.82(1) = 8.76 \text{ in} \qquad (17.111)$$

$$y = 2.26 - 9.64(1) + 5(1)^2 = -2.38 \text{ in} \qquad (17.112)$$

$$\theta = 1.98(1)^3 + 0.38 = 2.36 \text{ rad} = 135° \qquad (17.113)$$

The position of the plate at the end of 1 s is shown in Fig. 17.22.

b The *change* in position of the plate is given by

$$\Delta x = x \bigg|_{t=1} - x \bigg|_{t=0} = 8.76 - 3.94 = 4.82 \text{ in} \qquad (17.114)$$

$$\Delta y = y \bigg|_{t=1} - y \bigg|_{t=0} = -2.38 - 2.26 = -4.64 \text{ in} \qquad (17.115)$$

$$\Delta \theta = \theta \bigg|_{t=1} - \theta \bigg|_{t=0} = 135° - 21.8° = 113° \qquad (17.116)$$

c The velocity components of point *a* are

$$v_x = \dot{x} = \frac{d}{dt}(3.94 + 4.82t) = 4.82 \, \frac{\text{in}}{\text{s}} \qquad (17.117)$$

$$v_y = \frac{d}{dt}(2.26 - 9.64t + 5t^2) = [-9.64 + 2(5)t] \frac{\text{in}}{\text{s}}$$

$$\qquad (17.118)$$

At $t = 0$,

$$\dot{x}_0 = 4.82 \text{ in/s} \qquad \dot{y}_0 = -9.64 \text{ in/s} \qquad (17.119)$$

At $t = 1$ s,

$$\dot{x}_1 = 4.82 \text{ in/s} \qquad \dot{y}_1 = -9.64 + 10(1) = 0.36 \text{ in/s} \quad (17.120)$$

These components are shown in Fig. 17.23.

The magnitude of the velocity of point a is

$$v_a = \sqrt{\dot{x}_1^2 + \dot{y}_1^2} = \sqrt{4.82^2 + 0.36^2} = 4.83 \text{ in/s} \quad (17.121)$$

and the direction is

$$\beta = \tan^{-1}\frac{0.36}{4.82} = 4.27° \qquad (17.122)$$

d The change in the velocity of point a is given by

$$\Delta\dot{x} = \dot{x}_1 - \dot{x}_0 = 4.82 - 4.82 = 0 \qquad (17.123)$$

$$\Delta\dot{y} = \dot{y}_1 - \dot{y}_0 = 0.36 - (-9.64) = 10 \text{ in/s} \qquad (17.124)$$

e The angular velocity of line ab is

$$\dot{\theta} = \frac{d}{dt}(1.98t^3 + 0.38) = 3(1.98t^2) = 5.94t^2 \,\frac{\text{rad}}{\text{s}} \quad (17.125)$$

The change in the angular velocity is

$$\Delta\dot{\theta} = \dot{\theta}_1 - \dot{\theta}_0 = 5.94(1)^2 - 0 = 5.94 \text{ rad/s} \qquad (17.126)$$

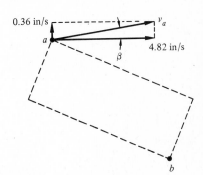

Fig. 17.23

17.9 INSTANT CENTER OF ROTATION

Figure 17.24 shows a plane rigid body which rotates about point a. The radial coordinate r, with its origin at the center of rotation, is attached to the body at an arbitrary location. The translational velocity v of points along the line r is related to the angular velocity ω by

$$v = r\omega \qquad (17.127)$$

It follows from Eq. (17.127) that v is a linear function of r, and this equation is plotted in the figure. It may be seen that points closer to the center of rotation have smaller translational velocities than points more distant from this reference axis. At the center of rotation, defined by $r = 0$, the linear velocity is zero. If this point is assumed to be physically part of the rigid body, then a very important conclusion may be drawn: *one point on the body, the center of rotation, has a velocity which is zero*. This point of zero velocity on a rotating body is referred to as the *instant center of rotation*. It is the point about which the body is rotating at *a given instant*.

In the above development, the instant center (IC), by implication, was seen to be located within the physical boundary of the rigid body. It may be shown that *the instant center does not have to be located on the body*. The concept of the instant center of rotation is used widely in the motion analysis of

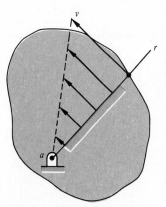

Fig. 17.24

mechanical linkages, where the velocities of different points on the links are to be obtained.

The techniques for locating the instant center will now be presented. Figure 17.25 shows a body which moves with plane rotation. The translational velocities of the points *a* and *b* are known; it is desired to find the location of the instant center of rotation. From the fundamental relationship between the linear velocity of a point that is on a rotating body, and the angular velocity of the body, it follows that the direction of the velocity is *perpendicular* to the line that joins the point and the center of rotation. A line *aa′*, perpendicular to v_a, is now drawn through point *a*, and it follows that the IC must lie on this line. By using a similar line of reasoning, the line *bb′* normal to v_b is drawn in Fig. 17.25, and the IC of the body must lie on this line. It follows from the discussion above that the only possible location of the IC which lies on both lines is the intersection of the two lines. This point is labeled IC in Fig. 17.25.

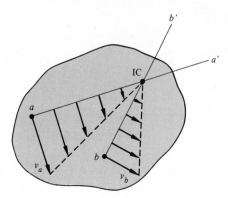

Fig. 17.25

It may be observed from the development above that the magnitude of the linear velocity was never considered. The only criteria which determine the location of the IC are the *directions* of the linear velocities at two points on the body. The general rule, then, for finding the location of the instant center of rotation is to draw lines perpendicular to the *known* directions of the linear velocities of two points on the body. The point of intersection of these two lines is then the instant center of rotation of the body.

A special case occurs if the known directions of the two velocities are parallel to each other. For this case the body is in translation, and the angular velocity is identically zero.

Example 17.8 Figure 17.26 shows a plane sliding mechanism. Slider block *A* moves leftward with a constant velocity of 4 m/s. For the position of the link shown in the figure,

   a Find the angular velocity of the link
   b Find the velocity of slider block *B*
   c Find the magnitude, direction, and sense of the velocity of point *a*

Solution

a The two slider blocks are assumed to be particles in rectilinear motion, and the link has general plane motion. The system is re-drawn in Fig. 17.27. The directions of the two slider tracks define the directions of the slider block velocities. The IC of the link is found by drawing lines perpendicular to these tracks, as shown in the figure. This is an example of a case where the IC does *not* physically lie on the rigid body. In the position shown, link *AB* and lines 0*A*, 0*B*, and 0*a* all instantaneously rotate about the IC with the same angular velocity ω. The angular velocity of line 0*A* is found from

$$v_A = r\omega \qquad \omega = \frac{v_a}{r} = \frac{4}{376/1000} = 10.6 \ \frac{\text{rad}}{\text{s}} \qquad (17.128)$$

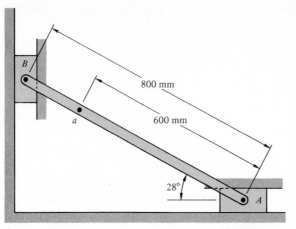

Fig. 17.26

$v_A = 4$ m/s

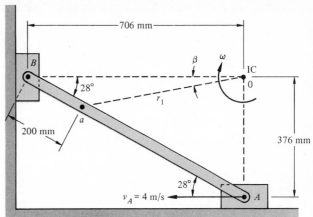

Fig. 17.27

b Since all lines on the link rotate about the IC with the *same* angular velocity, the velocity of slider block B is

$$v_B = r\omega = \frac{706}{1000}(10.6) = 7.48 \frac{\text{m}}{\text{s}} \qquad (17.129)$$

c The length of line $0a$ is designated r_1. From triangle $B0a$, using the law of cosines,

$$r_1^2 = 200^2 + 706^2 - 2(200)706 \cos 28° \qquad r_1 = 538 \text{ mm} \quad (17.130)$$

The angle β, using the law of sines, is found from

$$\frac{200}{\sin \beta} = \frac{538}{\sin 28°} \qquad \beta = 10.0° \qquad (17.131)$$

The magnitude of v_a is then

$$v_a = r_1\omega = \frac{538}{1000}(10.6) = 5.70 \frac{\text{m}}{\text{s}} \qquad (17.132)$$

The complete vector description of the velocities at the three points of interest is shown in Fig. 17.28.

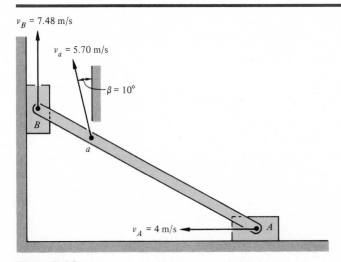

Fig. 17.28

17.10 PURE ROLLING OF RIGID BODIES

Figure 17.29 shows a wheel, in a vertical plane, which contacts a track. In terms of the motion of the wheel relative to the track, four states of motion are possible:

1. The wheel remains at rest.
2. The wheel does not rotate, and the rim of the wheel slides along the track.
3. The wheel rolls along the track without slipping.
4. The wheel moves along the track with a combination of rolling and sliding motion.

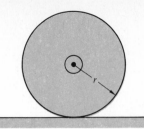

Fig. 17.29

Case 1 is a problem in statics. In case 2, since the wheel does not *rotate*, this element may be analyzed as a particle in translation. The situation described in case 4 is an undefined problem, unless additional information is provided which describes the relationship between the rolling and sliding motions. The remainder of this section will be concerned with case 3, where the wheel rolls without sliding. This type of motion is referred to as *pure rolling*.

Pure rolling of a cylindrical or spherical element is usually the desired operating condition for a device. Typical examples include the wheel of a vehicle, a ball in the race of a ball bearing, and a roller used to paint a wall. From consideration of the motion of a wheel which rolls without slipping, it may be concluded that this is a case of general plane motion. The center of the wheel translates along a path parallel to the track, while the wheel rotates about this center. The relationship between the angular motion of the wheel and the translation motion of the center of the wheel will now be obtained.

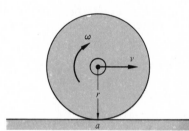

Fig. 17.30

Figure 17.30 shows the senses of motion of the wheel. The positive sense of the angular velocity ω is chosen to be clockwise, so that the center of the wheel moves to the right with the velocity v. The direction of the velocity of the center of the wheel is parallel to the track.

The contact point between the wheel and the track is designated point a. This point may be considered to be simultaneously on the wheel and the track. Since the problem of pure rolling implies no sliding motion between the wheel and the track, point a, as a point on the wheel which has zero velocity, must be an instant center of rotation of the wheel. All lines on the wheel, including line r, have the same angular velocity ω. It may be concluded then, by considering the wheel to instantaneously rotate about the contact point a, that

$$v = r\omega \qquad (17.133)$$

$$\omega = v/r \qquad (17.134)$$

The physical phenomenon of rolling of a wheel may be envisioned to be a succession of instantaneous rotations of the

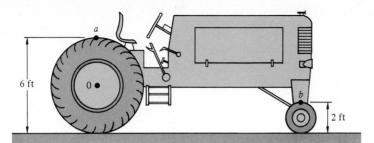

Fig. 17.31

wheel about the contact point between the wheel and the surface on which it rolls.

Example 17.9 The farm tractor shown in Fig. 17.31 moves with a constant speed of 10 mi/h.

a Find the angular velocity, in revolutions per minute, of the front and rear wheels.

b Find the velocity of point a on the top of the rear wheel.

c Find the relative velocity of point a with respect to the axle of the rear wheel.

Solution

a The linear velocity of both wheel centers is

$$v = 10 \frac{\text{mi}}{\text{h}} \left(\frac{5,280 \text{ ft}}{1 \text{ mi}}\right)\left(\frac{1 \text{ h}}{60 \text{ min}}\right) = 880 \frac{\text{ft}}{\text{min}} \qquad (17.135)$$

For the rear wheels,

$$\omega = \frac{v}{r} = \frac{880 \text{ ft/min}}{3 \text{ ft}} = 293 \frac{\text{rad}}{\text{min}} \qquad (17.136)$$

$$\omega = 293 \frac{\text{rad}}{\text{min}} \left(\frac{1 \text{ r}}{2\pi \text{ rad}}\right) = 46.6 \frac{\text{r}}{\text{min}} \qquad (17.137)$$

and for the front wheels

$$\omega = \frac{v}{r} = \frac{880}{1} = 880 \frac{\text{rad}}{\text{min}} \qquad (17.138)$$

$$\omega = 880 \left(\frac{1}{2\pi}\right) = 140 \frac{\text{r}}{\text{min}} \qquad (17.139)$$

b The rear wheel rotates about the contact point with the ground, which is the instant center, with the angular velocity of 293 rad/min. The linear velocity of point a on the upper rim of the wheel is then

$$v = r\omega \qquad (17.140)$$

$$= 6 \text{ ft} \left(293 \frac{\text{rad}}{\text{min}}\right) = 1,760 \frac{\text{ft}}{\text{min}} \qquad (17.141)$$

The distribution of the linear velocity of points on a vertical diameter of the rear wheel is shown in Fig. 17.32.

c The relative velocity of point a with respect to the wheel center is

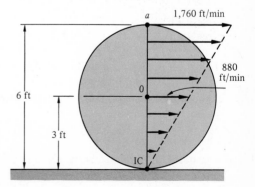

Fig. 17.32

$$v_{a0} = v_a - v_0 = 1{,}760 - 880 = 880 \text{ ft/min} \qquad (17.142)$$

This quantity is positive in the positive sense of v_a.

Example 17.10 Railroad wheels have flanges on them, as shown in Fig. 17.33, so that these wheels do not slide sideways off the track. Show that when the train is in motion, certain parts of the train are always moving in a sense *opposite* to the sense of the actual motion of the train.

Solution A train wheel is shown in Fig. 17.34, and the center a of the wheel is assumed to move to the right. Pure rolling is assumed, and point b is the instant center of rotation of the wheel. The line abc lies on the wheel and rotates with the angular velocity ω of the wheel. The velocity distribution of points of the wheel on a vertical diameter is shown in Fig. 17.35. It may be seen from Fig. 17.35 that the velocity relative to the track, and therefore to the ground, of all points on the flange of the wheel between b and c is *opposite* to the actual, rightward velocity of the train.

Since the train moves to the right with the absolute axle velocity v_a, the train will eventually arrive at the next station.

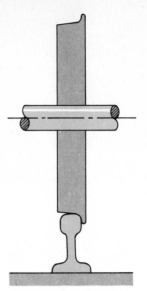

Fig. 17.33

17.11 SUMMARY

A rigid body is a body of unchanging dimensions. All points in a rigid body which moves with rectilinear, or plane curvilinear, translation move along parallel plane paths. The velocity and acceleration at all points in a body with this motion have the same magnitude, direction, and sense. If one point in a rigid body in plane motion is connected to an absolute reference system, such as the earth, the motion is referred to as rotation. Rotation, in its most general sense, is understood to mean motion in which a reference line on the rigid body experiences a changing angular position with respect to a fixed reference line in the plane of motion.

The angular displacement with respect to the reference system is designated θ. The angular velocity ω of a rigid body is the time rate of change of the angular displacement, or

$$\omega = \frac{d\theta}{dt} = \dot{\theta} \qquad (17.143)$$

The basic units of ω, in both USCS and SI units, are radians per second. The angular acceleration α of the rigid body is the time rate of change of the angular velocity, or

$$\alpha = \frac{d\omega}{dt} = \ddot{\theta} \qquad (17.144)$$

The basic units of α, in both USCS and SI units, are radians per second squared. The choice of a positive sense for θ automatically defines the same positive senses for ω and α.

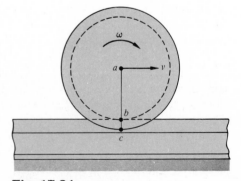

Fig. 17.34

584

The plots of angular displacement, velocity, and acceleration vs. time are referred to as motion diagrams. The value of the angular velocity at any time is the slope of the angular displacement–time curve. The area under the angular velocity–time curve between two times is equal to the change in angular displacement during this time interval. The value of the angular acceleration at any time is the slope of the angular velocity–time curve. The area under the acceleration–time curve between two times is equal to the change in angular velocity during this time interval.

If a rigid body in plane motion has constant angular acceleration, the angular displacement, velocity, and acceleration are related by

$$\omega = \omega_0 + \alpha t \qquad (17.145)$$

$$\theta = \theta_0 + \omega_0 t + \tfrac{1}{2}\alpha t^2 \qquad (17.146)$$

$$\omega^2 = \omega_0^2 + 2\alpha(\theta - \theta_0) \qquad (17.147)$$

where θ_0 and ω_0 are the initial angular displacement and velocity at initial time $t = 0$. These equations are the exact counterparts of the motion of a particle which moves in rectilinear translation with constant acceleration.

When a rigid body moves with plane rotation, the angular velocity ω is related to the translational velocity v of an arbitrary point on the body by

$$v = r\omega \qquad (17.148)$$

where r is the length from the center of rotation to the point of interest. The direction of the velocity v is normal to the direction of the line r. The components of acceleration of the point are related to the angular velocity and acceleration by

$$a_n = \frac{v^2}{r} = r\omega^2 \qquad a_t = r\alpha \qquad (17.149)$$

where n is the direction along the line r, and t is a direction normal to the line r.

The most general type of plane motion of a rigid body is a combination of rotation and translation. The position of the body at any time may be described by specifying the two coordinates of an arbitrary point on the body, and the angular displacement of the body with respect to an arbitrary reference line. All bodies which move with general plane motion may be considered to be instantaneously rotating about a fixed point in the plane. This point is called the instant center of rotation. The location of the instant center may be found if the directions of the absolute rectilinear velocity of two points on the body are known. Two lines, which are normal to these directions, are drawn through the points. The intersection of these two lines locates the instant center.

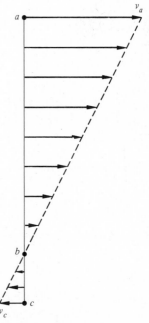

Fig. 17.35

When a wheel experiences pure rolling along a surface, the translational velocity v parallel to the track is related to the rotational velocity ω of the wheel by

$$v = r\omega \qquad (17.150)$$

where r is the radius of the wheel. Rolling of a wheel may be envisioned to be a succession of instantaneous rotations of the wheel about the contact point between the wheel and the surface on which it rolls.

PROBLEMS

17.1 The disk shown in Fig. P17.1 rotates about a fixed point. The position of an index line on the disk is given by θ. The angular displacement of the disk is given by $\theta = 1.9(t + 1)$, where θ is in radians and t is in seconds.

(*a*) Find the initial values of the angular displacement, velocity and acceleration when $t = 0$.

(*b*) Find the angular displacement, velocity, and acceleration of the disk when $t = 1$ s and $t = 2$ s; and sketch the position of the disk at these times.

(*c*) Find the time when the disk has completed one full revolution from its initial position.

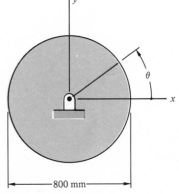

Fig. P17.1

17.2 Do the same as in Prob. 17.1, if $\theta = t^2 - 2$, where θ is in radians and t is in seconds.

17.3 Do the same as in Prob. 17.1, if $\theta = t^2 + t + 2$, where θ is in radians and t is in seconds.

17.4 Do the same as in Prob. 17.1, if $\theta = 2(1 + e^{-t})$, where θ is in radians and t is in seconds.

17.5 A disk rotates about a fixed point, with the displacement $\theta = at^2 + bt + c$, where a, b, and c are constants. When $t = 0$, the angular displacement is -1.2 rad, the angular velocity is 4 rad/s, and the angular acceleration is -2 rad/s^2.

(*a*) Find the values, and the units, of the constants a, b, and c.

(*b*) Find θ, ω, and α when $t = 4$ s.

17.6 Do the same as in Prob. 17.5 if, when $t = 2$ s, the angular displacement is 5 rad, the angular velocity is -8 rad/s, and the angular acceleration is 3 rad/s^2.

17.7 Do the same as in Prob. 17.5 if when $t = 1.5$ s, the angular displacement and velocity are zero and the angular acceleration is 10 rad/s^2.

17.8 through 17.12 The angular acceleration of a body that rotates about a fixed axis is given by the function shown. α is in radians per second squared and t is in seconds. At $t = 0$ the angular displacement and velocity are zero.

(a) Use graphical methods to find the angular velocity and angular displacement when $t = 1$ s and $t = 3$ s.

(b) Find the average values of angular velocity and angular acceleration in the interval $1 \leq t \leq 3$ s.

(c) Find the changes in the angular velocity and angular acceleration between $t = 1$ s and $t = 3$ s.

17.8 $\alpha = -18$.

17.9 $\alpha = -0.6t$.

17.10 $\alpha = (3t - 5)$.

17.11 $\alpha = (5 - 3t)$.

17.12 $\alpha = 9 - 5t \qquad 0 \leq t \leq 2.$
$\alpha = -1 \qquad\quad 2 \leq t \leq 3.$

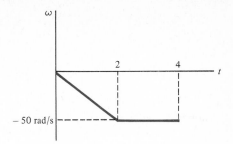

Fig. P17.13

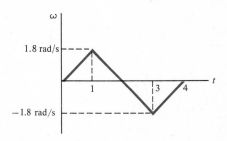

Fig. P17.14

17.13 through 17.15 The angular velocity-time diagram of a rigid body that rotates about a fixed axis is shown in each figure. All times are in seconds. At $t = 0$ the angular displacement is zero.

(a) Sketch the angular displacement and angular acceleration diagrams for the total time interval shown in the figure.

(b) Find the extreme value of the acceleration.

(c) Find the angular displacement of the body at the end of the time interval.

(d) Find the average values of the angular velocity and angular acceleration in the interval $0 \leq t \leq 4$ s.

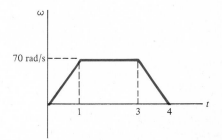

Fig. P17.15

17.16 through 17.24 A rigid body rotates about a fixed axis with the angular acceleration-time diagram shown and the initial velocity given. All times are in seconds, and the initial angular displacement is zero.

(a) Sketch the angular velocity and angular displacement diagrams.

(b) Identify the extreme values of angular velocity and angular displacement.

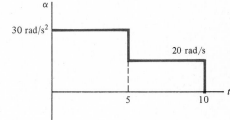

Figs. P17.16 to P17.18

17.16 Initial angular velocity = 0.

17.17 Initial angular velocity = 80 rad/s.

17.18 Initial angular velocity = −50 rad/s.

17.19 Initial angular velocity = 0.

17.20 Initial angular velocity = 30 rad/s.

17.21 Initial angular velocity = −45 rad/s.

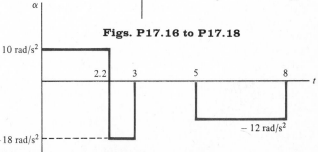

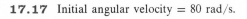
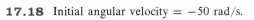

Figs. P17.19 to P17.21

17.22   Initial angular velocity = 0.

17.23   Initial angular velocity = −110 rad/s.

17.24   Initial angular velocity = 80 rad/s.

17.25   The angular velocity-time diagram of a body that rotates about a fixed axis is shown in Fig. P17.25. Find the required value of t_1 at which the angular displacement of the body is 115° from the initial position.

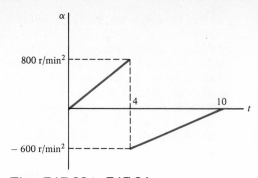

Figs. P17.22 to P17.24

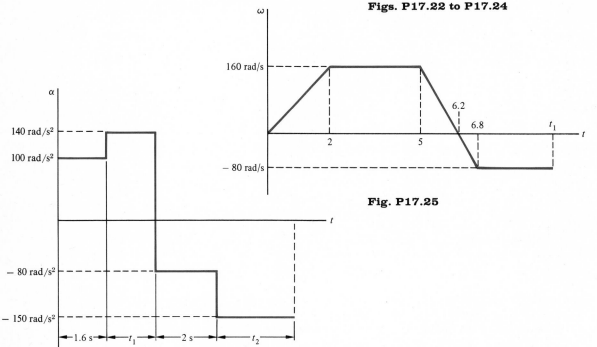

Fig. P17.25

Fig. P17.26

17.26   A disk that rotates about a fixed axis has the angular acceleration diagram shown in Fig. P17.26. The *magnitude* of the angular velocity may not exceed 4,000 r/min. Find the maximum values of the times t_1 and t_2, if $\omega = 0$ and $t = 0$.

17.27   A machinist sharpens a chisel against a grinding wheel, as shown in Fig. P17.27. The chisel is held against the wheel for 5 s. During this time the speed of the wheel changes from 3,600 r/min to 3,450 r/min.

(*a*) Find the value of the angular deceleration of the grinding wheel, if this quantity is assumed to be constant.

(*b*) Find the angular displacement of the grinding wheel during the time interval.

(*c*) When the chisel is removed, the motor accelerates the grinding wheel at 65 rad/s². How long does it take for the wheel to return to its original angular velocity?

Fig. P17.27

17.28 When the grinder in Prob. 17.27 is turned off, it is observed that it takes 140 s for the wheel to come to rest from its rated speed of 3,600 r/min.

(*a*) Find the value of the deceleration of the wheel, assuming this quantity to be constant.

(*b*) Through how many revolutions does the grinder turn in coming to rest from its rated speed?

17.29 (*a*) Find the time, when the grinder in Prob. 17.27 is turned on, for it to reach its rated speed of 3,600 r/min.

(*b*) Through how many revolutions does the grinder turn in going from rest to its rated speed?

17.30 In the manufacture of constant-angular-acceleration electric motors for a special application, a requirement is that the angular acceleration must not deviate more than 1 percent from a nominal design value of $\alpha = 80$ rad/s^2. Each motor coming off the assembly line is individually tested to meet this requirement.

(*a*) If each unit is started from rest and run for exactly 5 s, find the acceptable range of angular velocity, in revolutions per minute, that the motors should have at the end of this time interval.

(*b*) Find the corresponding range of total angular displacement during this time interval.

17.31 The link shown in Fig. P17.31 rotates about a fixed point with angular velocity $\omega = 6.5$ rad/s. For the position shown in the figure,

(*a*) Find the magnitude, direction, and sense of the velocity and acceleration of points *a* and *b*.

(*b*) Find the *x* and *y* components of the velocities and accelerations found in part *a*.

17.32 Do the same as in Prob. 17.31 if, at the instant shown in the figure, the link has a counterclockwise acceleration of 10 rad/s^2.

17.33 Do the same as in Prob. 17.31 if, at the instant shown in the figure, the angular velocity is 10 rad/s counterclockwise and the angular acceleration is 8 rad/s^2 clockwise.

17.34 At the instant shown in Fig. P17.34, the magnitude and direction of the acceleration of end *a* of the rigid rod have the known values $a = 860$ in/s^2 and $\theta = 67°$. The sense of the acceleration is as shown in the figure.

(*a*) Find the values of the normal and tangential components of acceleration of end *b* of the rod.

(*b*) Find the values of the angular velocity and angular acceleration of the rod.

(*c*) Find the magnitude, direction, and sense of the acceleration of end *b* of the rod.

(*d*) Is the rod speeding up or slowing down?

17.35 Do the same as in Prob. 17.34, if $a = 65$ ft/s^2 and $\theta = 102°$.

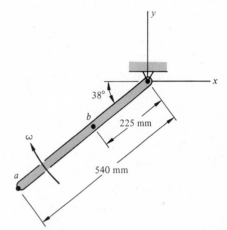

Fig. P17.31

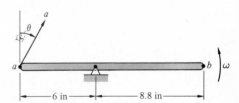

Fig. P17.34

17.36 Do the same as in Prob. 17.34, if $a = 200$ ft/s^2 and $\theta = 90°$.

17.37 A simple pendulum is released from rest at position a in Fig. P17.37. The velocity of the pendulum bob can be shown to have the form $v = \sqrt{2gl \cos \theta}$.

(*a*) Find the angular velocity of the pendulum and the normal acceleration of the bob when the pendulum is in position b.

(*b*) Find the position of the pendulum when the normal acceleration of the bob is half the value found in part a.

(*c*) Find the x and y components of the acceleration found in part b.

17.38 At the instant shown in Fig. P17.38, the stepped pulley rotates clockwise at 25 rad/s, with an angular acceleration of 6 rad/s^2.

(*a*) Find the velocity and acceleration of the weights A, B, and C.

(*b*) Find the relative velocity and acceleration of weight A with respect to weight B, of weight B with respect to weight C, and weight A with respect to weight C.

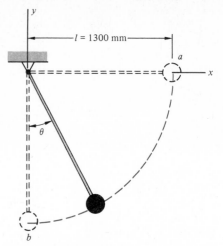

Fig. P17.37

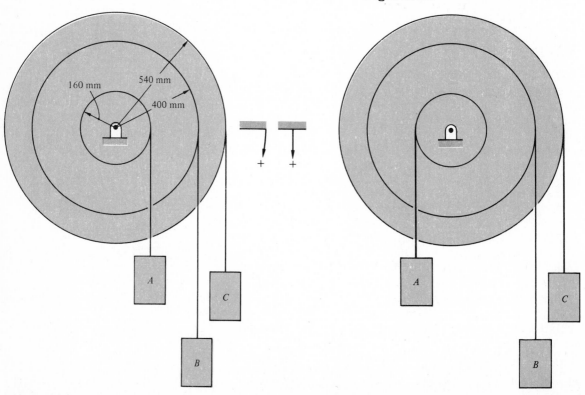

Fig. P17.38

Fig. P17.40

17.39 Do the same as in Prob. 17.38, if the sense of the angular acceleration changes to -6 rad/s^2.

17.40 Do the same as in Prob. 17.38, if the weights are arranged as shown in Fig. P17.40.

17.41 Do the same as in Prob. 17.39, for the arrangement shown in Fig. P17.40.

17.42 Do the same as in Prob. 17.38, if the weights are arranged as shown in Fig. P17.42.

17.43 Do the same as in Prob. 17.39, for the arrangement shown in Fig. P17.42.

17.44 The initial position at $t = 0$ of a flat plate which moves with general plane motion is shown in Fig. P17.44. The displacement of point a, and the angular displacement of line ab, are given by $x = 10$, $y = -4t + 8$, $\theta = 5t^2 + 65t + 30$ where x and y are in inches, θ is in degrees and t is in seconds.
 (a) Find the position of the plate when $t = 2$ s.
 (b) Find the magnitude, direction, and sense of the velocity of point a when $t = 2$ s.
 (c) Find the angular velocity of the plate when $t = 2$ s.

17.45 Do the same as in Prob. 17.44, if $x = -10(t^2 - 1)$, $y = 5t^2 + 8$, $\theta = 15(2 - t^2)$.

17.46 Do the same as in Prob. 17.44, if $x = 10 \cos \pi t$, $y = 8 \cos \pi t$, $\theta = 30 \cos \pi t$.

17.47 Do the same as in Prob. 17.44, if $x = -4t^2 + 10e^{-0.5t}$, $y = 2t^3 + 8e^{-0.6t}$, $\theta = 30e^{-0.6t}$

17.48 The body in Fig. P17.48 moves in plane motion. The velocity of point b is known to be along the direction ab.
 (a) Find the distance between the instant center and points a and b.
 (b) Find the angular velocity of the body.
 (c) Find the velocity of points b and c.

17.49 Do the same as in Prob. 17.48 for the body shown in Fig. P17.49. The velocity of point b is in a vertical direction.

17.50 The variation of velocity of points that lie on line ab on a rigid body rotating about a fixed axis is shown in Fig. P17.50.
 (a) Find the angular velocity of the body.
 (b) Find the velocity of point c.

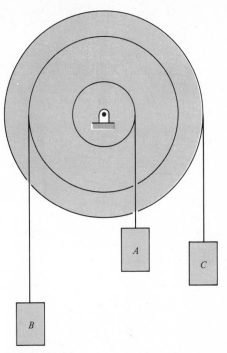

Fig. P17.42

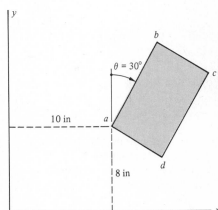

Fig. P17.44

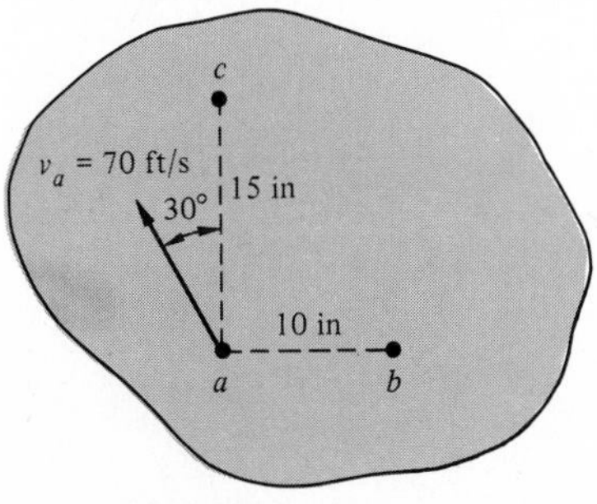

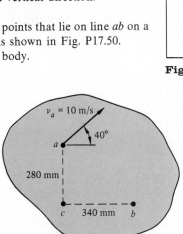

Fig. P17.48

Fig. P17.49

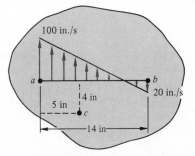

Fig. P17.50

591

17.51 Do the same as in Prob. 17.50, for the body shown in Fig. P17.51.

17.52 The crank arm *ab* shown in Fig. P17.52 rotates clockwise at 850 r/min. Find the velocity of the slider block, and the angular velocity of link *bc*, for the position shown in the figure.

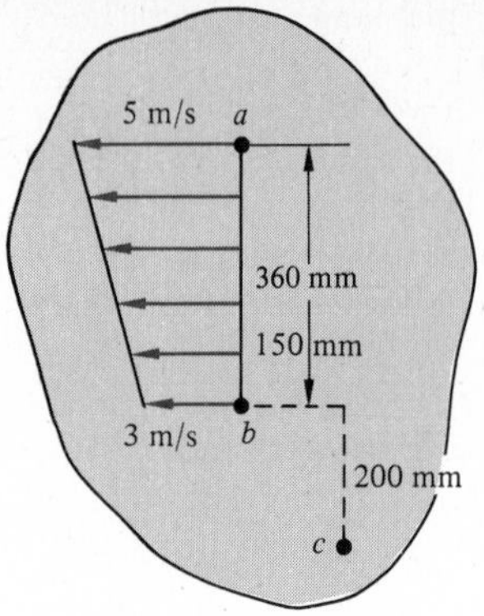

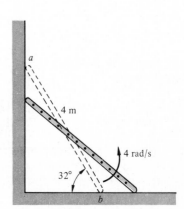

Fig. P17.51

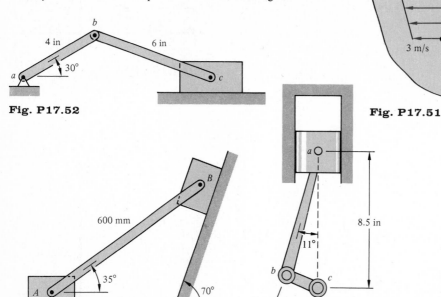

Fig. P17.52

Fig. P17.53

Fig. P17.54

17.53 For the position shown in Fig. P17.53, the angular velocity of the link which connects the two blocks is 22 rad/s, in a counterclockwise sense. Find the velocities of the two blocks.

17.54 Figure P17.54 shows an elementary model of the piston-cylinder-crank arrangement in an internal combustion engine. When the piston is in the position shown in the figure, it has a downward speed of 900 ft/min. Find the corresponding angular velocity of the crank *bc*.

17.55 The ladder in Fig. P17.55 is in a condition of impending sliding motion in the dashed position shown in the figure. It starts to slide. When it has rotated through 10° it has an angular velocity of 4 rad/s. Find the velocities of ends *a* and *b* of the ladder at this instant.

Fig. P17.55

17.56 Figure P17.56 shows an arrangement of two concentric cylinders joined to each other. The unit rolls without slipping on the horizontal rail. At the instant shown in the figure, $t = 0$ and the counterclockwise angular velocity is 52 rad/s, with a constant deceleration of 10 rad/s². Find the magnitude, direction, and sense of the velocity and acceleration of the uppermost points on the two cylindrical surfaces when $t = 2$ s.

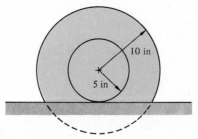

Fig. P17.56

17.57 A heavy crate is moved on rollers, as shown in Fig. P17.57, and pure rolling is assumed. At the instant shown in the figure, $v = 4$ ft/min and $a = 2$ ft/min^2. Find the angular velocity and acceleration of the rollers, and the velocity and acceleration of the centers of these two elements.

17.58 A thin inextensible string is wrapped around the inner diameter of the cylinder arrangement shown in Fig. P17.58. The velocity of the string is $v = 8$ m/s, and the unit rolls without sliding.
 (*a*) Find the velocity and acceleration of the uppermost points on the larger cylinder.
 (*b*) Find the relative velocity of the string with respect to the center of the cylinders.
 (*c*) Find the rate, in m/s, at which the string unwinds, from the cylinder.

17.59 Figure P17.59 is a kinematic model of a ball bearing. The balls are assumed to roll without sliding on both races. The angular velocity of the inner race is 1,500 r/min. Find the angular velocity of the balls and the velocity and acceleration of the centers of these elements, if $\omega_2 = 0$.

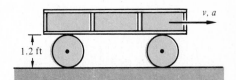

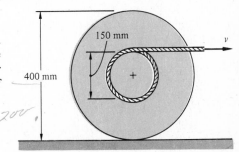

Fig. P17.57

Fig. P17.58

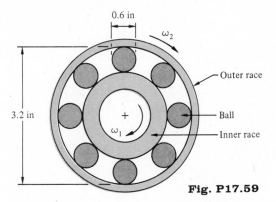

Fig. P17.59

17.60 Do the same as in Prob. 17.59, if $\omega_2 = 500$ r/min.

17.61 Do the same as in Prob. 17.59, if $\omega_2 = -500$ r/min.

17.62 For what value of ω_2 in Prob. 17.59 would the velocity of the ball centers be zero?

17.63 Figure P17.63 shows a rack and pinion gear arrangement. The rack moves downward with a constant acceleration of 15 ft/s^2. At $t = 0$, the rack has zero velocity and the position shown in the figure.
 (*a*) Find the time and corresponding velocity, when end *a* of the rack just loses contact with the pinion.
 (*b*) Find the angular velocity and angular acceleration of the pinion at the time found in part *a*.
 (*c*) Find the magnitude, direction, and sense of the velocity and acceleration of a point on the left end of a horizontal diameter of the pinion, at the time found in part *a*.

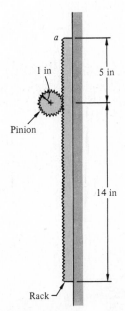

Fig. P17.63

17.64 Figure P17.64 shows a pair of meshing gears that lie in a common plane. The gears are designated 1 and 2, with the corresponding number of teeth N_1 and N_2. The kinematic action of the set of gears is that of pure rolling of two cylinders, with the pitch diameters d_1 and d_2, with no slipping. The equations that describe the motion and geometry relations between the gears are

$$\frac{\theta_1}{\theta_2} = \frac{\omega_1}{\omega_2} = \frac{d_2}{d_1} \qquad \frac{\omega_1}{\omega_2} = \frac{N_2}{N_1} \qquad \frac{N_1}{N_2} = \frac{d_1}{d_2}$$

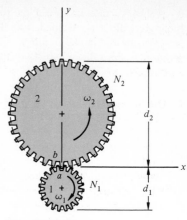

Fig. P17.64

At time $t = 0$, point a on gear 1 and point b on gear 2 are coincident points at the point of contact of the two pitch circles.

For the system shown in Fig. P17.64, $d_1 = 1$ in and $d_2 = 2.4$ in. Gear 1 rotates at 1,000 r/min in a clockwise sense.

(a) Find the magnitude, direction, and sense of the velocity and acceleration of point b after gear 1 has completed one full revolution.

(b) Find the x and y components of the velocity and acceleration found in part a.

(c) Do the same as in part a, for $t = 1$ s.

17.65 Do the same as in Prob. 17.64 if at $t = 0$, gear 1 starts to accelerate at 100 rad/s² in a clockwise sense.

17.66 Do the same as in Prob. 17.64 if at $t = 0$, gear 1 starts to decelerate at 60 rad/s² in a counterclockwise sense.

17.67 Figure P17.67 shows a set of three meshing gears. At $t = 0$, a and b are contact points between gears 1 and 2, and c and d are contact points between gears 2 and 3. Gear 1 rotates counterclockwise at 200 rad/s.

(a) Find the magnitude, direction, and sense of the velocity and acceleration of points a and d after gear 1 has completed one full revolution from the position shown in the figure.

(b) Find the x and y components of the velocity and acceleration found in part a.

(c) Do the same as in part a, for $t = 1$ s.

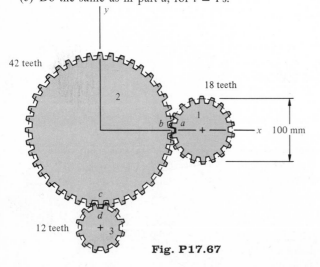

Fig. P17.67

594

17.68 Do the same as in prob. 17.67 if at $t = 0$, gear 1 starts to decelerate at 65 rad/s^2.

17.69 Do the same as in Prob. 17.67 if at $t = 0$, gear 1 starts to accelerate at 120 rad/s^2.

17.70 Do the same as in Prob. 17.67 if at $t = 0.8$ s, gear 1 starts to accelerate at 45 rad/s^2.

17.71 A thin inextensible string is wrapped around a cylinder, as shown in Fig. P17.71. At $t = 2.8$ s the motion of the string is to the right, with a velocity of 2 m/s and an acceleration of 1.2 m/s^2. At this instant, point a on the string is coincident with point b on the cylinder.
(*a*) Find the velocity and acceleration of points a and b when $t = 3.5$ s.
(*b*) Find the relative velocity and relative acceleration of point a with respect to point b when $t = 3.5$ s.

17.72 Do the same as in Prob. 17.71, if the string decelerates at 0.5 m/s^2.

17.73 Figure P17.73 shows the drive rod on a steam locomotive. The locomotive travels to the right at 50 mi/h. Find the magnitude, direction, and sense of the velocity and acceleration at points a, b, c, and d when the drive rod is in the position shown in the figure.

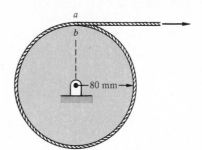

Fig. P17.71

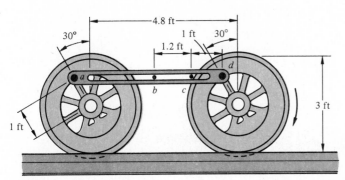

Fig. P17.73

17.74 The friction drive turntable shown in Fig. P17.74 permits an infinitely variable angular velocity ratio (ω_2/ω_1) $r_1 = 0.75$ in and r_2 may take on values between 1 in and 9 in, and pure rolling motion is assumed.
(*a*) Find the range of values of ω_2/ω_1.
(*b*) Find the acceleration of points on the rim of the disk if the angular velocity and acceleration of wheel 1 are 26 rad/s and 6 rad/s^2, respectively, and $r_2 = 7.6$ in.

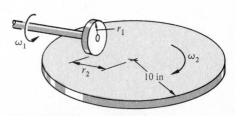

Fig. P17.74

17.75 Do the same as in Prob. 17.74, if $r_1 = 1$ in, $r_2 = 12$ in, and wheel 1 decelerates at 10 rad/s².

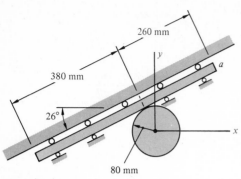

260 mm

380 mm

y

a

26°

x

80 mm

Fig. P17.76

17.76 At time $t = 0$ the wheel shown in Fig. P17.76 has an angular velocity of 3 rad/s clockwise and an angular acceleration of 0.6 rad/s² counterclockwise.

    (*a*) Find the *x* and *y* components of the velocity and acceleration of point *a* on the rod. Assume no relative sliding motion between the wheel and the rod.

    (*b*) Find the time at which the rod loses contact with the wheel.

17.77 Figure P17.77 shows a Yo-Yo modeled as a right circular cylinder about which is wrapped a thin, inextensible string. Find the relationship between the angular velocity of the Yo-Yo and the translational velocity of its center.

17.78 A right circular cylinder rolls without sliding in a track in the form of a circular arc, as shown in Fig. P17.78. The radius of the cylinder is *r*, and the radius of the track is *R*.

    (*a*) Find the angular velocity of the cylinder, and of the radial line *oa*, if the velocity of the center of the roller is v_a.

    (*b*) Find the numerical values for part *a*, if $r = 20$ mm, $R = 240$ mm, and $v_a = 3$ m/s.

17.79 Figure P17.79 shows the wheel and tire of an automobile. At the instant shown in the figure, the automobile is traveling at 45 mi/h to the right and decelerating at the rate of 6 ft/s². Find the velocity and acceleration of points *a*, *b*, and *c* on the tire.

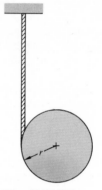

r

Fig. P17.77

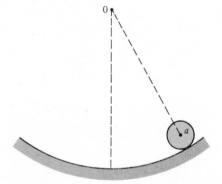

0

a

Fig. P17.78

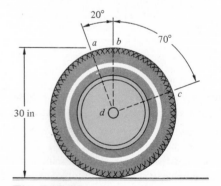

20°

a *b*

70°

c

30 in

d

Fig. P17.79

18

Centroids, and Mass Moments of Inertia, of Rigid Bodies

18.1 INTRODUCTION

Figure 18.1 shows a plane area A. The centroid of this area is located with respect to the x and y axes by the coordinates x_c and y_c, defined by

$$x_c = \frac{\int_A x\, dA}{\int_A dA} = \frac{\int_A x\, dA}{A} \tag{18.1}$$

$$y_c = \frac{\int_A y\, dA}{\int_A dA} = \frac{\int_A y\, dA}{A} \tag{18.2}$$

The *centroid* of a plane area is a specific point on the area which is a function only of the shape of the area, and not of the placement of coordinate axes with respect to this area. This concept is illustrated in Fig. 18.2, where an area is positioned with respect to three different sets of coordinate axes. Although the particular centroidal coordinates expressed in terms of each of these three sets of coordinate axes would be different

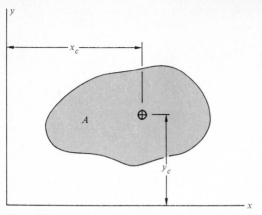

Fig. 18.1

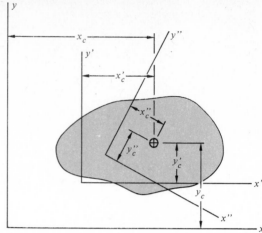

Fig. 18.2

from one another, *the actual location of the centroid on the plane area is the same.*

The centroid of a plane area has a very simple physical interpretation. The plane area is imagined to be a very thin, rigid, flat plate. If this plate rested on a straight knife edge which passes beneath the centroid, as shown in Fig. 18.3a or b, the plate would be in perfect balance in a horizontal plane.

An alternate interpretation of the centroid is shown in Fig. 18.4. Here, a thin wire of sufficient strength to support the plate is imagined to be attached to the plate at the centroid. The plate would then be in perfect balance in a horizontal plane.

A property of the *combined system,* consisting of the *area A* in Fig. 18.1 and the *position* of this area with respect to the *xy* coordinate axes, is called the *area moment of inertia.*

For the area shown in Fig. 18.1, two moments of inertia are defined to be

$$I_x = \int_A y^2 \, dA \qquad I_y = \int_A x^2 \, dA \qquad (18.3)$$

It may be seen from these equations that the fundamental units of area moment of inertia are length raised to the fourth power.

From consideration of Eq. (18.3), the following three special characteristics of area moment of inertia may be observed.

1. The distances x and y between the coordinate axes and the area elements dA are a function *only of the location of these axes relative to the area.* Thus, the position of these axes with respect to the area form an inherent part of the definition of the moment of inertia.
2. Moments of inertia are inherently positive quantities, since the terms x^2, y^2, and dA are always positive.
3. Area elements more distant from the reference axes have a proportionately greater effect on the magnitude of the moment of inertia, because of the squaring effect. Thus,

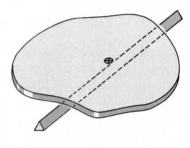

(a)

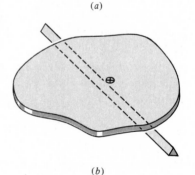

(b)

Fig. 18.3

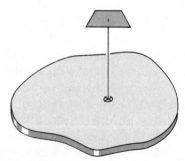

Fig. 18.4

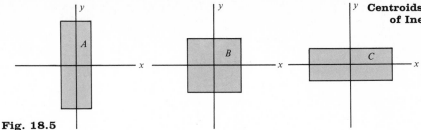

Fig. 18.5

the moment of inertia is a measure of the distribution, or shape, of the area with respect to the reference axis.

Effect 3 may be seen in Fig. 18.5, which shows three rectangles with the same surface area. It can be shown that

$$I_{xA} > I_{xB} > I_{xC} \tag{18.4}$$

Area moments of inertia have no particular physical significance. However, they are of fundamental importance in the stress and deflection analysis of structural elements, and in the analysis of certain distributed force systems.

In the following sections, the concept of the *centroid of an area*, as a unique point on the area, is extended to the case of the *centroid of a volume*. The concept of area moment of inertia will be extended to the interpretation of terms referred to as *mass moments of inertia*. It will be seen subsequently that mass moments of inertia have a distinct physical significance. It will also be seen that for thin plane rigid bodies, there is a unique relation between the *area* moment of inertia of the plane area of the body and the *mass* moment of inertia of the body.

18.2 CENTROIDS OF VOLUMES

Figure 18.6 shows a volume positioned with respect to a set of *xyz* coordinate axes. The volume is initially assumed to be a homogeneous solid of uniform density, so that it is a rigid body with an associated weight. A rigid body is a body within which any two points always have the same separation distance between them, no matter what type of force system acts on the body. As a consequence, the shape of a rigid body never changes. Throughout this book, the term body, or solid, will be understood to mean a rigid body. A particular point in the body is defined to be the centroid of the volume. Line *aa* in Fig. 18.6 is the top edge of an imagined knife edge, of vanishingly small lateral dimensions, which is parallel to the *zx* plane. The gravitational acceleration vector **g** has the direction and sense of the negative *y* axis. If the top edge of the knife is further imagined to pass through the centroid of the volume, then the body would be in perfect balance about this edge.

Figure 18.7 shows a true view of the body, in a plane which is

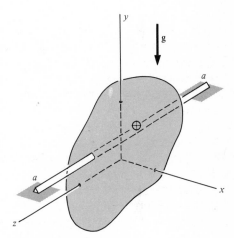

Fig. 18.6

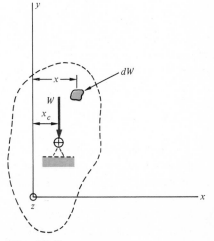

Fig. 18.7

normal to the knife edge, and of a typical weight element dW of the body. The x coordinate of the volume centroid is x_c. The body is in equilibrium when resting on the imagined knife edge through the centroid. Since the edge of the knife contacts the body only along a line through the centroid, it may be concluded that the reaction force of the knife edge on the body, and the weight force, are the only two forces acting on the body. It follows, then, that these two forces constitute a collinear-force system, and that the weight force must act through the centroid of the body. Furthermore, the direction of these two forces must be the same as that of the gravitational acceleration vector.

The moment of the weight force W about the z axis is given by

$$M_z = Wx_c \qquad (18.5)$$

This moment may also be expressed by summing all the moments of the elementary weight forces, or

$$M_z = \int_V x\,dW \qquad (18.6)$$

where V is the volume of the body. It follows that

$$Wx_c = \int_V x\,dW \qquad (18.7)$$

$$x_c = \frac{\int_V x\,dW}{W} \qquad (18.8)$$

Using γ, the specific weight of the material of the body, with the units of force per unit volume, Eq. (18.8) may be written as

$$x_c = \frac{\int_V x\,dW}{\int_V dW} = \frac{\int_V x(\gamma\,dV)}{\int_V \gamma\,dV} \qquad (18.9)$$

Since the body is assumed to be homogeneous, the specific weight is a constant, and this term may be moved outside the integral sign. The result is

$$x_c = \frac{\gamma \int_V x\,dV}{\gamma \int_V dV} = \frac{\int_V x\,dV}{V} \qquad (18.10)$$

By using an analysis similar to that shown above, the remaining two coordinates y_c and z_c of the centroid are

$$y_c = \frac{\int_V y\,dV}{V} \qquad (18.11)$$

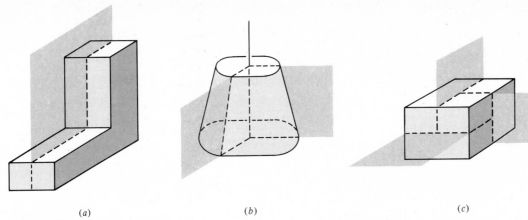

(a)   *(b)*   *(c)*

Fig. 18.8

$$z_c = \frac{\displaystyle\int_V z\,dV}{V} \qquad (18.12)$$

x_c, y_c, and z_c are the centroidal coordinates of the volume V. It may be seen that these equations have the same forms as Eqs. (18.1) and (18.2) which define the centroid of a plane area, with A and dA replaced by V and dV, respectively. Equations (18.10), (18.11), and (18.12) are the formal definition of the coordinates of the *centroid of a volume*. It is emphasized that the centroid of a volume is a point which has a *fixed* location within the volume, and this location is independent of the position of the coordinate axes with respect to the volume.

These three equations may be written in the forms

$$x_c V = \int_V x\,dV \qquad y_c V = \int_V y\,dV \qquad z_c V = \int_V z\,dV \quad (18.13)$$

The terms $x_c V$, $y_c V$, and $z_c V$ are referred to as the *first moments of the volume about the x, y, and z axes,* respectively. In Sec. 18.4 it will be shown how these terms are used in the computation of the centroidal coordinates of a composite volume.

If a volume has a plane of symmetry, then the centroid must lie in this plane. If there are two planes of symmetry, the centroid must lie in both planes. It follows that for the latter case the centroid must lie along the intersection line of the two planes. If the volume has three planes of symmetry, the centroid is located at the point of intersection of these three planes. For this last case, the common point of intersection of the three planes may be found by inspection. Figure 18.8 shows examples of bodies with one, two, and three planes of symmetry.

Example 18.1 Find the centroidal coordinates of the volume of the right circular cone shown in Fig. 18.9.

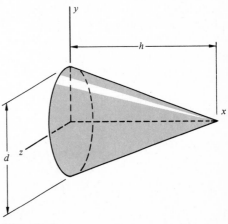

Fig. 18.9

Solution From symmetry considerations, the centroid of the volume must lie on the x axis, so that

$$y_c = z_c = 0 \qquad (18.14)$$

A cross-section view of the cone is shown in Fig. 18.10. The centroidal coordinate x_c is defined by

$$x_c = \frac{\int_V x\, dV}{V} \qquad (18.15)$$

The volume element dV is chosen to be the disk-shaped element in Fig. 18.10 since, in the limit, all points in this element are at the same distance x from the yz plane. The differential volume is

$$dV = \pi y^2\, dx \qquad (18.16)$$

From the shaded similar triangles shown in the figure,

$$\frac{y}{h - x} = \frac{d/2}{h} \qquad (18.17)$$

$$y = \frac{d}{2}\left(1 - \frac{x}{h}\right) \qquad (18.18)$$

Equation 18.18 is substituted into Eq. 18.16, to obtain:

$$dV = \pi \left(\frac{d}{2}\right)^2 \left(1 - \frac{x}{h}\right)^2 dx \qquad (18.19)$$

The total volume of the right circular cone is

$$V = \frac{1}{3}\left(\frac{\pi d^2}{4}\right)h = \frac{1}{12}\pi d^2 h \qquad (18.20)$$

Equation (18.15) now appears as

$$x_c = \frac{\int_V x\, dV}{V} = \frac{\int_0^h x\pi \left(\frac{d}{2}\right)^2 \left(1 - \frac{x}{h}\right)^2 dx}{\frac{1}{12}\pi d^2 h} \qquad (18.21)$$

$$x_c = \frac{\frac{\pi d^2}{4}\int_0^h \left(x - \frac{2x^2}{h} + \frac{x^3}{h^2}\right)dx}{\frac{1}{12}\pi d^2 h} \qquad (18.22)$$

$$x_c = \frac{3}{h}\left(\frac{x^2}{2} - \frac{2x^3}{3h} + \frac{x^4}{4h^2}\right)_0^h \qquad (18.23)$$

$$x_c = \frac{3}{h}\left(\frac{h^2}{2} - \frac{2h^3}{3h} + \frac{h^4}{4h^2}\right) = \frac{3}{h}\left(\frac{h^2}{12}\right) = \frac{1}{4}h \qquad (18.24)$$

It was observed earlier that the centroid of an area or volume is a unique and unchanging location with respect to the boundaries of the area or volume. The values of the *centroidal coordinates,* however, are not unique, since these quantities are determined by the placement of the reference axes relative to the area or volume. If the axes were attached to the cone of the present problem as shown in Fig. 18.11a, the centroidal x coordinate would be

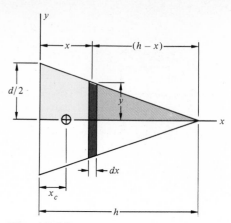

Fig. 18.10

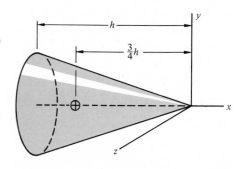

(a)

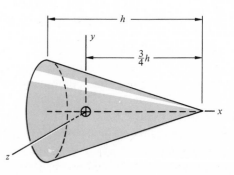

(b)

Fig. 18.11

$$x_c = -\frac{3}{4}h \qquad\qquad (18.25)$$

For placement of the axes as shown in Fig. 18.11b,

$$x_c = 0 \qquad\qquad (18.26)$$

18.3 CENTER OF MASS OF A RIGID BODY

The *center of mass* (CM) of a rigid body is a point in the body through which the total weight force acts. It is also a point at which all the mass of the body may be imagined to be "concentrated." Another commonly used description of this point is the *center of gravity*. An immediate, practical application of the concept of the center of mass is that the weight force of a body may be assumed to be a single resultant force, with magnitude equal to the total weight of the body, which acts through the center of mass. It is evident that knowing the location of the centroid of a rigid body is a prerequisite for showing the location of the weight force in a free-body diagram of the body.

Another use of the center of mass, or gravity, occurs in many problems in dynamics, where it is convenient to describe the motion of the body as a combined effect of translation of the center of mass and rotation about this point.

If the material of a body is *homogeneous,* the centroid of the volume of the body and the center of mass are coincident points. If the material of the body has a varying specific weight, the coordinates of the center of mass are given by

$$x_c = \frac{\int_V x\gamma\, dV}{\int_V \gamma\, dV} = \frac{\int_V x\gamma\, dV}{W} \qquad\qquad (18.27)$$

$$y_c = \frac{\int_V y\gamma\, dV}{\int_V \gamma\, dV} = \frac{\int_V y\gamma\, dV}{W} \qquad\qquad (18.28)$$

$$z_c = \frac{\int_V z\gamma\, dV}{\int_V \gamma\, dV} = \frac{\int_V z\gamma\, dV}{W} \qquad\qquad (18.29)$$

where γ, the specific weight of the material of the body, is a known function of the coordinates and W is the total weight of the body. γ may *not* be moved outside the integral sign in the above equations, since it is a variable quantity. (Table 18.5, located in the summary section of this chapter, gives the locations of the volume centroids of several elementary homo-geneous rigid bodies.)

Example 18.2 Figure 18.12 shows a container of rectangular cross section. A loose, soft material is packed, and compacted, into the container. The material at the bottom of the container is more tightly packed than the material at the top. An estimate of the variation of the specific weight with depth of packing is shown in Fig. 18.13. Find the centroidal coordinate y_c of the packed material in the container.

Solution The specific weight distribution curve is redrawn in Fig. 18.14. γ and y are a pair of points on the curve. From the similar triangles in the figure,

$$\frac{960 - \gamma}{y} = \frac{960 - 780}{600} \qquad \gamma = 960 - 0.3y \qquad (18.30)$$

where γ is in newtons per cubic meter and y is in millimeters.

The centroidal coordinate y_c is given by Eq. (18.28) as

$$y_c = \frac{\int_V y\gamma \, dV}{\int_V \gamma \, dV} \qquad (18.31)$$

The volume element dV is given by

$$dV = A \, dy \qquad (18.32)$$

where $A = 200(300) \text{ mm}^2$ is the cross-sectional area of the container. Equation (18.31) may be written as

$$y_c = \frac{\int_0^{600} y(960 - 0.3y)A \, dy}{\int_0^{600} (960 - 0.3y)A \, dy} \qquad (18.33)$$

$$= \frac{[960(y^2/2) - 0.3(y^3/3)]_0^{600}}{[960y - 0.3(y^2/2)]_0^{600}} = 290 \text{ mm} \qquad (18.34)$$

Had the material been homogeneous, the value of y_c, from inspection of the figure would have been 300 mm.

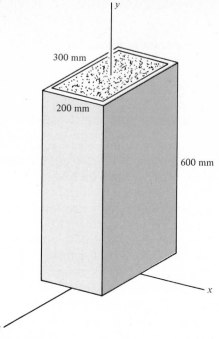

Fig. 18.12

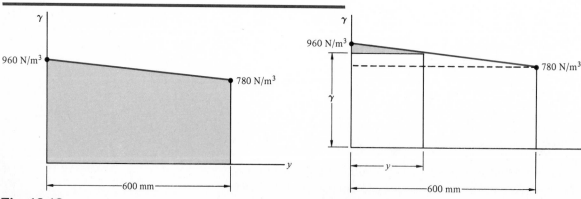

Fig. 18.13

Fig. 18.14

In many problems the volume of the rigid body whose centroid is desired is not one of the simple shapes shown in Table 18.5. In this case, it may be possible to subdivide the original body into elementary shapes whose centroidal coordinates are known. A centroidal coordinate of any body has the general form

$$x_c = \frac{\int_V x \, dV}{V} \qquad (18.35)$$

where V is the total volume of the body. This equation may be written as

$$x_c = \frac{\int_V x \, dV}{V} = \frac{\int_{V_1} x \, dV_1 + \int_{V_2} x \, dV_2 + \cdots + \int_{V_n} x \, dV_n}{V_1 + V_2 + \cdots + V_n} \qquad (18.36)$$

where n is the number of elementary volumes into which the original volume has been subdivided. The typical term $\int_{V_n} x \, dV_n$ in the numerator of the above equation, following Eqs. (18.13), may be written as

$$\int_{V_n} x \, dV_n = x_{cn} V_n \qquad (18.37)$$

where x_{cn} is the centroidal coordinate of the elementary volume V_n. The term $x_{cn} V_n$ may be recognized as the first moment of volume of the volume element V_n about the reference axis from which x_{cn} is measured. Using the above result, Eq. (18.36) may be written as

$$x_c = \frac{x_{c1} V_1 + x_{c2} V_2 + \cdots + x_{cn} V_n}{V_1 + V_2 + \cdots + V_n} \qquad (18.38)$$

The remaining two centroidal coordinates have the forms

$$y_c = \frac{y_{c1} V_1 + y_{c2} V_2 + \cdots + y_{cn} V_n}{V_1 + V_2 + \cdots + V_n} \qquad (18.39)$$

$$z_c = \frac{z_{c1} V_1 + z_{c2} V_2 + \cdots + z_{cn} V_n}{V_1 + V_2 + \cdots + V_n} \qquad (18.40)$$

It may be seen that Eqs. (18.38) and (18.39) have the same forms as the equations used to find the centroid of a composite area, if the term V_n is replaced by A_n.

If the composite volume contains holes or cutout portions, the volumes of these elements are considered to be *negative* quantities when used in the above equations.

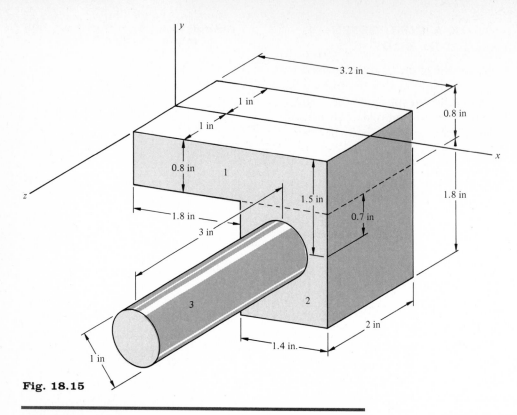

Fig. 18.15

Example 18.3

a Find the x, y, and z coordinates of the center of mass of the bracket shown in Fig. 18.15.

b Find the weight, and the mass in slugs, of the bracket. The bracket is made of bronze, with a specific weight of 0.295 lb/in³.

Solution a The bracket is divided into the three elementary shapes shown in Fig. 18.15. The volumes are

$$V_1 = 3.2(0.8)(2) = 5.12 \text{ in}^3 \tag{18.41}$$

$$V_2 = 1.4(1.8)(2) = 5.04 \text{ in}^3 \tag{18.42}$$

$$V_3 = \frac{\pi(1)^2}{4}3 = 2.36 \text{ in}^3 \tag{18.43}$$

The values of the nine required centroidal coordinates of the three elementary volumes are

$$x_{c1} = \frac{3.2}{2} = 1.6 \text{ in} \quad y_{c1} = -\frac{0.8}{2} = -0.4 \text{ in} \quad z_{c1} = 0$$

$$\tag{18.44}$$

$$x_{c2} = 1.8 + \frac{1.4}{2} \quad y_{c2} = -\left(0.8 + \frac{1.8}{2}\right) \quad z_{c2} = 0$$

$$= 2.5 \text{ in} \qquad\qquad = -1.7 \text{ in} \tag{18.45}$$

$$x_{c3} = 1.8 + \frac{1.4}{2} \quad y_{c3} = -1.5 \text{ in} \quad z_{c3} = 1 + \frac{3}{2} = 2.5 \text{ in}$$

$$= 2.5 \text{ in} \tag{18.46}$$

606

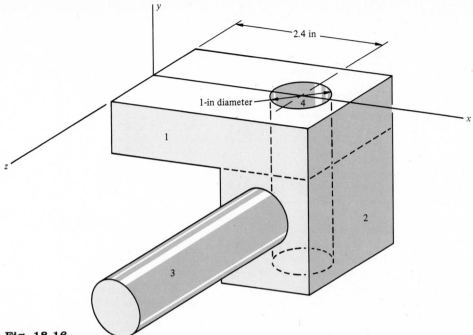

Fig. 18.16

The centroidal coordinates of the bracket are then

$$x_c = \frac{x_{c1}V_1 + x_{c2}V_2 + x_{c3}V_3}{V_1 + V_2 + V_3}$$

$$= \frac{1.6(5.12) + 2.5(5.04) + 2.5(2.36)}{5.12 + 5.04 + 2.36}$$

$$= \frac{26.7}{12.5} = 2.14 \text{ in} \qquad (18.47)$$

$$y_c = \frac{y_{c1}V_1 + y_{c2}V_2 + y_{c3}V_3}{V_1 + V_2 + V_3}$$

$$= \frac{-0.4(5.12) - 1.7(5.04) - 1.5(2.36)}{12.5}$$

$$= \frac{-14.2}{12.5} = -1.14 \text{ in} \qquad (18.48)$$

$$z_c = \frac{z_{c1}V_1 + z_{c2}V_2 + z_{c3}V_3}{V_1 + V_2 + V_3}$$

$$= \frac{0 + 0 + 2.5(2.36)}{12.5}$$

$$= \frac{5.9}{12.5} = 0.472 \text{ in} \qquad (18.49)$$

b The weight of the bracket is

$$W = 0.295(12.5) = 3.69 \text{ lb} \qquad (18.50)$$

The mass is

$$m = \frac{W}{g} = \frac{3.69}{32.2} = 0.115 \frac{\text{lb} \cdot \text{sec}^2}{\text{ft}} = 0.115 \text{ slugs} \qquad (18.51)$$

607

If the composite volume is a complicated shape which requires several elementary shapes for its description, the computation may be arranged in tabular form. A format for such a tabular organization is shown in Table 18.1.

Example 18.4 As part of a weight- and cost-reduction program, the bracket in Example 18.3 is modified by drilling a hole through it parallel to the y axis, as shown in Fig. 18.16.

a Find the centroidal coordinates of the bracket after the hole has been drilled.

b Find the weight of the modified bracket.

c Find the percent reduction from the weight of the original bracket.

Solution

a The solution can be organized in a tabular format, and Table 18.2 is constructed. The first three rows in the table record the results in Eqs. (18.41) through (18.46). The hole is designated element 4. A minus sign is affixed to the volume of this element to show that it represents material *removed* from the bracket. The new values of the centroidal coordinates are contained in the last row of the table.

b The weight of the modified bracket is

$$W = 0.295(10.5) = 3.10 \text{ lb} \qquad (18.52)$$

c The addition of the hole has the effect of reducing the original weight by $[(3.69 - 3.10)/3.69]100 = 16.0$ percent.

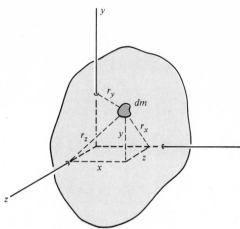

Fig. 18.17

18.5 MASS MOMENT OF INERTIA OF A HOMOGENEOUS RIGID BODY

Figure 18.17 shows a homogeneous, solid body. The typical mass element dm has the general position coordinates $x, y,$ and

TABLE 18.1							
Element	V_i	x_{ci}	$x_{ci}V_i$	y_{ci}	$y_{ci}V_i$	z_{ci}	$z_{ci}V_i$
1							
2							
n							
	$V = \sum_i V_i$		$\sum_i x_{ci}V_i$		$\sum_i y_{ci}V_i$		$\sum_i z_{ci}V_i$
		$x_c = \dfrac{\sum_i x_{ci}V_i}{V}$		$y_c = \dfrac{\sum_i y_{ci}V_i}{V}$		$z_c = \dfrac{\sum_i z_{ci}V_i}{V}$	

z. The true view of the mass element in a plane parallel to the xy plane is shown in Fig. 18.18. The z axis is normal to the plane of the figure, and r_z is the perpendicular distance between the mass element and the z axis.

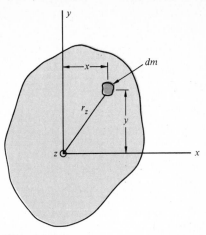

A quantity called the *mass moment of inertia about the z axis,* designated by the symbol I_z, is defined as

$$I_z = \int_V r_z^2 \, dm \qquad (18.53)$$

In the basic formulation of the mass moment of inertia given above, each mass element of the body is multiplied by the square of its distance to the reference axis. These products are then summed over the volume of the body. Since

$$r_z^2 = x^2 + y^2 \qquad (18.54)$$

the mass moment of inertia about the z axis may be written as

$$I_z = \int_V (x^2 + y^2) \, dm \qquad (18.55)$$

Fig. 18.18

The true views of the mass element in planes parallel to the yz and zx planes are shown in Fig. 18.19.

The mass moments of inertia about the x and y axes are defined to be

$$I_x = \int_V r_x^2 \, dm = \int_V (y^2 + z^2) \, dm \qquad (18.56)$$

$$I_y = \int_V r_y^2 \, dm = \int_V (z^2 + x^2) \, dm \qquad (18.57)$$

TABLE 18.2							
Element	V_i	x_{ci}	$x_{ci} V_i$	y_{ci}	$y_{ci} V_i$	z_{ci}	$z_{ci} V_i$
1	5.12	1.6	8.19	−0.4	−2.05	0	0
2	5.04	2.5	12.6	−1.7	−8.57	0	0
3	2.36	2.5	5.9	−1.5	−3.54	2.5	5.90
4	$\dfrac{-\pi(1)^2}{4}(2.6) = -2.04$	2.4	−4.90	−1.3	2.65	0	0
	$V = \sum_i V_i$ $V = 10.5$		$\sum_i x_{ci} V_i = 21.8$		$\sum_i y_{ci} V_i = -11.5$		$\sum_i z_{ci} V_i = 5.90$
			$x_c = \dfrac{21.8}{10.5} = 2.08 \text{ in}$	$y_c = \dfrac{-11.5}{10.5} = -1.10 \text{ in}$		$z_c = \dfrac{5.90}{10.5} = 0.562 \text{ in}$	

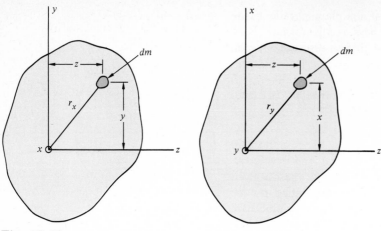

Fig. 18.19

Equations (18.55) to (18.57) are the formal definitions of the mass moments of inertia of the body about the three coordinate axes. The subscript on the symbol I always designates the axis to which the mass moment of inertia is referenced. It may be seen that the fundamental units of a mass moment of inertia are the product of mass and length squared. In USCS units, the typical units of mass moment of inertia are lb-sec²-in. The SI units of mass moment of inertia are kg-m². On engineering drawings in which USCS units are used, the mass moment of inertia often is stated in lb-in². This is a hybrid unit which may be converted to the required units by dividing by $g = 386$ in/s². It may also be observed that the mass moment of inertia is a *scalar* quantity.

The three distinguishing characteristics observed earlier for an area moment of inertia are also true for a mass moment of inertia:

1. The mass moment of inertia of a body is *not* an inherent characteristic of the body. Rather, it is a property of the combined system of the body and its position with respect to a set of coordinate reference axes.
2. The mass moments of inertia are always positive.
3. Mass elements which are more distant from the reference axis have a proportionately greater effect on the magnitude of the mass moment of inertia than do mass elements which are closer to this axis. Thus, the mass moment of inertia is a measure of the distribution, or placement, of the mass of the body.

The mass moment of inertia of a rigid body has a tangible physical interpretation. A reference axis, such as the x axis, is imagined to be the centerline of a shaft attached to the body. The mass moment of inertia with respect to this axis is then a measure of the resistance of the body to angular acceleration about the axis. This effect will be seen in the following chap-

ter, where the rotational form of Newton's second law is introduced.

The fundamental, formal definitions of the mass moments of
inertia are given by Eqs. (18.55) through (18.57). These equations usually are not used directly to compute the moments of
inertia, since integration over a volume is inherently a difficult,
triple-integration procedure. Rather, a technique is employed
which combines known solutions for mass moments of inertia,
and which uses a theorem which is referred to as the parallel-
axis, or transfer, theorem. This latter relationship is developed
in Sec. 18.6. Table 18.5, which is in the Summary section of
this chapter, contains the equations for the centroidal coordinates and mass moments of inertia of rigid bodies of elementary geometry. These general results are presented for the
moment of inertia with respect to a set of centroidal coordinates
x_0, y_0, z_0 that pass through the center of mass of the body. The
results are also presented for the moments of inertia about
selected axes parallel to the centroidal axes.

There is another mass-related property of a body that is
positioned with respect to a set of coordinate axes. This quantity is called the *mass product of inertia*. The products of
inertia are a measure of the symmetry of placement of the axes
with respect to the body. This subject is presented in Chap. 22,
where the mass products of inertia are used in the solution of
problems of dynamic unbalance.

18.6 PARALLEL-AXIS, OR TRANSFER, THEOREM FOR MASS MOMENTS OF INERTIA

A very useful relationship between the mass moments of inertia
of a rigid body about a centroidal axis and about an axis
parallel to this centroidal axis will be developed now. This
technique is the principal method used to find mass moments of
inertia in problems in engineering dynamics.

Figure 18.20 shows a plane section of a body which is normal
to the z axis. The x_0, y_0, z_0 axes, which pass through the center
of mass of the body, are parallel to the x, y, z axes. x_c, y_c, and
z_c are the position coordinates, measured in the x, y, z system,
of the center of mass of the body. d_z is the normal separation
distance between the z and z_0 axes. The fundamental definition of the mass moment of inertia of the body about the z axis
is

$$I_z = \int_V (x^2 + y^2)\, dm \qquad (18.58)$$

From Fig. 18.20,

$$x = x_c + x_0 \qquad y = y_c + y_0 \qquad (18.59)$$

These values are substituted into Eq. (18.58), with the result

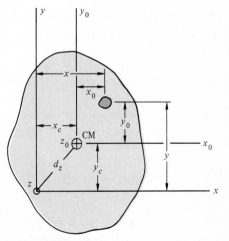

Fig. 18.20

$$I_z = \int_V [(x_c + x_0)^2 + (y_c + y_0)^2] \, dm \qquad (18.60)$$

$$I_z = \int_V [(x_c^2 + 2x_c x_0 + x_0^2) + (y_c^2 + 2y_c y_0 + y_0^2)] \, dm \qquad (18.61)$$

$$I_z = \int_V (x_c^2 + y_c^2) \, dm + 2x_c \int_V x_0 \, dm + 2y_c \int_V y_0 \, dm$$
$$+ \int_V (x_0^2 + y_0^2) \, dm \qquad (18.62)$$

The location of the center of mass CM of the body in the x_0, y_0 coordinate system is given by

$$x_{0c} = \frac{\int_V x_0 \, dm}{m} \qquad y_{0c} = \frac{\int_V y_0 \, dm}{m} \qquad (18.63)$$

Since the x_0 and y_0 axes both pass through the center of mass, the centroidal coordinates x_{0c} and y_{0c} must satisfy

$$x_{0c} = y_{0c} = 0 \qquad (18.64)$$

It follows from Eq. (18.63) that

$$\int_V x_0 \, dm = 0 \qquad \int_V y_0 \, dm = 0 \qquad (18.65)$$

and thus the middle two terms on the right-hand side of Eq. (18.62) are identically zero. The last term on the right side of this equation is the mass moment of inertia of the body about the centroidal z_0 axis, defined by

$$I_{0z} = \int_V (x_0^2 + y_0^2) \, dm \qquad (18.66)$$

From Fig. 18.20,

$$x_c^2 + y_c^2 = d_z^2 \qquad (18.67)$$

The first term on the right-hand side of Eq. (18.62) may then be written as

$$\int_V (x_c^2 + y_c^2) \, dm = \int_V d_z^2 \, dm = d_z^2 \int_V dm = m \, d_z^2 \qquad (18.68)$$

where m is the total mass of the body. Equations (18.66) and (18.68) are substituted into Eq. (18.62), and the final result is

$$I_z = I_{0z} + m \, d_z^2 \qquad (18.69)$$

By using an analysis similar to that shown above, it can be shown that

$$I_x = I_{0x} + m \, d_x^2 \qquad (18.70)$$

$$I_y = I_{0y} + m \, d_y^2 \qquad (18.71)$$

These equations are extremely useful results which are referred to as the *parallel-axis, or transfer, theorems*. In the usual application of these theorems, a mass moment of inertia, such as I_{0x} about the centroidal x_0 axis, is known and the mass moment of inertia about an axis parallel to the centroidal axis is to be found. The theorem states that the moment of inertia about the parallel axis is equal to the sum of

1. The centroidal mass moment of inertia
2. A correction term equal to the product of the mass of the body and the square of the separation distance between the two axes

When using the transfer theorem, the separation distance must be between the centroidal axis of the body and the reference axis about which the mass moment of inertia is desired. Failure to interpret this separation distance term correctly in a given problem is the usual reason for an incorrect result when using the parallel axis, or transfer, theorem.

Terms such as $m\,d_z^2$ are always positive. It follows from Eq. (18.69) that

$$I_z > I_{0z} \qquad (18.72)$$

This result shows that the mass moment of inertia about an axis through the *centroid* of a body is always less than the mass moment of inertia of the body about any other axis which is parallel to the centroidal axis.

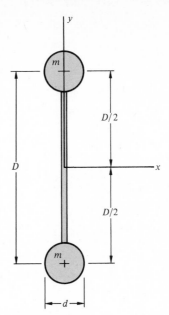

Fig. 18.21

Example 18.5 Two spherical masses are attached to a thin, massless rod to form the dumbbell shown in Fig. 18.21.

a Find the mass moment of inertia of the system about the x axis.

b If the diameters d of the spherical masses are small compared with the dimension D, the masses may be assumed to be point, or concentrated, masses located at $y = \pm D/2$. Based on this assumption, find the approximate value of the mass moment of inertia.

c Find the maximum permissible size of d relative to D if the approximate answer in part b is to be in error by no more than 5 percent.

d Do the same as in part c for a maximum error of 10 percent.

Solution a Mass moment of inertia of a homogeneous sphere, of mass m and diameter d, about a diameter is given by case 1 in Table 18.5 as $I_0 = \frac{1}{10}md^2$. One of the spherical masses is shown in Fig. 18.22 and the centroidal x_0 axis passes through the CM. The mass moment of inertia I_{0x} of the mass about its centroidal axis is

$$I_{0x} = \tfrac{1}{10}md^2 \qquad (18.73)$$

Using the transfer theorem, we find that the required value of the mass moment of inertia of the dumbbell is

$$I_x = 2(I_{0x} + m\,d_x^2) \qquad (18.74)$$

$$= 2\left[\frac{1}{10}md^2 + m\left(\frac{D}{2}\right)^2\right] \qquad (18.75)$$

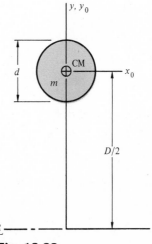

Fig. 18.22

613

$$= \frac{1}{10}m(5D^2 + 2d^2) \qquad (18.76)$$

b The appearance of the system, for the assumption of point masses, is shown in Fig. 18.23. The approximate value of the moment of inertia about the x axis is

$$I_x \approx 2\left[m\left(\frac{D}{2}\right)^2\right] = \frac{mD^2}{2} \qquad (18.77)$$

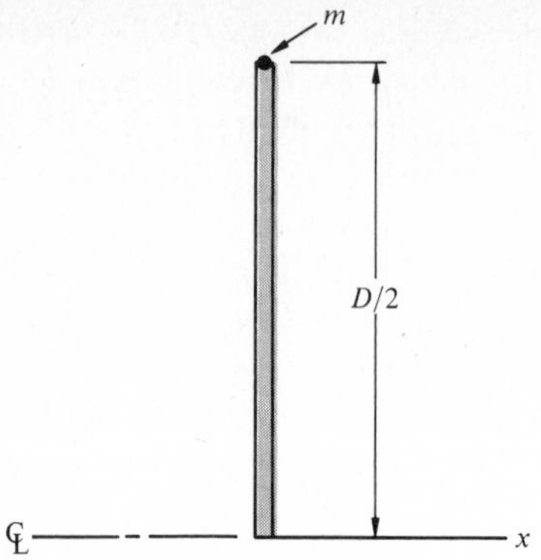

c A percent error between the exact and approximate solution is defined to be

$$\%D = \frac{\text{exact solution} - \text{approximate solution}}{\text{exact solution}} \qquad (18.78)$$

$$= \frac{(m/10)(5D^2 + 2d^2) - mD^2/2}{(m/10)(5D^2 + 2d^2)} = \frac{1}{1 + 2.5(D/d)^2} \qquad (18.79)$$

For an error of 5 percent,

$$\frac{1}{1 + 2.5(D/d)^2} = 0.05 \qquad d = 0.363D \qquad (18.80)$$

If $d \leq 36.3$ percent of D, the error in the mass moment of inertia will be less than 5 percent.

d For an allowable error of 10 percent,

$$\frac{1}{1 + 2.5(D/d)^2} = 0.10 \qquad d = 0.527D \qquad (18.81)$$

The error will be less than 10 percent if $d \leq 52.7$ percent of D.

The results of parts c and d are drawn to scale in Fig. 18.24.

Fig. 18.23

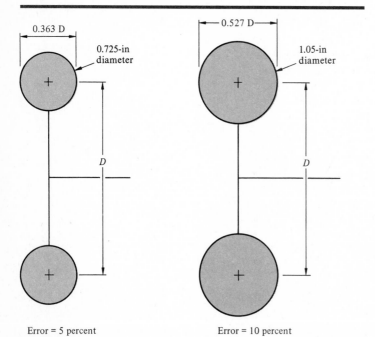

0.363 D

0.725-in diameter

D

Error = 5 percent

0.527 D

1.05-in diameter

D

Error = 10 percent

Fig. 18.24

18.7 RADIUS OF GYRATION

Each of the mass moments of inertia I_x, I_y, and I_z about the xyz coordinate axes have an associated term, the *radius of gyration,* defined by

$$I_x = k_x^2 m \qquad k_x = \sqrt{I_x/m} \qquad (18.82)$$

$$I_y = k_y^2 m \qquad k_y = \sqrt{I_y/m} \qquad (18.83)$$

$$I_z = k_z^2 m \qquad k_z = \sqrt{I_z/m} \qquad (18.84)$$

The radii of gyration have the unit of length, and k_x, k_y, and k_z are normal to the x, y, and z axes, respectively.

A radius of gyration has no particular physical significance. If all the mass of the body where imagined to be concentrated at a single point, as shown in Fig. 18.25, then a product such as $k_z^2 m$ would be equal to the mass moment of inertia I_z of the body about the z axis.

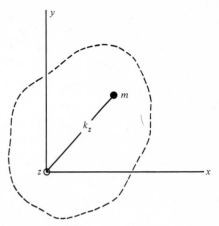

Fig. 18.25

18.8 MASS MOMENTS OF INERTIA OF HOMOGENEOUS THIN PLANE RIGID BODIES

Many physical objects for which a mass moment of inertia must be computed have the form of a thin plane rigid body. Such shapes include disks, flat plates, and rods. For these bodies, the forms for the mass moment of inertia may be simplified. The descriptive term *thin* is understood to mean that the thickness dimension is much less than the dimensions measured in the plane of the body. The theory developed in this section is approximate in nature. In Sec. 18.11, a comparison will be made of the exact and approximate solutions for a flat, rectangular plate, to obtain an estimate of the error associated with the use of the approximate solutions.

Figure 18.26 shows a thin plane rigid body of thickness t, and

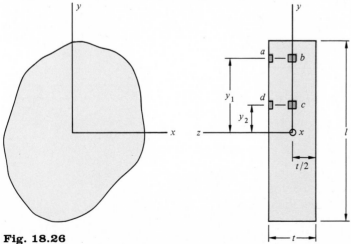

Fig. 18.26

it is desired to find the mass moment of inertia of the mass about the x axis. The formal definition of this quantity is

$$I_x = \int_V (y^2 + z^2)\, dm \qquad (18.85)$$

The contributions of four typical mass elements, with the locations shown in the figure, will now be obtained. A typical position coordinate for mass elements a and b which are not near the x axis is y_1. The differential mass element at b lies on the y axis and contributes

$$dI_{bx} = y_1^2\, dm \qquad (18.86)$$

The mass element a which forms part of the plane boundary surface of the body contributes the differential moment of inertia

$$dI_{ax} = \left[y_1^2 + \left(\frac{t}{2}\right)^2 \right] dm \qquad (18.87)$$

Since the plane body is assumed to be thin,

$$t \ll l \qquad \left(\frac{t}{2}\right)^2 \lll l \qquad (18.88)$$

Since y_1 is the same order of magnitude as l,

$$\left(\frac{t}{2}\right)^2 \lll y_1 \qquad (18.89)$$

and

$$y_1^2 + \left(\frac{t}{2}\right)^2 \approx y_1^2 \qquad (18.90)$$

The contribution of the mass element a is then approximately

$$dI_{ax} \approx y_1^2\, dm \qquad (18.91)$$

Mass element c lies on the y axis, where $z = 0$. The contribution of this element to I_x is

$$dI_{cx} = y_2^2\, dm \qquad (18.92)$$

The differential moment of inertia of element d is

$$dI_{dx} = \left[y_2^2 + \left(\frac{t}{2}\right)^2 \right] dm \qquad (18.93)$$

Although $t/2$ is not small compared to y_2, it still obeys the relationship in Eq. (18.89), so that

$$dI_{dx} \approx y_2^2\, dm \qquad (18.94)$$

It may be observed that the contributions of the four typical mass elements to the moment of inertia of the body about the x axis involve only the coordinate y and are independent of the coordinate z. The above results may now be generalized, and

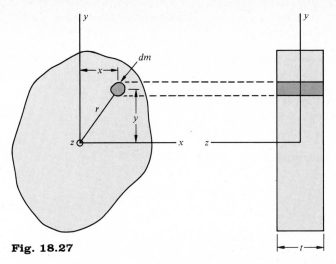

Fig. 18.27

the approximate form for the mass moment of inertia of the thin plane rigid body about the x axis is

$$I_x \approx \int_V y^2 \, dm \qquad (18.95)$$

where the mass element dm is taken to be a single mass element through the thickness of the plane body.

The thin plane body of Fig. 18.26 is redrawn in Fig. 18.27 and it is desired to find the mass moment of inertia of the body about the z axis.

The formal definition of I_z is

$$I_z = \int_V (x^2 + y^2) \, dm \qquad (18.96)$$

From the figure,

$$x^2 + y^2 = r^2 \qquad (18.97)$$

or

$$I_z = \int_V r^2 \, dm \qquad (18.98)$$

Since all the mass elements across the thickness of the plane body, for a given value of r, are at the same distance from the reference z axis, Eq. (18.98) is an exact solution for the mass moment of inertia about the z axis. The quantity I_z, defined above for the thin plane rigid body, is also referred to as the *polar mass moment of inertia.*

Example 18.6 The flat rectangular plate in Fig. 18.28 has mass m and thickness t. The origin of the coordinate axes is located at the volume centroid of the plate.

a Find the mass moment of inertia and the radius of gyration with respect to the x axis.

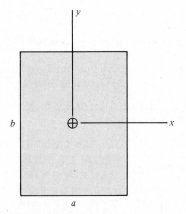

Fig. 18.28

b Do the same as in part *a* but with respect to the *y* axis.

c Do the same as in part *a*, for an axis which lies along the side of length *a*.

Solution

a The mass element *dm* shown in Fig. 18.29 is chosen, since all particles in this element, in the limit, are at the same distance *y* from the reference *x* axis. The magnitude of the differential mass is

$$dm = \rho(ta\,dy) \qquad (18.99)$$

where ρ is the mass density of the material. The required moment of inertia is then found from

$$dI_x = y^2\,dm = y^2(\rho ta\,dy) \qquad (18.100)$$

$$I_x = \int_{-b/2}^{b/2} y^2(\rho ta\,dy) = \rho ta \int_{b/2}^{b/2} y^2\,dy \qquad (18.101)$$

$$= \rho ta \left(\frac{y^3}{3}\bigg|_{-b/2}^{b/2}\right) = \frac{\rho ta}{3}\left[\left(\frac{b}{2}\right)^3 - \left(-\frac{b}{2}\right)^3\right] = \frac{1}{12}\rho tab^3 \quad (18.102)$$

The mass *m* of the plate is

$$m = \rho tab \qquad (18.103)$$

and final form for the mass moment of inertia is then

$$I_x = \frac{1}{12}mb^2 \qquad (18.104)$$

The radius of gyration is defined by

$$k_x = \sqrt{\frac{I_x}{m}} = \sqrt{\frac{mb^2}{12m}} = \frac{b}{\sqrt{12}} = 0.289b \qquad (18.105)$$

This radius of gyration is drawn to scale in Fig. 18.30.

b From the symmetry properties of the rectangular plate, with the dimensions *a* and *b* interchanged,

$$I_y = \frac{1}{12}ma^2 \qquad (18.106)$$

$$k_y = 0.289a \qquad (18.107)$$

c The x_1 axis is placed along the edge *a*, as shown in Fig. 18.31. Using the transfer theorem,

$$I_{x_1} = I_x + m\,d_x^2 = \frac{1}{12}mb^2 + m\left(\frac{b}{2}\right)^2 = \frac{1}{3}mb^2 \qquad (18.108)$$

It may be seen that the mass moment of inertia about the edge of the plate is four times as great as the mass moment of inertia about the centroidal axis.

18.9 RELATION BETWEEN MOMENTS OF INERTIA OF A PLANE AREA AND MASS MOMENTS OF INERTIA OF A HOMOGENEOUS THIN PLANE RIGID BODY

Figure 18.32 shows a thin plane body positioned with respect to a set of coordinate axes. The *area* moments of inertia I_{xA} and

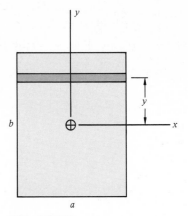

Fig. 18.29

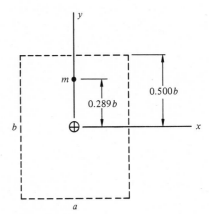

Fig. 18.30

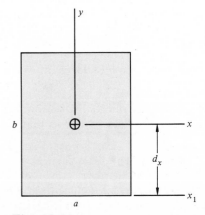

Fig. 18.31

I_{yA} of the *plane surface area* of the body are

$$I_{xA} = \int_A y^2\, dA \qquad I_{yA} = \int_A x^2\, dA \qquad (18.109)$$

The second subscript A has been added to the two moments of inertia to emphasize that these are *area* moments of inertia.

It was shown in Sec. 18.8 that if the plane body is thin, the mass moments of inertia I_{xM} and I_{yM} are given by the approximate equations

$$I_{xM} \approx \int_V y^2\, dm \qquad I_{yM} \approx \int_V x^2\, dm \qquad (18.110)$$

where the second subscript M has been added to indicate *mass* moment of inertia.

For a homogeneous, thin plane body, the surface area element dA is related to the plane mass element dm by the relationship

$$dm = \rho t\, dA \qquad (18.111)$$

where ρ is the mass density and t is the thickness of the body. By using the above result, Eq. (18.110) may be written as

$$I_{xM} \approx \int_A y^2 \rho t\, dA = \rho t \int_A y^2\, dA \qquad (18.112)$$

$$\approx \rho t I_{xA} \qquad (18.113)$$

$$I_{yM} \approx \int_A x^2 \rho t\, dA = \rho t \int_A x^2\, dA \qquad (18.114)$$

$$\approx \rho t I_{yA} \qquad (18.115)$$

The mass moment of inertia of the body in Fig. 18.32 about the z axis is

$$I_{zM} = \int_V r^2\, dm \qquad (18.116)$$

The $\approx$ sign is *not* used in Eq. (18.116) since this equation is an exact relationship. The polar moment of inertia about the z axis of the plane bounding area of the thin body is expressed by

$$I_{zA} = \int_A r^2\, dA = I_{xA} + I_{yA} = J \qquad (18.117)$$

where J is a term referred to as the polar moment of inertia. By using Eq. (18.111), it follows that

$$I_{zM} = \rho t I_{zA} = \rho t J \qquad (18.118)$$

A very important conclusion may now be drawn: for a thin, homogeneous rigid plane body, the mass moments of inertia of the body and the area moments of inertia of the plane bounding surface differ by only a constant factor. The magnitude of

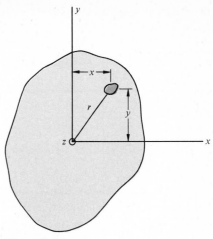

Fig. 18.32

this factor is the product of the thickness of the body and the mass density of the material.

Table 18.6, in the Summary section of this chapter, contains the centroidal coordinates and moments of inertia of several elementary plane areas.

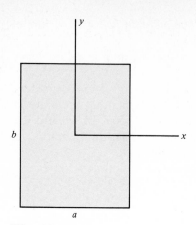

Example 18.7 The area moment of inertia of the surface area of the thin rigid plate of mass m shown in Fig. 18.33 is

$$I_{xA} = \frac{1}{12}ab^3 \qquad (18.119)$$

Find the mass moment of inertia I_x.

Fig. 18.33

Solution The area and mass moments of inertia, following Eq. (18.113), are related by

$$I_{xM} = \rho t I_{xA} \qquad I_{xM} = \rho t \left(\frac{ab^3}{12}\right) \qquad (18.120)$$

The mass of the plate is

$$m = \rho t a b \qquad (18.121)$$

and the final form for the mass moment of inertia is

$$I_{xM} = \frac{1}{12}mb^2 \qquad (18.122)$$

The above equation is the same result which was obtained in Example 18.6.

Example 18.8 The steel disk shown in Fig. 18.34 is 0.5 in thick.

a Find the three mass moments of inertia I_x, I_y, and I_z given that the area moments of inertia are

$$I_{xA} = I_{yA} = \frac{\pi d^4}{64} \qquad I_{zA} = J = \frac{\pi d^4}{32} \qquad (18.123)$$

where d is the diameter of the disk.

b Express the results for I_{xM} and I_{yM} in part a in the engineering drawing units of lb·in², and in the units of slug·ft². The specific weight of steel is $\gamma = 490$ lb/ft³.

Solution
a The area moments of inertia of the plane surface area are

$$I_{xA} = I_{yA} = \frac{\pi (9)^4}{64} = 322 \text{ in}^4 \qquad (18.124)$$

$$J = 2 I_{xA} = 644 \text{ in}^4 \qquad (18.125)$$

The mass density is found from the specific weight as

$$\rho = \frac{\gamma}{g} = \frac{(490 \text{ lb/ft}^3)(1 \text{ ft}^3/1,728 \text{ in}^3)}{386 \text{ in/s}^2} = 7.35 \times 10^{-4} \frac{\text{lb·s}^2}{\text{in}^4} \qquad (18.126)$$

The disc is assumed to be thin, and the mass moments of inertia are

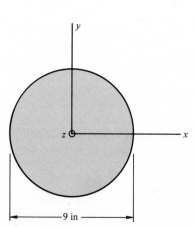

Fig. 18.34

620

$$I_{xM} = I_{yM} = \rho t I_{xA} = 7.35 \times 10^{-4} \, \frac{\text{lb} \cdot \text{s}^2}{\text{in}^4}(0.5 \text{ in})(322 \text{ in}^4) \quad (18.127)$$

$$= 0.118 \text{ lb} \cdot \text{s}^2 \cdot \text{in}$$

$$I_{zM} = 2I_{xM} = 0.236 \text{ lb} \cdot \text{s}^2 \cdot \text{in} \quad (18.128)$$

b The mass moments of inertia in terms of the engineering drawing units of lb·in² are

$$I_{xM} = I_{yM} = 0.118 \text{ lb} \cdot \text{s}^2 \cdot \text{in} \left(386 \, \frac{\text{in}}{\text{s}^2}\right) = 45.5 \text{ lb} \cdot \text{in}^2 \quad (18.129)$$

$$I_{zM} = 2I_{xM} = 2(45.5) = 91 \text{ lb} \cdot \text{in}^2 \quad (18.130)$$

Eq. (18.127) may be written in the form

$$I_{xM} = 0.118 \text{ lb} \cdot \text{s}^2 \cdot \text{in} \left(\frac{1 \text{ ft}}{12 \text{ in}}\right)\left(\frac{1 \text{ ft}}{1 \text{ ft}}\right) = 0.00983 \, \frac{\text{lb} \cdot \text{s}^2}{\text{ft}} \cdot \text{ft}^2 \quad (18.131)$$

Since 1 slug is equal to 1 lb·s²/ft, the final result is

$$I_{xM} = 0.00983 \text{ slug} \cdot \text{ft}^2 \quad (18.132)$$

18.10 MASS MOMENTS OF INERTIA OF COMPOSITE HOMOGENEOUS RIGID BODIES

If a body under consideration is not one of the simple shapes shown in Table 18.5, it may be possible to subdivide the body into several elementary shapes and sum the individual moments of inertia. In the process of this subdivision, elements are chosen whose centroidal mass moments of inertia about axes parallel to the desired axes are known. The parallel axis theorem may then be used to find the mass moment of inertia of the element about the reference axis. If the body consists of several elements, it may be desirable to organize the solution in a tabular form. This technique is shown in Example 18.10.

Example 18.9 Figure 18.35 shows a flywheel made of die cast zinc with a density of 7050 kg/m³.

a Find the mass, the polar mass moment of inertia, and the polar radius of gyration of the flywheel.

b In a proposed modification of this design the center section will have two holes, shown as the dashed circles in Fig. 18.35. Find the percent reduction in the mass, and in the polar mass moment of inertia, when the two holes are added to the original design.

c How would the results in part *a* change if the flywheel were fabricated of aluminum with a density of 2700 kg/m³?
The effects of the small center hole may be neglected.

Solution

a The original design consists of a flat, solid cylinder and a hollow cylinder, as shown in Fig. 18.36. The rim is designated element 1, and the plane center section is designated element 2. The results in cases 4 and 5 in Table 18.5 are used directly, and

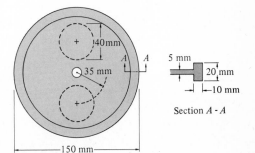

Section *A - A*

Fig. 18.35

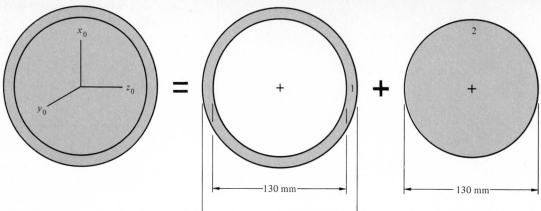

Fig. 18.36

$$m = m_1 + m_2 \tag{18.133}$$

$$= \frac{1}{4}\rho\pi h_1(d_{01}^2 - d_{i1}^2) + \frac{1}{4}\rho\pi\, d_2^2 h_2 \tag{18.134}$$

$$= \frac{1}{4}\left(7050\ \frac{\text{kg}}{\text{m}^3}\right)\pi(20\ \text{mm})(150^2 - 130^2)\ \text{mm}^2\left(\frac{1\ \text{m}}{1000\ \text{mm}}\right)^3$$

$$+ \frac{1}{4}(7050)\pi(130^2)5\left(\frac{1}{1000}\right)^3 \tag{18.135}$$

$$= 0.620 + 0.468 = 1.09\ \text{kg} \tag{18.136}$$

$$I_{0y} = \frac{1}{8}m_1(d_{01}^2 + d_{i1}^2) + \frac{1}{8}m_2\, d_2^2 \tag{18.137}$$

$$= \frac{1}{8}(0.620\ \text{kg})(150^2 + 130^2)\ \text{mm}^2\left(\frac{1\ \text{m}}{1000\ \text{mm}}\right)^2$$

$$+ \frac{1}{8}(0.468)130^2\left(\frac{1}{1000}\right)^2 \tag{18.138}$$

$$= 0.00305 + 0.000989 = 0.00404\ \text{kg}\cdot\text{m}^2 \tag{18.139}$$

It is interesting to observe that the contributions of the rim and center section from Eq. (18.139) are 76 and 24 percent, respectively, of the total mass moment of inertia. By comparison, from Eq. (18.136) the rim and center section contribute 57 and 43 percent, respectively, of the total mass of the assembly. The polar radius of gyration is found as

$$k_{0y} = \sqrt{\frac{I_{0y}}{m}} = \sqrt{\frac{0.00404}{1.09}} = 0.0609\ \text{m} = 60.9\ \text{mm} \tag{18.140}$$

b The mass of material which would occupy one hole is

$$m = \frac{1}{4}\rho\pi\, d^2 h = \frac{1}{4}(7050)\pi(40^2)5\left(\frac{1}{1000}\right)^3 = 0.0443\ \text{kg} \tag{18.141}$$

The total mass of the proposed design is

$$m_{\text{net}} = 1.09 - 2(0.0443) = 1.00\ \text{kg} \tag{18.142}$$

The corresponding mass moment of inertia of the material of one hole, about the center axis, is

$$I_y = I_{0y} + m\, d_y^2 \tag{18.143}$$

$$I_y = \frac{1}{8}m\, d^2 + m\, d_y^2 \tag{18.144}$$

$$I_y = \frac{1}{8}(0.0443)40^2 \left(\frac{1}{1000}\right)^2 + 0.0443\left(\frac{35}{1000}\right)^2 = 6.31 \times 10^{-5}\ \text{kg}\cdot\text{m}^2 \tag{18.145}$$

The mass moment of inertia of the flywheel with two holes is then

$$I_{\text{net}} = 0.00404 - 2(6.31 \times 10^{-5}) = 0.00391\ \text{kg}\cdot\text{m}^2 \tag{18.146}$$

The percent reduction in mass with the proposed design modification is $[(1.09 - 1.00)/1.09]100 = 8.3$ percent. The corresponding reduction in the mass moment of inertia is $[(0.00404 - 0.00391)/0.00404]100 = 3.2$ percent.

c The mass moment of inertia is directly proportional to the density of the material. Thus, if aluminum were substituted for zinc, the new values of m and I_{0y} would be

$$m = \frac{2700}{7050}(1.09) = 0.417\ \text{kg} \tag{18.147}$$

$$I_{0y} = \frac{2700}{7050}(0.00404) = 0.00155\ \text{kg}\cdot\text{m}^2 \tag{18.148}$$

Example 18.10 The bracket of Example 18.3 is shown in Fig. 18.37. Find

a The mass moment of inertia I_z
b The centroidal mass moment of inertia I_{0z}
c The mass moment of inertia I_{z1}
d The radius of gyration k_{0z}
e The radius of gyration k_z

The material is bronze, with a specific weight of $0.295\ \text{lb/in}^3$.

Solution

a The bracket is subdivided into the same three elements used in the computation of the volume centroid. A set of coordinate axes is attached to each element, as shown in Fig. 18.37.

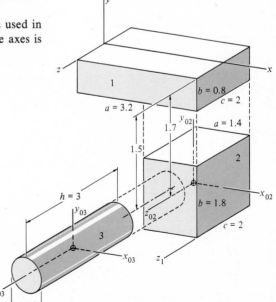

Fig. 18.37

TABLE 18.3

Element	m_i	d_{zi}	$I_{0z,i}$	$m_i d_{zi}^2$	I_{zi}
1	$m_1 = \rho abc$ $= \frac{0.295}{386}(3.2)0.8(2)$ $= 0.00391 \text{ lb·s}^2/\text{in}$	...	...	...	$I_{z1} = \frac{1}{3}m(a^2 + b^2)$ $= \frac{1}{3}(0.00391)(3.2^2 + 0.8^2)$ $= 0.0142 \text{ lb·s}^2\cdot\text{in}$
2	$m_2 = \rho abc$ $= \frac{0.295}{386}(1.4)1.8(2)$ $= 0.00385 \text{ lb·s}^2/\text{in}$	$d_{z2} = 3.02$	$I_{0z,2} = \frac{1}{12}m(a^2 + b^2)$ $= \frac{1}{12}(0.00385)(1.4^2 + 1.8^2)$ $= 0.00167 \text{ lb·s}^2\cdot\text{in}$	$m_2 d_{z2}^2 =$ $= (0.00385)3.02^2$ $= 0.0351 \text{ lb·s}^2\cdot\text{in}$	$I_{z2} = I_{0z,2} + m_2 d_{z2}^2$ $= 0.00167 + 0.0351$ $= 0.0368 \text{ lb·s}^2\cdot\text{in}$
3	$m_3 = \frac{1}{4}\rho\pi d^2 h$ $= \frac{1}{4}\left(\frac{0.295}{386}\right)\pi(1^2)3$ $= 0.00180 \text{ lb·s}^2/\text{in}$	$d_{z3} = 2.92$	$I_{0z,3} = \frac{1}{8}md^2$ $= \frac{1}{8}(0.00180)1^2$ $= 0.00023 \text{ lb·s}^2\cdot\text{in}$	$m_3 d_{z3}^2 =$ $= 0.0018(2.92^2)$ $= 0.0153 \text{ lb·s}^2\cdot\text{in}$	$I_{z3} = I_{0z,3} + m_3 d_{z3}^2$ $= 0.00023 + 0.0153$ $= 0.0155 \text{ lb·s}^2\cdot\text{in}$
	$m = \sum\limits_{i=1}^{i=3} m_i$ $= 0.00956 \text{ lb·s}^2/\text{in}$				$I_z = 0.0665 \text{ lb·s}^2\cdot\text{in}$ $= 25.7 \text{ lb·in}^2$

Reference axis: z

$$k_z = \sqrt{\frac{I_z}{m}} = \sqrt{\frac{0.0665}{0.00956}} = 2.64 \text{ in}$$

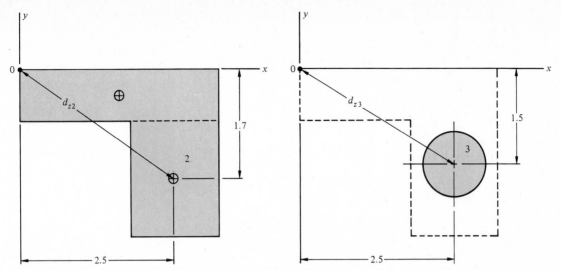

Fig. 18.38

Table 18.3 is next constructed. The solution for I_{z1} is found directly from case 10 in Table 18.5 as the mass moment of inertia about an edge of a rectangular parallelepiped. The solutions for $I_{0z,2}$ and $I_{0z,3}$ are found from cases 10 and 4, respectively, in the same table. The constructions used to find d_{z2} and d_{z3} are shown in Fig. 18.38. These terms are

$$d_{z2} = \sqrt{2.5^2 + 1.7^2} = 3.02 \text{ in} \qquad (18.149)$$

$$d_{z3} = \sqrt{2.5^2 + 1.5^2} = 2.92 \text{ in} \qquad (18.150)$$

The final result for I_z is

$$I_z = 0.0665 \text{ lb·s}^2\text{·in} = 25.7 \text{ lb·in}^2 \qquad (18.151)$$

b From the solution to Example 18.3, the two centroidal coordinates required in the present calculation are

$$x_c = 2.14 \text{ in} \qquad y_c = -1.14 \text{ in} \qquad (18.152)$$

The separation distance d_z between the z and z_0 axes, following Fig. 18.39, is

$$d_z = \sqrt{2.14^2 + 1.14^2} = 2.42 \text{ in} \qquad (18.153)$$

The centroidal moment of inertia is then found from

$$I_z = I_{0z} + m\, d_z^2 \qquad (18.154)$$

$$0.0665 = I_{0z} + 0.00956(2.42)^2 \qquad (18.155)$$

$$I_{0z} = 0.0105 \text{ lb·s}^2\text{·in} = 4.05 \text{ lb·in}^2 \qquad (18.156)$$

c The separation distance between the z_1 and z_0 axes is found from Fig. 18.39 as

$$d_{z1} = \sqrt{1.06^2 + 1.46^2} = 1.80 \text{ in} \qquad (18.157)$$

The mass moment of inertia about the z_1 axis is then

$$I_{z1} = I_{0z} + m\, d_{z1}^2 = 0.0105 + 0.00956(1.80)^2 = 0.0415 \text{ lb·s}^2\text{·in} \qquad (18.158)$$

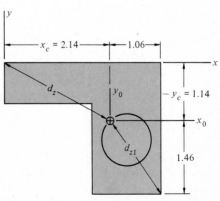

Fig. 18.39

625

A very common error, frequently made in the above type of calculation, is the attempt to find a moment of inertia, such as I_{z1}, by using the transfer theorem directly from another axis, such as z, which is not a centroidal axis. In the present problem, this incorrect form would be written as

$$I_{z1} \neq I_z + m\, d_{z,z1}^2 \qquad (18.159)$$

where $d_{z,z1}$ is the separation distance between the z and z_1 axes. The reader is urged to study Eq. (18.159) carefully and understand why it is an incorrect statement of the transfer, or parallel axis, theorem.

d The centroidal radius of gyration is found as

$$k_{0z} = \sqrt{\frac{I_{0z}}{m}} = \sqrt{\frac{0.0105}{0.00956}} = 1.05 \text{ in} \qquad (18.160)$$

e The radius of gyration about the z axis is

$$k_z = \sqrt{\frac{I_z}{m}} = \sqrt{\frac{0.0665}{0.00956}} = 2.64 \text{ in} \qquad (18.161)$$

18.11 COMPUTATION OF MASS MOMENTS OF INERTIA USING THE TRANSFER THEOREM AND A SINGLE INTEGRATION

A technique will now be presented that uses the transfer theorem, together with a single integration, to compute the mass moment of inertia of a rigid body. This method may be used if the body is a body of revolution, or if the body has a cross section of known variation. This basic method, by which all the results in Table 18.5 were obtained, will be illustrated in the following example.

Example 18.11 Find the mass moment of inertia I_z of the right circular cone shown in Fig. 18.40.

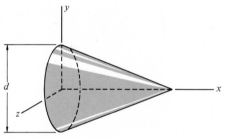

Fig. 18.40

Solution The side view of the cone is shown in Fig. 18.41. The mass moment of inertia of the disk-shaped differential mass element about its centroidal z_0 axis is

$$dI_{0z} = \rho t I_{0z,A} = \rho\, dx\, \frac{\pi(2y)^4}{64} = \frac{1}{4}\rho\pi y^4\, dx \qquad (18.162)$$

Using the transfer theorem, we find that the mass moment of inertia of this element about the z axis is

$$dI_z = dI_{0z} + (dm)x^2 \qquad (18.163)$$

$$dI_z = \frac{1}{4}\rho\pi y^4\, dx + (\rho\pi y^2\, dx)x^2 \qquad (18.164)$$

$$I_z = \rho\pi \int_0^h \left(\frac{1}{4}y^4 + y^2 x^2\right) dx \qquad (18.165)$$

The functional form of y was given by Eq. (18.18) as

$$y = \frac{d}{2}\left(1 - \frac{x}{h}\right) \qquad (18.166)$$

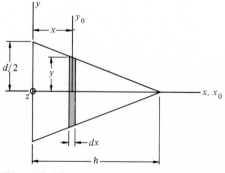

Fig. 18.41

Using the above equation, we find that Eq. (18.165) appears as

$$I_z = \rho\pi \int_0^h \left[\frac{1}{4}\left(\frac{d}{2}\right)^4\left(1 - \frac{4x}{h} + \frac{6x^2}{h^2} - \frac{4x^3}{h^3} + \frac{x^4}{h^4}\right)\right.$$

$$\left. + \left(\frac{d}{2}\right)^2\left(1 - \frac{2x}{h} + \frac{x^2}{h^2}\right)x^2 \right] dx \quad (18.167)$$

$$= \rho\pi \left[\frac{d^4}{64}\left(x - \frac{4x^2}{2h} + \frac{6x^3}{3h^2} - \frac{4x^4}{4h^3} + \frac{x^5}{5h^4}\right)\right.$$

$$\left. + \frac{d^2}{4}\left(\frac{x^3}{3} - \frac{2x^4}{4h} + \frac{x^5}{5h^2}\right)\right]_0^h \quad (18.168)$$

$$= \rho\pi\left[\frac{d^4h}{5(64)} + \frac{d^2h^3}{4(30)}\right] \quad (18.169)$$

The mass of the cone is

$$m = \rho\left[\frac{1}{3}\left(\frac{\pi d^2}{4}\right)h\right] = \frac{1}{12}\rho\pi \, d^2h \quad (18.170)$$

Eqs. (18.169) and (18.170) are combined to obtain the final value

$$I_z = \frac{1}{80}m(3 \, d^2 + 8h^2) \quad (18.171)$$

This equation is the result given as I_t in Table 18.5.

Example 18.12 Find the mass moment of inertia I_z of the rigid body shown in Fig. 18.42.

Solution The shaded mass element shown in Fig. 18.42 is a thin plane body. The mass moment of inertia dI_{0z} of this element about an axis through its centroid, parallel to the z axis, is

$$dI_{0z} = \frac{\rho \, dx \, cb^3}{12} \quad (18.172)$$

The moment of inertia of this element about the z axis, using the transfer theorem, is

$$dI_z = dI_{0z} + dm(x^2) \quad (18.173)$$

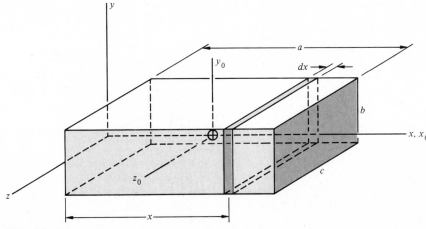

Fig. 18.42

$$= \frac{\rho cb^3}{12} dx + \rho bcx^2 \, dx \qquad (18.174)$$

$$I_z = \rho cb \int_0^a \left(\frac{b^2}{12} + x^2 \right) dx = \rho cb \left[\frac{b^2}{12} x + \frac{x^3}{3} \right]_0^a \qquad (18.175)$$

$$= \rho cb \left(\frac{b^2 a}{12} + \frac{a^3}{3} \right) = \rho abc \left[\frac{b^2}{12} + \frac{a^2}{3} \right] \qquad (18.176)$$

The mass m of the body is

$$m = \rho abc \qquad (18.177)$$

The final form for the mass moment of inertia I_z is then

$$I_z = \frac{1}{12} m(4a^2 + b^2) \qquad (18.178)$$

Using the transfer theorem, we get

$$I_z = I_{0z} + m \, d_z^2 \qquad (18.179)$$

$$\frac{1}{12} m(4a^2 + b^2) = I_{0z} + m \left(\frac{a}{2} \right)^2 \qquad (18.180)$$

$$I_{0z} = \frac{1}{12} m(a^2 + b^2) \qquad (18.181)$$

This equation is one of the results in case 10 in Table 18.5.

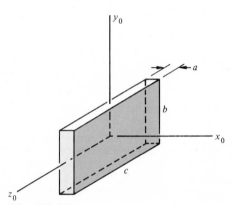

Fig. 18.43

Example 18.13 The dimension a of the rigid body in Example 18.12 is allowed to decrease until the shape of the body approaches a flat plate, as shown in Fig. 18.43. The approximate mass moment of inertia about the z_0 axis, assuming the body to be a thin plane mass, is

$$I_{0z} = \frac{1}{12} mb^2 \qquad (18.182)$$

Compute and plot the percent error between the exact and approximate mass moments of inertia I_{0z} for plate thicknesses up to one-half of the plate height b.

Solution The exact solution, from Eq. (18.181), is

$$I_{0z} = \frac{1}{12} m(a^2 + b^2) \qquad (18.183)$$

The percent error is defined to be

$$\% \text{ Error} = \frac{\text{exact solution} - \text{approximate solution}}{\text{exact solution}} (100) \qquad (18.184)$$

$$\frac{\frac{1}{12} m(a^2 + b^2) - \frac{1}{12} mb^2}{\frac{1}{12} m(a^2 + b^2)} (100) = \frac{1}{1 + \left(\frac{b}{a} \right)^2} (100) \qquad (18.185)$$

A plate thickness of one-half of the height of the plate corresponds to $a/b = \frac{1}{2}$. Equation (18.185) is solved for values of a/b from 0 to 0.5. The results are listed in Table 18.4, and plotted in Fig. 18.44. It may be seen that for small values of a/b, which characterize a thin plane

TABLE 18.4	
$\dfrac{a}{b}$	Percent error
0	0
0.1	1.0
0.2	3.8
0.3	8.3
0.4	13.8
0.5	20.0

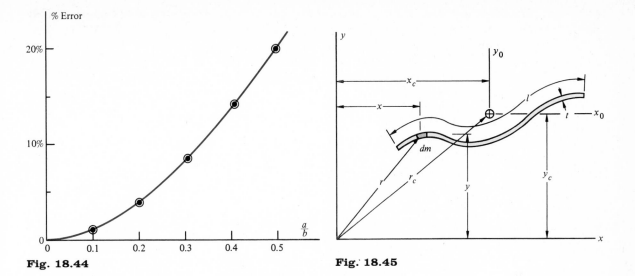

Fig. 18.44

Fig. 18.45

body, the error is very small. It may also be observed that the results are completely independent of the plate width dimension c.

18.12 CENTER OF MASS, AND MASS MOMENT OF INERTIA, OF PLANE BODIES FORMED OF THIN ROD SHAPES

Figure 18.45 shows a rigid body of plane form made of thin, homogeneous rod material with constant cross-section dimensions. The body lies in the xy plane, and the total length of the body, measured along the curvilinear axis, is l. The rod is considered to be thin if $t \ll l$.

The centroidal coordinates of the center of mass of the body are defined by

$$x_c = \frac{\int_m x \, dm}{\int_m dm} = \frac{\int_m x \, dm}{m} \qquad y_c = \frac{\int_m y \, dm}{\int_m dm} = \frac{\int_m y \, dm}{m}$$

$$(18.186)$$

The mass density per unit length of the rod material is designated ρ_0, and the Eq. (18.186) may be written as

$$x_c = \frac{\int_l x\rho_0 \, dl}{\int_l \rho_0 \, dl} = \frac{\int_l x \, dl}{l} \qquad y_c = \frac{\int_l y\rho_0 \, dl}{\int_l \rho_0 \, dl} = \frac{\int_l y \, dl}{l}$$

$$(18.187)$$

The right sides of Eq. (18.187) may be recognized as the centroidal coordinates of a plane curve. Thus, the center of mass

629

of the rigid plane body is located at the centroid of the plane curve which defines its shape. The mass moments of inertia of the body are defined by

$$I_x = \int_m y^2 \, dm \qquad I_y = \int_m x^2 \, dm \qquad (18.188)$$

$$I_z = \int_m r^2 \, dm = \int_m (x^2 + y^2) \, dm = I_x + I_y \quad (18.189)$$

Using $dm = \rho_0 \, dl$, we may express the mass moments of inertia by

$$I_x = \int_l y^2 \rho_0 \, dl = \rho_0 \int_l y^2 \, dl$$

$$\qquad (18.190)$$

$$I_z = \int_l (x^2 + y^2)\rho_0 \, dl = \rho_0 \int_l (x^2 + y^2) \, dl$$

The integral terms on the right sides of Eq. (18.190) may be recognized as the length moments of inertia of the plane curve about the x and y axes. With the notations for the moments of inertia of a plane curve, given by

$$I_{cx} = \int_l y^2 \, dl \qquad I_{cy} = \int_l x^2 \, dl \qquad I_{cz} = \int_l (x^2 + y^2)dl$$

$$\qquad (18.191)$$

the final forms for the mass moments of inertia of the plane rod form are

$$I_x = \rho_0 I_{cx} \qquad I_y = \rho_0 I_{cy} \qquad I_z = \rho_0 I_{cz} \quad (18.192)$$

It can be shown that the parallel axis, or transfer, theorem for the mass moments of inertia have the forms

$$I_x = I_{0x} + my_c^2$$

$$I_y = I_{0y} + mx_c^2 \qquad (18.193)$$

$$I_z = I_{0z} + mr_c^2$$

I_{0x}, I_{0y}, and I_{0z} are the centroidal moments of inertia about the $x_0 y_0 z_0$ axes shown in Fig. 18.45, x_c and y_c are the centroidal coordinates, and r_c is the separation distance between the z and z_0 axes.

Table 18.7 in the Summary section of this chapter, contains the centroidal coordinates and mass moments of inertia for several common curve shapes.

Example 18.14 A 16-mm-diameter rod is formed into the stirring blade shape shown in Fig. 18.46. When connected to a foot at the end of a shaft, the blade can be rotated about either the y axis or the y_1 axis.

a Find the location of the centroid of the blade shape.

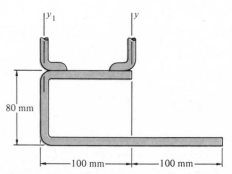

Fig. 18.46

b Find the mass moment of inertia of the blade about the y axis.

c Find the mass moment of inertia of the blade about the y_1 axis. The rod material is metal, with a density of 6760 kg/m³.

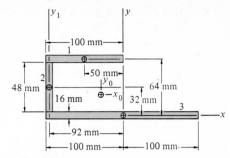

Fig. 18.47

Solution   The blade is divided into the three straight line elements, shown in Fig. 18.47. This particular subdivision places the center of mass of element 3 on the reference y axis, which will simplify the subsequent computations. The x axis is placed in the figure along element 3. The centroidal coordinates are

$$x_c = \frac{x_{c1}l_1 + x_{c2}l_2 + x_{c3}l_3}{l_1 + l_2 + l_3} = \frac{-50(100) - 92(48) + 0}{100 + 48 + 200}$$

$$= \frac{-9420}{348} = -27.1 \text{ mm} \quad (18.194)$$

$$y_c = \frac{y_{c1}l_1 + y_{c2}l_2 + y_{c3}l_3}{l_1 + l_2 + l_3} = \frac{64(100) + 32(48) + 0}{100 + 48 + 200}$$

$$= \frac{7940}{348} = 22.8 \text{ mm} \quad (18.195)$$

b For a rod of constant cross section area A and length l, the mass density ρ and mass density per unit length ρ_0 are related by

$$\rho A l = \rho_0 l \qquad \rho_0 = \rho A \qquad (18.196)$$

For the present problem

$$\rho_0 = 6760 \text{ kg/m}^3 \frac{\pi(16)^2}{4} \text{ mm}^2(1 \text{ m}/1000 \text{ mm})^2$$

$$= 1.36 \text{ kg/m} \qquad (18.197)$$

The masses of the three length elements are

$$m_1 = 1.36 \text{ kg/m} \left(\frac{100}{1000}\right) \text{m} = 0.136 \text{ kg}$$

$$m_2 = 1.36 \left(\frac{48}{1000}\right) = 0.0653 \text{ kg} \qquad (18.198)$$

$$m_3 = 1.36 \left(\frac{200}{1000}\right) = 0.272 \text{ kg}$$

The total mass of the blade is

$$m = m_1 + m_2 + m_3 = 0.136 + 0.0653 + 0.272 = 0.473 \text{ kg} \quad (18.199)$$

The equations for the mass moment of inertia of a straight rod element are contained in case 1 in Table 18.7. The mass moment of inertia about the y axis is

$$I_y = I_{y1} + I_{y2} + I_{y3} = \frac{1}{3}m_1 l_1^2 + m_2 y_2^2 + \frac{1}{12}m_3 l_3^2 \qquad (18.200)$$

$$= \frac{1}{3}(0.136)\left(\frac{100}{1000}\right)^2 + 0.0653\left(\frac{92}{1000}\right)^2 + \frac{1}{12}(0.272)\left(\frac{200}{1000}\right)^2$$

$$= 0.00191 \text{ kg·m}^2 \quad (18.201)$$

c To find the mass moment of inertia about the y_1 axis, the centroidal mass moment of inertia I_{0y} will first be found. Using the transfer theorem,

631

$$I_y = I_{0y} + mx_c^2 \qquad I_{0y} = I_y - mx_c^2 \qquad (18.202)$$

$$I_{0y} = 0.00191 - 0.473\left(\frac{-27.1}{1000}\right)^2 = 0.00156 \text{ kg·m}^2 \quad (18.203)$$

The separation distance between the centroidal y_0 axis and the y_1 axis is

$$d = 92 - 27.1 = 64.9 \text{ mm} \qquad (18.204)$$

The mass moment of inertia about the y_1 axis, using the transfer theorem, is

$$I_{y1} = I_{0y} + m\,d^2 = 0.00156 + 0.473\left(\frac{64.9}{1000}\right)^2$$

$$= 0.00355 \text{ kg·m}^2 \quad (18.205)$$

A very common mistake made in problems of this type is to attempt to transfer the moment of inertia about axis y directly to axis y_1. This incorrect application of the transfer theorem would then have the typical form

$$I_{y1} \neq I_y + m\,d_{y,y_1}^2 \qquad d_{y,y_1} = 92 \text{ mm} \qquad (18.206)$$

The reader is urged to carefully study Eq. (18.206) and to understand thoroughly why it is not a correct use of the transfer theorem.

18.13 SUMMARY

The centroid of a plane area is a point whose location is a function only of the shape of the area. The coordinates of the centroid of a plane area are

$$x_c = \frac{\int_A x\,dA}{A} \qquad y_c = \frac{\int_A y\,dA}{A} \qquad (18.207)$$

The centroid of a volume is a point whose location is a function only of the shape of the volume. The centroidal coordinates of a volume are

$$x_c = \frac{\int_V x\,dV}{V} \qquad y_c = \frac{\int_V y\,dV}{V} \qquad z_c = \frac{\int_V z\,dV}{V} \qquad (18.208)$$

The first moments of the volume are

$$x_c V = \int_V x\,dV \qquad y_c V = \int_V y\,dV \qquad z_c V = \int_V z\,dV \quad (18.209)$$

These quantities are used in the computation of the coordinates of the centroid of a composite volume.

A rigid body is one within which any two points always have the same separation distance between them. Thus, the shape

Body shape	Mass, and x, y, z coordinates of CM	Mass moments of inertia
1 Solid sphere: 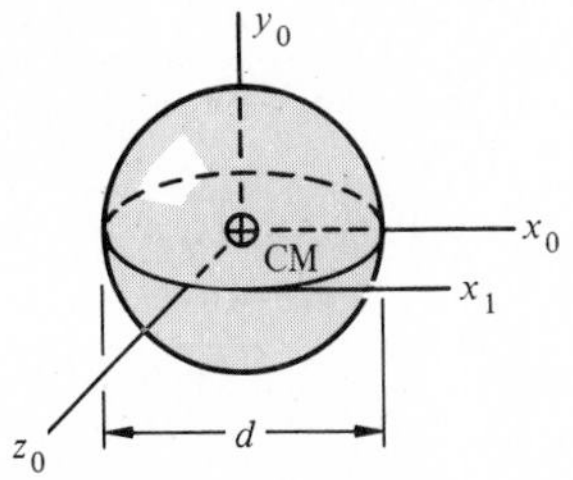 	$m = \dfrac{1}{6}\rho\pi d^3$	*centroidal* $I_{0x} = I_{0y} = I_{0z} = \dfrac{1}{10}md^2$ $I_{x_1} = \dfrac{7}{20}md^2$
2 Hollow sphere: 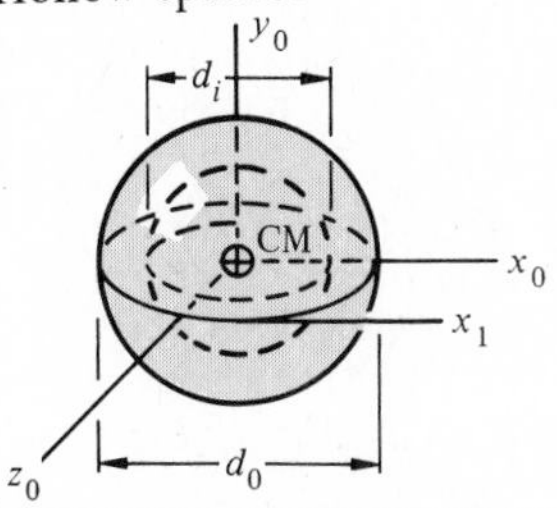 	$m = \dfrac{1}{6}\rho\pi(d_0^3 - d_i^3)$	$I_{0x} = I_{0y} = I_{0z}$ $I_{0x} = \dfrac{1}{10}m\left[\dfrac{d_0^5 - d_i^5}{d_0^3 - d_i^3}\right]$ $I_{x_1} = \dfrac{1}{20}m\left[\dfrac{7d_0^5 - 5d_0^2 d_i^3 - 2d_i^5}{d_0^3 - d_i^3}\right]$
3 Hemisphere: 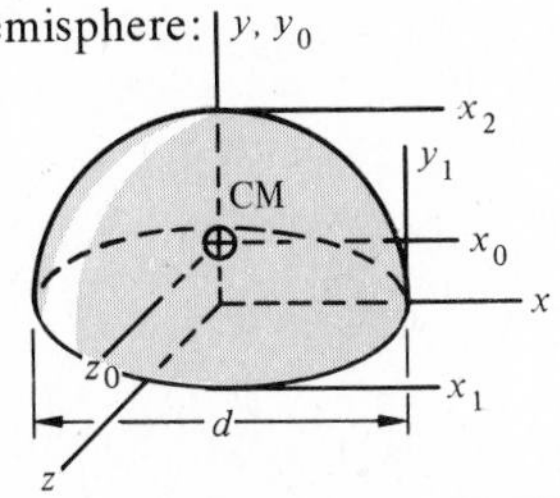 	$m = \dfrac{1}{12}\rho\pi d^3$ $x_c = z_c = 0$ $y_c = \dfrac{3}{16}d$	$I_{0x} = I_{0z} = 0.0648 md^2$ $I_x = I_y = I_z = I_{0y} = \dfrac{1}{10}md^2$ $I_{x_1} = 0.350\,md^2$ $I_{x_2} = 0.725 md^2$ $I_{y_1} = \dfrac{7}{20}md^2$
4 Right circular cylinder: 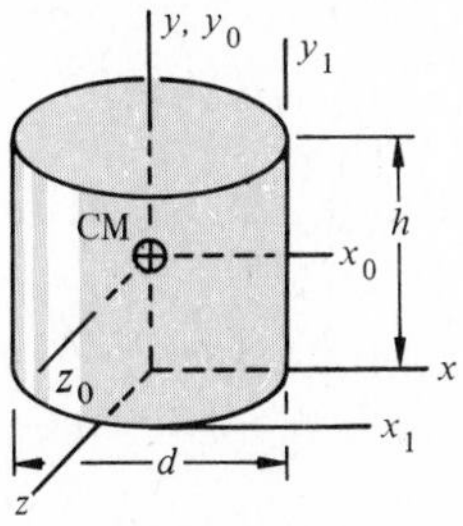 	$m = \dfrac{1}{4}\rho\pi d^2 h$ $x_c = z_c = 0$ $y_c = \dfrac{1}{2}h$	$I_{0x} = I_{0z} = \dfrac{1}{12}m\left(h^2 + \dfrac{3}{4}d^2\right)$ $I_{0y} = I_y = \dfrac{1}{8}md^2$ $I_x = I_z = \dfrac{1}{48}m(16h^2 + 3d^2)$ $I_{x_1} = \dfrac{1}{48}m(16h^2 + 15d^2)$ $I_{y_1} = \dfrac{3}{8}md^2$

(handwritten annotations) $\rho = \delta = \dfrac{g}{8}$ *density*

cylinder $A = \pi r^2$

$V = A \cdot lt$ *thickness or height*

$d - diameter$

Body shape	Mass, and x, y, z coordinates of CM	Mass moments of inertia
5 Hollow right circular cylinder:	$m = \frac{1}{4}\rho\pi h(d_0^2 - d_i^2)$ $x_c = z_c = 0$ $y_c = \frac{1}{2}h$	$I_{0x} = I_{0z} = \frac{1}{48}m(3d_0^2 + 3d_i^2 + 4h^2)$ $I_{0y} = I_y = \frac{1}{8}m(d_0^2 + d_i^2)$ $I_{x_1} = \frac{1}{48}m(15d_0^2 + 3d_i^2 + 16h^2)$ $I_{x_1} = \frac{1}{48}m(15d_0^2 + 3d_i^2 + 28h^2)$ $I_{y_1} = \frac{1}{8}m(3d_0^2 + d_i^2)$
6 Right circular cone:	$m = \frac{1}{12}\rho\pi d^2 h$ $x_c = z_c = 0$ $y_c = \frac{1}{4}h$	$I_{0x} = I_{0z} = \frac{3}{80}m(d^2 + h^2)$ $I_{0y} = I_y = \frac{3}{40}md^2$ $I_x = I_z = \frac{1}{80}m(3d^2 + 8h^2)$ $I_{x_1} = \frac{1}{80}m(23d^2 + 8h^2)$ $I_{x_2} = \frac{3}{80}m(d^2 + 16h^2)$ $I_{y_1} = \frac{13}{40}md^2$
7 Ellipsoid:	$m = \frac{1}{6}\rho\pi abc$	$I_{0x} = \frac{1}{20}m(b^2 + c^2)$ $I_{0y} = \frac{1}{20}m(a^2 + c^2)$ $I_{0z} = \frac{1}{20}m(a^2 + b^2)$ $I_{x_1} = \frac{1}{20}m(b^2 + 6c^2)$ $I_{y_1} = \frac{1}{20}m(c^2 + 6a^2)$ $I_{z_1} = \frac{1}{20}m(b^2 + 6a^2)$

Body shape	Mass, and x, y, z coordinates of CM	Mass moments of inertia
8 Paraboloid of revolution:	$m = \frac{1}{8}\rho\pi d^2 h$ $x_c = \frac{2}{3}h$ $y_c = z_c = 0$	$I_{0x} = I_x = \frac{1}{12}md^2$ $I_{0y} = I_{0z} = \frac{1}{72}m(3d^2 + 4h^2)$ $I_y = I_z = \frac{1}{24}m(d^2 + 12h^2)$ $I_{y_1} = I_{z_1} = \frac{1}{24}m(d^2 + 4h^2)$ $I_{x_1} = \frac{1}{3}md^2$
9 Cube:	$m = \rho a^3$ $x_c = y_c = z_c = \frac{1}{2}a$	$I_{0x} = I_{0y} = I_{0z} = \frac{1}{6}ma^2$ $I_x = I_y = I_z = \frac{2}{3}ma^2$ $I_{x_1} = \frac{5}{12}ma^2$
10 Rectangular parallelepipid:	$m = \rho abc$ $x_c = \frac{1}{2}a$ $y_c = \frac{1}{2}b$ $z_c = \frac{1}{2}c$	$I_{0x} = \frac{1}{12}m(b^2 + c^2)$ $I_{0y} = \frac{1}{12}m(a^2 + c^2)$ $I_{0z} = \frac{1}{12}m(a^2 + b^2)$ $I_x = \frac{1}{3}m(b^2 + c^2)$ $I_y = \frac{1}{3}m(a^2 + c^2)$ $I_z = \frac{1}{3}m(a^2 + b^2)$ $I_{x_1} = \frac{1}{12}m(4b^2 + c^2)$

TABLE 18.6: CENTROIDS, AND MOMENTS OF INERTIA OF ELEMENTARY PLANE AREAS

Case	Shape	A	x_c	y_c	I_{0x}	I_{0y}	I_{0z}
1		a^2	$\dfrac{a}{2}$	$\dfrac{a}{2}$	$\dfrac{a^4}{12}$	$\dfrac{a^4}{12}$	$\dfrac{a^4}{6}$
2		ab	$\dfrac{a}{2}$	$\dfrac{b}{2}$	$\dfrac{ab^3}{12}$	$\dfrac{ba^3}{12}$	$\dfrac{ab}{12}(a^2+b^2)$
3		$\dfrac{ab}{2}$	$\dfrac{2a}{3}$	$\dfrac{b}{3}$	$\dfrac{ab^3}{36}$	$\dfrac{ba^3}{36}$	$\dfrac{ab}{36}(a^2+b^2)$
4		$\dfrac{ab}{2}$	$\cdots$	$\dfrac{b}{3}$	$\dfrac{ab^3}{36}$		
5		$\pi a^2 = \dfrac{\pi d^2}{4}$	$a=\dfrac{d}{2}$	$a=\dfrac{d}{2}$	$\dfrac{\pi a^4}{4}=\dfrac{\pi d^4}{64}$	$\dfrac{\pi a^4}{4}=\dfrac{\pi d^4}{64}$	$\dfrac{\pi a^4}{2}=\dfrac{\pi d^4}{32}$
6		$\dfrac{\pi a^2}{2}$	a	$\dfrac{4a}{3\pi}$	$a^4\left(\dfrac{\pi}{8}-\dfrac{8}{9\pi}\right)$	$\dfrac{\pi a^4}{8}$	$a^4\left(\dfrac{\pi}{4}-\dfrac{8}{9\pi}\right)$
7		$\dfrac{\pi ab}{4}$	$\dfrac{a}{2}$	$\dfrac{b}{2}$	$\dfrac{\pi ab^3}{64}$	$\dfrac{\pi ba^3}{64}$	$\dfrac{\pi ab}{64}(a^2+b^2)$

*The area centroid of any triangle is at the common intersection of the three angle bisectors, at a height above each base of $\frac{1}{3}$ of the altitude.

TABLE 18.7 MASS MOMENTS OF INERTIA OF PLANE BODIES OF THIN ROD SHAPE*

Body shape	Mass, and x, y, z coordinates of CM	Mass moments of inertia
1 Thin straight rod:	$m = \rho_0 l$ $x_c = \dfrac{1}{2}l$ $y_c = z_c = 0$	$I_{0x} = I_x = 0$ $I_{0y} = I_{0z} = \dfrac{1}{12}ml^2$ $I_y = I_z = \dfrac{1}{3}ml^2$
2	$m = \rho_0 l$ $x_c = a + \dfrac{1}{2}l\sin\theta$ $y_c = b + \dfrac{1}{2}l\cos\theta$ $z_c = 0$	$I_{0x} = \dfrac{1}{12}ml^2\cos^2\theta$ $I_{0y} = \dfrac{1}{12}ml^2\sin^2\theta$ $I_{0z} = \dfrac{1}{12}ml^2$ $I_x = m\left(\dfrac{1}{3}l^2\cos^2\theta + bl\cos\theta + b^2\right)$ $I_y = m\left(\dfrac{1}{3}l^2\sin^2\theta + al\sin\theta + a^2\right)$ $I_z = m\left[\dfrac{1}{3}l^2 + l(a\sin\theta + b\cos\theta) + (a^2 + b^2)\right]$
3 Thin circular rod	$m = 2\rho_0 r\theta$ $x_c = \dfrac{r\sin\theta}{\theta}$ $y_c = z_c = 0$	$I_{0x} = I_x = mr^2\left(\dfrac{\theta - \sin\theta\cos\theta}{2\theta}\right)$ $I_{0y} = \dfrac{1}{2}mr^2\left(1 + \dfrac{\sin 2\theta}{2\theta} - \dfrac{2\sin^2\theta}{\theta^2}\right)$ $I_{0z} = mr^2\left(1 - \dfrac{\sin^2\theta}{\theta^2}\right)$ $I_y = mr^2\left(\dfrac{\theta + \sin\theta\cos\theta}{2\theta}\right)$ $I_z = mr^2$
4 Thin ring:	$m = \rho_0\pi d$ $x_c = y_c = \dfrac{d}{2}$ $z_c = 0$	$I_{0x} = I_{0y} = \dfrac{1}{8}md^2$ $I_{0z} = \dfrac{1}{4}md^2$ $I_x = I_y = \dfrac{3}{8}md^2$ $I_z = \dfrac{3}{4}md^2$

* ρ_0 = mass per unit length
     m = total mass of body
x_0, y_0, z_0 = centroidal coordinates, with origin at CM of body

I_{0x}, I_{0y}, I_{0z} = mass moments of inertia about centroidal axes
    x, y, z = axes which are parallel to centroidal axes x_0, y_0, z_0
    x_c, y_c, z_c = position coordinates, in xyz system, of CM of body

of a rigid body never changes. The center of mass CM of a rigid body is the point through which the weight force acts. If the material of the body is homogeneous, the center of mass and the centroid of the volume of the body are coincident points. If the material of the body is not homogeneous, the centroidal coordinates of the CM are given by

$$x_c = \frac{\int_V x\gamma \, dV}{\int_V \gamma \, dV} \qquad y_c = \frac{\int_V y\gamma \, dV}{\int_V \gamma \, dV} \qquad z_c = \frac{\int_V z\gamma \, dV}{\int_V \gamma \, dV} \qquad (18.210)$$

where γ, the specific weight, is a known function of the coordinates. If a volume has a plane of symmetry, the centroid must lie in this plane. If there are two planes of symmetry, the centroid must lie along the intersection line of the planes. If there are three planes of symmetry, the centroid is the common intersection point of the three planes.

The centroidal coordinates of a composite homogeneous rigid body are

$$x_c = \frac{x_{c1}V_1 + x_{c2}V_2 + \cdots + x_{cn}V_n}{V_1 + V_2 + \cdots + V_n} \qquad (18.211)$$

$$y_c = \frac{y_{c1}V_1 + y_{c2}V_2 + \cdots + y_{cn}V_n}{V_1 + V_2 + \cdots + V_n} \qquad (18.212)$$

$$z_c = \frac{z_{c1}V_1 + z_{c2}V_2 + \cdots + z_{cn}V_n}{V_1 + V_2 + \cdots + V_n} \qquad (18.213)$$

where $V_1, V_2, \ldots, V_n$ are the elementary volumes into which the body has been subdivided, and x_{cn}, y_{cn}, z_{cn} are the centroidal coordinates of these volumes. The volumes of any holes or cutouts are treated as negative quantities.

The moments of inertia of a plane area are defined by

$$I_x = \int_A y^2 \, dA$$

$$I_y = \int_A x^2 \, dA \qquad (18.214)$$

$$I_z = \int_A r^2 \, dA = \int_A (x^2 + y^2) \, dA = I_x + I_y$$

The area moments of inertia are a function of the shape of the area and of the placement of the reference axes with respect to this area. These quantities are always positive. They have the basic units of length raised to the fourth power. The area moments of inertia about the centroidal x_0, y_0 axes, and about the parallel x, y axes, are related by the transfer, or parallel axis, theorem, with the forms

$$I_x = I_{0x} + A \, d_x^2 \qquad I_y = I_{0y} + A \, d_y^2 \qquad (18.215)$$

where A is the magnitude of the area and d_x and d_y are the separation distances between the axes.

The moments of inertia of a rigid body are defined by

$$I_x = \int_V (y^2 + z^2)\, dm$$

$$I_y = \int_V (z^2 + x^2)\, dm \qquad (18.216)$$

$$I_z = \int_V (x^2 + y^2)\, dm$$

Mass moments of inertia are a function of both the distribution of mass in the body and of the placement of the reference axes with respect to the body. These terms are a measure of the resistance of the body to angular acceleration about the reference axes. Mass moments of inertia are always positive, with the basic units of mass times length squared.

The transfer, or parallel axis, theorem for mass moments of inertia has the typical form

$$I_x = I_{0x} + md_x^2 \qquad (18.217)$$

where m is the mass of the body and d_x is the separation distance between the centroidal x_0 axis and the parallel x axis.

The mass radii of gyration are defined by

$$k_x = \sqrt{\frac{I_x}{m}} \qquad k_y = \sqrt{\frac{I_y}{m}} \qquad k_z = \sqrt{\frac{I_z}{m}} \qquad (18.218)$$

The approximate solutions for the mass moments of inertia of a homogeneous thin plane rigid body are

$$I_x = \int_V y^2\, dm \qquad I_y = \int_V x^2\, dm$$

$$\qquad (18.219)$$

$$I_z = \int_V r^2\, dm = I_x + I_y$$

where $r^2 = x^2 + y^2$, and the xy axes lie in the plane of the area. For this type of thin plane body, the area moment of inertia of the plane boundary area and the mass moment of inertia of the body are related by the approximate equations

$$I_{xM} = \rho t I_{xA} \qquad I_{yM} = \rho t I_{yA}$$

$$\qquad (18.220)$$

$$I_{zM} = \rho t I_{zA} = \rho t (I_{xA} + I_{yA})$$

where the subscripts A and M refer to area and mass, respectively. The accuracy of these equations increases with decreasing thickness t of the body.

The centroidal coordinates of a plane body formed of thin rod shapes are the same as the centroidal coordinates of the plane curve which defines the shape of the body, given by

$$x_c = \frac{\int_l x \, dl}{l} \qquad y_c = \frac{\int_l y \, dl}{l} \qquad (18.221)$$

The mass moments of inertia are given by

$$I_x = \rho_0 I_{cx} \qquad I_y = \rho_0 I_{cy} \qquad I_z = \rho_0 I_{cz} \qquad (18.222)$$

where ρ_0 is the mass density per unit length of the rod, given by

$$\rho_0 = \rho A \qquad (18.223)$$

and I_{cx}, I_{cy}, and I_{cz} are the length moments of inertia of the plane curve shape.

PROBLEMS

18.1 The specific weight variation of the material from which the cone in Fig. P18.1a is fabricated is shown in Fig. P18.1b.
(a) Find the coordinate y_c of the center of mass of the cone.
(b) Find the percent difference between the result in part a and the centroidal coordinate y_c of the volume of the cone.

18.2 The material of the cylinder shown in Fig. P18.2a has the variation in specific weight shown in Fig. P18.2b. The equation of this curve is $\gamma = 6.7y^2 - 3.4y + 80$, where γ is in pounds per cubic feet and y is in feet.
(a) Find the coordinate y_c of the center of mass of the material.
(b) Find the percent difference between the result in part a and the centroidal coordinate y_c of the volume of the cylinder.

18.3 Do the same as in Prob. 18.2 for the body shape shown in Fig. P18.3.

18.4 The container with the form of a truncated cone, shown in Fig. P18.4, is filled with material whose specific weight varies according to Fig. 18.13.
(a) Find the coordinate y_c of the center of mass of the material.
(b) Find the percent difference between the result in part a and the centroidal coordinate y_c of the volume of the truncated cone.

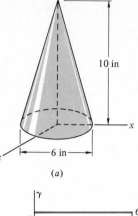

(a)

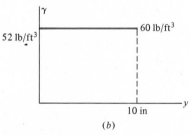

(b)

Fig. P18.1

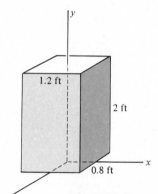

Fig. P18.3

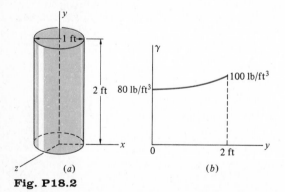

Fig. P18.2

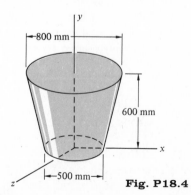

Fig. P18.4

18.5 A cylindrical container exposed to freezing temperatures formed the ice layer shown in Fig. P18.5. Find the y coordinate of the center of mass of the container. The specific weight of ice is 56 lb/ft³, and the specific weight of water is 62.4 lb/ft³. The mass of the container may be neglected.

18.6 A tank of square cross section contains water and oil, as shown in Fig. P18.6. The density of the water is 1,000 kg/m³, and the density of the oil is 920 kg/m³. If the weight of the tank is neglected, find the centroidal coordinate of the center of mass of the material in the tank.

18.7 A cylindrical tank is 1 ft in diameter and 4 ft high. Into the tank is poured 12 gal of water and 10 gal of oil with a specific gravity of 0.89. Find the location of the center of mass of the tank. The mass of the tank may be neglected, and 7.48 gal = 1 ft³.

18.8 through 18.14 The figure shows a machine part made of thin homogeneous material of constant thickness. The xy plane bisects the thickness dimension.

(a) Find the mass moments of inertia I_x, I_y, and I_z.

(b) Find the mass of the part and the radii of gyration k_x, k_y, and k_z.

(c) Using the parallel axis theorem, find the centroidal mass moments of inertia I_{ox}, I_{oy}, and I_{oz}. The centroidal axes x_o, y_o, and z_o are parallel to the x, y, and z axes.

(d) Find the radii of gyration k_{ox}, k_{oy}, and k_{oz}.

The material, and thickness, of each part is indicated. (Certain of these problems were first presented in Chap. 10, where the area moments of inertia, and radii of gyration, were to be found. The original problem numbers are shown in parentheses.)

18.8 (Prob. 10.2) Bronze: $\rho = 8,800$ kg/m³; thickness = 4 mm.

density

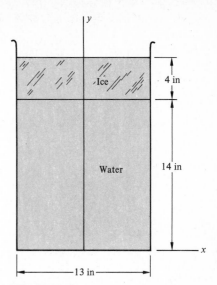

Fig. P18.5

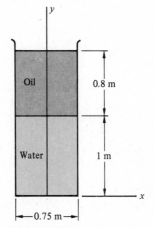

Fig. P18.6

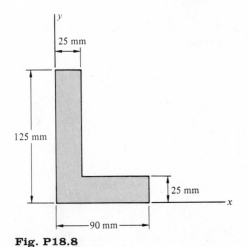

Fig. P18.8

18.9 (Prob. 10.3) Bronze: $\rho = 8,800$ kg/m³; thickness = 4 mm.

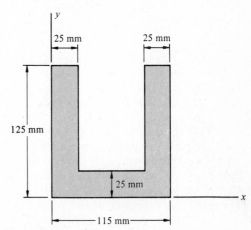

Fig. P18.9

18.10 (Prob. 10.4) Bronze: $\rho = 8{,}800 \text{ kg/m}^3$; thickness $= 4$ mm.

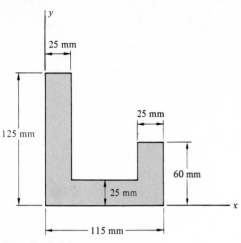

Fig. P18.10

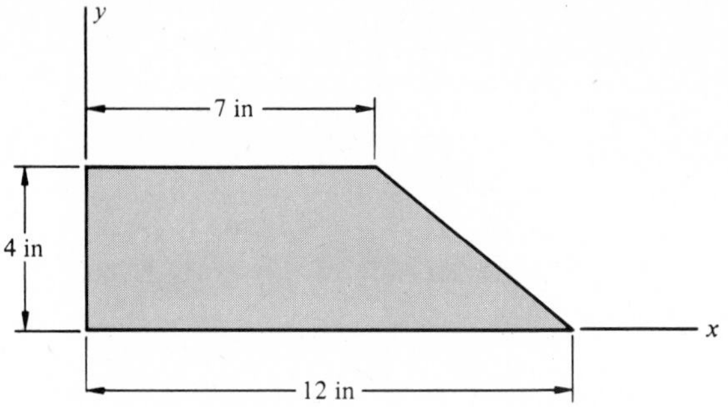

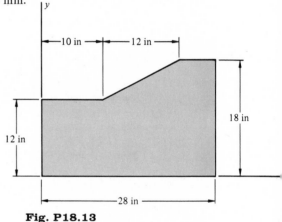

Fig. P18.11

18.11 (Prob. 10.6) Steel: $\gamma = 489 \text{ lb/ft}^3$; $t = 0.375$ in.

18.12 (Prob. 10.7) Aluminum: $\rho = 2{,}770 \text{ kg/m}^3$; $t = 75$ mm.

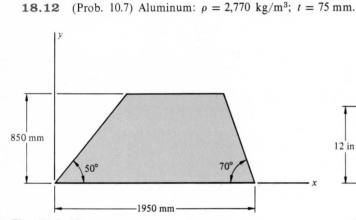

Fig. P18.12

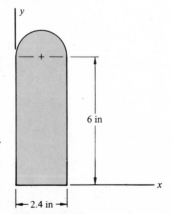

Fig. P18.13

18.13 (Prob. 10.8) Copper: $\gamma = 556 \text{ lb/ft}^3$; $t = 1$ in.

18.14 (Prob. 10.9) Brass: $\gamma = 534 \text{ lb/ft}^3$, $t = 0.25$ in.

18.15 through 18.23 The figure shows a machine part made of thin homogeneous material of constant thickness. The xy plane bisects the thickness dimension.
(a) Find the mass moments of inertia I_x, I_y.
(b) Find the mass of the part and the radii of gyration k_x and k_y.
(c) Using the parallel axis theorem, find the mass moment of inertia I_{ox}. The x_o axis is parallel to the x axis.
(d) Find the radius of gyration k_{ox}.
The material and thickness of each part is indicated. (Certain of the problems were first presented in Chap. 10. The original problem numbers are shown in parentheses.)

Fig. P18.14

18.15 (Prob. 10.11) Rolled monel metal: $\gamma = 555$ lb/ft³; $t = 0.3$ in.

18.16 (Prob. 10.28) Copper: $\rho = 8{,}910$ kg/m³; $t = 10$ mm.

18.17 (Prob. 10.29) Aluminum: $\rho = 2{,}770$ kg/m³; $t = 70$ mm.

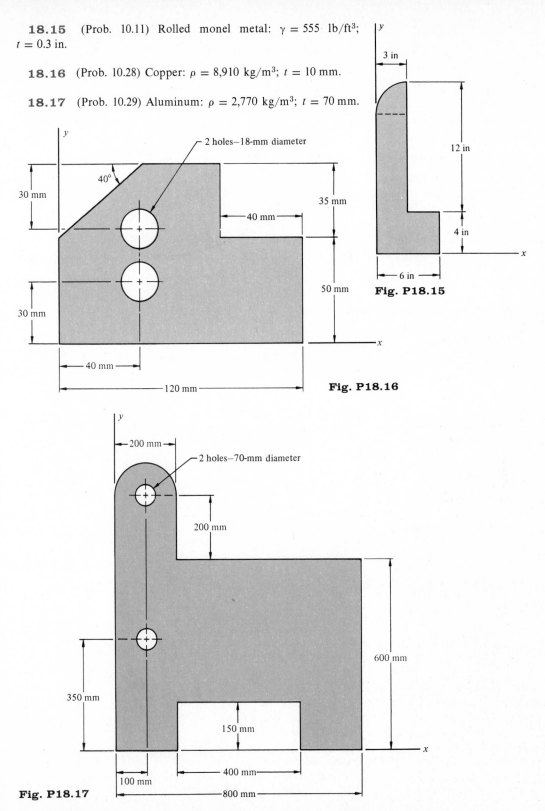

2 holes—18-mm diameter

40°

30 mm

30 mm

40 mm

120 mm

35 mm

40 mm

50 mm

Fig. P18.16

y

3 in

12 in

4 in

6 in

x

Fig. P18.15

2 holes—70-mm diameter

200 mm

200 mm

350 mm

150 mm

600 mm

100 mm

400 mm

800 mm

Fig. P18.17

643

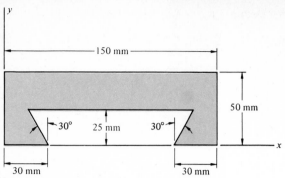

Fig. P18.18

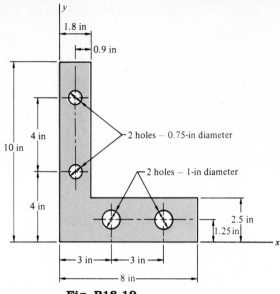

Fig. P18.19

18.18 (Prob. 10.30) Steel: $\rho = 7{,}830 \text{ kg/m}^3$; $t = 4$ mm.

18.19 (Prob. 10.31) Nickel alloy: $\gamma = 0.315 \text{ lb/in}^3$; $t = 0.125$ in.

18.20 (Prob. 10.32) Titanium: $\rho = 4{,}510 \text{ kg/m}^3$; $t = 30$ mm.

18.21 (Prob. 10.33) Gray cast iron: $\gamma = 442 \text{ lb/ft}^3$; $t = 1$ in.

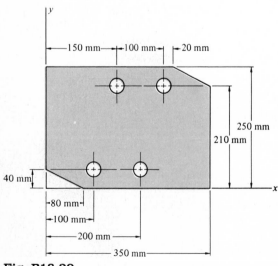

Fig. P18.20

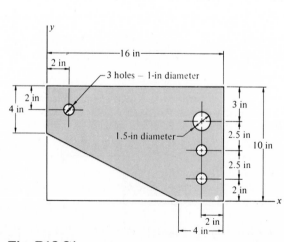

Fig. P18.21

18.22 (Prob. 10.34) Die cast zinc: $\rho = 6{,}570 \text{ kg/m}^3$; $t = 75$ mm.

18.23 (Prob. 10.36) Steel: $\rho = 7{,}830 \text{ kg/m}^3$; $t = 4$ mm.

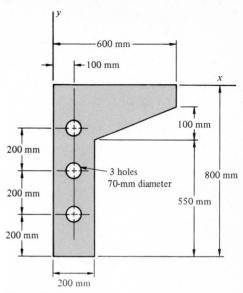

Fig. P18.22

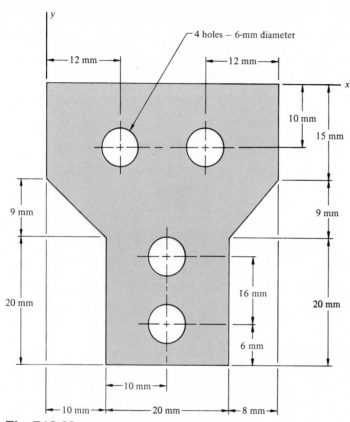

Fig. P18.23

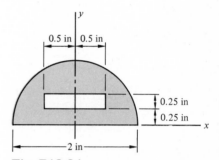

Fig. P18.24

18.24 A plate with a rectangular cutout, shown in Fig. P18.24, is made of brass strip of 0.125-in thickness. Find the mass moment of inertia of the plate about the x axis. The specific weight of brass is 534 lb/ft³.

18.25 Do the same as in Prob. 18.24, if the design of the plate is changed to the elliptical shape with two rectangular cutouts shown in Fig. P18.25.

18.26 Use the parallel axis theorem to verify the results for I_{x_1}, in case 1 of Table 18.5.

18.27 Do the same as in Prob. 18.26, for I_{x_1}, in case 2 of Table 18.5.

18.28 Do the same as in Prob. 18.26, for I_{x_1}, I_{x_2}, and I_{y_1} in case 3 of Table 18.5.

18.29 Do the same as in Prob. 18.26, for I_x, I_{x_1}, and I_{y_1} in case 4 of Table 18.5.

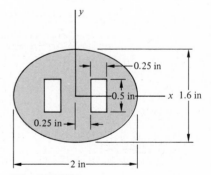

Fig. P18.25

18.30 Do the same as in Prob. 18.26, for I_x, I_{x_1}, I_{x_2}, and I_{y_1} in case 6 of Table 18.5.

18.31 Do the same as in Prob. 18.26, for I_{x_1}, I_{y_1}, and I_{z_1} in case 7 of Table 18.5.

18.32 Figure P18.32 shows a homogeneous right circular cylinder. The differential mass element dm has the form $dm = \rho(\pi d^2/4)t$. Find the mass moment of inertia I_x and compare this result with the value given in case 4 of Table 18.5.

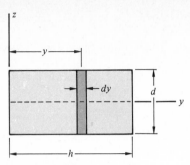

Fig. P18.32

18.33 Figure P18.33 shows a cross-section view of a steel pulley with three different diameters. (*a*) Find the mass moment of inertia of the pulley about its center axis. (*b*) Express the result in the engineering drawing units of lb·in². The specific weight of steel is 489 lb/ft³.

18.34 Find the radius of gyration of the pulley in Fig. P18.33 about its center axis.

18.35 Do the same as in Prob. 18.33, for the steel pulley shown in Fig. P18.35.

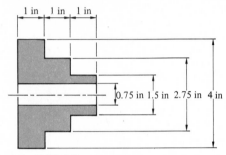

Fig. P18.33

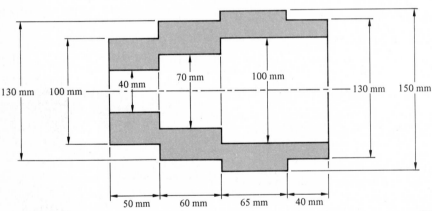

Fig. P18.35

18.36 Find the radius of gyration of the pulley in Fig. P18.35 about its center axis.

18.37 The disk shown in Fig. P18.37 has two holes in it and is made of 0.5-in-thick aluminum plate.

(*a*) Find the mass moment of inertia of the disk about its center axis.

(*b*) Find the radius of gyration of the disk about its center axis. The specific weight of aluminum is 173 lb/ft³.

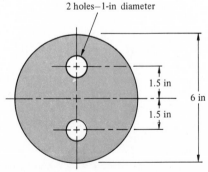

Fig. P18.37

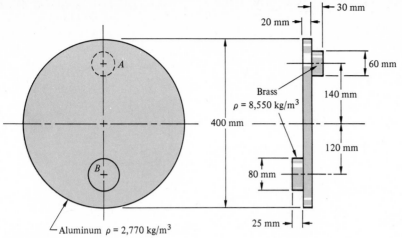

Fig. P18.38

18.38 Two cylindrical weights are attached to a circular disk, as shown in Fig. P18.38.

(a) Find the mass moment of inertia of the assembly about the center axis.

(b) Find the radius of gyration of the assembly about the center axis.

18.39 Find the mass moment of inertia of the steel body, shown in Fig. P18.39, about its center axis. The specific weight of steel is 489 lb/ft³. Neglect the effect of the center hole.

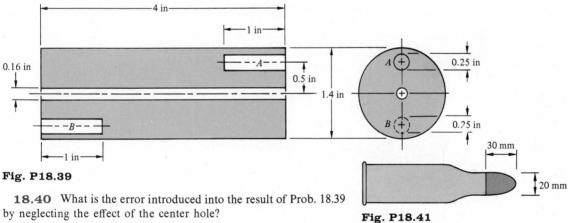

Fig. P18.39

18.40 What is the error introduced into the result of Prob. 18.39 by neglecting the effect of the center hole?

18.41 Figure P18.41 shows a proposed design for the nose shape, in the form of a paraboloid of revolution, of an antiaircraft shell. Find the mass moment of inertia of the nose about its axis of revolution. The nose material is lead, with a density of 11,400 kg/m³.

18.42 A hardened steel dowel pin has hemispherical ends, as shown in Fig. P18.42. Find the mass moments of inertia I_{ox} and I_{oy}. The specific weight of steel is 489 lb/ft³.

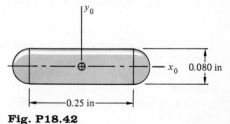

Fig. P18.41

Fig. P18.42

647

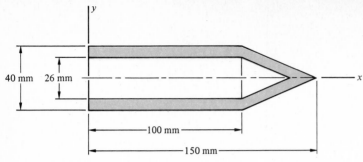

Fig. P18.43

18.43 Figure P18.43 shows a cross-section view of an aluminum housing with a cone-cylinder form. Find the mass moments of inertia I_x, and the radius of gyration k_x. The density of aluminum is 2,770 kg/m³.

18.44 Find the mass moment of inertia I_y, and the radius of gyration k_y, of the housing shown in Fig. P18.43. The density of aluminum is 2,770 kg/m³.

18.45 Figure P18.45 shows a cross-section view of a steel pin. The density of steel is 7,830 kg/m³.
(*a*) Find the mass moments of inertia I_x and I_y.
(*b*) Find the radii of gyration k_x and k_y.

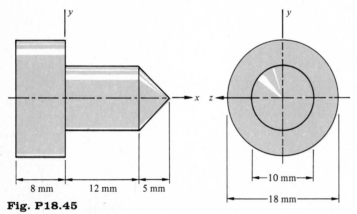

Fig. P18.45

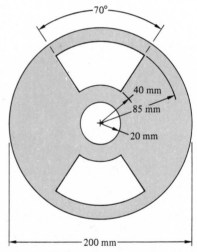

Fig. P18.46

18.46 Find the mass moment of inertia of the disk in Fig. P18.46 about its center axis. The thickness of the disk is 40 mm and the material is bronze, with $\rho = 8,800$ kg/m³.

18.47 In a certain testing machine, a very precise value of mass moment of inertia is required. This is accomplished by drilling pairs of equally spaced holes on a diameter of a disk, as shown in Fig. P18.47. Find the percent reduction in the mass moment of inertia about the center axis for each pair of holes drilled. Use the mass moment of inertia of a disk with a center hole as the reference value. The material is aluminum, and $\rho = 2,770$ kg/m³.

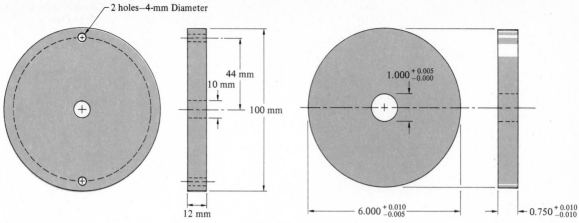

Fig. P18.47

Fig. P18.48

18.48 The tolerances on the dimensions of a disk are shown in Fig. P18.48. The disk is made of steel. The range of values of the specific weight of the steel used is 485 to 495 lb/ft³. Find the maximum and minimum computed values of the mass moment of inertia of the disk about its center axis. Use four significant figures.

18.49 Find the mass moments of inertia I_x, I_y, and I_z of the body shown in Fig. P18.49. The material is steel, with $\rho = 7{,}830$ kg/m³.

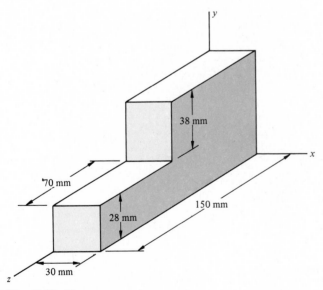

Fig. P18.49

18.50 Find the centroidal coordinates x_c, y_c, and z_c, and the mass moments of inertia I_{ox}, I_{oy}, and I_{oz} of the body shown in Fig. P18.49.

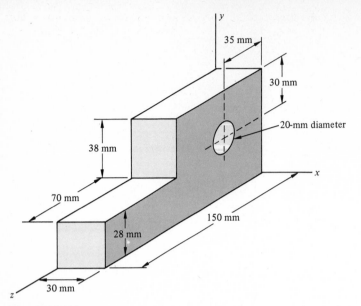

Fig. P18.51

18.51 Do the same as in Prob. 18.49 if a hole is drilled in the part, as shown in Fig. P18.51.

18.52 Find the centroidal coordinates x_c, y_c, and z_c, and the mass moments of inertia I_{ox}, I_{oy}, and I_{oz}, of the body shown in Fig. P18.51.

18.53 Find the mass moments of inertia I_x, I_y, and I_z of the body shown in Fig. P18.53. The body is made of die cast zinc, with $\gamma = 410$ lb/ft³.

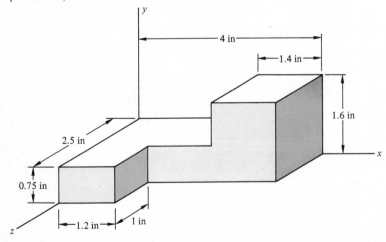

Fig. P18.53

18.54 Find the centroidal coordinates x_c, y_c, and z_c, and the mass moments of inertia I_{ox}, I_{oy}, and I_{oz} of the body shown in Fig. P18.53.

18.55 Do the same as in Prob. 18.53, if two holes are drilled in the body, as shown in Fig. P18.55.

Centroids, and Mass Moments | **651** **of Inertia, of Rigid Bodies**

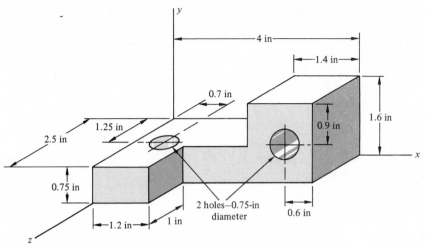

Fig. P18.55

18.56 Find the centroidal coordinates x_c, y_c, and z_c, and the mass moments of inertia I_{ox}, I_{oy}, and I_{oz}, of the body shown in Fig. P18.55.

18.57 A copper spacer plate has the dimensions shown in Fig. P18.57. A square hole is cut through the plate thickness. Find the mass moments of inertia I_x, I_y, and I_z. The density of the material is 8,910 kg/m³.

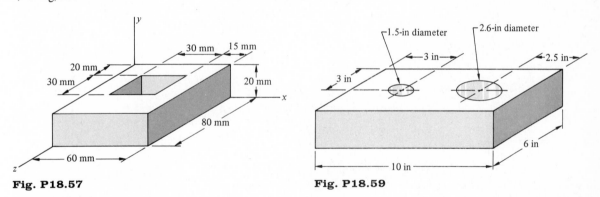

Fig. P18.57

Fig. P18.59

18.58 Find the centroidal coordinates x_c, y_c, and z_c, and the mass moments of inertia I_{ox}, I_{oy}, and I_{oz}, of the body shown in Fig. P18.57.

18.59 A brass plate has two holes drilled through it, as shown in Fig. P18.59. Find the mass moment of inertia of the plate about an axis which is normal to the plane of the plate, and which passes through the centroid of the plate. The specific weight of brass is 534 lb/ft³. The plate thickness is 1.75 in.

18.60 Find the mass moment of inertia of the plate in Fig. P18.59 about the center axis of the smaller hole.

18.61 A machine part is fabricated by welding two cylindrical steel stubs onto a plate, as shown in Fig. P18.61. Find the mass moments of inertia I_x, I_{x_1}, and I_y. The mass of the weld material may be neglected. The density of steel is 7,830 kg/m³.

18.62 (a) Find the mass moment of inertia of the part in Prob. 18.61 about the centroidal x_o axis. The x_o axis is parallel to the x and x_1 axes.
 (b) Find the radius of gyration k_{ox}.

18.63 Do the same as in Prob. 18.61, for the welded machine part shown in Fig. P18.63.

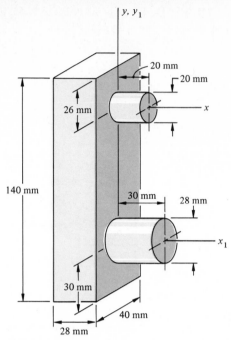

Fig. P18.61

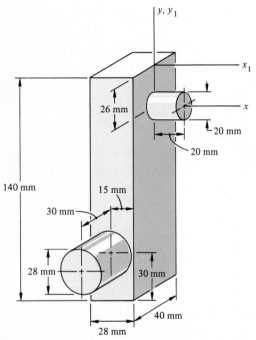

Fig. P18.63

18.64 Figure P18.64 shows the cross section of a proposed lightweight flywheel design. The density of steel is 7,830 kg/m³, and the density of aluminum is 2,770 kg/m³.
 (a) Find the weight of the flywheel and the mass moment of inertia about the center axis.
 (b) Do the same as in part a, if the flywheel is made entirely of steel. Compare the results with those in part a.

18.65 Figure P18.65 shows a latching lever formed from a steel strip, with attached cylindrical brass plugs. Find the mass moment of inertia I_z of the lever assembly. The effect of the hole may be neglected. The specific weight of brass is 534 lb/ft³, and the specific weight of steel is 489 lb/ft³.

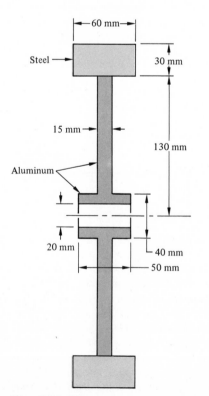

Fig. P18.64

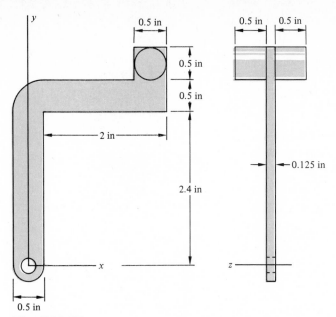

Fig. P18.65

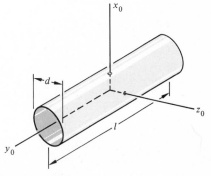

Fig. P18.69

18.66 (a) Using the techniques in Examples 18.1 and 18.11, verify the results for the centroidal location, and the mass moment of inertia I_x, for the right circular cylinder in case 4 of Table 18.5.

(b) Using the results from part a and the transfer theorem, verify the results for I_{ox}.

18.67 Do the same as in Prob. 18.66, for the paraboloid in case 8 of Table 18.5.

18.68 Find the error introduced in Example 18.5 by neglecting the mass moment of inertia of the rod. The masses and rod are a one piece assembly of magnesium, with $\gamma = 108$ lb/ft³, $d = 0.5$ in, and $D = 4$ in.

18.69 Figure P18.69 shows a thin, right, circular cylinder. For what values of the length to diameter ratio l/d will the expression $I_{ox} = I_{oz} = \frac{1}{12}ml^2$ be no more than 5 percent in error?

18.70 Two cube-shaped masses are attached to the end of a massless rod, as shown in Fig. P18.70. It is desired to find the mass moment of inertia of the assembly about the x axis. As a first approximation, the masses may be assumed to be point masses at the ends of the rod of length l.

(a) For what range of values a/l will the error in the above assumption not exceed 5 percent?

(b) Do the same as in part a, for a maximum permissible error of 10 percent.

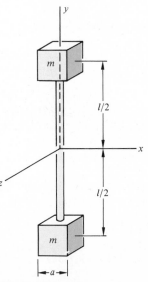

Fig. P18.70

18.71 If the disk in Fig. P18.71 is considered to be thin, the mass moment of inertia about the z_o axis has the approximate form $I_{oz} = \frac{1}{16}md^2$, where m is the mass of the disk.

(a) For what range of values of the ratio a/d will the use of the approximate solution result in an error of no more than 5 percent in the value of the mass moment of inertia about the z_o axis?

(b) Do the same as in part a, for an error of 10 percent.

18.72 A stirring blade is formed of 0.75-in-diameter steel wire into the shape shown in Fig. P18.72. The specific weight of steel is 489 lb/ft³.

(a) Find the mass moment of inertia about the y axis.

(b) Find the mass moment of inertia about the y_1 axis.

(c) Find the mass moment of inertia about the vertical centroidal axis of the wire form.

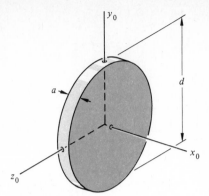

Fig. P18.71

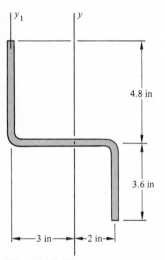

Fig. P18.72

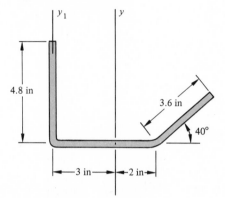

Fig. P18.73

18.73 Do the same as in Prob. 18.72, for the shape shown in Fig. P18.73.

18.74 Do the same as in Prob. 18.72, for the shape shown in Fig. P18.74.

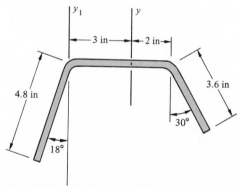

Fig. P18.74

18.75 The circular hoop in Fig. P18.75 is formed of thin, brass rod of 6.5 mm diameter. The mean diameter of the rod is 100 mm, and the density of the brass is 8,550 kg/m³.

(a) Find the mass moment of inertia of the hoop about the z_o axis.

(b) Find the diameter of a homogeneous, solid brass disk of 6.5 mm thickness which would have the same mass moment of inertia about the z_o axis.

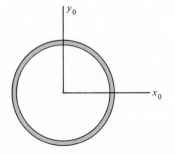

Fig. P18.75

19

Dynamics of Rigid Bodies in Plane Motion

19.1 INTRODUCTION

In Chap. 15 the concept of a particle was introduced. A particle is a mathematical idealization of an element of *mass* which has vanishingly small dimensions. As a consequence, a particle can be envisioned to be a *point* which travels on a path in space. Newton's second law was shown in Chap. 16 to relate the force acting on the particle to the resulting motion of this element.

In Chap. 17 the kinematics of a rigid body in plane motion was considered. A rigid body may be imagined to be a system of individual mass elements. If the subdivision of the body into smaller and smaller mass elements is continued without limit, the size of each of these elements approaches that of a particle. All the relations previously developed for the dynamic motion of a particle may then be used to characterize the dynamic motion of a rigid body.

In this chapter, the technically significant problem of a rigid body in plane motion will be considered. It is probably safe to say that a major portion of the problems in engineering dynamics fall into this category. When a body moves in plane motion, all points in the body maintain the same respective distance, from some fixed reference plane, throughout the entire motion. Not all the forces acting on the body must lie in the plane of motion of the body. If any of these forces has a component normal to the plane of motion, then this component must be balanced out by a reaction force component, of the ground on the body, which is normal to the plane of motion.

Only the components of force which lie in the plane contribute to the motion in this plane.

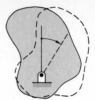

Fig. 19.1

There are three general classifications of problems in plane motion of a rigid body. In the first type, one point on the body is a fixed point which is attached to the ground. Figure 19.1 shows such a body. For this case, the motion of the body is fully described by defining the angular, or rotational, motion of the body about the fixed point. The case of rotation about a fixed point includes the very important case of one body rolling on another body. The point of contact between the two bodies may be considered to be a fixed point, or instant center, about which, at any given instant, one body rotates with respect to the other body.

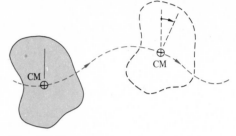

Fig. 19.2

In the second general type of plane motion, the total planar motion of the body is described by the translational motion of the center of mass (CM) and the rotation of the body about this point. This effect is illustrated in Fig. 19.2, which shows the position of the body at two different times. The CM in this case may travel along either a straight or a curvilinear path.

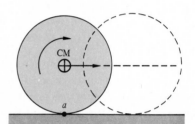

Fig. 19.3

The third general type of plane motion of a rigid body is similar to the case described above. The motion of the body is described by the translational motion of an arbitrary point on the body and the rotation about this point. The essential difference between the above two cases is that, for the last case, the reference point on the body is not the CM of the body. This last problem is of a more advanced nature than the first two types, and it is not considered further in this text.

Certain problems may be described as either rotation about a fixed point or motion of the CM. The homogeneous cylinder shown in Fig. 19.3 which rolls, without slipping, on a plane is such a problem. As the cylinder rolls along the plane, the CM translates along a straight line. The cylinder simultaneously rotates about the CM. The contact point a between the cylinder and the plane is an instant center. The motion of the cylinder along the plane may thus be thought of as a succession of instantaneous rotations about the point of contact. Both of the above approaches will be used in the subsequent examples.

As in the analysis of problems in static equilibrium, an operation of fundamental importance is to draw a complete free-body diagram of the rigid body. On this diagram are shown both the applied forces or moments acting on the body and the reaction forces or moments exerted on the body by the ground, which is imagined to be removed. In problems of static analysis, a necessary condition for equilibrium is that the resultants of all the forces and moments which act on a body must be identically zero. In dynamics, the reverse of this situation must always be true. That is, a resultant force or moment on the body is *required* to impart to this element a translational or rotational acceleration.

656

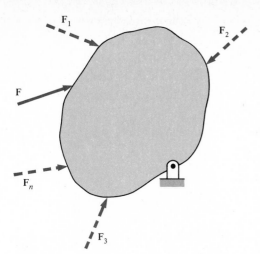

Fig. 19.4

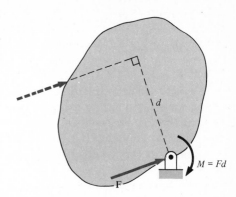

Fig. 19.5

19.2 DYNAMIC MOTION OF A RIGID BODY ABOUT A FIXED POINT

Figure 19.4 shows a body acted on by a system of external forces $\mathbf{F}_1, \mathbf{F}_2, \ldots, \mathbf{F}_n$. The magnitude, direction, sense, and location of the resultant of this system of forces may be found by using the techniques of static analysis. This resultant force is designated $\mathbf{F}$.

It is shown in statics that any force which acts on a body can be replaced by an equal, parallel force at another location, and a couple. The operation is now performed on the body shown in Fig. 19.4, and the result is seen in Fig. 19.5. The term $M = Fd$ is the resultant external couple, or moment, which acts on the body.

It should be noted that Fig. 19.5 does *not* show a free-body diagram of the body. Rather, it portrays the operation of replacing a force by a force and a couple at a parallel location. If a free-body diagram were drawn, the force $\mathbf{F}$ would be simply a force which acts on the body at the location of the hinge pin.

As the body rotates about the fixed point, all the points on the body translate along circular paths which are concentric about the fixed point. A typical mass element m_i of the body, located at distance r_i from the fixed point, is shown in Fig. 19.6. This element experiences motion as a particle in circular plane translation, with the normal and tangential acceleration components a_n and a_t. The forces F_{in} and F_{it} are the rectangular components of the total force $\mathbf{F}_i$ which acts on the particular mass element m_i. This force may be either a reaction force exerted by adjacent mass elements on the element being considered, or an external force which acts directly on the element.

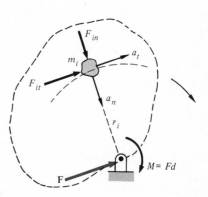

Fig. 19.6

Newton's second law, for the mass element as a particle in curvilinear translation, is

$$F_{in} = m_i a_n \qquad F_{it} = m_i a_t \qquad (19.1)$$

The particle m_i moves along a circular path, so that

$$a_n = r_i \omega^2 \qquad a_t = r_i \alpha \qquad (19.2)$$

where r_i is the constant radial distance between the mass particle and the fixed point, and ω and α are the angular velocity and acceleration, respectively, of the body about the fixed point. It may be noted that the latter two terms are not subscripted i, since they are the same for *all* mass elements of the body.

The two components of force which act on m_i now have the forms

$$F_{in} = m_i r_i \omega^2 \qquad F_{it} = m_i r_i \alpha \qquad (19.3)$$

The relationship between the force components F_{in} and F_{it} on the mass element m_i, and the moment about the fixed point which is required to produce these forces, will now be developed. Since the line of action of F_{in} passes through the fixed point, this force contributes no moment. The moment about the fixed point, which is required to produce the force F_{it}, is

$$M_i = F_{it} r_i \qquad (19.4)$$

F_{it} is eliminated from between Eqs. (19.3) and (19.4), with the result

$$M_i = m_i r_i^2 \alpha \qquad (19.5)$$

The magnitude of the total moment M which is required to accelerate all the mass elements of the body is then

$$M = \sum_i M_i = \sum_i m_i r_i^2 \alpha \qquad (19.6)$$

where the summation is over all the mass elements of the body. Since the angular acceleration α has the same value for all the mass elements in the body, it may be moved outside the summation sign. The result is

$$M = \alpha \sum_i m_i r_i^2 \qquad (19.7)$$

The subdivision of the mass elements is now allowed to continue without limit, so that

$$m_i \to dm \qquad r_i \to r \qquad (19.8)$$

Equation (19.7) now appears as

$$M = \alpha \int_V r^2\, dm \qquad (19.9)$$

where the integration is over the volume V. The integral in Eq. (19.9) may be recognized as the *mass moment of inertia* of the rigid body about an axis which is normal to the plane of motion and which passes through the fixed point. With the designation

$$I = \int_V r^2\, dm \qquad (19.10)$$

the final form of Eq. (19.9) is

$$M = I\alpha \qquad (19.11)$$

This equation is a statement of Newton's second law for the rotational motion of a rigid body about a point which is fixed to the ground. *This equation is of fundamental importance in engineering dynamics.* M is the resultant external couple, moment, or torque, with respect to the fixed point, which acts on the rigid body. I is the mass moment of inertia of the body about the fixed point, and α is the angular acceleration of the body. In many problems, the mass moment of inertia I_0 of the rigid body about the centroidal axis is known. The mass moment of inertia I about the fixed point may be found readily by using the transfer theorem, with the form

$$I = I_0 + m\, d^2 \qquad (19.12)$$

where m is the mass of the body and d is the separation distance, measured in the plane of the motion, between the CM and the fixed point.

If M has a *constant magnitude,* it follows that the angular acceleration α must be constant. For this case, all the equations presented in Chap. 17 for the case of rotational motion with constant acceleration are directly applicable. The forms of these equations are

$$\omega = \omega_0 + \alpha t \qquad (19.13)$$

$$\theta = \theta_0 + \omega_0 t + \tfrac{1}{2}\alpha t^2 \qquad (19.14)$$

$$\omega^2 = \omega_0^2 + 2\alpha(\theta - \theta_0) \qquad (19.15)$$

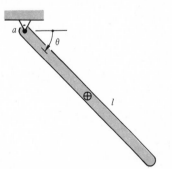

where θ_0 and ω_0 are the initial angular displacement and velocity, respectively, at $t = 0$.

The techniques used to find the force exerted by the hinge pin on the body are presented in the following section.

Example 19.1 Figure 19.7 shows a slender rod of mass m and length l. The rod is released with zero initial velocity from the position $\theta = 0°$.

a Find the maximum value of the angular acceleration of the rod and the corresponding tangential acceleration a_t of the tip of the rod.

Fig. 19.7

b Find the numerical results for part a, if $l = 1200$ mm and $m = 2.4$ kg.

Solution   a The free-body diagram of the rod, for an arbitrary value of θ, is shown in Fig. 19.8. The weight force mg produces a moment about point a. The rotational form of Newton's second law for the rod is

$$M_a = I_a \alpha \qquad mg\left(\frac{l}{2}\cos\theta\right) = I_a\alpha \qquad (19.16)$$

The mass moment of inertia of a slender rod about its end, case 1 in Table 18.7, is

$$I_a = \frac{1}{3}ml^2 \qquad (19.17)$$

and

$$mg\left(\frac{l}{2}\cos\theta\right) = \frac{1}{3}ml^2\alpha \qquad \alpha = \frac{3g}{2l}\cos\theta \qquad (19.18)$$

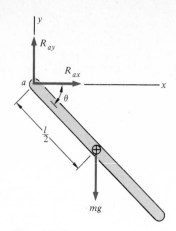

Fig. 19.8

The angular acceleration in this problem is a function of the angle θ. It has its maximum value when $\theta = 0$, so that

$$\alpha_{\max} = \frac{3g}{2l}\cos 0° = \frac{3g}{2l} \qquad (19.19)$$

The corresponding value of a_t is

$$a_{t,\max} = l\alpha_{\max} = l\left(\frac{3g}{2l}\right) = \frac{3}{2}g \qquad (19.20)$$

It may be observed from Eq. (19.18) that the acceleration is zero when $\theta = 90°$. This corresponds to the rod being in a vertical position.
b For $l = 1200$ mm,

$$\alpha_{\max} = \frac{3(9.81)}{2(1200)/1000} = 12.3 \text{ rad/s}^2 \qquad a_t = \frac{3}{2}(9.81) = 14.7 \text{ m/s}^2$$
$$(19.21)$$

It may be observed that α is not a constant in this problem. Thus, the equations of motion given by Eqs. (19.13) through (19.15) may not be used.

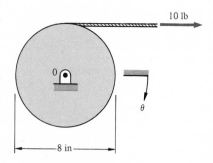

Fig. 19.9

Example 19.2   A 20-lb disk is hinged at its center, as shown in Fig. 19.9. A thin, inextensible string is wrapped around the outside of the disk. The disk is initially at rest. At time $t = 0$, a constant force of 10 lb is applied to the string.
a Find the angular acceleration when the force is applied to the string.
b Find the time and the angular velocity of the disk, in revolutions per minute, when 42 in of string has been unwound from the disk.
c If the force is removed from the string at the time that the conditions of part b are reached, what constant tangential force on the rim of the disk would be required to bring this element to rest in 1 s?

Solution
a The mass moment of inertia of the disk is

$$I_0 = \frac{1}{8}m\,d^2 = \frac{1}{8}\left(\frac{20}{386}\right)(8^2) = 0.415 \text{ lb·s}^2\text{·in} \qquad (19.22)$$

Using Newton's second law, we have

$$M_0 = I_0\alpha \qquad 10(4) = 0.415\alpha \qquad \alpha = 96.4 \text{ rad/s}^2 = \text{constant} \quad (19.23)$$

b The angular displacement which corresponds to unwinding 42 in of string from the disk is found from

$$s = r\theta \qquad 42 = 4(\theta) \qquad \theta = 10.5 \text{ rad} \qquad (19.24)$$

The corresponding velocity ω and time t are given by

$$\omega^2 = \omega_0^2 + 2\alpha\theta \qquad \omega^2 = 0 + 2(96.4)(10.5) \qquad (19.25)$$

$$\omega = 45 \text{ rad/s} = 45\left(\frac{60}{2\pi}\right) = 430 \text{ r/min} \qquad (19.26)$$

$$\omega = \omega_0 + \alpha t \qquad 45 = 0 + 96.4t \qquad t = 0.467 \text{ s} \quad (19.27)$$

c At the instant that the force is removed from the string, the disk has an angular velocity of 45 rad/s. The acceleration α_1 required to bring the disk to come to rest in 1 s, under the influence of a constant retarding torque, is found from

$$\omega = \omega_0 + \alpha_1 t \qquad 0 = 45 + \alpha_1(1) \qquad \alpha_1 = -45 \text{ rad/s}^2 \quad (19.28)$$

The corresponding value of the torque is

$$M_0 = I_0\alpha = 0.415(-45) = -18.7 \text{ in·lb} \qquad (19.29)$$

The minus sign in Eq. (19.29) indicates that the sense of this torque is opposite to the sense of rotation at the beginning of the time interval under consideration.

The required value of the tangential rim force is

$$F = \frac{M_0}{r} = \frac{18.7}{4} = 4.68 \text{ lb} \qquad (19.30)$$

19.3 DYNAMIC MOTION DESCRIBED BY TRANSLATION OF THE CENTER OF MASS, AND ROTATION ABOUT THIS POINT

The general plane body shown in Fig. 19.4 is redrawn in Fig. 19.10. The body is no longer attached to the ground, but may have any general type of plane motion. The equations which govern the motion of the body will now be developed.

Figure 19.11 shows the body positioned with respect to a set of coordinates which are attached to the ground. The CM is located with respect to the ground by the position vector $\mathbf{s}_c$. The mass element m_i is located relative to the CM by the displacement vector $\mathbf{r}_i$. The *absolute displacement* of m_i is given by the vector $\mathbf{s}_i$ measured from the ground. From the figure,

$$\mathbf{s}_i = \mathbf{s}_c + \mathbf{r}_i \qquad (19.31)$$

This equation is understood to be a vector summation. Each of the mass elements m_i may be envisioned to move in general curvilinear translation. Newton's second law for each such element is then

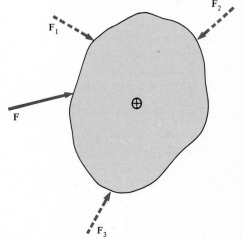

Fig. 19.10

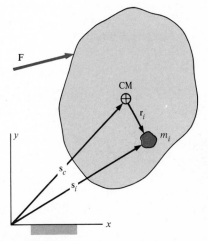

Fig. 19.11

$$F_i = m_i \ddot{s}_i \qquad (19.32)$$

where $\ddot{s}_i$, the second time derivative of s_i, is the absolute acceleration of the mass element. As before, F_i may represent the force of adjacent mass elements on the element under consideration, or it may represent an external force which acts directly on the element. The resultant force which acts on the body is F and, from the definition of a resultant force,

$$F = \sum_i F_i \qquad (19.33)$$

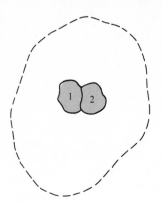

The summation on the right side of Eq. (19.33) is of *all* the forces acting on *all* the mass elements. In the process of performing this summation, all the internal forces in the body, of one mass element on another mass element, are identically self-canceling in pairs. This effect is illustrated in Fig. 19.12, which shows two typical, adjacent mass elements. The force exerted by element 1 on element 2 is designated F_{12}, and F_{21} is a similar designation for the force of element 2 on element 1. The free-body diagrams of these two particles are shown in Fig. 19.13. The mass elements 1 and 2 physically contact each other. Thus, the forces F_{12} and F_{21}, following Newton's third law, must be a pair of action-reaction forces, and

Fig. 19.12

$$F_{12} = -F_{21} \qquad (19.34)$$

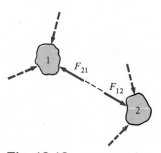

The elements 1 and 2 in Fig. 19.13 may have other internal forces acting on them, in addition to external forces, if these elements form a portion of the boundary of the rigid body. All the other internal forces are self-canceling in pairs when taken together with the corresponding mating element, and it is only the external forces on the body which contribute to the resultant force.

Fig. 19.13

Equations (19.32) and (19.33) are now combined, with the following result:

$$F = \sum F_i = \sum m_i \ddot{s}_i \qquad (19.35)$$

From Eq. (19.31), we get

$$s_i = s_c + r_i \qquad (19.36)$$

This equation is differentiated twice with respect to time, with the result

$$\ddot{s}_i = \ddot{s}_c + \ddot{r}_i \qquad (19.37)$$

The term $\ddot{s}_c$ is the absolute acceleration of the CM of the body, and the term $\ddot{r}_i$ is the acceleration of the typical mass particle m_i with respect to the CM of the body.

Equation (19.37) is now substituted into Eq. (19.35):

$$F = \sum m_i (\ddot{s}_c + \ddot{r}_i) = \sum m_i \ddot{s}_c + \sum m_i \ddot{r}_i \qquad (19.38)$$

The term $\ddot{\mathbf{s}}_c$ is the absolute acceleration of the CM of the body, and this quantity will be written as

$$\ddot{\mathbf{s}}_c = \mathbf{a}_c \qquad (19.39)$$

The first term on the right side of Eq. (19.38) is then written as

$$\sum m_i \ddot{\mathbf{s}}_c = \sum m_i \mathbf{a}_c \qquad (19.40)$$

Since $\mathbf{a}_c$ is the same for all mass elements of the body, it may be moved outside of the summation sign, so that

$$\sum_i m_i \mathbf{a}_c = \mathbf{a}_c \sum_i m_i = m \mathbf{a}_c \qquad (19.41)$$

where m is the mass of the body.

The last term on the right side of Eq. (19.38) may be written as

$$\sum_i m_i \ddot{\mathbf{r}}_i = \sum_i m_i \frac{d^2}{dt^2}(\mathbf{r}_i) \qquad (19.42)$$

Since the operations of time differentiation and summation over the mass elements of the body are independent of each other, the order of these operations may be interchanged, with the result

$$\sum_i m_i \ddot{\mathbf{r}}_i = \frac{d^2}{dt^2} \sum_i m_i \mathbf{r}_i \qquad (19.43)$$

It will now be shown that the quantity $\sum_i m_i \mathbf{r}_i$ has the form of a first moment of the mass of the body. Figure 19.14 shows a set of xy axes attached to the body. The center of mass of the body is located by $\mathbf{r}_c$. The position vector $\mathbf{r}_i$ is the displacement of the typical mass particle m_i. This vector has the components r_{ix} and r_{iy}. The components of $\mathbf{r}_c$ are the centroidal coordinates x_c and y_c, defined by

$$x_c = \frac{\displaystyle\sum_i r_{ix} m_i}{m} \qquad (19.44)$$

$$y_c = \frac{\displaystyle\sum_i r_{iy} m_i}{m} \qquad (19.45)$$

In the present problem the quantity $\mathbf{r}_i$ is measured from the CM, as shown in Fig. 19.11. Thus,

$$\mathbf{r}_c = 0 \qquad (19.46)$$

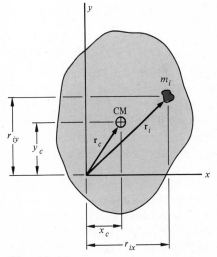

Fig. 19.14

and, as a result,

$$x_c = y_c = 0 \qquad (19.47)$$

It follows from Eqs. (19.44) and (19.45) that

$$\sum_i r_{ix}m_i = 0 \qquad \sum_i r_{iy}m_i = 0 \qquad (19.48)$$

Since r_{ix} and r_{iy} are components of the vector $\mathbf{r}_i$, it may be concluded that

$$\sum_i m_i \mathbf{r}_i = 0 \qquad (19.49)$$

Using this result in Eq. (19.43), Eq. (19.38) then has the final form

$$\mathbf{F} = m\mathbf{a}_c \qquad (19.50)$$

This equation is a very important fundamental relationship in engineering dynamics. $\mathbf{F}$ is the resultant force which acts on the rigid body, and this quantity may be found by using the techniques of static analysis. The absolute *translational* acceleration of the CM is $\mathbf{a}_c$. If all the mass of the rigid body were imagined to be concentrated at the CM, then this mass would move as a particle in translation which is acted on by the force $\mathbf{F}$. All the previously developed equations for rectilinear or curvilinear translation of a particle may then be applied directly. It is emphasized that Eq. (19.50) is true for any direction of the force $\mathbf{F}$, and for any point of application of this force on the rigid body. It should also be noted that this equation yields no information whatsoever about the rotational motion of the body. This observation is another fundamentally important concept which is illustrated in Fig. 19.15. Here, a plane rigid body has the *same* resultant force applied at three different locations on the body. In all three cases, the translational equation of motion would be written as

$$\mathbf{F} = m\mathbf{a}_c \qquad \mathbf{a}_c = \frac{\mathbf{F}}{m} \qquad (19.51)$$

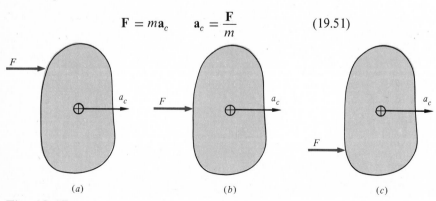

(a)   (b)   (c)

Fig. 19.15

and the CM of the body would experience *the same magnitude, direction, and sense of acceleration* $\mathbf{a}_c$ at the instant shown. It may also be observed that *the line of action of the resultant force which acts on the body is generally not collinear with the line of action of the acceleration*. This effect can be seen in Fig. 19.15. In all three cases, the line of action of the acceleration of the CM is the single horizontal line which passes through this point. The lines of action of the resultant forces, by comparison, are collinear with these forces and have the three different positions shown in Fig. 19.15.

The reader may intuitively sense that the three cases shown in Fig. 19.15 are basically different problems, and indeed they are. In view *a*, the body would experience clockwise, angular acceleration. In view *b*, the body would experience no angular acceleration. In view *c*, the body would experience counterclockwise acceleration. The central observation in the above discussion is that *the translational motion of the center of mass CM is independent of the rotational motion of the body* and is a function of only the magnitude, sense, and direction of the resultant force which acts on the body. This independence of the translation of the CM, and the rotation about this point, is the basis of the description of general plane motion as the sum of the translational motions of the center of mass and the rotational motion about this point.

The force components F_{in} and F_{it} which act on the mass elements of the rigid body were shown in Fig. 19.6 and defined by Eqs. (19.1) in terms of the acceleration components a_n and a_t. These two terms are given by Eqs. (19.2) and they are both functions of r_i, the distance from the reference point on the body to the mass element under consideration. It follows that both acceleration components are quantities which are *relative* to the reference point, since these terms vanish when $r_i \to 0$. Thus it may be concluded that the relationship between the resultant moment acting on the rigid body and the angular acceleration of the body holds true regardless of whether the reference point is stationary or moving. This reference point is now chosen to be the CM of the body, and the equation which describes the rotational motion about the CM, following Eq. (19.11), has the form

$$M_0 = I_0 \alpha \qquad (19.52)$$

In this equation, I_0 is the mass moment of inertia of the rigid body about the CM, M_0 is the resultant external couple, moment or torque about the CM, and α is the angular acceleration of the body.

The complete description of the general plane motion of a rigid body is given by the two equations

$$F = ma_c \qquad (19.53)$$

$$M_0 = I_0\alpha \qquad (19.54)$$

The first equation describes the translational motion of the CM, while the second describes the rotational motion about the CM. It may be observed that Eq. (19.53) is a vector equation, and it can have at most two rectangular components in the plane of the motion. Equation (19.54) is written in scalar form, since the direction of the external moment M_0 on the body is always that of the plane of the motion.

Example 19.3 Figure 19.16 shows a Yo-Yo modeled as a homogeneous disk of mass m connected to an inextensible string.

a Find the translation and rotational accelerations of the Yo-Yo, by writing the equations of motion of translation of the CM, and rotation about the CM.

b Find the translational and rotational accelerations by using point a as a fixed point about which the Yo-Yo instantaneously rotates.

c If the Yo-Yo is released from rest, find the translational and angular velocities after the center has moved through a distance of 30 in. The radius of the Yo-Yo is 1.3 in.

d If the string is cut at any arbitrary time, discuss the subsequent motion of the Yo-Yo.

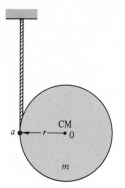

Fig. 19.16

Solution

a The free-body diagram is shown in Fig. 19.17. The vertical displacement of the CM is y, and θ is the angular motion about this point. The string tensile force is designated P. The resultant force on the body, acting vertically downward, is $mg - P$. The equation of motion of the CM is

$$F = ma_c \qquad mg - P = ma_y \qquad (19.55)$$

The resultant moment about the CM is Pr. The rotational equation of motion is

$$M_0 = I_0\alpha \qquad Pr = I_0\alpha \qquad (19.56)$$

The string is assumed to be inextensible. If a length of string $r\theta$ is imagined to be unwound, the CM will lower by the amount

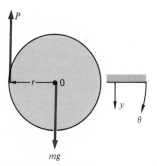

Fig. 19.17

$$y = r\theta \qquad (19.57)$$

Since $r = $ constant,

$$a_y = r\alpha \qquad (19.58)$$

α is eliminated from Eqs. (19.56) and (19.58), and P is eliminated from the resulting two equations, to obtain

$$a_y = \frac{g}{1 + I_0/(mr^2)} \qquad (19.59)$$

a_y is eliminated between Eqs. (19.55) and (19.59), to obtain

$$P = \frac{mg}{1 + mr^2/I_0} \qquad (19.60)$$

Equations (19.58) and (19.59) are combined, with the result

$$\alpha = \frac{g}{r[1 + I_0/(mr^2)]} \qquad (19.61)$$

For the circular disk shown in Fig. 19.16,

$$I_0 = \tfrac{1}{8}m\,d^2 = \tfrac{1}{2}mr^2 \qquad (19.62)$$

The final results are then

$$a_y = \frac{2}{3}g \qquad \alpha = \frac{2g}{3r} \qquad P = \frac{1}{3}mg \qquad (19.63)$$

It may be seen that a_y, α and P are all constants.

b Since the string is inextensible, the distance from point a to the attachment point of the string to the ground is a constant at any given instant of time. Point a thus behaves as an instantaneous fixed point, and it is an instant center of rotation of the disk with respect to the string. This configuration is shown in Fig. 19.18.

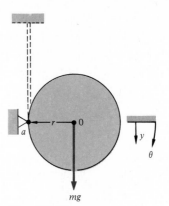

Fig. 19.18

The equation of rotational motion of the body about the fixed point a is given by

$$M = I\alpha \qquad (19.64)$$

From the figure,

$$M = mgr \qquad I = I_a = I_0 + mr^2 \qquad (19.65)$$

so that

$$mgr = (I_0 + mr^2)\alpha \qquad (19.66)$$

$$\alpha = \frac{g}{r[1 + I_0/(mr^2)]} \qquad (19.67)$$

The result above is the same as Eq. (19.61).

The relationship

$$a_y = r\alpha \qquad (19.68)$$

is still true, and a_y would have the form given by Eq. (19.59). It is interesting to note that the string force P is not obtained in the method of solution used in this part of the problem.

c From Eqs. (19.63),

$$a_y = \tfrac{2}{3}g = \tfrac{2}{3}(32.2) = 21.5 \text{ ft/s}^2 \qquad (19.69)$$

The translational velocity when the CM has moved through 30 in is found from

$$v^2 = v_0^2 + 2a_y s \qquad v^2 = 2(21.5)\tfrac{30}{12} \qquad v = 10.4 \text{ ft/s} \quad (19.70)$$

The corresponding angular velocity is given by

$$v = r\omega \qquad \omega = \frac{v}{r} = \frac{10.4}{1.3/12} = 96\frac{\text{rad}}{\text{s}} \qquad (19.71)$$

$$\omega = 96\left(\frac{60}{2\pi}\right) = 917\frac{\text{r}}{\text{min}} \qquad (19.72)$$

d If the string is cut, the string force P becomes zero and thus vanishes from the problem. Under these conditions, the method of solution in part *b* is no longer valid, since point *a* is no longer a fixed point. From consideration of the free-body diagram in Fig. 19.17, the resultant force which acts on the disk is mg, the static weight of the disk. The resultant moment about the CM is zero. The equations of motion of the disk are then

$$F = ma_c \qquad mg = ma_y \qquad a_y = g \qquad (19.73)$$

$$M_0 = I_0\alpha \qquad 0 = I_0\alpha \qquad \alpha = 0 \qquad (19.74)$$

Since the angular acceleration is zero, it follows that

$$\omega = \text{constant} \qquad (19.75)$$

At the instant that the string is cut, the disk will have a downward acceleration which is equal to the gravitational acceleration of free fall. In addition, it will have a *constant* angular velocity which is equal to its angular velocity at the instant the string was cut.

Example 19.4 The disk which represents the Yo-Yo in Example 19.3 is assumed to have a symmetrical variable mass distribution. The exterior shape of the Yo-Yo is assumed to be the right circular cylinder of radius *r* and mass *m* shown in Fig. 19.19*a*. In one extreme configuration, all the mass is assumed to be located near the rim, as shown in Fig. 19.19*b*. In the other extreme distribution of mass, all the mass is assumed to be located near the CM, as shown in Fig. 19.19*c*. Find the range of values of the translational acceleration of the Yo-Yo for the extremes of mass distribution shown in the figures.

Solution   From Eq. (19.59),

$$a_y = \frac{g}{1 + I_0/(mr^2)} \qquad (19.76)$$

I_0 is the mass moment of inertia about the CM, and this quantity may be expressed in terms of the radius of gyration k_0 by

$$I_0 = k_0^2 m \qquad (19.77)$$

Equation (19.76) now appears as

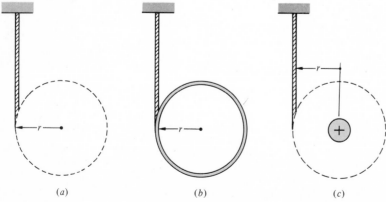

(a)   (b)   (c)

Fig. 19.19

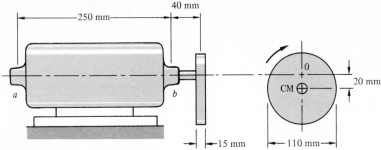

40 mm

250 mm

20 mm

a

b

CM

0

15 mm

110 mm

Fig. 19.20

$$a_y = \frac{g}{1 + mk_0^2/(mr^2)} = \frac{g}{1 + (k_0/r)^2}, \qquad (19.78)$$

For the case in Fig. 19.19b of mass distribution near the rim,

$$I_0 \approx mr^2 = mk_0^2 \qquad k_0 = r \qquad (19.79)$$

$$a_y = \frac{g}{1 + (r/r)^2} = \frac{1}{2}g \qquad (19.80)$$

When the mass is distributed near the center,

$$I_0 \approx 0 \qquad k_0 \approx 0 \qquad a_y \approx g \qquad (19.81)$$

It may be seen that the range of possible values of acceleration of the CM of the Yo-Yo is approximately 50 to 100 percent of the value of the gravitational acceleration. For the case of mass distribution near the center, the motion of the CM is the same as the case where the string is cut.

It is left as an exercise for the reader to decide which of the two extreme constructions shown in Fig. 19.19b and c might result in a better Yo-Yo. This problem is considered further in Example 20.11.

Example 19.5 The motor shown in Fig. 19.20 is firmly mounted on the wall of a vertical chute through which fine granular material flows. The disk is mounted off center on the motor. When the unit is running, a pulsating force is transmitted through the motor base to the wall to prevent clogging of the material as it flows through the chute. Find the forces exerted on the bearings at a and b when the disk is in the position shown. The motor speed is 1725 r/min and the density of the disk material is 7830 kg/m³.

Solution The mass of the disk is

$$m = 7830 \text{ kg/m}^3 \frac{\pi(110)^2}{4} 15 \text{ mm}^3 \left(\frac{1 \text{ m}}{1000 \text{ mm}}\right)^3 = 1.12 \text{ kg} \quad (19.82)$$

The disk is a body which rotates about a fixed point 0. Since the disk rotates with constant speed, the angular acceleration is zero. Thus, the external moment which acts on the disk is zero. The center of mass of the disk, however, travels in a circular path and experiences normal acceleration a_n. The free body-diagram of the disk is shown in Fig. 19.21. F_n is the force exerted on the disk by the shaft, with the *known* radial direction shown in the figure. The equation of motion is

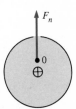

F_n

0

Fig. 19.21

$$F = ma_c \qquad F_n = ma_n = mr\omega^2 \tag{19.83}$$

$$F_n = 1.12 \text{ kg} \left(\frac{20}{1000}\right) m \left[1725 \left(\frac{2\pi}{60}\right)\right]^2 \frac{\text{rad}^2}{\text{s}^2} = 731 \text{ N} \tag{19.84}$$

The free-body diagram of the shaft is shown in Fig. 19.22. For equilibrium of this element,

$$\sum M_a = 0 \qquad -R_b(250) + 731(290) = 0 \qquad R_b = 848 \text{ N} \tag{19.85}$$

$$\sum F_y = 0 \qquad R_a + R_b - 731 = 0 \tag{19.86}$$

$$R_a + 848 - 731 = 0 \qquad R_a = -117 \text{ N}$$

The forces which act on the bearings due to the rotating unbalance, for the position of the disc in Fig. 19.20, are 177 N acting *upward* at bearing a, and 848 N acting *downward* at bearing b.

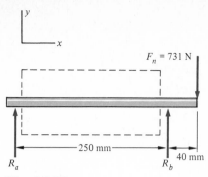

Fig. 19.22

19.4 PURE ROLLING OF A CYLINDRICAL BODY

Figure 19.23 shows a cylindrical body which is acted on by a horizontal force P and which rolls along a straight, horizontal track. The conditions necessary to ensure that the cylinder will roll without slipping will now be established.

If slipping is assumed to not occur, then point a is an instant center of rotation. The equation of motion of the cylinder about this point is

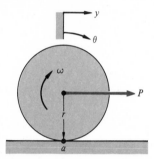

Fig. 19.23

$$M = I\alpha \qquad Pr = I\alpha \tag{19.87}$$

where I is the mass moment of inertia of the cylinder about point a. This term may be written as

$$I = I_0 + mr^2 \tag{19.88}$$

where I_0 is the centroidal mass moment of inertia. Equation (19.87) now appears as

$$Pr = (I_0 + mr^2)\alpha \qquad \alpha = \frac{Pr}{I_0 + mr^2} \tag{19.89}$$

This equation gives the relationship between the angular acceleration and the applied force P, based on the assumption of no slipping.

The free-body diagram of the cylinder is shown in Fig. 19.24. The force F is the friction force exerted by the track on the cylinder. It is this force, and this force alone, which causes angular acceleration of the cylinder. Since the actual sense of the angular acceleration is known to be clockwise, the force F must act to the left, as shown in Fig. 19.24. The equation of motion of the cylinder about its CM is

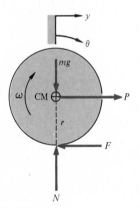

Fig. 19.24

$$M_0 = I_0\alpha \qquad Fr = I_0\alpha \tag{19.90}$$

α is eliminated between Eqs. (19.89) and (19.90), with the result

$$F = \frac{P}{1 + mr^2/I_0} \qquad (19.91)$$

It may be seen that the applied force P and the friction force F are directly proportional to each other. If the applied force P increases, the friction force F will increase until it reaches its maximum possible value. This limiting value is given by

$$F_{\max} = \mu_s N \qquad (19.92)$$

where μ_s is the coefficient of static friction and N is the normal force.

From consideration of Fig. 19.24, we find that

$$N = mg \qquad (19.93)$$

and Eq. (19.92) then has the form

$$F_{\max} = \mu_s mg \qquad (19.94)$$

The maximum permissible value $P_{\max}$ of the applied force P, for no slipping, is found by combining Eqs. (19.91) and (19.94):

$$P_{\max} = \mu_s mg\left(1 + \frac{mr^2}{I_0}\right) \qquad (19.95)$$

It is emphasized that Eq. (19.95) is valid only when sliding motion of the cylinder on the plate is impending.

If the body is a homogeneous, right circular cylinder,

$$I_0 = \tfrac{1}{2}mr^2 \qquad (19.96)$$

and the maximum force which may be applied without causing sliding is

$$P_{\max} = \mu_s mg\left(1 + \frac{mr^2}{\tfrac{1}{2}mr^2}\right) = 3\mu_s mg \qquad (19.97)$$

The quantity $\mu_s mg$ is the maximum friction force which may exist between the plane and the cylinder if nonrolling, sliding motion of the cylinder were impending. It may be seen that the applied force P may have a magnitude which is up to 3 times this value before slipping of the cylinder occurs.

Example 19.6 The cylindrical body shown in Fig. 19.25 rolls, without sliding, down the inclined plane with known direction β.

a Derive an expression for the minimum required value of the coefficient of static friction μ_s if slipping is not to occur.

b Find the numerical value of μ_s if the cylinder is homogeneous, with a mass of 2 kg, a diameter of 150 mm, and $\beta = 30°$.

Solution a The free-body diagram of the cylinder is shown in Fig. 19.26.

Point a is an instant center. For no slipping of the cylinder,

$$M = I_a\alpha \qquad (mg\sin\beta)(r) = (I_0 + mr^2)\alpha \qquad (19.98)$$

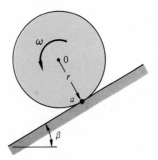

Fig. 19.25

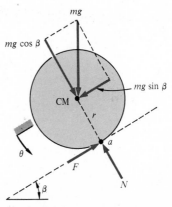

Fig. 19.26

$$\alpha = \frac{mgr \sin \beta}{I_0 + mr^2} \qquad (19.99)$$

It may be seen that the angular acceleration will increase if the slope of the plane increases.

The friction force exerted by the plane on the cylinder is F. The rotational equation of motion about the CM is

$$M_0 = I_0 \alpha \qquad Fr = I_0 \alpha \qquad (19.100)$$

If α, given by Eq. (19.99), increases with increasing values of β, then Eq. (19.100) shows that the required friction force must also increase.

The limiting value of F, when sliding motion is impending, is given by

$$F_{\text{max}} = \mu_s N \qquad (19.101)$$

where

$$N = mg \cos \beta \qquad (19.102)$$

Equations (19.99) through (19.102) are now combined to obtain

$$\mu_s = \frac{\tan \beta}{1 + mr^2/I_0} \qquad (19.103)$$

This equation gives the *minimum required value of* μ_s if the cylinder is to roll without slipping down the plane of inclination β.

For a homogeneous cylinder,

$$I_0 = \tfrac{1}{2}mr^2 \qquad (19.104)$$

and Eq. (19.103) appears as

$$\mu_s = \frac{\tan \beta}{1 + mr^2/(\tfrac{1}{2}mr^2)} = \frac{1}{3} \tan \beta \qquad (19.105)$$

It is interesting to compare this result with the case where the cylinder is a nonrolling object. The value of μ_s at which sliding motion for this case is impending is

$$\mu_s = \tan \beta \qquad (19.106)$$

It may be seen that the *tangents of the angles* of the inclines differ by a factor of 3.

b It follows from Eq. (19.105) that, for a homogeneous cylinder, μ_s *is independent of both the mass and the dimensions of the cylinder.* This quantity is a function only of the inclination angle of the plane on which the cylinder rolls. When $\beta = 30°$, the minimum required value of μ_s is

$$\mu_s = \tfrac{1}{3} \tan \beta = \tfrac{1}{3} \tan 30° = 0.192 \approx 0.2 \qquad (19.107)$$

Example 19.7 The following example is one which this author was exposed to in his first course in dynamics. It had a very lasting impression, and it was presented as the "red cylinders" problem.

Figure 19.27 shows two cylinders at rest on an inclined plane. Both cylinders have identical *dimensions* and identical *weights*. The surfaces of both cylinders, and of the plane, are slightly roughened, and angle β is sufficiently small so that the cylinders definitely roll without slipping. Both cylinders are released from rest at the same instant.

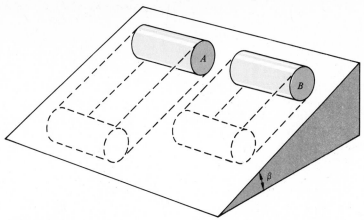

Fig. 19.27

A short time later, cylinder A has advanced down the plane an observably greater distance than cylinder B. Explain how this phenomenon is possible.

Solution The equation for the angular acceleration which governs the motion of a right circular cylinder which rolls without slipping down an inclined plane is given by Eq. (19.99), which is repeated here:

$$\alpha = \frac{mgr \sin \beta}{I_0 + mr^2} \qquad (19.108)$$

Since the cylinders have the same weight, m is the same for both. The dimensions are the same, so that r is a constant. β is a constant which defines the inclination of the plane. The only term in Eq. (19.108) which may vary, and thus explain the behavior of the cylinders, is I_0, the mass moment of inertia about the center axis of the cylinder. For cylinders of the same weight and dimensions, the term I_0 will vary *if the cylinders are made of different materials.* Figure 19.28 shows the cross sections of the two cylinders. Cylinder A is a homogeneous solid. Cylinder B is a homogeneous, hollow cylinder made of material with a density greater than that of cylinder A. Thus,

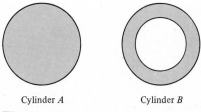

Cylinder A Cylinder B

Fig. 19.28

$$I_{0B} > I_{0A} \qquad (19.109)$$

and, from Eq. (19.108),

$$\alpha_B < \alpha_A \qquad (19.110)$$

Thus, in a given time, cylinder A will have traveled farther than cylinder B.

As an example, the dimensions of the cylinders are chosen as shown in Fig. 19.29. Cylinder A is made of aluminum, with $\gamma = 173$ lb/ft^3, and cylinder B is made of steel, with $\gamma = 489$ lb/ft^3. The inclination of the plane is 10°, and it is desired to find the distance between the two cylinders 1 s after they are released from rest.

For cylinder A,

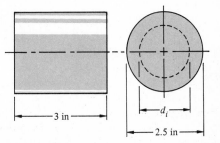

Fig. 19.29

$$W_A = \frac{\pi(2.5)^2}{4}(3) \text{ in}^3 \left(\frac{1 \text{ ft}^3}{1{,}728 \text{ in}^3}\right)\left(173 \frac{\text{lb}}{\text{ft}^3}\right) = 1.47 \text{ lb} \quad (19.111)$$

$$I_{0A} = \frac{1}{8}m_A d_A^2 = \frac{1}{8}\left(\frac{1.47}{386}\right)(2.5)^2 = 0.00298 \text{ lb} \cdot \text{s}^2 \cdot \text{in} \quad (19.112)$$

The inside diameter d_i of cylinder B is found from

$$\frac{\pi}{4}(2.5^2 - d_i^2)(3)\left(\frac{489}{1{,}728}\right) = 1.47 \text{ lb} \qquad d_i = 2.01 \text{ in} \quad (19.113)$$

The mass moment of inertia of cylinder B is found from

$$I_{0B} = \rho t J \qquad (19.114)$$

where J is the polar moment of inertia of the *annular cross-sectional area* about the center axis and ρ is the mass density.

For a hollow cylinder,

$$J = \frac{\pi}{32}(d_o^4 - d_i^4) \qquad (19.115)$$

where d_i and d_o are the inner and outer diameters.

$$I_{0B} = 489 \frac{\text{lb}}{\text{ft}^3}\left(\frac{1 \text{ ft}^3}{1{,}728 \text{ in}^3}\right)\left(\frac{1}{386 \text{ in/s}^2}\right)(3 \text{ in})\left(\frac{\pi}{32}\right)$$
$$\cdot [(2.5^4 - 2.01^4)] \text{ in}^4 \quad (19.116)$$

$$I_{0B} = 0.00492 \text{ lb} \cdot \text{s}^2 \cdot \text{in} \qquad (19.117)$$

The angular accelerations of the cylinders, from Eq. (19.99), are

$$\alpha = \frac{mgr \sin \beta}{I_0 + mr^2} \qquad (19.118)$$

$$\alpha_A = \frac{1.47(2.5/2)(\sin 10°)}{0.00298 + (1.47/386)(2.5/2)^2} = 35.7 \frac{\text{rad}}{\text{s}^2} \quad (19.119)$$

$$\alpha_B = \frac{1.47(2.5/2)(\sin 10°)}{0.00492 + (1.47/386)(2.5/2)^2} = 29.4 \text{ rad/s}^2 \quad (19.120)$$

If the cylinders start from rest, the angular displacements are

$$\theta = \tfrac{1}{2}\alpha t^2 \qquad (19.121)$$

The translational displacements s of the rolling cylinders are given by $s = r\theta$. At the end of 1 s,

$$\theta_A = \tfrac{1}{2}(35.7)(1^2) = 17.9 \text{ rad} \qquad (19.122)$$

$$s_A = \frac{2.5}{2}(17.9) = 22.4 \text{ in} \qquad (19.123)$$

$$\theta_B = \tfrac{1}{2}(29.4)(1^2) = 14.7 \text{ rad} \qquad (19.124)$$

$$s_B = \frac{2.5}{2}(14.7) = 18.4 \text{ in} \qquad (19.125)$$

The separation distance ΔS between the two cylinders at this time is

$$\Delta s = s_A - s_B = 22.4 - 18.4 = 4 \text{ in} \qquad (19.126)$$

19.5 DYNAMIC MOTION OF CONNECTED RIGID BODIES

In Chap. 16, the motion of connected particles was considered. The technique of solution consisted of drawing a free-body diagram and writing the equation of motion for *each* mass particle. The forces in elements such as cables or links which connect the particles are unknown quantities which may be found from the solution of the several simultaneous equations of motion of the entire system.

This method of solution may be extended to the case of connected rigid bodies, and Example 19.8 shows a typical calculation for a case where the mass moment of inertia of a pulley is to be considered in the solution.

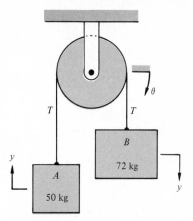

Fig. 19.30

Example 19.8 The system of Example 16.4 is repeated in Fig. 19.30. In this earlier problem the pulley was considered to be massless. The translational acceleration of the blocks was found to be

$$a_y = 1.77 \text{ m/s}^2 \qquad (19.127)$$

and the cable tension T had the value

$$T = 579 \text{ N} \qquad (19.128)$$

The pulley has a mass of 10 kg, is 800 mm in diameter, and is assumed to have the shape of a circular disk.

a If the cable is assumed to not slip on the rim of the pulley, find the force in each cable, the acceleration of the masses, and the hinge pin force when the system is released from rest.

b What is the minimum required value of the coefficient of static friction between the cable and the rim of the pulley if slipping is not to occur?

The hinge is assumed to be frictionless.

Solution a The free-body diagrams of the three mass elements of the system are shown in Fig. 19.31. R is the force exerted by the hinge pin on the pulley, and T_A and T_B are the cable tensile forces. The mass moment of inertia I_0 of the pulley is

$$I_0 = \tfrac{1}{8}md^2 = \tfrac{1}{8}(10)(\tfrac{800}{1,000})^2 = 0.8 \text{ kg·m}^2 \qquad (19.129)$$

The equation of motion of the pulley is

$$M = I_0\alpha \qquad (T_B - T_A)(\tfrac{400}{1,000}) = 0.8\alpha \qquad (19.130)$$

and the equations of motion of the masses are

$$\sum F = m_B a_y \qquad 706 - T_B = 72a_y \qquad (19.131)$$

$$\sum F = m_A a_y \qquad T_A - 491 = 50a_y \qquad (19.132)$$

The kinematic relationship between y and α is

$$a_y = \tfrac{400}{1,000}\alpha = 0.4\alpha \qquad (19.133)$$

These equations are solved simultaneously, and the result is

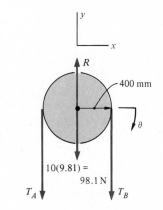

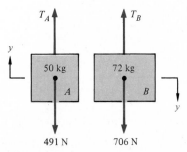

Fig. 19.31

$$a_y = 1.70 \text{ m/s}^2 \qquad T_A = 575 \text{ N} \qquad T_B = 584 \text{ N} \qquad (19.134)$$

The percent difference in the computed values of the acceleration of the masses is

$$\text{Percent } D = \frac{1.70 - 1.77}{1.77} \, 100 = -4 \text{ percent} \qquad (19.135)$$

It may be seen that a small error is introduced by neglecting the mass moment of inertia of the pulley. In engineering calculations, unless the dimensions of the pulley are large, with a correspondingly large value of the mass moment of inertia, the mass effects of the pulley are usually negligible. The hinge pin force R, from Fig. 19.31, is

$$\sum F_y = 0 \qquad R - T_A - T_B - 98.1 = 0 \qquad (19.136)$$

$$R = 575 + 584 + 98.1 = 1{,}260 \text{ N} \qquad (19.137)$$

When the system is at rest, the pin force is

$$R_{\text{initial}} = 491 + 706 + 98.1 = 1{,}300 \text{ N} \qquad (19.138)$$

It may be seen that the motion has the effect of *reducing* the hinge pin force.

b The equation which describes the condition of impending sliding motion of a cable with respect to a curved surface is

$$\frac{T_1}{T_2} = e^{\mu_s \beta} \qquad (19.139)$$

T_1 and T_2 are the tensile forces in the cable on either side of the pulley, and $T_1 > T_2$. β is the angle of contact, and μ_s is the coefficient of static friction.

For the present example

$$T_1 = T_B = 584 \text{ N} \qquad T_2 = T_A = 575 \text{ N} \qquad \beta = 180° = \pi \text{ rad} \qquad (19.140)$$

Equation (19.139) now appears as

$$\frac{584}{575} = e^{\mu_s \pi} \qquad 1.016 = e^{\mu_s \pi} \qquad (19.141)$$

$$\ln 1.016 = \mu_s \pi \qquad \mu_s = 0.005 \qquad (19.142)$$

If $\mu_s \geq 0.005$, the cable will not slip on the pulley.

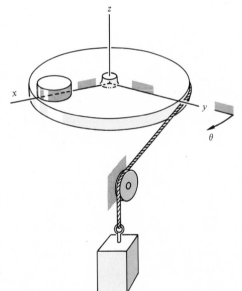

Example 19.9 The rotor in Fig. 19.32 consists of a solid aluminum disk to which is attached a brass plug. The rotor assembly is mounted in a horizontal plane and a set of xyz axes is attached to the disk. An inextensible string is wrapped around the rim of the disk and is connected to a 600-g mass.

a Find the mass, and the location of the center of mass, of the rotor assembly, and the mass moment of inertia of this assembly about the axis of rotation.

b Find the acceleration of the mass and of the rotor assembly, and the cable tensile force.

Fig. 19.32

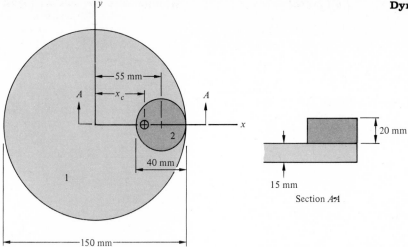

Fig. 19.33

c Find the horizontal components of the force on the rotor assembly hinge pin 2 s after the mass is released from rest. Assume that the initial angular position of the rotor assembly was such that, at $t = 2$ s, the string force is parallel to the y axis, and acting in the negative sense of this axis.

The density of brass is 8,550 kg/m^3 and the density of aluminum is 2,770 kg/m^3.

Solution

a Figure 19.33 shows the rotor assembly. The aluminum disk is element 1 and the brass plug is element 2. The masses of these two elements are

$$m_1 = \frac{\pi}{4}(150)^2 15 \text{ mm}^3 (2770 \text{ kg/m}^3)\left(\frac{1 \text{ m}}{1000 \text{ mm}}\right)^3 = 0.734 \text{ kg}$$

$$m_2 = \frac{\pi}{4}(40)^2 20(8550)\left(\frac{1}{1000}\right)^3 = 0.215 \text{ kg} \qquad (19.143)$$

$$m = m_1 + m_2 = 0.734 + 0.215 = 0.949 \text{ kg} \qquad (19.144)$$

The centroidal coordinate x_c is found from

$$x_c = \frac{x_1 m_1 + x_2 m_2}{m_1 + m_2} = \frac{0 + 55(0.215)}{0.734 + 0.215} = 12.5 \text{ mm} \quad (19.145)$$

The mass moment of inertia of the rotor assembly about the axis of rotation is

$$I = I_{01} + I_2 = I_{01} + I_{02} + md^2 \qquad (19.146)$$

$$I = \frac{1}{8}m_1 d_1^2 + \frac{1}{8}m_2 d_2^2 + m_2 d^2 \qquad (19.147)$$

$$I = \frac{1}{8}(0.734)\left(\frac{150}{1000}\right)^2 + \frac{1}{8}(0.215)\left(\frac{40}{1000}\right)^2 + 0.215\left(\frac{55}{1000}\right)^2$$

$$= 2.76 \times 10^{-3} \text{ kg} \cdot \text{m}^2 \qquad (19.148)$$

b The tensile force in the string is designated P. The equation of motion of the rotor is

$$M_0 = I_0\alpha \qquad P\left(\frac{75}{1000}\right)\text{N} \cdot \text{m} = (2.76 \times 10^{-3} \text{ kg} \cdot \text{m}^2)\alpha \quad (19.149)$$

The equation of motion of the mass is

$$\sum F = ma \qquad \frac{600}{1000}(9.81) - P = \frac{600}{1000}a \qquad (19.150)$$

Since the string is inextensible,

$$a = r\alpha \qquad a = \frac{75}{1000}\alpha \qquad (19.151)$$

The solutions to these equations are

$$\alpha = 71.9 \frac{\text{rad}}{\text{s}^2} \qquad P = 2.65 \text{ N} \qquad a_y = 5.39 \frac{\text{in}}{\text{s}^2} \quad (19.152)$$

c The angular acceleration of the rotor is constant, and the angular velocity of this element two seconds after starting from rest is

$$\omega = \omega_0 + \alpha t = 71.9(2) = 144 \frac{\text{rad}}{\text{s}} \qquad (19.153)$$

The center of mass of the rotor assembly travels in a circular path. The two components of the hinge pin force, in the horizontal plane, which act on the disk are shown in Fig. 19.34. The components of the acceleration of the center of mass are

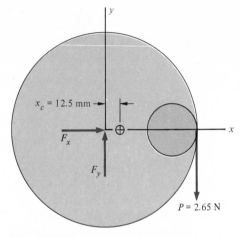

Fig. 19.34

$$a_n = x_c\omega^2 = \frac{12.5}{1000}(144)^2 = 259 \text{ m/s}^2 \qquad (19.154)$$

$$a_t = x_c\alpha = \frac{12.5}{1000}(71.9) = 0.9 \text{ m/s}^2 \qquad (19.155)$$

The equations for the translational motion of the CM are

$$F_n = ma_n \qquad -F_x = ma_n = 0.949(259) = 246 \text{ N} \qquad F_x = -246 \text{ N}$$
$$(19.156)$$

$$F_t = ma_t \qquad -F_y + P = ma_t \qquad (19.157)$$
$$-F_y + 2.65 = 0.949(0.9) \qquad F_y = 1.8 \text{ N} \qquad (19.158)$$

It may be seen that the normal component is the predominant force effect.

19.6 SOLUTIONS USING THE D'ALEMBERT, OR INERTIA, FORCES AND MOMENTS

In Sec. 16.6 the concept of the D'Alembert, or inertia, force on a mass particle was introduced. It was seen that the addition of another force, namely the inertia force, to the particle had the effect of transforming a problem in dynamics to a problem in static equilibrium.

The concept of an inertia force acting on a particle may be extended readily to the case of a rigid body in plane motion.

Figure 19.35 shows a body which is hinged to the ground. The equation of rotational motion is

$$M = I\alpha \qquad (19.159)$$

This equation may be written in the form

$$M - I\alpha = 0 \qquad M + (-I\alpha) = 0 \qquad (19.160)$$

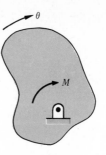

Fig. 19.35

The quantity $(-I\alpha)$ is called the inertia, or D'Alembert, moment. If this quantity is imagined to be an applied moment which acts on the body, then the equation of motion would have the form

$$\sum M = 0 \qquad (19.161)$$

which is the basic form of moment equilibrium in statics.

The general rules which govern the formulation of the inertia force or moment acting on a particle or a rigid body are as follows.

1. An arrow is drawn on the free-body diagram of the particle or rigid body in the actual, or assumed positive sense of the motion coordinate. In the case of a rigid body, this arrow would be drawn through the CM, for the case of translation, or about a known reference point, for the case of rotation.
2. The magnitude of this arrow is indicated by the product of mass and acceleration, for the case of translation, or by the product of mass moment of inertia and angular acceleration, for the case of angular motion.
3. *A minus sign is inserted in front of the quantity described in step 2.* The quantity formulated above, *including* the minus sign, is then the inertia force or moment which acts on the element under consideration. This quantity is considered to be positive in the actual, or positive sense of the motion coordinate, and it may then be treated as simply another force which acts in the system. The equations of static equilibrium may then be used to solve for the unknowns in the problem.

In the following problems, the concept of an inertia force will be used to characterize certain types of problems in general plane motion. For these problems, the inertia force technique will be found to be a particularly convenient way of formulating the problem. In one problem, the solutions will be obtained by using both the inertia force and the direct application of Newton's second law, and the two methods of solution may then be compared.

The addition of the inertia force to a particle changes the interpretation of the problem from "the resultant force is equal to the product of the mass of the particle and the acceleration of the particle" to "the sum of all of the forces acting on the

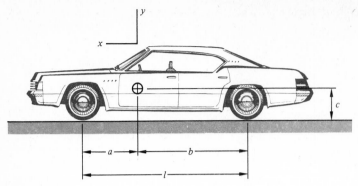

Fig. 19.36

particle is zero." In certain problems the use of the inertia force is particularly convenient. The disadvantage of this method, however, is that its use tends to obscure and blur the actual physical phenomenon that an unbalanced force causes a particle to accelerate. The beginning reader is urged to commence the study of dynamics by formulating problems in terms of the resultant force found from the free-body diagram. At this level of the study of dynamics, the inertia force technique should be used principally to check the results obtained by Newton's second law.

Example 19.10 Figure 19.36 shows a side view of an automobile of mass m. Find the maximum possible theoretical value of the acceleration of the vehicle for the case of **a** rear-wheel drive only, **b** front-wheel drive only, and **c** four-wheel drive.

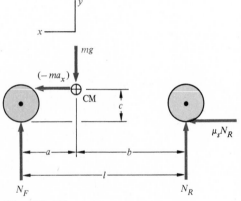

Fig. 19.37

Solution

a *Solution for rear wheel drive only, using the inertia force* Since rear-wheel drive is assumed, the friction force of the ground on the tires acts at the rear wheels only, and μ_s is the coefficient of static friction. The free-body diagram for the case of rear-wheel drive only is shown in Fig. 19.37. The inertia force is placed at the CM, in accordance with the rules given.

The equations of motion are

$$\sum M_{N_F} = 0 \qquad mg(a) - (-ma_x)c - N_R l = 0 \qquad (19.162)$$

$$\sum F_x = 0 \qquad -ma_x + \mu_s N_R = 0 \qquad (19.163)$$

$$\sum F_y = 0 \qquad N_F - mg + N_R = 0 \qquad (19.164)$$

The solutions to the above equations are

Rear-wheel drive only:

$$a_x = \frac{\mu_s ag}{l - \mu_s c} \qquad (19.165)$$

$$N_R = \frac{amg}{l - \mu_s c} \qquad N_F = mg\frac{(b - \mu_s c)}{l - \mu_s c} \qquad (19.166)$$

Solution for front wheel drive only, by direct use of Newton's second law. The automobile is a body in general plane motion. Thus, the equations of motion are

$$M_0 = I_0\alpha \qquad F = ma_c \qquad (19.167)$$

In the present problem $\alpha = 0$, so that the summation of moments about the center of mass is zero. The force F is expressed in terms of its components along the x and y axes. The equations which describe the motion of the automobile are then

$$\sum F_x = ma_x \qquad \mu_s N_R = ma_x \qquad (19.168)$$

$$\sum F_y = ma_y = 0 \qquad N_F - mg + N_R = 0 \qquad (19.169)$$

$$\sum M_0 = 0 \qquad N_F a - N_R b + \mu_s N_R c = 0 \qquad (19.170)$$

a_x is found from these equations as

$$a_x = \frac{\mu_s ag}{l - \mu_s c} \qquad \text{rear-wheel drive only} \qquad (19.171)$$

Equation (19.171) is the result obtained previously in Eq. (19.165). Several very interesting conclusions may be drawn from the above equations. From Eq. (19.171), it may be concluded that the magnitude of the maximum possible acceleration a_x will increase if a or c increases. This corresponds to placing the center of mass as far from the ground, and as close to the rear wheels, as possible.

From Eq. (19.166), it may be seen that the normal force between the front wheels and the ground will be negative if $\mu_s c > b$. Since N_F is defined as a *compressive* force, the interpretation of the above result is that, when $\mu_s c = b$, the front wheels lose contact with the ground. This is the effect referred to as a "wheelie." It is comparable to the effect observed when a child riding a two wheel bicycle lunges backward in such a way that the front wheel lifts off the ground.

b *Solution for front wheel drive only, using the inertia force* The free-body diagram for the case of front-wheel drive only is shown in Fig. 19.38. The equations of motion are

$$\sum M_{N_R} = 0 \qquad N_F l - (-ma_x)c - mgb = 0 \qquad (19.172)$$

$$\sum F_x = 0 \qquad (-ma_x) + \mu_s N_F = 0 \qquad (19.173)$$

The solution is

$$a_x = \frac{\mu_s bg}{l + \mu_s c} \qquad \text{front-wheel drive only} \qquad (19.174)$$

Solution for front wheel drive only, by direct use of Newton's second law The equations of motion of the CM, and about this point, are

$$M_0 = I_0\alpha \qquad F = ma_c \qquad (19.175)$$

Since $\alpha = 0$, the summation of moments about the center of mass is zero, and

$$\sum F_x = ma_x \qquad \mu_s N_F = ma_x \qquad (19.176)$$

$$\sum F_y = ma_y = 0 \qquad N_F - mg + N_R = 0 \qquad (19.177)$$

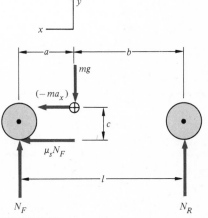

Fig. 19.38

$$\sum M_0 = 0 \qquad N_F a - N_R b + \mu_s N_F c = 0 \qquad (19.178)$$

The solution to this system of equations is

$$a_x = \frac{\mu_s bg}{l + \mu_s c} \qquad \text{front-wheel drive only} \qquad (19.179)$$

which is the result obtained in Eq. (19.174), and

$$N_F = \frac{bmg}{l + \mu_s c} \qquad N_R = \frac{(a + \mu_c c)mg}{l + \mu_s c} \qquad (19.180)$$

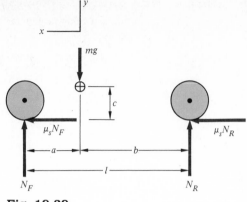

Fig. 19.39

It may be observed that a_x N_F, and N_R are always positive. Thus, there is no condition of motion with front-wheel drive only which would permit the wheels to loose contact with the ground.

c The free-body diagram, for the case of four-wheel drive, is shown in Fig. 19.39. Using Newton's second law directly, we get

$$\sum F_x = ma_x \qquad \mu_s N_R + \mu_s N_F = ma_x \qquad (19.181)$$

$$\sum F_y = ma_y = 0 \qquad N_F - mg + N_R = 0 \qquad (19.182)$$

$$\sum M_0 = 0 \qquad N_F a - N_R b + \mu_s N_F c + \mu_s N_R c = 0 \quad (19.183)$$

The solutions to these equations are

$$a_x = \mu_s g \qquad (19.184)$$

$$N_F = \frac{(b - \mu_s c)mg}{l} \qquad N_R = \frac{(a + \mu_s c)mg}{l} \qquad (19.185)$$

It may be seen from these equations that, as in the case of rear wheel drive only, the front wheels loose contact with the ground when $\mu_s c > b$.

It is interesting to note that all the results above for the acceleration are independent of the mass of the vehicle.

Example 19.11 The vehicle described in the last Example has the following dimensions.

$$a = 45 \text{ in} \qquad (19.186)$$

$$b = 65 \text{ in} \qquad (19.187)$$

$$c = 21 \text{ in} \qquad (19.188)$$

$$l = a + b = 110 \text{ in} \qquad (19.189)$$

The coefficient of static friction between the tires and the pavement is assumed to have the value 0.68.

a If it is assumed that the vehicle has the required power, find the minimum times to accelerate from rest to 60 mi/h for rear-wheel drive only, front-wheel drive only, and four-wheel drive.

b Find the normal forces N_F and N_R which correspond to maximum acceleration of the automobile for the three types of drive in part *a*. Compare these values with the corresponding values of the normal forces when the vehicle is at rest.

Solution **a** For the case of rear-wheel drive only,

$$a_x = \frac{\mu_s ag}{l - \mu_s c} = \frac{0.68(45)(32.2)}{110 - 0.68(21)} = 10.3 \text{ ft/s}^2 \qquad (19.190)$$

The final velocity is

$$v = \left(60\, \frac{\text{mi}}{\text{h}}\right)\left(\frac{5{,}280\ \text{ft}}{1\ \text{mi}}\right)\left(\frac{1\ \text{h}}{3{,}600\ \text{s}}\right) = 88\, \frac{\text{ft}}{\text{s}} \qquad (19.191)$$

The required time is then found from

$$v = v_0 + at \qquad 88 = 0 + 10.3t \qquad t = 8.54\ \text{s} \qquad (19.192)$$

When only the front wheels drive the vehicle,

$$a_x = \frac{\mu_s bg}{l + \mu_s c} = \frac{0.68(65)(32.2)}{110 + 0.68(21)} = 11.5\, \frac{\text{ft}}{\text{s}^2} \qquad (19.193)$$

$$v = v_0 + at \qquad\qquad\qquad\qquad\qquad (19.194)$$

$$88 = 0 + 11.5t \qquad t = 7.65\ \text{s} \qquad (19.195)$$

When all four wheels are driving the vehicle,

$$a_x = \mu_s g = 0.68(32.2) = 21.9\ \text{ft/s}^2 \qquad (19.196)$$

$$v = v_0 + at \qquad 88 = 0 + 21.9t \qquad t = 4.02\ \text{s} \qquad (19.197)$$

When the vehicle is at rest, following Fig. 19.39,

$$\sum M_{N_F} = 0 \qquad (mg)a - N_R l = 0 \qquad N_R = \frac{a}{l} mg \quad (19.198)$$

$$\sum M_{N_R} = 0 \qquad N_F l - (mg)b = 0 \qquad N_F = \frac{b}{l}(mg) \quad (19.199)$$

For the numerical values of the problem

$$N_R = \frac{45}{110}(mg) = 0.41\,(mg) \qquad N_F = \frac{65}{110}(mg) = 0.59\,(mg) \quad (19.200)$$

The values of N_F and N_R, for front and rear wheel drives, are computed from the above equations, and the results are summarized in Table 19.1. It may be seen that the effect of the acceleration of the vehicle, for all three types of drive, is to "shift the weight" from the

TABLE 19.1			
		Weight Distribution	
		Automobile at Rest, percent	Maximum Acceleration, percent
Rear-wheel drive	Front wheels	59	53
	Rear wheels	41	47
Front-wheel drive	Front wheels	59	52
	Rear wheels	41	48
Four-wheel drive	Front wheels	59	46
	Rear wheels	41	54

front wheels to the rear wheels. This effect is most pronounced in the case of four wheel drive.

It follows from the solutions above that front-wheel drive is more effective traction than rear-wheel drive. Although the four-wheel-drive vehicle has the maximum traction, it is unlikely that such a vehicle would be equipped with an engine of sufficient power output to satisfy the conditions of the problem.

This vehicle example is considered further in Probs. 19.56 through 19.70. Here, the effectiveness of front-wheel and rear-wheel braking is compared, in addition to the cases of accelerating or braking in traveling up or down an inclined surface.

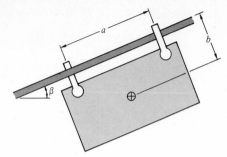

Fig. 19.40

Example 19.12 Figure 19.40 shows a conveyor system used to transport heavy steel plates. The two carriages have shoes which slide along an inclined steel rail, with clamping mechanisms to attach to the plate. The maximum value of the coefficient of kinetic friction is assumed to be 0.015, which would correspond to an inadequate rail lubrication maintenance schedule. The plates are released with zero velocity from the top of the incline.

a Find the acceleration of the plate.

b Find the normal contact forces between the shoes and the rail.

c Find the numerical results for parts a and b, if $a = 6$ ft, $b = 3$ ft, $\beta = 28°$, and the weight of the plate is 750 lb.

d Are there any conditions which would cause a shoe to lose contact with the rail?

Solution

a The free-body diagram of the carriage-plate assembly is shown in Fig. 19.41, together with the inertia force. For dynamic equilibrium of the plate,

$$\sum F_x = 0 \qquad -\mu_k N_L + (-ma_x) - \mu_k N_R + mg \sin \beta = 0 \qquad (19.201)$$

$$\sum F_y = 0 \qquad N_L - mg \cos \beta + N_R = 0 \qquad (19.202)$$

$$\sum M_{N_L} = 0 \qquad (mg \sin \beta - ma_x)\frac{b}{2} + (mg \cos \beta)\frac{a}{2} - N_R a = 0$$
$$(19.203)$$

The acceleration is found from these equations to be

$$a_x = g(\sin \beta - \mu_k \cos \beta) \qquad (19.204)$$

b Equations (19.201) and (19.203) are solved simultaneously, and the normal contact forces are

$$N_L = \left(\frac{a - \mu_k b}{2a}\right) mg \cos \beta \qquad (19.205)$$

$$N_R = \left(\frac{a + \mu_k b}{2a}\right) mg \cos \beta \qquad (19.206)$$

c The numerical results are

$$a_x = g(\sin \beta - \mu_k \cos \beta) = 32.2(\sin 28° - 0.15 \cos 28°) = 10.9 \text{ ft/s}^2$$
$$(19.207)$$

$$N_L = \left(\frac{a - \mu_k b}{2a}\right) mg \cos \beta = \left[\frac{6 - 0.15(3)}{2(6)}\right] 750 \cos 28° = 306 \text{ lb}$$

$$(19.208)$$

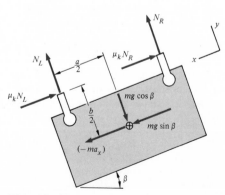

Fig. 19.41

$$N_R = \left(\frac{a + \mu_k b}{2a}\right) mg \cos\beta = \left[\frac{6 + 0.15(3)}{2(6)}\right] 750 \cos 28° = 356 \text{ lb}$$

$$(19.209)$$

It can be shown that, if the rail is frictionless, $N_L = N_R = 331$ lb. Thus, the friction forces have the effect of increasing the right-side normal-reaction force, and decreasing the left-side normal-reaction force.

d The left shoe will lose contact with the rail for computed values of $N_L \leq 0$. The required condition for this shoe to remain in contact with the rail, from Eq. (19.205), is

$$\mu_k b < a \qquad \mu_k < \frac{a}{b} = \frac{6}{3} = 2 \qquad (19.210)$$

For the present problem, $\mu_k = 0.15$. Thus, the shoes remain in contact with the rail.

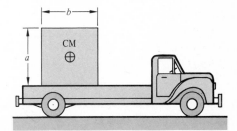

Fig. 19.42

19.7 CRITERIA FOR SLIDING OR TIPPING

One type of problem in which the concept of an inertia force is extremely useful is the determination of whether an object will slide or tip.

A typical example is shown in Fig. 19.42, which shows a crate resting on a flatbed truck. With no loss of generality, the crate is assumed to be a homogeneous material, so that the CM is located at the centroid of the volume. As the driver applies the brakes, the crate may decelerate with the truck, slide relative to the flatbed, or tip over. Each case will be considered now.

When the truck is at rest or moving with constant velocity, the free-body diagram of the crate is as shown in Fig. 19.43. The weight force mg is equal to the normal force N of the truck on the crate.

Figure 19.44 shows the free-body diagram when the driver brakes. The inertia force is drawn in accordance with the positive x coordinate axis shown in the figure. The truck is decelerating, so that a_x is positive. *The actual sense of the inertia force, interpreted as an external force applied to the crate, is to the right.* Since this force tends to rotate the crate clockwise, the line of action of the reaction force of the truck on the crate moves to the right of its original position. The force F is the friction force exerted by the truck bed on the crate.

The magnitude of the deceleration is now imagined to increase. If the crate is temporarily assumed not to tip, sliding motion of this object will be impending when the friction force attains its maximum value of

$$F_{\max} = \mu_s N \qquad (19.211)$$

where μ_s is the coefficient of static friction. The equations of motion for this case are

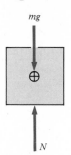

Fig. 19.43

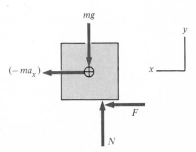

Fig. 19.44

$$\sum F_y = 0 \qquad -mg + N = 0 \qquad N = mg \quad (19.212)$$

$$\sum F_x = 0 \qquad (-ma_x) + \mu_s N = 0 \qquad (19.213)$$

$$ma_x = \mu_s N = \mu_s mg \qquad a_x = \mu_s g \qquad (19.214)$$

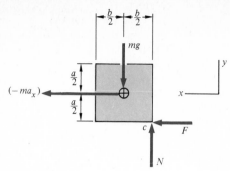

If the magnitude of the deceleration of the truck exceeds $\mu_s g$, the crate will slide.

As the magnitude of the deceleration of the truck increases, the line of action of the reaction force of the crate continues to move rightward. A limiting condition is reached when this force acts at the forward edge of the crate, as shown in Fig. 19.45. If the friction force F at this condition is less than the maximum possible value $\mu_s N$, the crate will be in a condition of impending tipping motion about the forward edge. The equilibrium requirements are

Fig. 19.45

$$\sum F_y = 0 \qquad -mg + N = 0 \qquad N = mg \quad (19.215)$$

$$\sum M_N = 0 \qquad -mg\frac{b}{2} - (-ma_x)\left(\frac{a}{2}\right) = 0 \qquad a_x = \frac{b}{a}g$$

$$(19.216)$$

It may be observed that b/a defines the shape of the crate. A short, squat crate would have a large b/a ratio, while a tall, slender crate would have a small value of b/a.

The following possible motions of the crate on the bed of the truck may now be identified.

1. If $a_x \le \mu_s g$ and $a_x \le (b/a)g$, the crate will neither slide nor tip.
2. If $a_x > \mu_s g$ and $\mu_s < b/a$, the crate will slide without tipping.
3. If $a_x > (b/a)g$ and $\mu_s > b/a$, the crate will tip without sliding.

A special case occurs if $\mu_s = b/a$. In this case, sliding and tipping are equally likely and the effects could occur simultaneously.

Example 19.13 A crate rests on the back of a truck, as shown in Fig. 19.46. The truck bed is made of rough wood, and the coefficient of static friction between the bed and the crate is estimated to be 0.6. Find the magnitude of the maximum deceleration which the truck may experience if the crate is not to move relative to the bed.

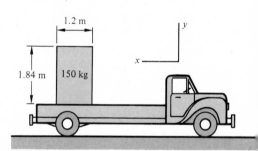

Fig. 19.46

Solution Sliding motion of the crate is impending when

$$a_x = \mu_s g = 0.6(9.81) = 5.89 \text{ m/s}^2 \qquad (19.217)$$

Tipping will occur if

$$a_x = \frac{b}{a}g = \frac{1.2}{1.84}9.81 = 6.40 \text{ m/s}^2 \qquad (19.218)$$

Sliding motion will occur first, and the maximum permissible deceleration is 5.89 m/s².

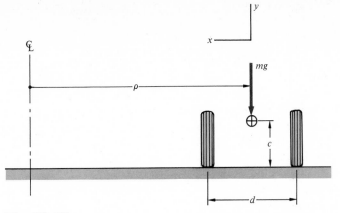

Fig. 19.47

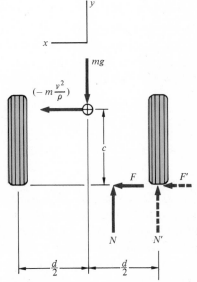

Fig. 19.48

Example 19.14 A vehicle travels with constant speed around a horizontal, circular track, as shown in Fig. 19.47.

a Develop the criteria for the velocities at which sliding or tipping of the vehicle will occur.

b If $c = 21$ in, $d = 57$ in, $\rho = 300$ ft, and $\mu_s = 0.81$, find the limiting value of the speed at which sliding or tipping will occur.

Solution

a The center of mass of the vehicle travels with constant speed in a plane circular path which is parallel to the track. The plane motion which is considered in this problem is in a radial plane which is normal to the track. This plane is the plane of the illustration in Fig. 19.47. The free-body diagram of the vehicle is shown in Fig. 19.48. The centripetal acceleration has the magnitude v^2/ρ and is directed toward the center of the track, in the sense of positive x. For the case where tipping is *not* impending, the normal force N has the general position shown in the figure. The equilibrium requirements are

$$\sum F_y = 0 \qquad -mg + N = 0 \qquad N = mg \qquad (19.219)$$

$$\sum F_x = 0 \qquad \left(-m\frac{v^2}{\rho}\right) + F = 0 \qquad F = \frac{mv^2}{\rho} \qquad (19.220)$$

When sliding motion is impending,

$$F = F_{\max} = \mu_s N = \mu_s mg \qquad (19.221)$$

where μ_s is the coefficient of static friction. F is eliminated between Eqs. (19.220) and (19.221), with the result

$$\mu_s mg = m\frac{v_{\max}^2}{\rho} \qquad v_{\max} = \sqrt{\mu_s \rho g} \qquad (19.222)$$

When tipping motion is impending, the normal reaction force component N' has the limiting position shown in Fig. 19.48. For equilibrium,

$$\sum M_{N'} = 0 \qquad -\left(-\frac{mv^2}{\rho}\right)c - mg\frac{d}{2} = 0 \qquad v_{\max} = \sqrt{\frac{d}{2c}\rho g}$$

$$(19.223)$$

If

$$\mu_s < \frac{d}{2c} \qquad (19.224)$$

the vehicle will slide before it tips.

b The limiting condition is

$$\mu_s \overset{?}{<} \frac{d}{2c} = \frac{57}{2(21)} = 1.36 \qquad (19.225)$$

Since $\mu_s = 0.81 < 1.36$, the vehicle will slide before it tips. The value of the speed when sliding motion is impending is

$$v_{\max} = \sqrt{\mu_s \rho g} = \sqrt{0.81(300)32.2} = 88.5 \text{ ft/s} = 60.3 \text{ mi/h} \quad (19.226)$$

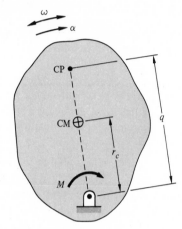

19.8 CENTER OF PERCUSSION $_{\textit{omit}}$

When a rigid body experiences *angular acceleration about a fixed point* there is a point on the body, which is *never* coincident with the CM, that has a unique property. This property is that the sum about this point of all the moments which act on the body is always zero. This point is defined to be the *center of percussion*. A familiar example is when a baseball is struck by a bat at the "wrong" location along the bat and an unpleasant stinging sensation is felt in the hands. The location of the center of percussion (CP) will now be determined.

Fig. 19.49

Figure 19.49 shows a rigid body which moves with plane motion about a fixed point. The point CP is defined to be the center of percussion. This point lies on a straight line through the CM and the fixed point, at the distance q from the fixed point. The body is acted upon by the resultant moment M.

The free-body diagram is shown in Fig. 19.50, and on this diagram are shown the acceleration components of the CM. The forces F_n and F_t, with the directions shown in the figure, are the two components of the total force exerted by the hinge pin on the body. These two force components act in the actual senses of the two acceleration components.

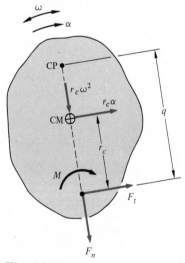

The equations of motion of the CM of the body are

$$F_n = mr_c\omega^2 \qquad F_t = mr_c\alpha \qquad (19.227)$$

In any given problem, these equations may be used directly to find the hinge pin force.

The equation of motion about the fixed point is

$$M = I\alpha = (I_0 + mr_c^2)\alpha \qquad (19.228)$$

where I_0 is the mass moment of inertia of the body about the CM.

Fig. 19.50

The CP is the point about which the sum of all the moments acting on the body is identically zero. This condition may be written as

$$\sum M_{CP} = 0 \qquad M - F_t q = 0 \qquad (19.229)$$

F_t and M from Eqs. (19.227) and (19.228) are substituted into Eq. (19.229), with the result

$$(I_0 + mr_c^2)(\alpha) - mr_c \alpha q = 0 \qquad (19.230)$$

$$q = \frac{I_0 + mr_c^2}{mr_c} = r_c + \frac{I_0}{mr_c} \qquad (19.231)$$

The term I_0 may be written as

$$I_0 = k_0^2 m \qquad (19.232)$$

where k_0 is the centroidal radius of gyration. Equation (19.231) now appears as

$$q = r_c + \frac{k_0^2 m}{mr_c} = r_c + \frac{k_0^2}{r_c} \qquad (19.233)$$

The separation distance δ between CP and CM is

$$\delta = q - r_c = r_c + \frac{k_0^2}{r_c} - r_c \qquad \delta = \frac{k_0^2}{r_c} \qquad (19.234)$$

It may be seen from Eq. (19.234) that δ is never zero.

The body shown in Fig. 19.50 is now imagined to represent a baseball bat. The player's hands are at the fixed point, and the moment applied by the player's hands imparts the angular acceleration α to the bat. If the bat strikes the ball so that the line of action of the force between these two elements passes through the CP, this force will cause no moment about the CP. If, however, the bat strikes the ball at a different location, a moment about the CP is produced. This moment must be counteracted by a sudden change in the value of F_t, the force exerted by the player's hands on the bat handle.

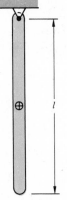

Fig. 19.51

Example 19.15 Figure 19.51 shows a slender rod of mass m which is hinged at one end. Find the location of the center of percussion.

Solution For a slender rod,

$$I_0 = \tfrac{1}{12}ml^2 \qquad (19.235)$$

and

$$k_0 = \sqrt{\frac{I_0}{m}} = \sqrt{\frac{\frac{1}{12}ml^2}{m}} = 0.289l \qquad (19.236)$$

Using Eq. (19.233), we get

$$q = r_c + \frac{k_0^2}{r_c} = 0.5l + \frac{(0.289l)^2}{0.5l} = 0.667l \qquad (19.237)$$

The distance between the CP and the hinge is exactly two-thirds the length of the rod.

When a rigid body moves in plane motion, all points in the body maintain the same respective distance from some fixed reference plane throughout the entire motion. Only the components of force which lie in the plane of motion contribute to the motion of the body.

A preliminary, necessary step in the solution of any problem in plane motion of a rigid body is to draw a complete free body diagram. If the body rotates about a fixed point, the rotational equation of motion is

$$M = I\alpha \tag{19.238}$$

where M = resultant external moment which acts on the body
I = mass moment of inertia about the fixed point
α = angular acceleration of the body

The force **F** exerted by the ground on the body at the fixed point is found from

$$\mathbf{F} = m\mathbf{a}_c \tag{19.239}$$

where $\mathbf{a}_c$ is the translational acceleration of the center of mass and m is the mass of the body. The force **F** can have at most two rectangular components which lie in the plane of the motion. If the resultant external moment M has a constant magnitude, the angular acceleration is constant. For this case, the angular velocity and displacement satisfy the equations

$$\omega = \omega_0 + \alpha t \tag{19.240}$$

$$\theta = \theta_0 + \omega_0 t + \tfrac{1}{2}\alpha t^2 \tag{19.241}$$

$$\omega^2 = \omega_0^2 + 2\alpha(\theta - \theta_0) \tag{19.242}$$

The case of general plane motion of a rigid body may be described by the sum of the translational motion of the center of mass, and the rotational motion about this point. The two governing equations of motion are

$$M_0 = I_0\alpha \qquad \mathbf{F} = m\mathbf{a}_c \tag{19.243}$$

where I_0 is the mass moment of inertia about the center of mass. The force **F** can have at most two rectangular components which lie in the plane of the motion.

In pure rolling of a rigid cylindrical body,

$$v_c = r\omega \qquad a_c = r\alpha \tag{19.244}$$

where v_c and a_c = translational velocity and acceleration, respectively, of the center of mass
ω and α = angular velocity and acceleration, respectively, of the body
r = radius of the body

In order to have pure rolling motion, the tangential friction force exerted by the plane on the body must satisfy the equations

$$M_0 = I_0 \alpha \qquad M_0 = Fr \qquad F < F_{max} = \mu_s N \quad (19.245)$$

where F = friction force
N = normal force on the body
μ_s = coefficient of static friction

The problem of plane motion of a rigid body may be solved by using inertia forces and moments. It is recommended that the beginning reader formulate the problem in terms of the resultant force or moment found from a free-body diagram, and then use the inertia force method to verify the solutions.

A certain point on a rigid body which experiences angular acceleration about a fixed point is called the center of percussion. The sum about this point of all of the moments which act on the body is always zero. The center of percussion is located at the distance q from the fixed point, where

$$q = r_c + \frac{I_0}{mr_c} \qquad (19.246)$$

The distance between the center of mass and the fixed point is r_c, and the center of percussion, the center of mass, and the fixed point all lie on the same straight line.

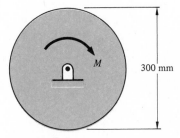

Fig. P19.1

PROBLEMS

19.1 The disk in Fig. P19.1 is acted upon by a couple M with constant magnitude 10 N·m. The mass of the disk is 5 kg.
(a) Find the angular acceleration of the disk.
(b) Find the angular velocity after the disk has completed two revolutions, starting from rest.

19.2 Figure P19.2 shows a slender rigid rod of weight 10 lb. Find the value of the moment M that acts on the rod, if the magnitude of the angular acceleration is 26 rad/s^2.

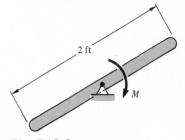

Fig. P19.2

19.3 Figure P19.3 shows a heavy cast-iron flywheel that rotates at a constant speed of 150 r/min. A friction braking system is used to bring the flywheel to rest. When the flywheel is braked, it experiences a constant retarding moment of 5 N·m. The mass moment of inertia of the flywheel about its center axis is 6.25 kg·m^2.
(a) How long does it take the flywheel to come to rest?
(b) Through how many revolutions does the flywheel rotate before coming to rest?

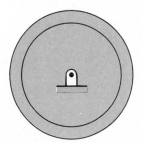

Fig. P19.3

19.4 A machinist sharpens a chisel against a grinding wheel, as shown in Fig. P19.4. The chisel is held against the wheel for 5 s. During this time the speed of the wheel changes from 3,600 r/min to 3,450 r/min. The mass moment of inertia of the wheel is 0.044 lb·s²·in.

Find the tangential component of the force exerted by the chisel on the wheel. Assume the chisel exerts a constant force on the wheel.

19.5 The motor that drives the grinding wheel in Prob. 19.4 exerts a constant torque of 3 in·lb. How long does it take the wheel to return to its original speed after the chisel is removed?

19.6 Figure P19.6 shows a slender rod on which are positioned two masses. These masses may be considered to be point masses, and the mass of the rod may be neglected. A constant moment, about the hinge, is applied to the system when the masses are in solid position shown, and the resulting acceleration is 68.4 rad/s². Find the acceleration if the same moment is applied to the system when the masses are in the dashed positions shown in the figure.

19.7 The angular velocity-time diagram of a rigid body that rotates about a fixed axis is shown in Fig. P19.7. If the mass moment of inertia of the body about the fixed axis is 0.125 lb·s²·in, find the value of the moment that acts on the body during the time interval $0 \le t \le 2s$.

19.8 See Fig. P19.8 for the angular acceleration-time diagram of a rigid body that rotates about a fixed axis. The maximum value of the magnitude of the moment, about the fixed axis, that acts on the body is 12 N·m. Find the value of the mass moment of inertia of the body.

19.9 Do the same as in P19.8, for the angular acceleration-time diagram shown in Fig. P19.9.

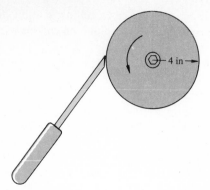

Fig. P19.4

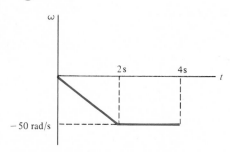

Fig. P19.6

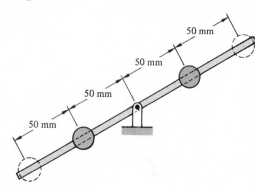

Fig. P19.7

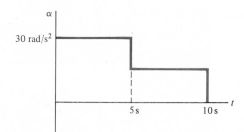

Fig. P19.8

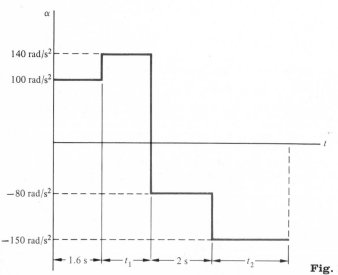

Fig. P19.9

19.10 Figure P19.10 shows a pulley about which passes a belt. At a certain instant, the belt forces have the constant values shown in the figure, and the mass moment of inertia of the pulley is $0.4\ \text{lb·s}^2\text{·in}$. Find the angular acceleration of the pulley, if the belts are assumed not to slip.

19.11 The 4-kg disk shown in Fig. P19.11 is initially at rest at time $t = 0$. A force of 50 N is applied to the thin, inextensible cable wrapped around the disk.
(*a*) Find the angular acceleration of the disk.
(*b*) Find the angular velocity, and the total angular displacement, of the disk 4 s after the force has been applied.
(*c*) Find the angular velocity of the disk after this element has completed four revolutions.

19.12 Do the same as in Prob. 19.11 if, at the time that the force is applied, the disk has a counterclockwise angular velocity of 30 rad/s.

19.13 Do the same as in Prob. 19.11 if, in addition to the cable force, the disk is acted on by a counterclockwise couple of magnitude $2\ \text{N·m}$. The couple acts in the plane of the disk.

19.14 A thin, inextensible string is wrapped around a cylinder, as shown in Fig. P19.14. At $t = 3$ s the motion of the string is to the right, with a velocity of 2 m/s and with constant acceleration. At this instant, point *a* on the string is coincident with point *b* on the cylinder. At $t = 5$ s, point *a* has moved 2.4 m to the right of its original position. If the string tensile force is 12 N, find the mass moment of inertia of the cylinder.

19.15 A belt drives a roller with a mass moment of inertia of $0.025\ \text{lb·s}^2\text{·in}$, as shown in Fig. P19.15. At a certain instant, the angular acceleration of the roller is 200 rad/s².
(*a*) Find the tangential force exerted by the belt on the roller.
(*b*) Is it necessary in solving part *a* to assume that the belt does not slip with respect to the roller?

19.16 The cylinder arrangement shown in Fig. P19.16 rests in a trough. Find the value of the constant forces P applied to the thin, inextensible cables, if the unit experiences an angular acceleration of 40 rad/s². The mass moment of inertia of the cylinder arrangement is $0.164\ \text{kg·m}^2$, and the mass is 185 kg.

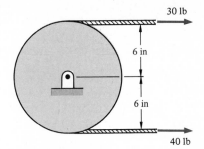

Fig. P19.10

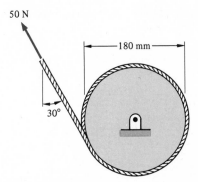

Fig. P19.11

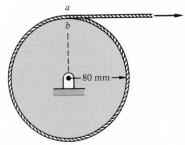

Fig. P19.14

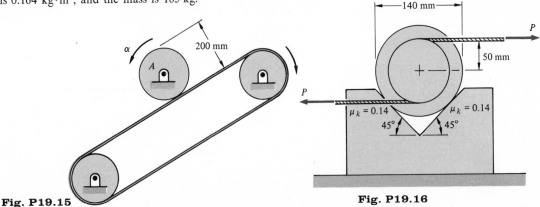

Fig. P19.15

Fig. P19.16

19.17 A cylinder of mass 6 kg rests in a trough, as shown in Fig. P19.17. A counterclockwise couple in the plane of the figure, of constant magnitude 3.8 N·m, is applied to the cylinder. Find the resulting angular acceleration.

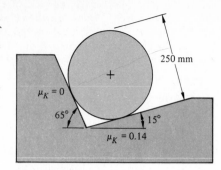

Fig. P19.17

19.18 The disk in Fig. P19.18 is attached to a shaft supported by two bearings equally spaced from the disc. When the disk rotates at a speed of 3,000 r/min, a force of 600 N is transmitted to the bearings. Find the eccentricity of the disk. (The eccentricity is the distance between the center of mass and the axis of rotation.) The thickness of the disk is 18 mm, and the density is 7,830 kg/m³.

Note: Several of the following problems use mass moments of inertia found as solutions to certain problems in Chapter 18. The original problem number is indicated in parentheses.

19.19 Figure P19.19 shows a cross-section view of a steel pulley with three different diameters. Find the value of the applied moment, about the center axis, which will accelerate the pulley at 250 rad/s². The specific weight of steel is 489 lb/ft³. (Prob. 18.33.)

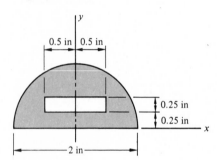

Fig. P19.18

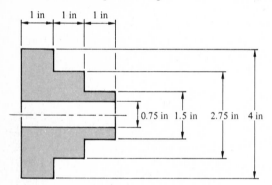

Fig. P19.19

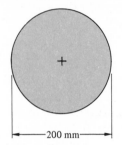

Fig. P19.20

19.20 A plate with a rectangular cutout, shown in Fig. P19.20, is made of brass strip of thickness 0.125 in. The plate is attached to a shaft, supported by bearings, which is collinear with the x axis. The specific weight of brass is 534 lb/ft³. (Prob. 18.24.)

(a) Find the value of the moment acting on the plate, about the x axis, that will produce an angular acceleration of 300 rad/s².

(b) Find the force exerted on the shaft when the plate rotates at 4,000 r/min.

19.21 Do the same as in Prob. P19.20, if the design of the plate is changed to the elliptical shape with two rectangular cutouts, shown in Fig. P19.21. (Prob. 18.25.)

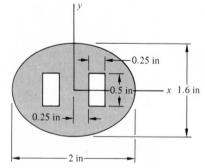

Fig. P19.21

19.22 The disk shown in Fig. P19.22 is made of bronze, with $\rho = 8,800$ kg/m³. It is mounted on a shaft of negligible mass. When a constant moment is applied to the shaft, the disk reaches a speed of 1,500 r/min in 10.8 s. Find the magnitude of the moment. (Prob. 18.46.)

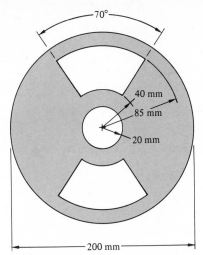

Fig. P19.22

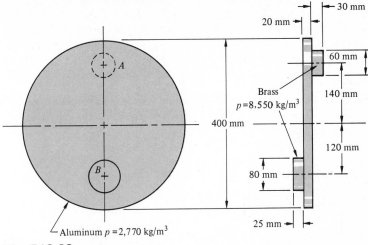

Fig. P19.23

19.23 Two cylindrical weights are attached to a circular disk, Fig. P19.23, which is attached to the midpoint of a shaft supported by bearings. Find the force exerted by the bearings on the shaft when the disk rotates at 160 r/min. (Prob. 18.38.)

19.24 Figure P19.24 shows the cross section of a proposed lightweight flywheel design. The density of steel is 7,830 kg/m³, and the density of aluminum is 2,770 kg/m³. Find the required value of the applied moment, about the center axis, that will accelerate the flywheel at 80 rad/s². (Prob. 18.64.)

19.25 At the instant shown in Fig. P19.25, the rod has an angular velocity of 26 r/min.
(*a*) Find the angular acceleration of the rod at this instant.
(*b*) State how the result in part *a* would change if the angular velocity of the rod, at the instant shown in the figure, were 50 r/min in a clockwise sense.

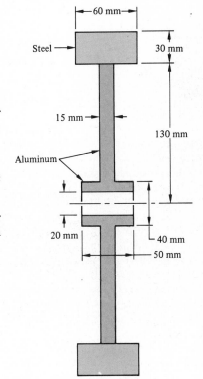

Fig. P19.24

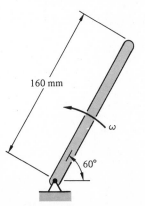

Fig. P19.25

19.26 The rod of weight 6 lb in Fig. P19.26 is initially supported by a cable.

(*a*) Find the angular acceleration of the rod at the instant that the string is cut.

(*b*) Find the angular velocity of the rod at this instant.

19.27 A simple pendulum is released from rest at position *a* in Fig. P19.27. The velocity of the pendulum bob can be shown to have the form $v = \sqrt{2\,gl\cos\theta}$. Find the force acting on the hinge pin when the pendulum is in position *b*.

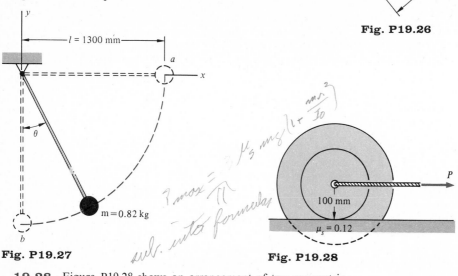

Fig. P19.26

Fig. P19.27

Fig. P19.28

19.28 Figure P19.28 shows an arrangement of two concentric cylinders joined to each other and moving in the plane of the figure. (*a*) Find the maximum permissible value of the cable tensile force *P* if the unit is to roll without slipping. (*b*) Find the maximum value of the angular acceleration of the cylinder, if the unit is to roll without slipping. The mass is 6 kg and the centroidal mass moment of inertia is 0.1 kg·m².

19.29 The cable that acts on the cylinder unit in Fig. P19.28 is now inclined, as shown in Fig. P19.29.

(*a*) Derive a general expression for the maximum value of force *P* for which the cylinder unit may roll without slipping. Express the answer in terms of μ_s, *r*, *m*, θ and I_o, the centroidal mass moment of inertia.

(*b*) Find the numerical value of the result in part *a*, and compare it with the solution to Prob. 19.28. $\mu_s = 0.12$, *r* = 100 mm, *m* = 6 kg, and $I_o = 0.1$ kg·m². Use values of θ of 15°, 30°, and 45°.

19.30 A thin, inextensible string is wrapped around the inner diameter of the cylinder arrangement shown in Fig. P19.30. The mass of the unit is 8.2 kg, and the mass moment of inertia about the center axis is 0.15 kg·m². (*a*) Find the maximum permissible value of the cable tensile force, if the unit is to roll without slipping. (*b*) Find the maximum value of the angular acceleration of the cylinder, if the unit is to roll without slipping.

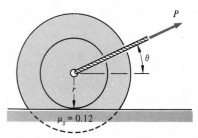

Fig. P19.29

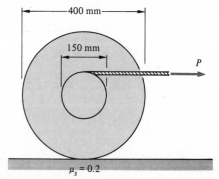

Fig. P19.30

19.31 Do the same as in Prob. 19.30, if the string is arranged as shown in Fig. P19.31.

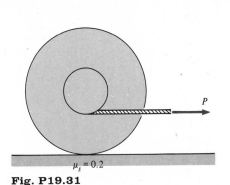

$\mu_s = 0.2$

Fig. P19.31

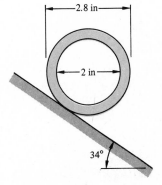

$\mu_s = 0.2$

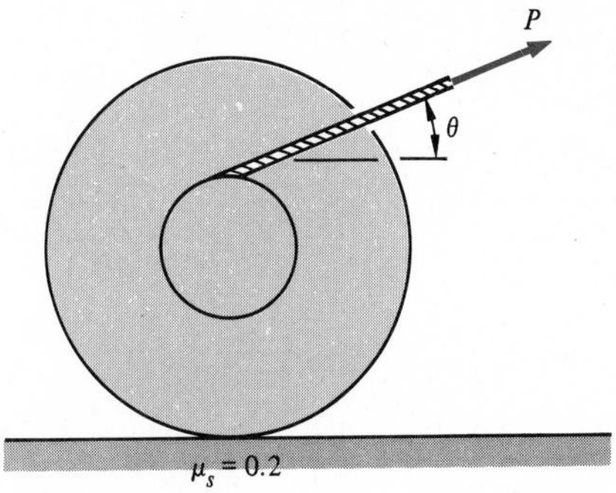

Fig. P19.32

19.32 Do the same as in Prob. 19.30, if the cable which acts on the cylinder unit is inclined, as shown in Fig. P19.32. $\theta = 20°$.

19.33 A hollow cylinder rolls down the incline shown in Fig. P19.33. The material of the cylinder is aluminum, with $\gamma = 0.1$ lb/in³, and the length is 3.6 in. For what range of values of the coefficient of static friction will the cylinder roll without sliding?

19.34 A homogeneous cylinder is released from rest at position a in Fig. P19.34. It rolls without sliding until it reaches position b. Length bc of the inclined plane is contaminated with lubricant and, for the purpose of this problem, the coefficient of friction on this surface may be assumed to be zero.
(a) Find the initial angular acceleration of the cylinder.
(b) Find the value of the friction force that acts on the cylinder in the regime ab.
(c) Find the angular velocity, and the velocity of the center, when the cylinder reaches position b.
(d) Do the same as in part c, when the cylinder reaches position c.

2.8 in
2 in
34°

Fig. P19.33

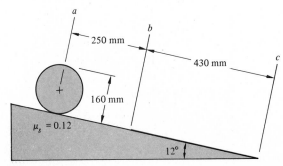

a
250 mm
b
430 mm
c
160 mm
$\mu_s = 0.12$
12°

Fig. P19.34

19.35 A cylinder is released from rest in the position shown in Fig. P19.35.

(a) For what value of β will the cylinder roll, without slipping, down the plane in the minimum time?

(b) Find the time for the motion in part a.

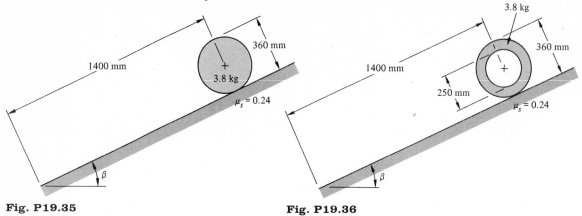

Fig. P19.35   Fig. P19.36

19.36 Do the same as in Prob. 19.35 if the cylinder is hollow, as shown in Fig. P19.36.

19.37 Fig. P19.37 shows the two cylinders of Example 19.7. Both cylinders start from rest and roll down the inclined plane, and $\beta = 10°$. Find the position of cylinder B, given by the distance l, if both cylinders reach the 18-in displacement at the same time.

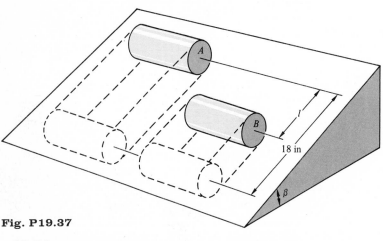

Fig. P19.37

19.38 Figure P19.38 shows a Yo-Yo of weight 0.15 lb modeled as a cylindrical disk connected to an inextensible cable. At the instant shown in the figure, the Yo-Yo has a counterclockwise angular velocity of 30 rad/s.

(a) Find the maximum height that the Yo-Yo will attain.

(b) Find the time that corresponds to the motion in part a.

(c) Do the same as in part a if, at a time 0.1 s later than that shown in the figure, the cable is cut.

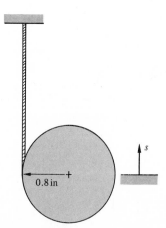

Fig. P19.38

19.39 (*a*) Find the maximum value of β in Fig. P19.39 for which the solid sphere can roll down the plane without sliding.

(*b*) Find the numerical value of β if the coefficient of static friction is 0.23.

19.40 Do the same as in Prob. 19.39, if the sphere is hollow, with an outside diameter 40 percent greater than the inside diameter.

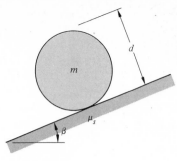

Fig. P19.39

19.41 The system of Example 19.8 is repeated in Fig. P19.41. Because of poor lubrication, the pulley must overcome a constant friction moment of 1.2 N·m as it rotates. $m_c = 1.2$ kg; $m_A = 2.8$ kg.

(*a*) Find the cable tensile forces, and the acceleration of the masses.

(*b*) Find the hinge pin force.

(*c*) Find the velocity of the blocks after block *B*, starting from rest, has moved downward 1 m.

The cable is assumed not to slip on the pulley.

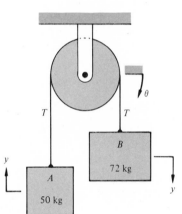

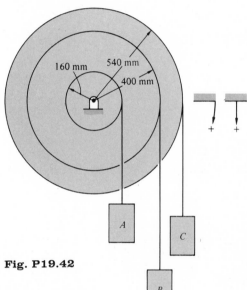

Fig. P19.41   **Fig. P19.42**

19.42 At the instant shown in Fig. P19.42, the stepped pulley rotates clockwise at 25 rad/s, with a clockwise angular acceleration of 6 rad/s². The masses of the three blocks are $m_A = 2$ kg, $m_B = 1.5$ kg, and $m_C = 1.2$ kg, and the cables are inextensible. Find the mass moment of inertia of the pulley.

19.43 Figure P19.43 shows a system of weights and pulleys. The cable is assumed not to slip on the pulleys.

(*a*) Find the acceleration of the weights, the tensile forces in the cable, and the hinge pin forces, when the system is released from rest. Neglect the mass moments of inertia of the pulleys.

(*b*) Find the velocities of the weights and pulleys when weight *B*, starting from rest, has moved upward 900 mm.

(*c*) Do the same as in part *a*, but include the effect of the mass moments of inertia of the pulleys. The masses and mass moments of inertia are $m_A = 20$ kg, $m_B = 14$ kg, $I_C = 0.005$ kg·m², and $I_D = 0.010$ kg·m².

(*d*) Do the same as in part *b*, for the conditions of part *c*.

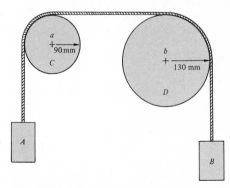

Fig. P19.43

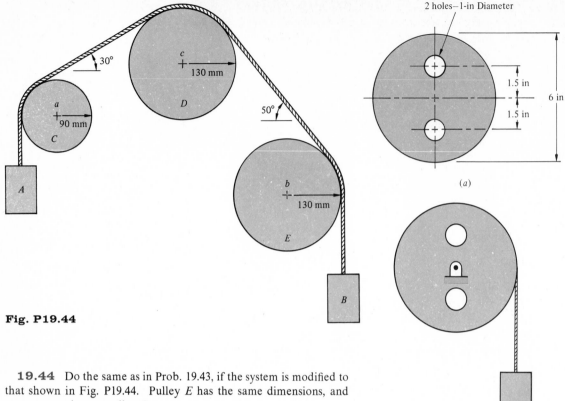

2 holes—1-in Diameter

1.5 in

6 in

1.5 in

(a)

Fig. P19.44

(b)

Fig. P19.45

19.44 Do the same as in Prob. 19.43, if the system is modified to that shown in Fig. P19.44. Pulley E has the same dimensions, and mass properties, as pulley D.

19.45 The disk shown in Fig. P19.45a has two holes in it and is made of 0.5-in-thick aluminum plate. The specific weight of aluminum is 173 lb/ft³. A thin, inextensible cable is wrapped around the rim of the disk and attached to a block, as shown in Fig. P19.45b. When the system is released from rest, the weight moves downward through a distance of 26 in in 12 s. Find the weight of the block. (Prob. 18.37.)

19.46 A body with the form of a rectangular parallelepiped rolls without slipping on two cylindrical rollers, as shown in Fig. P19.46. The mass of each roller is 1,200 kg, and the mass of the body is 2,200 kg. Find the acceleration of the body.

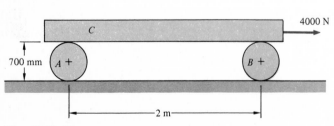

Fig. P19.46

19.47 Figure P19.47 shows a rack-and-pinion gear arrangement. The rack may be approximated as a steel rod of 0.5-in by 0.5-in square cross section, and the pinion may be approximated as a 0.5-in-thick steel disk. All frictional effects may be neglected. The specific weight of steel is 489 lb/ft³. At $t = 0$ the system is released from rest in the position shown in the figure.

(a) Find the acceleration of the rack.

(b) Find the time at which the rack loses contact with the pinion.

(c) Find the velocity of the rack at the position where the rack loses contact with the pinion.

(d) How would the results in parts b and c change if the pinion had zero mass?

19.48 Do the same as in Prob. 19.47, if the pinion must overcome a constant friction moment of 1.2 in·lb.

19.49 Figure P19.49 shows a pair of meshing gears that lie in a common plane. The gears are designated 1 and 2, with the corresponding number of teeth N_1 and N_2. The kinematic action of the set of gears is that of pure rolling of two cylinders, with the pitch diameters d_1 and d_2, with no slipping. The equations which describe the motion and geometry relationships between the gears are

$$\frac{\theta_1}{\theta_2} = \frac{\omega_1}{\omega_2} = \frac{\alpha_1}{\alpha_2} = \frac{d_2}{d_1} = \frac{N_2}{N_1} \qquad \frac{N_1}{N_2} = \frac{d_1}{d_2}$$

The mass moment of inertia of a gear is assumed to be the same as that of a disk whose diameter is equal to that of the pitch diameter of the gear, and with the thickness of the gear.

(a) Find the accelerations of gears 1 and 2, if a clockwise moment of magnitude 15 in·lb, in the plane of the gear, is applied to gear 1.

(b) Do the same as in part a, if the moment is applied to gear 2 instead of gear 1.

The gears are steel, with $\gamma = 489$ lb/ft³, $d_1 = 4$ in, and $d_2 = 10$ in. The thickness of the gears is 1 in.

19.50 Do the same as in Prob. 19.49, if the same clockwise moment of 15 in·lb is applied to both gears.

19.51 A counterclockwise moment of magnitude 1.2 N·m is applied to gear 1 in Fig. P19.51. Find the angular accelerations of the three gears. The gears are made of 20-mm-thick gray cast iron, with $\rho = 7,080$ kg/m³.

19.52 Do the same as in Prob. 19.51, if the moment is applied to gear 2.

19.53 Do the same as in Prob. 19.51, if the moment is applied to gear 3.

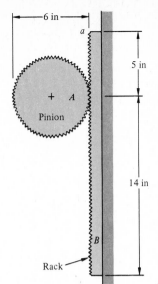

Fig. P19.47

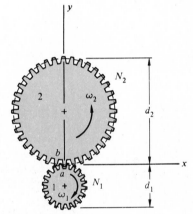

Fig. P19.49

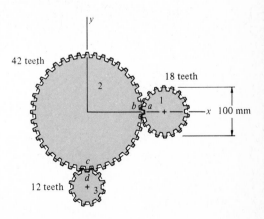

Fig. P19.51

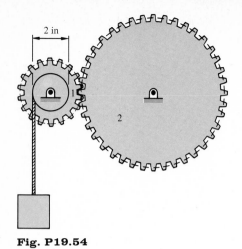

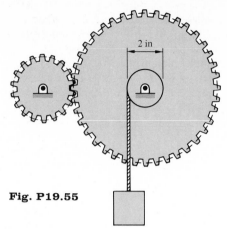

Fig. P19.54

Fig. P19.55

19.54 The gears of Prob. 19.49 are shown in Fig. P19.54. An inextensible cable is wrapped around a cylinder, of negligible mass, attached to gear 1. An 8-lb weight is attached to the cable.

(*a*) Find the acceleration of the weight and the force· in the cable.

(*b*) Find the velocity of the weight after this element, starting from rest, has lowered through a distance of 20 in.

19.55 Do the same as in Prob. 19.54, if the gears and weight are arranged as shown in Fig. P19.55.

19.56 Figure P19.56 shows an automobile that moves along a horizontal roadway. The coefficient of static friction between the tires and the roadway is 0.68, and the dimensions of the vehicle are $a = 45$ in, $b = 65$ in, and $c = 21$ in. The automobile is assumed to have brakes on the rear wheels only; and $W = 3,000$ lb.

(*a*) Find the maximum possible value, in symbolic form, of the braking deceleration of the automobile, by the direct application of Newton's second law.

(*b*) Do the same as in part *a*, by using the inertia force technique.

(*c*) Find the numerical value of the result found in parts *a* and *b*.

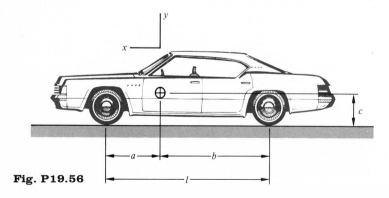

Fig. P19.56

19.57 Do the same as in Prob. 19.56, if the automobile has brakes on the front wheels only.

19.58 (*a*) Do the same as in Prob. 19.56, if the automobile has brakes on all four wheels.

(*b*) Find the reaction forces of the roadway on the tires for the cases when the automobile is stationary and when it experiences maximum deceleration.

19.59 The automobile in Prob. 19.56 ascends the straight inclined roadway shown in Fig. P19.59. $\beta = 15°$. The automobile is assumed to have rear-wheel drive only.

(*a*) Find the maximum possible value, in symbolic form, of the theoretical acceleration of the automobile, by direct application of Newton's second law.

(*b*) Do the same as in part *a*, by using the inertia force technique.

(*c*) Find the numerical value of the result found in parts *a* and *b*.

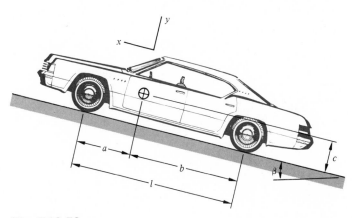

Fig. P19.59

19.60 Do the same as in Prob. 19.59, if the automobile has front-wheel drive only.

19.61 (*a*) Do the same as in Prob. 19.59, if the automobile has four-wheel drive.

(*b*) Find the reaction forces of the roadway on the tires for the cases when the automobile is stationary, and when it experiences maximum acceleration.

19.62 Do the same as in Prob. 19.56, if the vehicle ascends the roadway shown in Fig. P19.59.

19.63 Do the same as in Prob. 19.57, if the vehicle ascends the roadway shown in Fig. P19.59.

19.64 Do the same as in Prob. 19.58, if the vehicle ascends the roadway shown in Fig. P19.59.

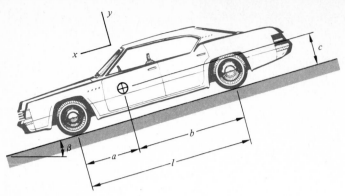

Fig. P19.65

19.65 The automobile in Prob. 19.56 descends the straight inclined roadway shown in Fig. P19.65. $\beta = 15°$. The automobile is assumed to have rear-wheel drive only.

(a) Find the maximum possible value, in symbolic form, of the theoretical acceleration of the automobile, by direct application of Newton's second law.

(b) Do the same as in part a, by using the inertia force technique.

(c) Find the numerical value of the result found in parts a and b.

19.66 Do the same as in Prob. 19.65, if the automobile has front-wheel drive only.

19.67 (a) Do the same as in Prob. 19.65, if the automobile has four-wheel drive.

(b) Find the reaction forces of the roadway on the tires for the cases when the automobile is stationary and when it experiences maximum acceleration.

19.68 Do the same as in Prob. 19.56, if the vehicle descends the roadway shown in Fig. P19.65.

19.69 Do the same as in Prob. 19.57, if the vehicle descends the roadway shown in Fig. P19.65.

19.70 Do the same as in Prob. 19.58, if the vehicle descends the roadway shown in Fig. P19.65.

19.71 A crate slides down an incline, as shown in Fig. P19.71. Find the normal and friction forces exerted on edges a and b.

19.72 Do the same as in Prob. 19.71, if the crate slides down the incline in the position shown in Fig. P19.72.

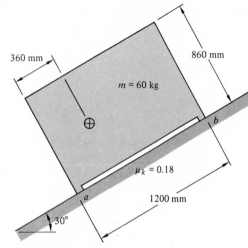

Fig. P19.71

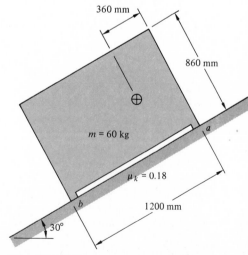

Fig. P19.72

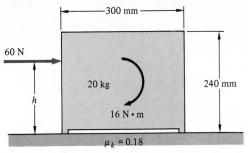

Fig. P19.73

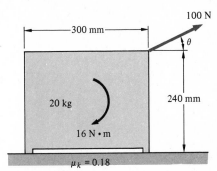

Fig. P19.74

19.73 For what range of values of h will the crate in Fig. P19.73 slide without tipping?

19.74 (a) Find the value of θ that will result in the maximum acceleration of the crate in Fig. P19.74.
(b) Do the same as in part a, if the 16-N·m moment is removed.

19.75 A cabinet on casters is pulled to the right on a horizontal floor by a constant force P, as shown in Fig. P19.75.
(a) Find the value of the acceleration of the cabinet that will just cause the rear wheels to lose contact with the floor.
(b) Find the value of the force P that corresponds to part a.
The mass of the cabinet is 160 kg.

19.76 Do the same as in Prob. 19.75, if the direction of the force is that shown in Fig. P19.76.

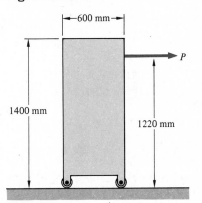

Fig. P19.75

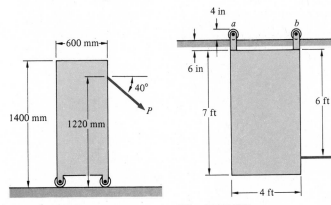

Fig. P19.76   Fig. P19.77

19.77 Figure P19.77 shows a heavy metal plate that moves on rollers along a conveyor rail. The constant force P causes the plate to accelerate to the right. Find the maximum value of acceleration that the plate may have if the rollers are not to lose contact with the rail. The plate is made of 0.5-in steel plate, with a specific weight of 489 lb/ft^3.

19.78 Do the same as in Prob. 19.77, if the plate is modified by cutting a hole through it, as shown in Fig. P19.78.

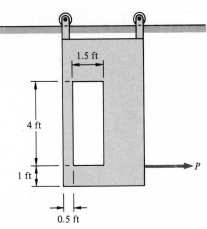

Fig. P19.78

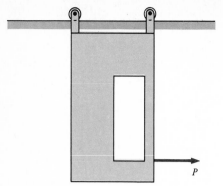

Fig. P19.79

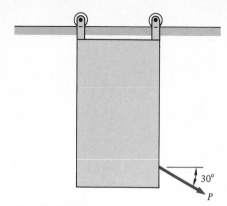

Fig. P19.80

19.79 Do the same as in Prob. 19.77, if the modified plate of Fig. P19.78 is mounted as shown in Fig. P19.79.

19.80 Do the same as in Prob. 19.77, if the force has the direction shown in Fig. P19.80.

19.81 A truck ascends the straight inclined roadway shown in Fig. P19.81.
(*a*) Develop the criteria for sliding or tipping motion of the crate as the truck accelerates.
(*b*) Do the same as in part *a,* for the case when the truck decelerates.
(*c*) Find the numerical results for parts *a* and *b,* using $\beta = 15°$ and the numerical data from Example 19.13.

19.82 Figure P19.82 shows a motorcycle driving around a horizontal circular track at constant speed.
(*a*) Find the value of angle β when the motorcycle travels at 40 mi/h.
(*b*) Find the maximum value of the speed of the motorcycle, if sliding motion is not to occur.
(*c*) Find the angle β that corresponds to the motion in part *b.*

19.83 A stunt driver in a circus drives a motorcycle around the inside wall of a cylindrical drum, as shown in Fig. P19.83. The coefficient of friction between the tires and the wall is 0.6.
(*a*) Find the minimum value of speed required if the motorcycle is not to slide down the wall.
(*b*) Find the maximum value of speed of the rider if, for physiological reasons, his body must not experience an acceleration greater than six times the gravitational acceleration.
(*c*) Find the angle β that corresponds to the motion in part *b.*

Fig. P19.81

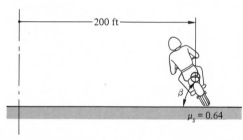

Fig. P19.82

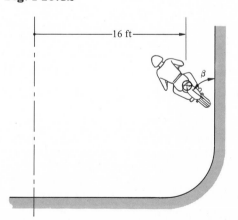

Fig. P19.83

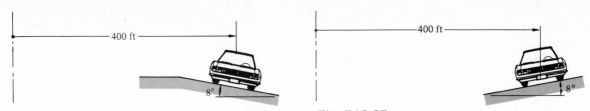

Fig. P19.84   **Fig. P19.85**

19.84 The vehicle of Example 19.14 travels with constant speed around the horizontal circular track shown in Fig. P19.84. Develop the criteria for the speeds at which sliding, and tipping, of the vehicle will occur.

19.85 Do the same as in Prob. 19.84, if the track is banked as shown in Fig. P19.85.

19.86 Figure P19.86 shows an experimental automobile testing track. Sliding motion of the automobile is impending when the vehicle is at rest. Find the resultant normal force on the inner and outer wheels, when the automobile travels at 200 km/h. Use the dimensions of Example 19.14.

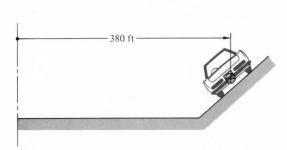

Fig. P19.86

19.87 through 19.89 Find the x coordinate of the center of percussion of the plane body shown.

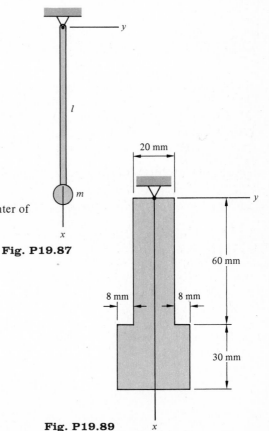

Fig. P19.87

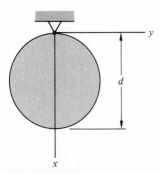

Fig. P19.88   **Fig. P19.89**

707

Fig. P19.90 shows a latching lever formed from a steel strip, to which is attached two cylindrical brass plugs. The specific weight of brass is 534 lb/ft³, and the specific weight of steel is 489 lb/ft³. (Prob. 18.65.)

(*a*) Find the value of the constant moment, about the *z* axis, that will cause the latch to rotate through 90° in 0.14 s.

(*b*) Find the *x* and *y* coordinates of the center of percussion.

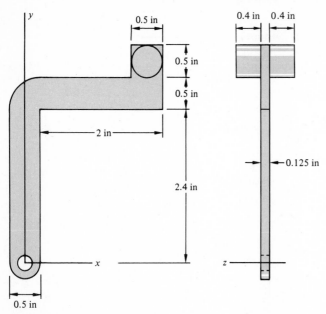

Fig. P19.90

20

Work-Energy Methods for Particles and Rigid Bodies

20.1 INTRODUCTION

This chapter considers a technique, referred to as the *work-energy method,* which may be used to solve problems in dynamics. The problems are formulated in terms of a quantity called energy. In its most fundamental conception, *energy* is understood to mean the capacity for doing work. It will be shown that energy may be stored in two forms in a mass element. The first form is due to the *position* of the mass element, and this energy is *potential energy.* The second way that energy may be stored in a mass element is when the body is in motion and thus has a nonzero velocity. This energy is called *kinetic energy.* The work-energy method considers states, or conditions, of motion *only at the beginning and end of the time interval* of interest in the problem. The solution yields no information whatsoever about the conditions *during* this interval. Also, when the work-energy method is used, a free-body diagram of the mass element is not necessarily required, and *the acceleration of the mass element never enters directly into the analysis.* This technique rests on the basic premise that matter can be neither created nor destroyed, and thus all the energy in the system must be accounted for.

The work-energy method has two major useful applications. It may be used either to obtain results which are directly useful, or to check the correctness of results obtained by the use of Newton's second law. Both of these outcomes will be illustrated in the examples in this chapter.

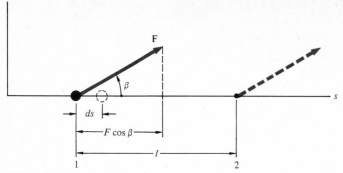

Fig. 20.1

20.2 WORK OF A FORCE

Figure 20.1 shows a force F which acts on a particle that is constrained to move along the s axis. The infinitesimal work dW done by the force on the particle as this element translates through the distance ds is defined to be

$$dW = (F \cos \beta) \, ds \qquad (20.1)$$

Equation (20.1) is the fundamental definition of the *work done* when a force acts through a displacement. Work is a scalar quantity, and the units of this term are the product of force and length. In U.S. Customary System (USCS) units, typical units for work would be the foot-pound (ft·lb) or pound-foot (lb·ft). Both ways of writing the work units are correct, but the foot-pound, or inch-pound (in·lb), is preferred in this book. In SI units, the basic unit of work is the product of newtons and meters, abbreviated N·m. It may be observed that the units of work are the same as those of couple, moment, and torque. In the case of SI units, the distinction between work units and moment units is clearly made. A magnitude of work of one newton-meter is defined to be one *joule,* with the symbol J. Thus, *all work and energy quantities in SI units are in joules.* No such distinction between work and moment units exists in USCS units. The conversion factor between work, or energy, in USCS units and SI units is 1 ft·lb = 1.356 J.

The force in Fig. 20.1 is now assumed to be of *constant* magnitude, direction, and sense. As the point of application of this force on the particle moves along the s axis in the positive coordinate sense, through distance l, the total work W_{12} done by the force on the particle is

$$W_{12} = (F \cos \beta) l \qquad (20.2)$$

where 1 and 2 represent the endpoints of the interval l. Equation (20.2) contains an implicit sign convention for work. If $-90° < \beta < 90°$, the component of force is in the direction of the motion of the particle, and the work term is positive. If

$90° < \beta < 270°$, then the senses of the force component and of the displacement are opposite, and the work term is negative. It follows that the work done by a force on a particle is positive if the sense of the component of force in the direction of motion is the same as the sense of motion of the particle.

It follows from Eq. (20.1) that the work done by the force is zero if $\beta = 90°$. Thus, *if the force is normal to the path of motion of the particle, this force does no work on the particle.* A common application of this statement occurs in the case of a particle which slides along a surface. In this case, the normal contact forces *do no work* since these forces, by definition, are normal to the direction of the sliding motion. Thus, only the friction forces may do work on the particle.

If either the force acting on the particle shown in Fig. 20.1 or the direction between this force and the displacement of the particle is not constant, then the expression for the work done on the particle has the general form

$$W_{12} = \int_0^l F \cos \beta \, ds \qquad (20.3)$$

This equation may be solved if the force F is a known function of the displacement s of the particle. This effect is illustrated in Example 20.3.

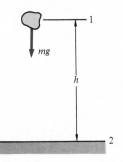

Fig. 20.2

Example 20.1 A particle is located at a distance h above the ground, as shown in Fig. 20.2.

a. Find the work done if the particle is allowed to fall to the ground.

b Find the magnitude of the work if the weight of the particle is 2.8 lb and $h = 100$ ft.

All air resistance effects may be neglected.

Solution

a The force acting on the particle is the static weight force mg, which has constant magnitude, direction, and sense. This weight force acts along the vertical direction, and there is no component of force normal to this direction. The work done by the force is

$$W_{12} = (F \cos \beta)l = mg(\cos 0°)h = mgh \qquad (20.4)$$

b For the numerical values of this example,

$$W_{12} = 2.8(100) = 280 \text{ ft} \cdot \text{lb} \qquad (20.5)$$

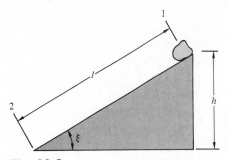

Fig. 20.3

Example 20.2 The particle in Example 20.1 is now allowed to slide down the frictionless, inclined plane shown in Fig. 20.3. Find the work done on the particle as this element travels through the distance l.

Solution The components of the weight force parallel and normal to the inclined plane are shown in Fig. 20.4. The normal component of the weight force does no work, since this force has no

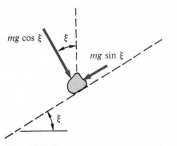

Fig. 20.4

component in the direction of the motion. The work done as the particle slides down the plane is

$$W_{12} = (F \cos \beta)l = (mg \sin \xi)l \qquad (20.6)$$

From Fig. 20.3,

$$l \sin \xi = h \qquad (20.7)$$

and the final expression for the work done on the particle is

$$W_{12} = mgh \qquad (20.8)$$

It may be seen that this result is exactly the same as that for the case of free fall of the particle. These two cases are examples of a *conservative force field,* and this concept will be considered further in a subsequent section of this chapter. It should also be noted that Fig. 20.4 is not a free-body diagram of the particle, but rather depicts the components of the applied force acting on the particle.

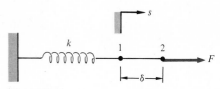

Fig. 20.5

Example 20.3 Figure 20.5 shows a helical spring which is acted on by a force F. The spring is assumed to be linear. This means that the spring constant k, which is a measure of the stiffness of the spring, is a constant with units of force divided by length. When $F = 0$, the end of the spring is at position 1.

a Find the work done by the force F on the spring as the end of the spring moves through the distance δ from 1 to 2.

b Find the work done by the internal force in the spring for the motion of part *a*.

The spring is assumed to be massless, so that all acceleration effects may be neglected.

Solution

a The general force relationship on the tip particle of the spring is shown in Fig. 20.6. The applied force F is opposed by the internal spring force F_s. The equilibrium requirement of the particle is

Fig. 20.6

$$\sum F = 0 \qquad F - F_s = 0 \qquad F = F_s \qquad (20.9)$$

Since the spring is linear,

$$F_s = ks \qquad (20.10)$$

and therefore

$$F = ks \qquad (20.11)$$

The work W_{12} done by the force F as the tip of the spring is stretched from position 1 to position 2 is

$$W_{12} = \int_1^2 (F \cos \beta) \, ds = \int_0^\delta (F \cos 0°) \, ds = \int_0^\delta F \, ds \quad (20.12)$$

$$= \int_0^\delta ks \, ds = \frac{ks^2}{2} \Big|_0^\delta = \frac{1}{2} k\delta^2 \qquad (20.13)$$

The spring force F_s acts in a sense which is opposite to the sense of motion of the tip of the spring. The work done by this force is, then,

$$W_s = \int_1^2 (F \cos \beta) \, ds = \int_0^\delta (F_s \cos 180°) \, ds = -\int_0^\delta F_s \, ds \quad (20.14)$$

$$= -\int_0^\delta ks\,ds = -\frac{ks^2}{2}\bigg|_0^\delta = -\frac{1}{2}k\delta^2 = -W_{12} \qquad (20.15)$$

It may be seen that the work done by the spring force is the *negative* of the work done by the applied force.

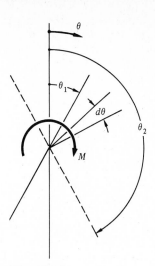

20.3 WORK OF A COUPLE, MOMENT, OR TORQUE

The work done by a couple, moment, or torque which acts through an angular displacement is defined in a similar way as the work of a force. Figure 20.7 shows a moment M which acts in the plane of the figure. The differential work which is done by the moment, as this quantity acts through the angle $d\theta$, is defined to be

$$dW = M\,d\theta \qquad (20.16)$$

Fig. 20.7

This equation is the fundamental definition of the work done when a moment acts through an angular displacement.

The work done as the moment acts through the angle between θ_1 and θ_2 is

$$W_{12} = \int_{\theta_1}^{\theta_2} M\,d\theta \qquad (20.17)$$

If the magnitude of the moment is *constant*, then Eq. (20.17) may be written as

$$W_{12} = \int_{\theta_1}^{\theta_2} M\,d\theta = M\int_{\theta_1}^{\theta_2} d\theta = M\theta\bigg|_{\theta_1}^{\theta_2} = M(\theta_2 - \theta_1) \quad (20.18)$$

The work quantity will be *positive* if the senses of the moment and the angular displacement are the *same*. It may be seen that the units of the work done by a couple, moment, or torque are again the product of force and length.

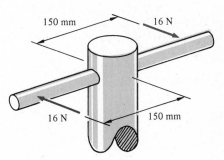

Example 20.4 A machinist uses a T-handle wrench to finish-ream a large drilled hole. The machinist applies equal and opposite forces of 16 N, at 150 mm from the center, as shown in Fig. 20.8. Find the work done when the reamer has rotated through 375°.

Fig. 20.8

Solution The forces applied to the handle are assumed to be constant, and the couple applied to the reamer is

$$M = 16\left(\frac{300}{1,000}\right) = 4.8 \text{ N·m} \qquad (20.19)$$

The work done is thus

$$W = M(\theta_2 - \theta_1) = (4.8 \text{ N·m})(375°)\frac{2\pi \text{ rad}}{360°} = 31.4 \text{ J} \quad (20.20)$$

20.4 ENERGY DUE TO POSITION— POTENTIAL ENERGY OF A PARTICLE

An energy term, which is a function only of the position of a particle, will now be considered. Figure 20.9 shows a particle resting on the ground. It is desired to raise the particle from the ground to the ledge at height h above the ground. A force F is applied to the particle, as shown in Fig. 20.9b, to elevate this mass element in a quasi-static manner. The term *quasi-static* means that the motion of the particle, as evidenced by the magnitude of the velocity, is so gradual that this motion may be thought of as a succession of states, in each of which the particle is in static equilibrium. Thus, all acceleration effects and the associated forces may be neglected. It follows that the force F must be only infinitesimally greater than the static weight mg, or

$$F \approx mg \qquad (20.21)$$

The work done by the force F in raising the particle is thus

$$W_{12} = (F \cos \beta)l = (mg \cos 0°)h = mgh \qquad (20.22)$$

At the conclusion of the process of raising the weight from the ground to the ledge, the work done on the weight in raising it is now "stored" in the weight, *by virtue of its position with respect to the ground from which it was raised.* This energy content is defined to be the *potential energy* of the weight. In its most basic conception, the potential energy of a body may be thought of as the ability of a body to do work when the position of the body changes. Since work is a scalar quantity, it follows that the potential energy is also a scalar quantity. In the above example, work was done on the weight as this element was moved from the ground to the ledge. When the weight rests on the ledge, the work done to place it in this position is transformed to a *stored* energy of the body. If the weight is imagined to return to the ground, then the stored potential energy could be used to do work as the weight force moves downward through the distance h.

The symbol V will be used to represent the potential energy of a mass element. In using energy methods to solve problems in dynamics, only the *change* in the potential energy, designated by ΔV, has any significance. This change is defined to be

$$\Delta V = V_2 - V_1 \qquad (20.23)$$

where the subscripts 1 and 2 represent the initial and final endpoints, respectively, of the interval of interest.

A concept of fundamental importance in the definition of potential energy is that of the datum. A *datum* is a position of the body at which the potential energy is arbitrarily defined to

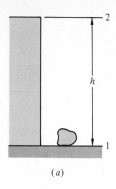

(a)

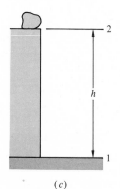

(b)

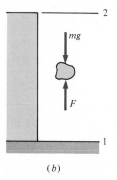

(c)

Fig. 20.9

714

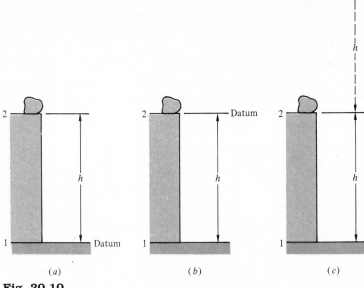

Fig. 20.10

be zero. Three possible choices of a datum for the system of Fig. 20.9 are shown in Fig. 20.10. In each case, the weight is raised through the distance h from the ground to the ledge. Numbers 1 and 2 designate the endpoints of the interval of interest in all three cases. Three different, arbitrary datums are chosen, as shown. The descriptions of the potential energy and the changes in this quantity are then as follows:

Datum at ground level (Fig. 20.10a):

$$V_1 = 0 \qquad V_2 = mgh \qquad (20.24)$$

$$\Delta V = V_2 - V_1 = mgh - 0 = mgh \qquad (20.25)$$

Datum at ledge (Fig. 20.10b):

$$V_1 = -mgh \qquad V_2 = 0 \qquad (20.26)$$

$$\Delta V = V_2 - V_1 = 0 - (-mgh) = mgh \qquad (20.27)$$

Datum at height h above ledge (Fig. 20.10c):

$$V_1 = -2mgh \qquad V_2 = -mgh \qquad (20.28)$$

$$\Delta V = V_2 - V_1 = -mgh - (-2mgh) = mgh \quad (20.29)$$

Terms such as V_1 and V_2 are defined in terms of the arbitrarily chosen datum of the problem. The *change* in the potential energy, by comparison, is completely independent of the choice of the datum. It may be seen in the above problem that the *change* in potential energy is the same for all three cases. This is an expected result, since a single physical problem is under consideration.

In this chapter two types of potential energy in mechanical systems will be considered. The first type is referred to as *raising a weight*. If a weight is raised, work is done *on* the weight, and potential energy is stored *in* the weight. The magnitude of the *increase* in the potential energy is simply the product of the magnitudes of the weight and the vertical distance through which the weight is raised. If the weight is lowered, work is done *by* the weight as the potential energy decreases. The second type of potential energy is the energy stored in a spring because of the deflection of this element. The following example illustrates this effect.

Fig. 20.11

Example 20.5 The linear, helical spring shown in Fig. 20.11 is initially in static equilibrium when acted on by a force $F_1 = 40$ N. The magnitude of this force is now increased until the end of the spring moves to point 2.

a Find the change in the potential energy stored in the spring as the end is stretched from 1 to 2.

b Find the total potential energy stored in the spring when the end of the spring is at position 2.

Solution

a The work required to stretch a linear, helical spring through a distance s is given by

$$W = \tfrac{1}{2}ks^2 \qquad (20.30)$$

where k is the spring constant, with the units of force per unit length. This work done on the spring is stored as potential energy in the spring. It may be seen that the datum for this energy quantity is implicitly given by Eq. (20.30) as $s = 0$.

At position 1,

$$F_1 = ks_1 \qquad s_1 = \frac{F_1}{k} = \frac{40 \text{ N}}{3,200 \text{ N/m}} = 0.0125 \text{ m} \qquad (20.31)$$

The displacement at point 2 is

$$s_2 = s_1 + 28 \text{ mm} = 0.0125 + \frac{28}{1,000} = 0.0405 \text{ m} \qquad (20.32)$$

The change in the potential energy as the spring is stretched from 1 to 2 is

$$\Delta V = V_2 - V_1 = \tfrac{1}{2}ks_2^2 - \tfrac{1}{2}ks_1^2 = \tfrac{1}{2}k(s_2^2 - s_1^2) \qquad (20.33)$$

$$= \tfrac{1}{2}(3,200)(0.0405^2 - 0.0125^2) = 2.37 \text{ N·m} = 2.37 \text{ J} \qquad (20.34)$$

b The *total* potential energy when the spring is stretched to position 2 is

$$V_2 = \tfrac{1}{2}ks_2^2 = \tfrac{1}{2}(3,200)(0.0405^2)$$
$$= 2.62 \text{ N·m} = 2.62 \text{ J} \qquad (20.35)$$

20.5 ENERGY DUE TO MOTION—KINETIC ENERGY OF A PARTICLE

Section 20.4 considered a form of energy, referred to as potential energy, which is stored by virtue of the position of a particle. In this section a second, distinct form of energy of a particle will be identified. This energy quantity is *kinetic energy,* and it is associated with the *motion* of a particle.

Figure 20.12 shows a particle which moves along a curved path in a horizontal plane. The coordinate of the length along the curved path is s. Since the path of the particle is horizontal, there is no change in the elevation of the particle with respect to a datum plane. Thus, there is no change in the potential energy of the particle. The particle is acted on by a resultant force F, with the normal and tangential components F_n and F_t. Newton's second law in the tangential direction is written as

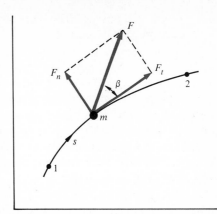

Fig. 20.12

$$F_t = ma_t \qquad (20.36)$$

The tangential acceleration a_t may be written as

$$a_t = \frac{dv}{dt} \qquad (20.37)$$

where v is the scalar magnitude of the velocity, or the speed, of the particle.

The force F_t may be written as

$$F_t = F \cos \beta \qquad (20.38)$$

and Eq. (20.36) now appears as

$$F \cos \beta = m \frac{dv}{dt} \qquad (20.39)$$

The term v is defined in terms of the length coordinate s along the curve by

$$v = \frac{ds}{dt} \qquad (20.40)$$

from which

$$dt = \frac{ds}{v} \qquad (20.41)$$

The dt term is eliminated from Eqs. (20.39) and (20.41), with the result

$$F \cos \beta = m \frac{dv}{(ds/v)} = mv \frac{dv}{ds} \qquad (20.42)$$

$$(F \cos \beta)\, ds = mv\, dv \qquad (20.43)$$

Equation (20.43) is now integrated between the two positions 1 and 2 shown in the figure, and the result is

717

$$\int_1^2 (F \cos \beta) \, ds = \int_1^2 mv \, dv = m \int_1^2 v \, dv \qquad (20.44)$$

$$= m \frac{v^2}{2} \Big|_{v_1}^{v_2} = \tfrac{1}{2}mv_2^2 - \tfrac{1}{2}mv_1^2 \qquad (20.45)$$

The term on the left side of Eq. (20.45), by comparison with Eq. (20.3), is seen to be the work done on the particle between positions 1 and 2. The terms on the right side have the form $\tfrac{1}{2}mv^2$. This latter term is referred to as the *kinetic energy of the particle*. The symbol T is used to designate this quantity, and

$$T = \tfrac{1}{2}mv^2 \qquad (20.46)$$

The kinetic energy of a particle is an energy which the particle possesses because of its motion. Since Newton's second law was used to derive the above result, the term v is an *absolute velocity* which must be defined, or measured, in an inertial coordinate system. It may be seen that the kinetic energy of a particle is zero only when the velocity of the particle is zero, and at no other time. Thus, the datum for all kinetic energy terms is the condition of zero velocity. In its most basic conception, the kinetic energy of a body may be thought of as the ability of a body to do work when the velocity of the body changes.

In the problem above *work was done on the particle,* as the force F_t acted through a certain displacement, to give this mass element an increase in velocity. If the particle is imagined to slow down to a lower velocity, then the stored kinetic energy of the particle could be used to do work. Since work is a scalar quantity, it follows from Eq. (20.45) that kinetic energy is also a scalar quantity.

A significant difference between potential and kinetic energy terms may be observed. In the case of potential energy, a datum is chosen and the potential energy is arbitrarily defined to be zero at this point. The criterion for the selection of this datum is solely convenience. In the case of the kinetic energy, the datum of zero energy *must* correspond to the state of zero velocity of the particle. From consideration of Eq. (20.45), it may be seen that the work done by the force on the particle produces a change in the kinetic energy, and therefore a change in the velocity, of the particle.

The path, shown in Fig. 20.12, of the particle was assumed to lie in a horizontal plane. Thus, there are no changes in the potential energy of the particle. This fact does not limit the generality of the final result obtained in Eq. (20.45). If the path of the particle did not lie in a horizontal plane, part of the applied force would be used to change the potential energy, while the remainder would be used to change the kinetic energy of the particle.

Finally, if the force acting on the particle has *constant* magnitude, direction, and sense, then the work done is the product of the component of this force in the direction of motion and the displacement of the particle. If the force is variable, then the integral form on the left side of Eq. (20.45) must be used.

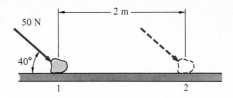

Fig. 20.13

Example 20.6 A particle of mass 2.4 kg is at rest in position 1 on the frictionless, horizontal track shown in Fig. 20.13. If a 50-N force at a constant inclination of 40° to the track is applied to the particle, find the speed of the particle as it passes position 2.

Solution The work done on the particle as it moves from 1 to 2 is

$$W_{12} = (F \cos \beta)l = (50 \cos 40°)2 = 76.6 \text{ N·m} = 76.6 \text{ J} \quad (20.47)$$

Equation (20.45) then has the form

$$W_{12} = \tfrac{1}{2}mv_2^2 - \tfrac{1}{2}mv_1^2 \quad (20.48)$$

$$76.6 = \tfrac{1}{2}(2.4)v_2^2 \qquad v_2 = 7.99 \text{ m/s} \quad (20.49)$$

20.6 CONSERVATION OF ENERGY—THE WORK-ENERGY METHOD FOR A PARTICLE

When a particle is acted on by a force, the particle's potential energy, kinetic energy, or both may be changed. A general formulation of this problem will be developed now. As a preliminary step, the concept of conservation of energy will be considered.

In the absence of nuclear effects, *energy in the physical universe can be neither created nor destroyed.* Energy may exist in one of four basic forms:

1. Mechanical energy
2. Electric energy
3. Chemical energy
4. Heat energy

Potential and kinetic energies of a mass particle are forms of mechanical energy. An example of electric energy is a charged capacitor. Chemical energy may be released during a chemical reaction, such as an explosion or a combustion process. Finally, the effect of heat energy is to change the temperature of a substance.

The relationships among potential and kinetic energies of mass particles, and work, heat, and chemical energy, are studied in detail in thermodynamics. The central objective in thermodynamics is the efficient transformation of heat energy into mechanical work. In this text, only the mechanical potential and kinetic energies of mass elements will be considered.

In problems in dynamics it is convenient to identify two types

719

of forces, referred to as conservative and nonconservative forces. The *conservative* forces produce changes in potential and kinetic energy which are fully recovered if the system is imagined to operate in reverse until the original condition is reached. An alternate statement of this effect is that the *conservative forces produce no permanent energy losses*. The energy changes caused by the application of *nonconservative* forces, by comparison, are not fully recovered if the system is imagined to operate in reverse. Typical examples of conservative forces are weight forces and spring forces. Friction forces are examples of nonconservative forces.

The work done by the conservative forces may be expressed in terms of changes in the potential energy of the particle. The work done by the nonconservative forces may *not* be expressed in this fashion. The nonconservative work, designated by the symbol W_{NC}, *must* be found from an equation of the form

$$W_{NC} = \int (F_{NC} \cos \beta) \, ds \qquad (20.50)$$

where F_{NC} is the nonconservative force.

The most general statement of the conservation of energy in a mechanical system may now be written as

$$\begin{array}{c} \text{Mechanical} \\ \text{energy in} \\ \text{system in} \\ \text{position 1} \end{array} + \begin{array}{c} \text{nonconservative} \\ \text{work done on} \\ \text{the particle} \end{array} = \begin{array}{c} \text{mechanical} \\ \text{energy in} \\ \text{system in} \\ \text{position 2} \end{array} \qquad (20.51)$$

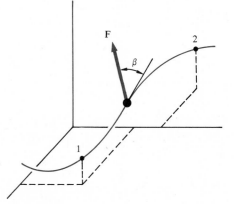

Fig. 20.14

Figure 20.14 shows a general situation of a particle which moves along a path from 1 to 2 and is acted on by a force **F**. Locations 1 and 2 are the endpoints of the interval of interest. At the initial position 1, the total mechanical energy content of the particle is described by the sum of the potential energy V_1 and the kinetic energy T_1. The nonconservative work, *if any,* done on the particle between positions 1 and 2 is designated W_{NC}. When the particle is at position 2, the total mechanical energy content is V_2 plus T_2.

By using the above notations, Eq. (20.51) may be written as

$$(T_1 + V_1) + W_{NC} = (T_2 + V_2) \qquad (20.52)$$

This equation may be rearranged to the form

$$W_{NC} = (T_2 - T_1) + (V_2 - V_1) \qquad (20.53)$$

Using the notations

$$\Delta T = T_2 - T_1 \qquad \Delta V = V_2 - V_1 \qquad (20.54)$$

the final form of Eq. (20.52) is

$$W_{NC} = \Delta T + \Delta V \qquad (20.55)$$

This equation is a concise, formal statement of the *conservation of energy for a particle in motion.* This equation states that the nonconservative work done on a particle results in a change in kinetic energy, a change in potential energy, or both.

In many problems in dynamics no nonconservative forces act on the particle. For this case, the statement of conservation of energy reduces to

$$0 = \Delta T + \Delta V \qquad \text{Conservative forces only} \qquad (20.56)$$

$$\Delta T = -\Delta V \qquad \text{Conservative forces only} \qquad (20.57)$$

This equation has a very simple physical interpretation. A positive change, or increase, in the kinetic energy of the particle corresponds to a negative change, or decrease, of the potential energy. Thus, although the *total* energy of the particle must remain constant, potential energy may be converted to kinetic energy, and vice versa. Familiar examples of these effects are a falling object, which exchanges potential energy for kinetic energy; a ball thrown up in the air, which exchanges kinetic energy for potential energy; and an automobile suspension spring, which stores the kinetic energy of the wheel hitting a hole in the road as potential energy.

A very important characteristic of the above equations must be observed. These equations describe relationships between the potential and kinetic energies *only at the endpoints of the interval* of interest in the problem. They provide no information whatsoever about conditions within the interval. Also, at no place does the acceleration appear in these equations. *The work-energy problem is formulated solely in terms of position coordinates and velocities.*

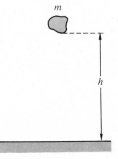

Fig. 20.15

Example 20.7 The system of Example 15.5 is shown in Fig. 20.15. The particle is initially at rest and is dropped from a height h to the ground.

a Use the work-energy method to find the general result for the velocity with which the particle strikes the ground.

b Find the value of this velocity which corresponds to a height $h = 100$ ft.

Solution

a The system is redrawn in Fig. 20.16. The initial position is designated 1, and the ground is designated 2. The ground is taken to be the datum for potential energy, and there is no nonconservative work term.

The energy terms at the endpoints of the time interval are

$$T_1 = 0 \qquad V_1 = mgh \qquad (20.58)$$

$$T_2 = \tfrac{1}{2}mv^2 \qquad V_2 = 0 \qquad (20.59)$$

The statement of work energy is thus

$$0 = \Delta T + \Delta V \qquad 0 = (T_2 - T_1) + (V_2 - V_1) \qquad (20.60)$$

$$0 = (\tfrac{1}{2}mv^2 - 0) + (0 - mgh) \qquad v = \sqrt{2gh} \qquad (20.61)$$

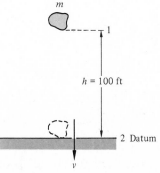

Fig. 20.16

It may be observed that this result is *independent* of the mass of the particle.

b For the numerical values of this example,

$$v = \sqrt{2gh} = \sqrt{2(32.2)(100)} = 80.2 \text{ ft/s} \qquad (20.62)$$

This is the result obtained in Example 15.5 for a particle with constant acceleration. This problem was also considered in Example 20.1. It is left as an exercise for the reader to show that the result of this latter problem may be used with Eq. (20.44) to obtain Eq. (20.62).

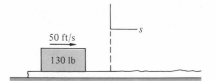

Fig. 20.17

Example 20.8 The system of Example 16.2 is shown in Fig. 20.17. The block slides along a smooth, horizontal track at a constant velocity of 50 ft/s. At a certain point the smooth track joins a section of rough, horizontal track. The coefficient of kinetic friction between the block and the rough track is estimated to be 0.24. How far along the rough track will the block slide before coming to rest?

Solution The distance traveled by the block along the rough track is l. The nonconservative force is the friction force F, given by

$$F = \mu_k \, mg \qquad (20.63)$$

The nonconservative work is given by

$$W_{\text{NC}} = \int_0^l (F \cos \beta) \, ds \qquad (20.64)$$

Since the friction force acts *opposite* to the motion of the block,

$$\cos \beta = 180° \qquad (20.65)$$

and

$$W_{\text{NC}} = \int_0^l (F \cos 180°) \, ds = \int_0^l (-\mu_k mg) \, ds \qquad (20.66)$$

$$= -\mu_k mgl \qquad (20.67)$$

Since there are no elevation changes of the block, the potential energy change ΔV of the block is zero. The equation of work energy has the form

$$W_{\text{NC}} = \Delta T + \Delta V = T_2 - T_1 \qquad (20.68)$$

$$-\mu_k mgl = 0 - \tfrac{1}{2}mv_1^2 \qquad l = \frac{v_1^2}{2\mu_k g} \qquad (20.69)$$

It may be observed that this result is independent of the mass of the block. For the present case, $v_1 = 50$ ft/s and $\mu_k = 0.24$. Equation (20.69) then appears as

$$l = \frac{50^2}{2(0.24)(32.2)} = 162 \text{ ft} \qquad (20.70)$$

This is the result obtained earlier in Eq. (16.29).

Example 20.9 Figure 20.18 shows a model of a spring-operated toy pistol which shoots plastic pellets. In the uncocked position the tip of the spring is at position 2. When the pistol is loaded, the tip of the spring is at position 1. The mass of the pellet is m, and the spring constant is k.

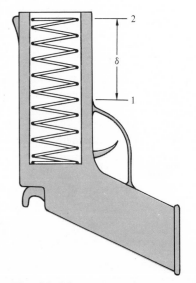

Fig. 20.18

a Derive a general expression for the velocity with which the pellet leaves the spring and for the maximum height which the pellet will reach when the pistol is fired.

b Find the numerical values for part *a* if the pellet weighs 15 g, $k = 70$ N/m and $\delta = 100$ mm.

All frictional effects, and the mass of the spring, may be neglected.

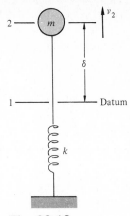

Solution

a The model of the pistol spring is shown in Fig. 20.19. Since both the spring and the mass may store potential energy, the potential energy terms for each of these elements will be written separately. The subscripts m and s are used to designate the pellet mass and the spring, respectively. The required energy terms are

$$W_{\mathrm{NC}} = 0 \qquad T_1 = 0 \qquad V_{1m} = 0 \qquad V_{1s} = \tfrac{1}{2}k\delta^2 \qquad (20.71)$$

$$T_2 = \tfrac{1}{2}mv_2^2 \qquad V_{2m} = mg\delta \qquad V_{2s} = 0 \qquad (20.72)$$

Fig. 20.19

The equation of work energy has the form

$$W_{\mathrm{NC}} = \Delta T + \Delta V \qquad (20.73)$$

$$= (T_2 - T_1) + (V_{2m} - V_{1m}) + (V_{2s} - V_{1s}) \qquad (20.74)$$

$$0 = (\tfrac{1}{2}mv_2^2 - 0) + (mg\delta - 0) + (0 - \tfrac{1}{2}k\delta^2) \qquad (20.75)$$

$$\tfrac{1}{2}mv_2^2 = \tfrac{1}{2}k\delta^2 - mg\delta \qquad v_2 = \sqrt{\frac{\delta}{m}(k\delta - 2mg)} \qquad (20.76)$$

It is interesting to note that a limiting condition occurs if

$$2mg = k\delta \qquad mg = \tfrac{1}{2}k\delta \qquad (20.77)$$

For this case the velocity of the mass at position 2 would be zero, and the pellet would not leave the spring. The corresponding weight of the mass, from Eq. (20.77), would be *exactly one half* of the force required to compress the spring by the amount δ.

When the pellet leaves the spring, it has the velocity given by Eq. (20.76). The model of the rise of the pellet to its maximum height h is shown in Fig. 20.20. Position 2 is defined to be a new datum, and the required energy terms are

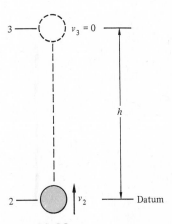

Fig. 20.20

$$T_2 = \tfrac{1}{2}mv_2^2 \qquad V_2 = 0 \qquad (20.78)$$

$$T_3 = 0 \qquad V_3 = mgh \qquad (20.79)$$

From Eq. (20.76),

$$\tfrac{1}{2}mv_2^2 = T_2 = \tfrac{1}{2}k\delta^2 - mg\delta \qquad (20.80)$$

and the equation of work energy appears as

$$W_{\mathrm{NC}} = \Delta T + \Delta V \qquad 0 = (T_3 - T_2) + (V_3 - V_2) \qquad (20.81)$$

$$0 = [0 - (\tfrac{1}{2}k\delta^2 - mg\delta)] + (mgh - 0) \qquad (20.82)$$

$$= -\tfrac{1}{2}k\delta^2 + mg\delta + mgh \qquad (20.83)$$

$$h = \frac{\tfrac{1}{2}k\delta^2 - mg\delta}{mg} = \delta\left(\frac{k\delta}{2mg} - 1\right) \qquad (20.84)$$

b For the present problem,

$$m = 15 \text{ g} \qquad k = 70 \text{ N/m} \qquad \delta = 100 \text{ mm}$$

Using Eq. (20.76), we get

$$v = \sqrt{\frac{100/1,000}{15/1,000}\left[70\left(\frac{100}{1,000}\right) - 2\left(\frac{15}{1,000}\right)(9.81)\right]}$$

$$= 6.69 \frac{m}{s} \quad (20.85)$$

From Eq. (20.84),

$$h = \frac{100}{1,000}\left[\frac{70(100/1,000)}{2(15/1,000)(9.81)} - 1\right] = 2.28 \text{ m} \quad (20.86)$$

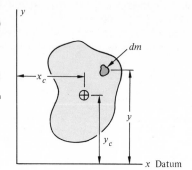

Fig. 20.21

20.7 POTENTIAL ENERGY OF A RIGID BODY IN PLANE MOTION

Figure 20.21 shows a rigid body positioned with respect to a set of coordinate axes lying in a vertical plane. It is desired to find the potential energy of the body with respect to the x axis, which is defined to be the datum for potential energy.

The potential energy dV of a typical mass element dm is

$$dV = dm\, gy \quad (20.87)$$

where $dm\, g$ is the weight of the element. The total potential energy is then found as

$$V = \int_{\text{vol}} dm\, gy = g\int_{\text{vol}} y\, dm \quad (20.88)$$

The definition of the centroidal coordinate y_c is

$$y_c = \frac{\displaystyle\int_{\text{vol}} y\, dm}{m} \quad (20.89)$$

or

$$\int_{\text{vol}} y\, dm = my_c \quad (20.90)$$

The term $\int_{\text{vol}} y\, dm$ is eliminated between Eqs. (20.88) and (20.90), with the result

$$V = g(my_c) = (mg)y_c \quad (20.91)$$

The term mg is the *total weight* of the rigid body. Thus, the potential energy of a body may be found by imagining all the weight to be concentrated at the center of mass (CM) and treating this point as a particle in translation.

20.8 KINETIC ENERGY OF A RIGID BODY IN PLANE MOTION

Figure 20.22 shows a rigid body which is in plane rotational motion about a *fixed point*.

The *absolute* velocity of the typical mass element dm is

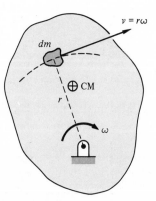

Fig. 20.22

$$v = r\omega \qquad (20.92)$$

The kinetic energy of this element is

$$dT = \tfrac{1}{2}(dm)v^2 = \tfrac{1}{2}(dm)(r\omega)^2 \qquad (20.93)$$

The total kinetic energy of the body is found by summing the contributions of all the individual mass elements, in the form

$$T = \int dT = \int_{\text{vol}} \tfrac{1}{2}(dm)(r\omega)^2 = \tfrac{1}{2}\omega^2 \int_{\text{vol}} r^2\, dm \qquad (20.94)$$

The integral in Eq. (20.94) may be recognized as the *mass moment of inertia* of the rigid body about the fixed point, or

$$I = \int_{\text{vol}} r^2\, dm \qquad (20.95)$$

The kinetic energy T then has the final form

$$T = \tfrac{1}{2}I\omega^2 \qquad (20.96)$$

Equation (20.96) is of fundamental importance when the work-energy method is used to solve problems of plane motion of rigid bodies.

Figure 20.23 shows a rigid body which moves with general plane motion. It was shown in Chap. 3 that when a body rotates with general plane motion, there is a fixed point about which the body may be assumed to be instantaneously rotating. This point is the instant center (IC) shown in the figure. The velocity v_0 of the CM of the body is an *absolute* velocity, so that the IC is a point which is *fixed* with respect to a set of inertial coordinates. The kinetic energy of the body in general plane rotation about a fixed point, following Eq. (20.96), is

$$T = \tfrac{1}{2}I\omega^2 \qquad (20.97)$$

For the present problem, I is the mass moment of inertia of the body about the fixed point which is the instant center. Using the transfer theorem for moments of inertia, we get

$$I = I_0 + mr_0^2 \qquad (20.98)$$

where I_0 is the mass moment of inertia of the body about the CM. The kinetic energy term now has the form

$$T = \tfrac{1}{2}(I_0 + mr_0^2)\omega^2 = \tfrac{1}{2}I_0\omega^2 + \tfrac{1}{2}mr_0^2\omega^2 \qquad (20.99)$$

Since $v_0 = r_0\omega$, the final form of Eq. (20.99) is

$$T = \tfrac{1}{2}mv_0^2 + \tfrac{1}{2}I_0\omega^2 \qquad (20.100)$$

It may be seen that the kinetic energy of a body in general plane motion has two distinct components. The first is the term $\tfrac{1}{2}mv_0^2$. This term represents the *translational* kinetic energy due to the absolute velocity v_0 of the CM. The second

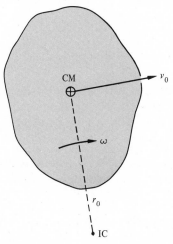

Fig. 20.23

term $\frac{1}{2}I_0\omega^2$ is the *rotational* kinetic energy due to the angular velocity ω of the body.

20.9 CONSERVATION OF ENERGY— THE WORK-ENERGY METHOD FOR A RIGID BODY IN PLANE MOTION

The work-energy equation for a mass particle was given by Eq. (20.55) as

$$W_{NC} = \Delta T + \Delta V \qquad (20.101)$$

This equation is also valid for the case of a rigid body in plane motion. The term W_{NC} is the nonconservative work done on the rigid body, and it may be expressed in general symbolic form as

$$W_{NC} = \int (F_{NC} \cos \beta)\, ds + \int M_{NC}\, d\theta \qquad (20.102)$$

where F_{NC} is the nonconservative force, and M_{NC} is the nonconservative moment, acting on the rigid body. The kinetic energy terms are found by using Eq. (20.97) or (20.100). The potential energy terms due to elevation changes of the body are found by using Eq. (20.91).

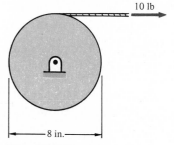

Fig. 20.24

Example 20.10 The system of Example 19.2 is shown in Fig. 20.24. The weight of the disk is 20 lb. A thin, inextensible string is wrapped around the outside of the disk. The disk is initially at rest when a constant force of 10 lb is applied to the string. Find the angular velocity of the disk, in revolutions per minute, when 42 in of string has been unwound from the disk. The mass moment of inertia of the disk about its center was earlier found to be 0.415 lb·s²·in.

Solution The angular displacement of the disk which corresponds to unwinding 42 in of string is found from

$$s = r\theta \qquad 42 = 4(\theta) \qquad \theta = 10.5 \text{ rad} \qquad (20.103)$$

The string force is a nonconservative force, and the nonconservative moment is

$$M_{NC} = 10(4) = 40 \text{ in·lb} \qquad (20.104)$$

Since this moment is constant, the equation for the nonconservative work has the form

$$W_{NC} = M_{NC}(\theta_2 - \theta_1) = 40(10.5 - 0) = 420 \text{ in·lb} \qquad (20.105)$$

The required energy terms are

$$T_1 = 0 \qquad T_2 = \tfrac{1}{2}I\omega^2 = \tfrac{1}{2}(0.415)\omega^2 = 0.208\omega^2 \qquad (20.106)$$

$$V_1 = 0 \qquad V_2 = 0 \qquad (20.107)$$

The equation of work energy appears as

$$W_{NC} = \Delta T + \Delta V = (T_2 - T_1) + (V_2 - V_1) \qquad (20.108)$$

$$420 = (0.208\omega^2 - 0) + (0 - 0) \tag{20.109}$$

$$\omega = 44.9 \frac{\text{rad}}{\text{s}} \qquad \omega = 44.9 \left(\frac{60}{2\pi}\right) = 429 \frac{\text{r}}{\text{min}} \tag{20.110}$$

This is the result, within computational roundoff error, which was obtained in Eq. (19.26).

Example 20.11 The Yo-Yo of Example 19.3 is shown in Fig. 20.25. This element is modeled as a homogeneous disk of mass m connected to an inextensible string.

a If the Yo-Yo is released from rest, find the general forms for the translational and rotational velocities of this element after the center has moved downward through a distance h.

b Find the numerical values for part a if $r = 1.3$ in and $h = 30$ in.

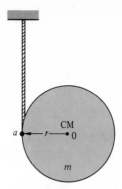

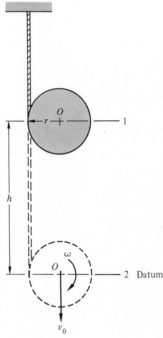

Fig. 20.25

Solution The initial and final positions are designated 1 and 2, as shown in Fig. 20.26, and position 2 is taken as the datum.

a The required energy terms in the initial and final positions are

$$T_1 = 0 \qquad V_1 = mgh \tag{20.111}$$

$$T_2 = \tfrac{1}{2}mv_0^2 + \tfrac{1}{2}I_0\omega^2 \qquad V_2 = 0 \tag{20.112}$$

By using

$$v_0 = r\omega \qquad I_0 = \tfrac{1}{2}mr^2 \tag{20.113}$$

the kinetic energy in the final position may be written as

$$T_2 = \frac{1}{2}mv_0^2 + \frac{1}{2}\left(\frac{1}{2}mr^2\right)\left(\frac{v_0^2}{r^2}\right) = \frac{3}{4}mv_0^2 \tag{20.114}$$

There is no nonconservative work term, and the equation of work energy has the form

$$0 = \Delta T + \Delta V \qquad 0 = (T_2 - T_1) + (V_2 - V_1) \tag{20.115}$$

$$0 = (\tfrac{3}{4}mv_0^2 - 0) + (0 - mgh) \qquad v_0 = \sqrt{\tfrac{4}{3}gh} \tag{20.116}$$

b For the numerical values of the problem,

$$v_0 = \sqrt{\frac{4}{3}(32.2)\left(\frac{30}{12}\right)} = 10.4 \frac{\text{ft}}{\text{s}} \qquad \omega = \frac{v_0}{r} = \frac{10.4}{1.3/12} = 96 \frac{\text{rad}}{\text{s}} \tag{20.117}$$

The above results were obtained in Eqs. (19.70) and (19.71) of Example 19.3. It may again be observed that the above results are independent of the mass of the body.

Fig. 20.26

Example 20.12 A homogeneous disk of diameter d and mass m rolls without slipping up an inclined surface, as shown in Fig. 20.27.

a If the angular velocity of the disk at a certain point is ω_1, find the additional distance l through which the disk will roll along the inclined surface before coming to rest.

b Find the numerical value for part a if $\beta = 26°$, $d = 200$ mm, and $\omega_1 = 80$ r/min.

c. Do the same as in parts a and b if the disk has a set of holes drilled on a concentric circle about the center, so that the radius of gyration k_0 is equal to $0.4d$.

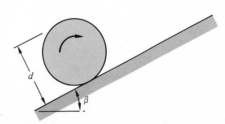

Fig. 20.27

d For what theoretical symmetrical mass distribution of the disk would the distance l found in part a be maximum?

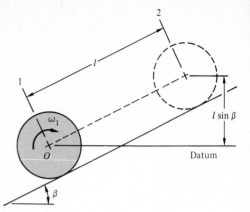

Fig. 20.28

Solution

a The initial and final locations are designated 1 and 2, as shown in Fig. 20.28. The required energy terms are

$$T_1 = \tfrac{1}{2}I_0\omega_1^2 + \tfrac{1}{2}mv_0^2 \qquad V_1 = 0 \qquad (20.118)$$

$$T_2 = 0 \qquad V_2 = mgl\sin\beta \qquad (20.119)$$

There is no nonconservative work done, and the equation of work energy has the form

$$0 = \Delta T + \Delta V = [0 - (\tfrac{1}{2}I_0\omega_1^2 + \tfrac{1}{2}mv_0^2)] + (mgl\sin\beta - 0) \quad (20.120)$$

With a view toward the solution of part c, the mass moment of inertia will be expressed in terms of the radius of gyration, with the form

$$I_0 = k_0^2 m \qquad (20.121)$$

Using

$$v_0 = r\omega_1 \qquad (20.122)$$

Eq. (20.120) appears as

$$0 = -[\tfrac{1}{2}(k_0^2 m)\omega_1^2 + \tfrac{1}{2}m(r\omega_1)^2] + mgl\sin\beta \qquad (20.123)$$

$$l = \frac{k_0^2 + r^2}{2g\sin\beta}\omega_1^2 \qquad (20.124)$$

It is interesting to observe that this result is independent of the mass of the disk.

b The radius of gyration of the homogeneous disk is found as

$$k_0 = \sqrt{\frac{I_0}{m}} = \sqrt{\frac{\tfrac{1}{2}mr^2}{m}} = \frac{r}{\sqrt{2}} = 0.707r \qquad (20.125)$$

Using

$$\omega_1 = 80\left(\frac{2\pi}{60}\right) = 8.38 \;\frac{\text{rad}}{\text{s}} \qquad r = \tfrac{1}{2}(200) = 100 \text{ mm} \, (20.126)$$

in Eq. (20.124), the value of l is

$$l = \frac{(0.707r)^2 + r^2}{2g\sin\beta}\omega_1^2$$

$$= \frac{(0.707^2 + 1)(100)^2}{2(9.81)\sin 26^\circ}(8.38)^2\left(\frac{1 \text{ m}}{1{,}000 \text{ mm}}\right)^2 = 0.122 \text{ m} \quad (20.127)$$

c For the case where the radius of gyration of the disk is $0.4d = 0.8r$, the distance traveled by the disk is

$$l = \frac{(0.8^2 + 1)(100)^2}{2(9.81)\sin 26^\circ}(8.38)^2\left(\frac{1}{1{,}000}\right)^2 = 0.134 \text{ m} \quad (20.128)$$

d From consideration of Eq. (20.124), it may be seen that the distance l will be maximum when k_0 has its maximum value. The theoretical limiting maximum value of k_0 corresponds to the case where all the mass of the disk is assumed to be concentrated along the rim. For this case, $k_0 = r$, and the theoretical maximum value of l is

$$l_{\text{max}} = \frac{(1 + 1)(100)^2}{2(9.81) \sin 26°} (8.38)^2 \left(\frac{1}{1,000}\right)^2 = 0.163 \text{ m} \quad (20.129)$$

An interesting effect may be seen in the solution to this example. The basic physical phenomenon is that the rolling disk exchanges kinetic energy for potential energy as it rolls up the incline. If the mass of the disk is constant, then the increase in potential energy for a given movement up the incline is constant. The initial kinetic energy is the sum of the translational and rotational kinetic energies. The initial angular velocity is assumed to be constant. Thus, since the mass is constant, the part of the initial kinetic energy due to translation is constant. The part of the initial kinetic energy due to rotation has the form $\frac{1}{2}I_0\omega_1^2$. This quantity will be maximum when I_0, the mass moment of inertia of the disk, has its maximum value. The above phenomenon forms the theoretical basis for the design of mechanical flywheels, where an attempt is made to distribute the maximum amount of mass as near to the rim of the flywheel as possible.

20.10 THE WORK-ENERGY METHOD FOR CONNECTED BODIES

The case of motion of connected bodies was first presented in Chap. 16. The solution technique was shown to consist of drawing a free-body diagram of each mass element and writing Newton's second law for each of these elements. In the process of doing this, the cable or link forces between the bodies were treated as unknown quantities. The resulting system of equations was then solved simultaneously to obtain the accelerations and the cable, or link, forces.

The motion of certain types of systems of connected bodies also may be obtained by using the work-energy method. The solution technique consists of expressing the potential energies of all the bodies in terms of position coordinates measured from a common datum. The kinetic energy of the system is then expressed in terms of the velocities of the mass elements. If both angular and translational motions occur in the system, the velocities may be related by equations of the form

$$v = r\omega \quad (20.130)$$

If the nonconservative work is zero, the problem may be solved directly by applying the work-energy equation in the form

$$0 = \Delta T + \Delta V \quad (20.131)$$

If there is nonconservative work and this quantity may be expressed in a form *which does not include the unknown cable or link forces,* then the work-energy equation has the form

$$W_{\text{NC}} = \Delta T + \Delta V \quad (20.132)$$

An example of a problem of motion of connected bodies which cannot be solved conveniently by using the work-energy method is shown in Fig. 20.29. This system was considered in Example 16.5. As the pair of connected blocks slides down the plane, nonconservative work is done as the friction forces on the blocks act through a distance. These friction forces are functions of the normal forces acting on the blocks. These normal forces are functions of the *unknown force* in the link which connects the two blocks. Since this link force is not known at the outset of the problem, this problem cannot be solved directly by using the work-energy method.

This problem can be solved by the energy method, however, if a free-body diagram of each block is drawn, as was shown in Fig. 16.15, and the work-energy equation is written for *each* mass element. This operation yields two equations in two unknowns. One unknown is the link force, and the other is the particular position coordinate or velocity which is to be found. For a case such as this, it may be more convenient to solve the problem by the direct use of Newton's second law, as was done in Example 16.5.

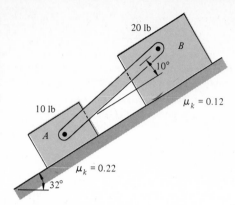

Fig. 20.29

Example 20.13 The system of Example 16.4 is shown in Fig. 20.30. If the blocks are released from rest in the position shown, find the velocity of each block when these elements have moved through a displacement of 1.5 m. The cable is inextensible, the pulley pin is assumed to be frictionless, and the mass moment of inertia of the pulley may be neglected.

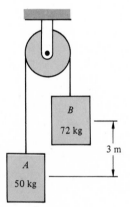

Fig. 20.30

Solution The position chosen for the datum for potential energy is shown in Fig. 20.31. The required energy terms are

$$T_{A1} = 0 \qquad V_{A1} = 0 \qquad (20.133)$$

$$T_{B1} = 0 \qquad V_{B1} = 72(9.81)3 = 2{,}120 \text{ N} \cdot \text{m} = 2{,}120 \text{ J} \qquad (20.134)$$

$$T_{A2} = \tfrac{1}{2}m_A v_A^2 \qquad V_{A2} = 50(9.81)1.5 = 736 \text{ N} \cdot \text{m} = 736 \text{ J} \qquad (20.135)$$

$$T_{B2} = \tfrac{1}{2}m_B v_B^2 \qquad V_{B2} = 72(9.81)1.5 = 1{,}060 \text{ N} \cdot \text{m} = 1{,}060 \text{ J} \qquad (20.136)$$

Since the cable is inextensible,

$$v_{A2} = v_{B2} = v_2 \qquad (20.137)$$

and

$$T_2 = T_{A2} + T_{B2} = \tfrac{1}{2}(m_A + m_B)v_2^2 = \tfrac{1}{2}(50 + 72)v_2^2 = 61v_2^2 \qquad (20.138)$$

There is no nonconservative work done, and the equation of work energy has the form

$$0 = \Delta T + \Delta V \qquad 0 = (T_2 - T_1) + (V_2 - V_1) \qquad (20.139)$$

$$0 = [(T_{A2} + T_{B2}) - (T_{A1} + T_{B1})] + [(V_{A2} + V_{B2}) - (V_{A1} + V_{B1})] \qquad (20.140)$$

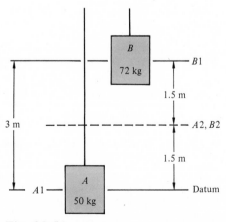

Fig. 20.31

$$0 = [61v_2^2 - (0 + 0)] + [(736 + 1,060) - (0 + 2,120)] \quad (20.141)$$

$$v_2 = 2.30 \text{ m/s} \quad (20.142)$$

This is the value which was obtained in Eq. (16.42).

20.11 THE WORK-ENERGY METHOD USED TO FIND THE VALUE OF THE NORMAL ACCELERATION OF A PARTICLE

Figure 20.32 shows a particle which moves along a plane curve in a vertical plane. The normal component a_n of the acceleration of the particle was shown in Chap. 1 to have the form

$$a_n = \frac{v^2}{\rho} \quad (20.143)$$

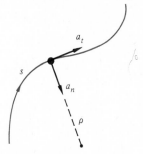

Fig. 20.32

where ρ is the radius of curvature. The physical interpretation of normal acceleration is that this quantity is required *to change the direction of the velocity* of the particle so that this element will follow the curved path of motion. In many problems it is particularly convenient to use the work-energy method to obtain the value of v in Eq. (20.143). This technique will be illustrated in the following three examples.

Example 20.14 A small particle is at rest on top of a fixed cylinder, as shown in Fig. 20.33. The surface of the cylinder is assumed to be frictionless.

a If the mass is given an infinitesimal lateral displacement to set it into motion, find the position at which this particle loses contact with the cylindrical surface.

b How would the result in part *a* be affected if there is sliding friction between the particle and the cylinder?

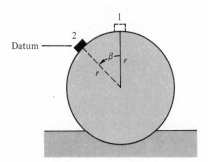

Fig. 20.33

Solution

a The initial position is designated 1, and an arbitrary subsequent position is designated 2, as shown in Fig. 20.34. The radius of the cylinder is r, and the datum for potential energy is at position 2. The required energy terms are

$$T_1 = 0 \qquad V_1 = mgr(1 - \cos\beta) \quad (20.144)$$

$$T_2 = \tfrac{1}{2}mv^2 \qquad V_2 = 0 \quad (20.145)$$

The equation of work energy is then

$$0 = \Delta T + \Delta V = (T_2 - T_1) + (V_2 - V_1) \quad (20.146)$$

$$= (\tfrac{1}{2}mv^2 - 0) + [0 - mgr(1 - \cos\beta)] \quad (20.147)$$

The free-body diagram of the mass particle in position 2 is shown in Fig. 20.35. Newton's second law for the particle has the form

$$\sum F_n = ma_n \qquad mg\cos\beta - N = ma_n = m\frac{v^2}{r} \quad (20.148)$$

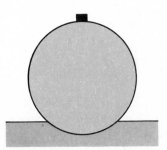

Fig. 20.34

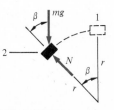

Fig. 20.35

The limiting condition $N = 0$ corresponds to loss of contact between the mass element and the cylinder. Using this condition, and eliminating v^2 from Eqs. (20.147) and (20.148), results in

$$\cos \beta = \tfrac{2}{3} \qquad \beta = 48.2° \qquad (20.149)$$

It is interesting to note that Eq. (20.149) is independent of *both* the mass of the particle and the dimensions of the cylinder.

b If sliding friction exists between the particle and the cylinder, there is a *negative* nonconservative work term, since the friction forces act opposite to the actual sense of the motion. The equation of work energy has the form

$$W_{\mathrm{NC}} = \Delta T + \Delta V \qquad W_{\mathrm{NC}} < 0 \qquad (20.150)$$

The terms ΔT and ΔV are the same as before, so that

$$W_{\mathrm{NC}} = \tfrac{1}{2}mv^2 - mgr(1 - \cos \beta) \qquad (20.151)$$

The term v^2 is eliminated between Eqs. (20.148) and (20.151). Using the condition $N = 0$ and defining β_f to be the position, for the case of sliding friction, at which contact is lost, we have

$$\cos \beta_f = \frac{2 + [2/(rmg)]W_{\mathrm{NC}}}{3} \qquad (20.152)$$

Since W_{NC} is a *negative* quantity, it follows that

$$\cos \beta_f < \cos \beta \qquad \beta_f > \beta \qquad (20.153)$$

It may be seen that when sliding friction is present, the particle has a larger arc of contact with the cylinder.

Example 20.15 Figure 20.36 shows a circular hoop which lies in a vertical plane. The internal surface of the hoop is a slightly grooved, frictionless track. Initially, a small particle of mass m rests on the lowest portion of the track. A spring-loaded arm is used to impart an initial velocity to the mass element. This mass has a magnitude of 35 g, and the diameter of the hoop is 400 mm.

a Find the minimum required value of the initial velocity of the particle at position 1 if, when this element is in position 2, it is not to lose contact with the track.

b If the initial velocity v_1 is 2.80 m/s, find the position where the particle loses contact with the track.

c For the position of part *b*, find the tangential acceleration of the particle and discuss the magnitude, direction, and sense of the total acceleration of the particle.

Solution

a The free-body diagram of the mass particle in position 2 is shown in Fig. 20.37. The normal force exerted by the track on the particle is N. Newton's second law in the normal direction is written as

$$\sum F_n = ma_n \qquad N + mg = ma_n = m\frac{v^2}{\rho} \qquad (20.154)$$

Since N is a compressive reaction force, it may have only positive values. Thus, a limiting condition is reached when $N = 0$. The

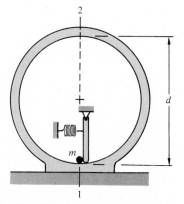

Fig. 20.36

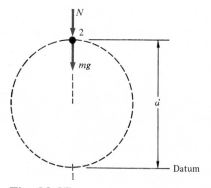

Fig. 20.37

corresponding value of the velocity is designated v_2. For this case, Eq. (20.154) appears as

$$0 + mg = \frac{mv_2^2}{d/2} \qquad v_2^2 = \tfrac{1}{2}dg \qquad (20.155)$$

The equation of work energy is now written between positions 1 and 2. The required energy terms are

$$T_1 = \tfrac{1}{2}mv_1^2 \qquad V_1 = 0 \qquad (20.156)$$

$$T_2 = \tfrac{1}{2}mv_2^2 \qquad V_2 = mgd \qquad (20.157)$$

and

$$0 = \Delta T + \Delta V \qquad (20.158)$$

$$0 = (T_2 - T_1) + (V_2 - V_1) = (\tfrac{1}{2}mv_2^2 - \tfrac{1}{2}mv_1^2) + (mgd - 0)$$
$$(20.159)$$

$$v_2^2 = v_1^2 - 2gd \qquad (20.160)$$

The term v_2^2 is eliminated between Eqs. (20.155) and (20.160), with the result

$$v_1^2 = \tfrac{5}{2}dg \qquad v_1 = \sqrt{\tfrac{5}{2}dg} \qquad (20.161)$$

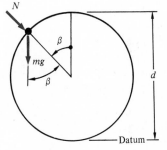

Fig. 20.38

Using $d = 400$ mm, we have

$$v_1 = \sqrt{\frac{5}{2}\left(\frac{400}{1,000}\right)9.81} = 3.13 \ \frac{\text{m}}{\text{s}} \qquad (20.162)$$

If the initial velocity of the mass particle is 3.13 m/s, the element will just lose contact with the track at position 2. It may be observed that this result is independent of the mass.

b Figure 20.38 shows the free-body diagram when the mass particle is at an arbitrary position defined by angle β. Newton's second law in the normal direction has the form

$$\sum F_n = ma_n \qquad N + mg \cos \beta = ma_n = \frac{mv^2}{d/2} \qquad (20.163)$$

The kinetic and potential energies, when the particle is in the position defined by angle β, are

$$T = \frac{1}{2}mv^2 \qquad V = mg\left(\frac{d}{2}\right)(1 + \cos \beta) \qquad (20.164)$$

The initial energy terms T_1 and V_1 are given by Eq. (20.156). The equation of work energy is written as

$$0 = \Delta T + \Delta V = (T - T_1) + (V - V_1) \qquad (20.165)$$

$$= \left(\frac{1}{2}mv^2 - \frac{1}{2}mv_1^2\right) + \left[mg\left(\frac{d}{2}\right)(1 + \cos \beta) - 0\right] \qquad (20.166)$$

The position at which the particle loses contact with the track is defined by $N = 0$. Using this condition, v^2 is eliminated between Eqs. (20.163) and (20.166) to obtain

$$\cos \beta = \frac{2}{3dg}(v_1^2 - dg) \qquad (20.167)$$

With the values $v_1 = 2.80$ m/s and $d = 400$ mm,

$$\cos \beta = \frac{2}{3(9.81)(400/1{,}000)} \left[2.80^2 - \frac{400}{1{,}000}(9.81) \right]$$

$$= 0.667 \qquad \beta = 48.2° \tag{20.168}$$

It may be observed that the above value for β is exactly the same as the value obtained in Eq. (20.149) in Example 20.14. It is left as an exercise for the reader to show that these are equivalent problems.

c From consideration of Fig. 20.38, Newton's second law in the normal and tangential directions has the forms

$$\sum F_n = ma_n \qquad mg \cos \beta = ma_n \qquad a_n = g \cos \beta \tag{20.169}$$

$$\sum F_t = ma_t \qquad mg \sin \beta = ma_t \qquad a_t = g \sin \beta \tag{20.170}$$

It may be seen that a_n and a_t are the components of the gravitational acceleration vector g. Thus, at the instant when the particle loses contact with the track, the total acceleration of the particle is equal to g.

Example 20.16 Figure 20.39 shows a preliminary engineering design for a roller coaster track to be built for an amusement park. The car is towed up a ramp to position 1. A slight leftward horizontal force is then applied to the car, and it rolls down the track. All the dimensions of the car are small compared with the length and radii of curvature of the track. Thus, all rotation effects may be neglected, and the car may be assumed to move as a particle in translation. In addition, all friction effects may be neglected. The heights are $h_1 = 60$ ft, $h_2 = 25$ ft, and $h_3 = 40$ ft.

a Find the maximum acceleration which a passenger would experience when the car is in position 2.

b Find the minimum permissible value of the radius of curvature when the car is in position 3, if the wheels of the car are not to lose contact with the track at this location.

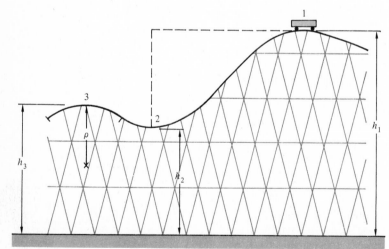

Fig. 20.39

Solution

a The velocity at position 2 will be found first. The ground is chosen to be the datum, and

$$T_1 = 0 \qquad V_1 = mgh_1 \qquad (20.171)$$

$$T_2 = \tfrac{1}{2}mv_2^2 \qquad V_2 = mgh_2 \qquad (20.172)$$

$$0 = \Delta T + \Delta V = (\tfrac{1}{2}mv_2^2 - 0) + (mgh_2 - mgh_1) \quad (20.173)$$

$$v_2^2 = 2g(h_1 - h_2) \qquad (20.174)$$

The normal acceleration of the car at position 2 is

$$a_n = \frac{v_2^2}{\rho} \qquad (20.175)$$

Fig. 20.40

v_2^2 from Eq. (20.174) is substituted into Eq. (20.175). Using $h_1 - h_2$ for the radius of curvature results in

$$a_n = \frac{2g(h_1 - h_2)}{h_1 - h_2} = 2g \qquad (20.176)$$

At position 2 the passenger would experience an acceleration which is twice the value of the gravitational acceleration.

b The free-body diagram of the car in position 3 is shown in Fig. 20.40. Newton's second law has the form

$$\sum F_n = ma_n \qquad mg - N = ma_n = \frac{mv_3^2}{\rho} \qquad (20.177)$$

The work-energy equation is written between positions 1 and 3, with the result

$$0 = \Delta T + \Delta V = (T_3 - T_1) + (V_3 - V_1) \qquad (20.178)$$

$$= (\tfrac{1}{2}mv_3^2 - 0) + (mgh_3 - mgh_1) \qquad (20.179)$$

$$v_3^2 = 2g(h_1 - h_3) \qquad (20.180)$$

The car will lose contact with the track when $N = 0$. Using this result, v_3^2 is eliminated between Eqs. (20.177) and (20.180) to obtain

$$mg = \frac{2mg(h_1 - h_3)}{\rho} \qquad \rho = 2(h_1 - h_3) \qquad (20.181)$$

$$\rho = 2(60 - 40) = 40 \text{ ft} \qquad (20.182)$$

This result is a *minimum* value for the radius of curvature at position 3.

20.12 WORK OR ENERGY PER UNIT TIME—POWER

Figure 20.41 shows a particle which is acted on by a resultant force **F** and which is constrained to move along the s axis. The fundamental definition of the work dW done on the particle, as this element translates through the displacement ds, was given by Eq. (20.1) as

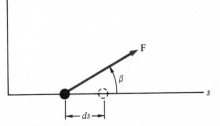

Fig. 20.41

$$dW = (F \cos \beta)\, ds \qquad (20.183)$$

This result is *independent of the time it took for the event to occur.* A term will now be introduced which characterizes the time required for a given amount of work to be done. This quantity is called *power,* and in its most fundamental definition, power is the work done per unit time. The distinguishing characteristic of a more powerful machine versus a less powerful machine is that the former can do a certain amount of work faster than the latter.

Both sides of Eq. (20.183) are divided by dt, with the result

$$P = \frac{dW}{dt} = (F \cos \beta)\frac{ds}{dt} \qquad (20.184)$$

where P is the symbol used to represent power. The term ds/dt is the magnitude of the velocity, or the speed, of the particle, and this quantity may be written as

$$\frac{ds}{dt} = v \qquad (20.185)$$

Equations (20.184) and (20.185) are combined to obtain

$$P = (F \cos \beta)v \qquad (20.186)$$

It may be seen from this equation that the *product of force and velocity is the basic definition of power.* It follows from this equation that the power will be constant only if both the component of force in the direction of motion, and the velocity, are constant.

The basic units of power are energy divided by time. In USCS units, typical power units are foot-pounds per second or foot-pounds per minute. A very useful unit is the horsepower, designated hp, and defined by

$$1 \text{ hp} = 550 \ \frac{\text{ft} \cdot \text{lb}}{\text{s}} = 33{,}000 \ \frac{\text{ft} \cdot \text{lb}}{\text{min}} \qquad (20.187)$$

In SI units, the basic unit of power is $1 \ \text{N} \cdot \text{m/s} = 1 \ \text{J/s}$. A power of 1 joule per second is defined to be one watt, designated by the symbol W. Thus,

$$1 \text{ W} = 1\,\frac{\text{J}}{\text{s}} \qquad (20.188)$$

The conversion relationship between the power in the USCS and SI units is

$$1 \text{ hp} = 746 \text{ W} \qquad (20.189)$$

Figure 20.42 shows a shaft which rotates with angular velocity ω and transmits a moment, or torque, of magnitude M. By using an analysis similar to that for the case of a force acting on

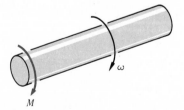

Fig. 20.42

a particle, it can be shown that the power transmitted through the shaft is

$$P = M\omega \qquad (20.190)$$

The units of power in the rotational case are the same as those in the translational case. A very convenient relationship among the torque, angular speed, and power, in USCS units, is given by

$$M = 63,000 \left(\frac{\text{hp}}{N} \right) \qquad (20.191)$$

In Eq. (20.191), T is in inch-pounds and N is in revolutions per minute.

In SI units, the relation of torque, angular speed, and power is

$$M = 9.55 \left(\frac{P}{N} \right) \qquad (20.192)$$

where M is in newton-meters, P is in watts, and N is in revolutions per minute.

In any physical, mechanical system there are certain inherent power losses due to friction, hysteresis losses in materials, and resistance effects in electric conductors. A convenient macroscopic representation of all these losses is contained in a term which is referred to as *efficiency*. This quantity is represented by the symbol η and is defined to be

$$\eta = \frac{\text{energy, or power, output}}{\text{energy, or power, input}} \qquad (20.193)$$

For a system which had no losses of any kind, $\eta = 1$. This case represents a theoretical upper limit for any real system. Thus, for actual mechanical systems,

$$\eta < 1$$

For convenience of interpretation, problems in power may be of two general types. In the first type, the power output is *constant*. A typical example would be an electric motor driving a blower. The required torque output of the motor to drive the blower is constant, and the blower operates at constant speed. In the second type either the force (or moment) required, or the velocity, or both, are variable. For this case, Eq. (20.186) or (20.190) is still valid, but the power must be thought of in terms of *instantaneous values*. A typical example of this type of problem is an automobile in motion. Because of changing conditions such as speed, roadway inclination, and wind conditions, the power requirements of the vehicle are changing almost continually. Both types of problems will be illustrated in the following example problems.

Example 20.17 The system of Examples 20.1 and 20.7 is shown in Fig. 20.43.

a Find the maximum power output of the mass particle as it falls freely in the gravitational field.

b Express the answer to part *a* in SI units.

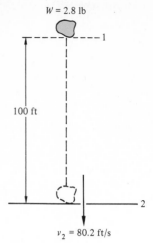

W = 2.8 lb

100 ft

v_2 = 80.2 ft/s

Fig. 20.43

Solution

a The resultant force in the direction of motion is the static weight force $W = 2.8$ lb. The particle is released from rest, so that the velocity increases monotonically from zero to the maximum value $v_2 = \sqrt{2g(100)} = 80.2$ ft/s at position 2. The maximum power output occurs at position 2, with the value

$$P_{max} = Wv_2 = 2.8 \text{ lb}\left(80.2 \frac{\text{ft}}{\text{s}}\right) = 225 \frac{\text{ft·lb}}{\text{s}} \qquad (20.194)$$

$$= 225 \frac{\text{ft·lb}}{\text{s}}\left(\frac{1 \text{ hp}}{550 \text{ ft · lb/s}}\right) = 0.409 \text{ hp} \qquad (20.195)$$

b The maximum power output in SI units is

$$P_{max} = 0.409 \text{ hp}\left(\frac{746 \text{ } W}{1 \text{ hp}}\right) = 305 \text{ } W \qquad (20.196)$$

In this example the power varies continually with time. Thus, Eqs. (20.195) and (20.196) represent the *instantaneous* power output of the mass particle at position 2.

Example 20.18 Figure 20.44 shows a forklift truck. The fork elevates a crate of mass 820 kg uniformly through a vertical distance of 2 m in 10 s. The truck is powered by a battery-operated motor. The total power efficiency of the motor and lift assembly is 0.62. Find the required electric power input to the system in watts and in horsepower.

Fig. 20.44

Solution The weight force of the crate is

$$W = mg = 820(9.81) = 8,040 \text{ N} \qquad (20.197)$$

and the constant vertical velocity of this element is

$$v = \frac{2 \text{ m}}{10 \text{ s}} = 0.2 \frac{\text{m}}{\text{s}} \qquad (20.198)$$

The theoretical power P_t required to raise the load is

$$P_t = Wv = 8,040(0.2) = 1,610 \text{ J/s} = 1,610 \text{ W} \qquad (20.199)$$

The actual power P_a required to operate the system is

$$P_a = \frac{P_t}{\eta} = \frac{1,610}{0.62} = 2,600 \text{ W} \qquad (20.200)$$

$$= 2,600 \text{ W}\left(\frac{1 \text{ hp}}{746 \text{ W}}\right) = 3.49 \text{ hp} \qquad (20.201)$$

Example 20.19 Figure 20.45 shows a shaft with four gears mounted on it. The system is driven through gear *B*, and power is

738

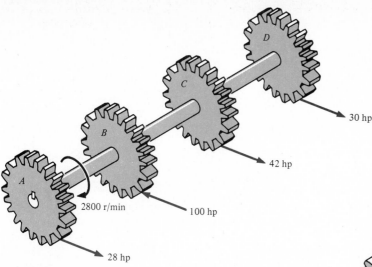

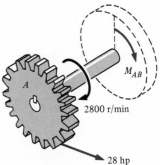

Fig. 20.45

taken out through the remaining three gears. Find the torque transmitted through shaft sections AB, BC, and CD. The rotational speed
of the shaft is 2,800 r/min.

Fig. 20.46

Solution Gear A and shaft section AB are isolated from the
system, as shown in Fig. 20.46. Power from gear B enters end B of
shaft length AB and leaves at end A through gear A. The speed of the
shaft is constant. It may thus be concluded, from Eq. (20.191), that
the torque in shaft length AB is constant. This value is

$$M_{AB} = 63{,}000 \left(\frac{\text{hp}_{AB}}{N} \right) = 63{,}000 \left(\frac{28}{2{,}800} \right) = 630 \text{ in} \cdot \text{lb} \quad (20.202)$$

Gears C and D and shaft length BCD are isolated from the system, as
shown in Fig. 20.47. The torque transmitted through shaft length BC
is then

$$T_{BC} = 63{,}000 \left(\frac{\text{hp}_{BC}}{N} \right) \quad (20.203)$$

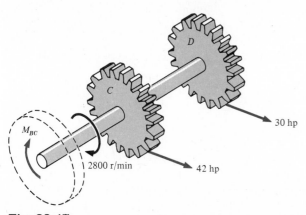

Fig. 20.47

The power transmitted through shaft length BC must satisfy the output requirements of gears C and D. Thus,

$$\text{hp}_{BC} = 42 + 30 = 72 \text{ hp} \qquad (20.204)$$

Equation (20.191) now appears as

$$M_{BC} = 63,000 \left(\frac{72}{2,800}\right) = 1,620 \text{ in·lb} \qquad (20.205)$$

By using a similar analysis, it can be shown that the torque transmitted through the shaft length CD is

$$M_{CD} = 63,000 \left(\frac{30}{2,800}\right) = 675 \text{ in·lb} \qquad (20.206)$$

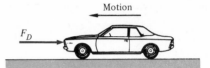

Motion

Example 20.20 Figure 20.48 shows an automobile which moves with constant speed along a horizontal road surface. As the vehicle moves, it must displace stationary air. The total resisting force of the air on the vehicle is represented by the resultant force F_D. This force is referred to as a *drag force*. It is shown in Chap. 24 that an approximate description of this force is given by

$$F_D = C_D(\tfrac{1}{2}\rho v^2)A \qquad (20.207)$$

where ρ is the mass density of the air, A is the projected area of the vehicle on a plane which is normal to the direction of motion, v is the speed, and C_D is a constant called the drag coefficient.

a Find the power output of the automobile engine required to overcome the air resistance if the vehicle moves with a constant speed of 50 mi/h.

b Do the same as in part *a* if the speed of the vehicle is 70 mi/h.

The specific weight of the air is 0.07637 lb/ft³, the projected area of the automobile is 20.6 ft², and the drag coefficient is assumed to have the value 0.68.

Fig. 20.48

Solution
a At 50 mi/h,

$$v = 50 \frac{\text{mi}}{\text{h}} \left(\frac{5,280 \text{ ft/mi}}{3,600 \text{ s/h}}\right) = 73.3 \frac{\text{ft}}{\text{s}} \qquad (20.208)$$

The drag force is

$$F_D = C_D \left(\frac{1}{2}\rho v^2\right)A = 0.68 \left[\frac{1}{2}\left(\frac{0.07637}{32.2}\right)(73.3)^2\right]20.6 = 89.3 \text{ lb} \qquad (20.209)$$

The required power is then

$$P = F_D v = 89.3(73.3)\left(\frac{1 \text{ hp}}{550 \text{ ft·lb/s}}\right) = 11.9 \text{ hp} \qquad (20.210)$$

b At 70 mi/h,

$$v = 70\left(\frac{5,280}{3,600}\right) = 103 \text{ ft/s} \qquad (20.211)$$

The drag force is

$$F_D = C_D \left(\frac{1}{2}\rho v^2\right)A = 0.68 \left[\frac{1}{2}\left(\frac{0.07637}{32.2}\right)(103)^2\right]20.6 = 176 \text{ lb} \qquad (20.212)$$

and the required power is

$$P = F_D v = \frac{176(103)}{550} = 33.0 \text{ hp} \qquad (20.213)$$

It may be seen that a 40 percent increase in the speed of the vehicle almost triples the magnitude of the required power. These results illustrate the effects which are responsible for the drastic increase in fuel consumption when an automobile operates at high speed.

20.13 SUMMARY

In its most fundamental conception energy is understood to mean the capacity for doing work. Energy may be stored in a mass particle by virtue of the motion of this element. This form of energy is called kinetic energy, with the basic form

$$T = \tfrac{1}{2}mv^2 \qquad (20.214)$$

Energy may also be stored in a mass particle by virtue of the position of the particle. This form of energy is called potential energy. When motion of a particle occurs, potential energy can be converted to kinetic energy, and kinetic energy can be converted to potential energy.

The work done by a force is defined to be

$$W_{12} = \int_0^l (F \cos \beta) \, ds \qquad (20.215)$$

where 1 and 2 represent the endpoints of l, the distance through which the point of application of the force moves. If both the magnitude and the orientation of the force with respect to the displacement are constant, then the work may be expressed as

$$W_{12} = (F \cos \beta)l \qquad (20.216)$$

The work done by a couple, moment, or torque M is

$$W_{12} = \int_{\theta_1}^{\theta_2} M \, d\theta \qquad (20.217)$$

where $\theta_2 - \theta_1$ is the angle through which the moment acts. If the moment has constant magnitude, direction, and sense, then the work may be expressed as

$$W_{12} = M(\theta_2 - \theta_1) \qquad (20.218)$$

Work is positive if the sense of the force or moment is the same as the sense of the displacement. The units of work or energy are the product of force and length. The usual USCS units are inch-pounds or foot-pounds. In SI units, the fundamental work and energy units are joules, written as J, where

$$1 \text{ J} = 1 \text{ N} \cdot \text{m} \qquad (20.219)$$

Conservative forces produce changes in the kinetic and potential energy which are fully recoverable if the system is imagined to operate in reverse and return to the original condition. Thus, conservative forces produce no permanent energy losses. Weight and spring forces are examples of conservative forces. Nonconservative forces produce permanent energy losses. A friction force is an example of a nonconservative force.

The general statement of conservation of energy in a mechanical system is

$$\begin{matrix}\text{Mechanical} \\ \text{energy in} \\ \text{system in} \\ \text{position 1}\end{matrix} + \begin{matrix}\text{nonconservative} \\ \text{work done on} \\ \text{the particle}\end{matrix} = \begin{matrix}\text{mechanical} \\ \text{energy in} \\ \text{system in} \\ \text{position 2}\end{matrix} \quad (20.220)$$

This equation may be written in the form

$$W_{NC} = \Delta T + \Delta V \quad (20.221)$$

where W_{NC} is the nonconservative work, ΔT is the change in kinetic energy, and ΔV is the change in potential energy. If there is no nonconservative work done, the work-energy equation has the form

$$0 = \Delta T + \Delta V = (T_2 - T_1) + (V_2 - V_1) \quad (20.222)$$

The potential energy of a rigid body may be found by imagining all the mass of the body to be concentrated at the CM and treating this point as a particle in translation. The kinetic energy of a rigid body which rotates about a fixed point with angular velocity ω is

$$T = \tfrac{1}{2}I\omega^2 \quad (20.223)$$

where I is the mass moment of inertia about the fixed point. If the rigid body moves in general plane motion, the kinetic energy has the form

$$T = \tfrac{1}{2}mv_0^2 + \tfrac{1}{2}I_0\omega^2 \quad (20.224)$$

where v_0 is the absolute velocity of the CM and I_0 is the mass moment of inertia of the body about this point.

The work-energy method considers states, or conditions, at only the endpoints of the time interval of interest. The solutions yield no information whatsoever about the conditions during the interval. The acceleration terms never enter directly into these solutions.

The normal acceleration of a particle which moves in plane curvilinear translation is given by

$$a_n = \frac{v^2}{\rho} \quad (20.225)$$

where ρ is the radius of curvature of the path. In many problems the path of the motion lies in a vertical plane. For such cases the work-energy method may be used to find the velocity at the point of interest. This value may then be used in Eq. (20.225) to find the normal acceleration of the particle.

Power is defined to be the work done per unit time. In translational systems, the power is given by

$$P = (F \cos \beta)v \qquad (20.226)$$

In rotational systems, the power is expressed as

$$P = M\omega \qquad (20.227)$$

The fundamental units of power are the units of energy divided by time. In USCS units, the power is given in foot-pounds per second or foot-pounds per minute. The unit horsepower is defined by

$$1 \text{ hp} = 550 \, \frac{\text{ft} \cdot \text{lb}}{\text{s}} = 33,000 \, \frac{\text{ft} \cdot \text{lb}}{\text{min}} \qquad (20.228)$$

In SI units the power is expressed in newton-meters per second, where

$$1 \, \frac{\text{N} \cdot \text{m}}{\text{s}} = 1 \, \frac{\text{J}}{\text{s}} = 1 \text{ W} \qquad (20.229)$$

In Eq. (20.229), the symbols J and W represent joules and watts, respectively. The conversion relationship for power in the two systems is

$$1 \text{ hp} = 746 \text{ W} \qquad (20.230)$$

The efficiency of a mechanical system is defined by

$$\eta = \frac{\text{energy, or power, output}}{\text{energy, or power, input}} \qquad (20.231)$$

Since all real systems have power losses, it follows that

$$\eta < 1 \qquad (20.232)$$

PROBLEMS

20.1 through 20.6 The particle shown in the figure is acted on by the system of forces shown. It moves with rectilinear translation in a frictionless guide.

(*a*) Find the work done on the particle when this element moves through a distance of 2 ft.

(*b*) Find the velocity of the particle when this element has moved through a distance of 2 ft.

(*c*) Find the change in potential energy of the particle after this element has moved through a distance of 2 ft.

(*d*) Verify the result in part *b* by solving for the acceleration and using this result in the equations for motion with constant acceleration.

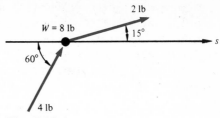

Fig. P20.1

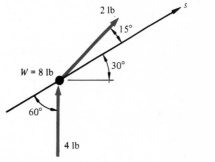

Fig. P20.2

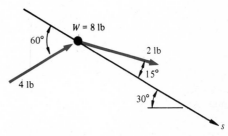

Fig. P20.3

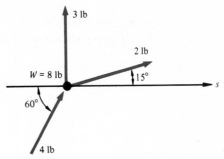

Fig. P20.4

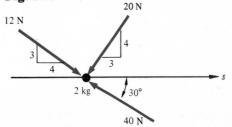

Fig. P20.5

20.6 (*a*) Do the same as in Prob. P20.2, if both forces are removed from the particle.

(*b*) Do the same as in part *a,* for Prob 20.3.

20.7 A 3600-lb automobile moves along a straight horizontal roadway.

(*a*) Find the change in the kinetic energy of the automobile when its speed changes from 30 mi/h to 40 mi/h.

(*b*) Do the same as in part *a*, if the speed changes from 40 mi/h to 50 mi/h.

20.8 The disk in Fig. P20.8 is acted upon by a couple *M* with a constant magnitude of 10 N·m. The mass of the disk is 5 kg.

(*a*) Find the work done by the couple when the disk has completed two revolutions, starting from rest.

(*b*) Find the angular velocity of the disk that corresponds to the position in part *a*.

(*c*) Compare the results in part *b* with the solution to Prob. 19.1, part *b*.

20.9 Figure P20.9 shows a heavy cast-iron flywheel that rotates at a constant speed of 150 r/min. A friction braking system is used to bring the flywheel to rest. When the flywheel is braked, it experiences a constant retarding moment of 5 N·m. The mass moment of inertia of the flywheel about its center axis is 6.25 kg·m².

(*a*) Determine how many revolutions the flywheel rotates through before coming to rest.

(*b*) Compare the result in part *a* with the solution to Prob. P19.3, part *b*.

20.10 The 4-kg disk shown in Fig. P20.10 is initially at rest. A force of 50 N is applied to the thin, inextensible cable wrapped around the disk.

(*a*) Find the angular velocity of the disk after this element has completed four revolutions.

(*b*) Compare the result in part *a* with the solution to Prob. 19.11, part *c*.

20.11 (*a*) Do the same as in Prob. 20.10, part *a*, if in addition to the cable force, the disk is acted on by a counterclockwise couple of magnitude 2 N·m. The couple acts in the plane of the disk.

(*b*) Compare the result in part *a* with the solution to Prob. 19.13.

20.12 A 6-kg cylinder rests in a trough, as shown in Fig. P20.12. A couple of constant magnitude $M = 3.8$ N·m is applied to the cylinder. Through how many revolutions has the cylinder rotated at the instant that its angular velocity is 110 rad/s?

20.13 Figure P20.13 shows a slender rod of mass *m* and length *l*. The rod is released with zero initial velocity from the position $\theta = 0°$.

(*a*) Find the kinetic energy of the rod as a function of θ.

(*b*) Find the angular velocity of the rod as a function of θ.

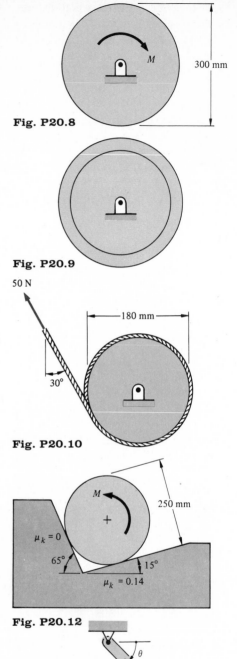

Fig. P20.8

Fig. P20.9

50 N

180 mm

30°

Fig. P20.10

M

250 mm

$\mu_k = 0$

65°   15°

$\mu_k = 0.14$

Fig. P20.12

θ

l

Fig. P20.13

744

(c) Find the numerical results for parts a and b, if $l = 1200$ mm and $m = 2.4$ kg.

(d) Find the maximum value of the angular velocity of the rod.

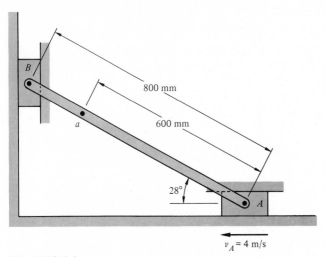

Fig. P20.14

20.14 The plane sliding mechanism of Example 17.8 is shown in Fig. P20.14. The velocity of block B was found to be $v_B = 7.48$ m/s. $m_A = 2.4$ kg and $m_B = 3.2$ kg, and the mass of the connecting link may be neglected. Find the kinetic energy of the system at the instant shown in the figure.

20.15 A particle is projected downward from a height of 100 ft with a velocity of 35 ft/s. Find the velocity with which it strikes the ground.

20.16 An archer shoots an arrow vertically upward.

(a) If the arrow ascends to a height of 90 ft, find the required value of the initial velocity of the arrow.

(b) Compare the result in part a with the solution to Prob. 15.69, part a.

20.17 The particle in Fig. P20.17 is projected upward from location a with an initial velocity of 12 m/s.

(a) Find the maximum height above the ground that the particle attains.

(b) Find the velocity with which the particle passes point b.

(c) Find the velocity with which the particle strikes the ground.

20.18 (a) Figure P20.18 shows a ball rebounding from a pavement. Find the maximum height to which the ball will rise.

(b) Compare the result in part a with the solution to Prob. 15.76, part a.

20.19 Use the work-energy method to verify the equation given in Prob. 15.92.

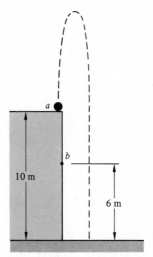

Fig. P20.17

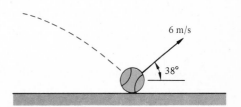

Fig. P20.18

20.20 A block slides along a horizontal plane with a constant value of deceleration, as shown in Fig. P20.20. The speed of the particle decreases from 35 in/s to zero over a length of 100 in.

(a) Find the value of the coefficient of kinetic friction.

(b) A second block, weighing 6 lb, is attached to the top of the 14-lb block. Find the distance through which the system of blocks will move before coming to rest, if the initial speed is 35 in/s.

(c) Compare the results of parts a and b with the solution to Prob. 16.31.

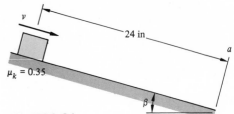

Fig. P20.20

20.21 The velocity of the block in the position shown in Fig. P20.21 is $v = 20$ in/s, and $\beta = 15°$. How much further will the block travel before it comes to rest?

20.22 It is desired to have the block in Fig. P20.21 come to rest at position a.

(a) If $\beta = 15°$, find the required value of v.

(b) If $v = 20$ in/s, find the required value of β.

Fig. P20.21

20.23 The block in Fig. P20.23 is released from rest at the position shown in the figure. The coefficient of kinetic friction over length ab is 0.22; and over length bc, this quantity has the value 0.16. Find the velocity with which the block passes position c.

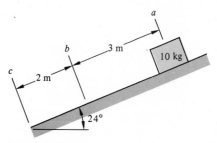

Fig. P20.23

20.24 A force P is applied to the initially stationary block in Fig. P20.24. When the block has covered a distance of 12 ft, the force is removed. Find the velocity with which the block passes its initial position. Magnitude of force is 40 lb.

20.25 A constant force P is applied to the crate shown in Fig. P20.25 when this element is moving to the right at 1.2 m/s. After the crate has moved through 4 m, the velocity is 3.7 m/s. Find the magnitude of the force P.

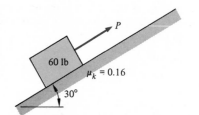

Fig. P20.24

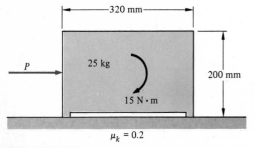

Fig. P20.25

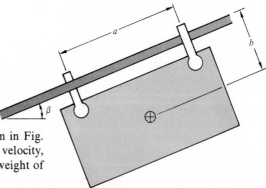

20.26 The conveyor system of Example 19.12 is shown in Fig. P20.26. At the instant shown in the figure, the plate has a velocity, with a sense which is down and to the left, of 8 ft/s. The weight of the plate is 750 lb. $a = 6$ ft, $b = 3$ ft, and $\beta = 28°$.

(a) If $\mu_k = 0.15$, find how far the plate moves before its velocity is 10.5 ft/s.

(b) Do the same as in part a, if $\mu_k = 0$.

Fig. P20.26

20.27 The inclined plane in Fig. P20.27 is assumed to be frictionless along the length *ab*. Length *bc* is rough, with a constant coefficient of friction $\mu_k \approx \mu_s$. The block is released from rest in position *a*.

(*a*) Find the maximum value of μ_k for which the block will continue to slide, without tipping, down the plane.

(*b*) Find the velocity of the block at position *c*, for the conditions of part *a*.

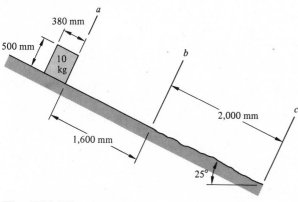

Fig. P20.27

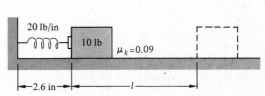

Fig. P20.28

20.28 The free length of the spring in Fig. P20.28 is 4 in. Find the distance *l* through which the block will move when this element is released from rest in the position shown in the figure.

20.29 Do the same as in Prob. 20.28, for the arrangement of the system shown in Fig. P20.29.

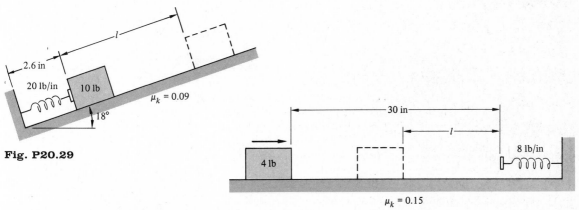

Fig. P20.29

Fig. P20.30

20.30 At the instant shown in Fig. P20.30, the block has a velocity of 8 ft/s.

(*a*) Find the maximum value of the deflection of the spring.

(*b*) Find the distance *l* through which the block travels, after rebound, before it comes to rest.

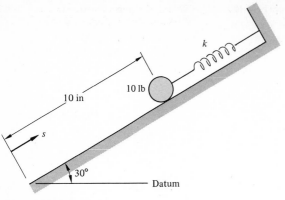

Fig. P20.31

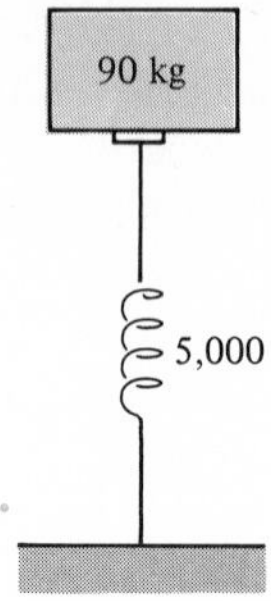

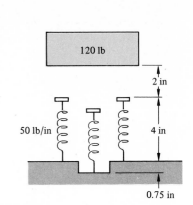

Fig. P20.32

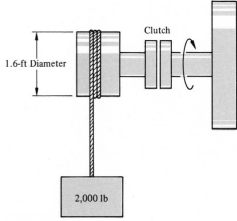

Fig. P20.33

20.31 The body in P20.31 is released from rest in the position shown. The initial value of the tensile spring force is 12 lb. Find the maximum value of the displacement s of the particle. $\mu_k = 0.18$.

20.32 In the position shown in Fig. P20.32, the block just contacts the free end of the spring.

(a) If the block is released instantaneously with zero initial velocity, find the maximum displacement of the spring.

(b) Do the same as in part a, if the block is very gradually lowered onto the spring.

20.33 A weight is dropped with zero initial velocity onto the springs shown in Fig. P20.33. If all three springs have the same dimensions, find the maximum values of the deflections of the springs.

20.34 Do the same as in Prob. 20.33, if the weight has a downward velocity of 10 in/s in the position shown in Fig. P20.33.

20.35 The flywheel in Fig. P20.35 rotates at 100 r/min. When the clutch is engaged, the stored energy of the flywheel may be used to raise the weight. The mass moment of inertia of the flywheel is 5.9×10^5 lb·in², and the mass moment of inertia of the drum on which the cable winds may be neglected. It may be assumed that there is a loss of 5 percent of the initial energy as a result of slippage during the clutch engagement. Find the distance through which the weight is raised when the flywheel is engaged.

20.36 Figure P20.36 shows a Yo-Yo of weight 0.15 lb, modeled as a cylindrical disk connected to an inextensible cable. At the instant shown in the figure, the Yo-Yo has a counterclockwise angular velocity of 30 rad/s.

(a) Find the increase in height that the Yo-Yo will attain.

(b) Compare the result in part a with the solution to Prob 19.38, part a.

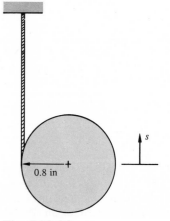

Fig. P20.35

Fig. P20.36

20.37 The cylinder in Fig. P20.37 rolls without slipping on the inclined surface. It is released from rest in position *a*.

(*a*) Find the kinetic energy of the cylinder when it reaches position *b*.

(*b*) Find the translational and rotational velocities of the cylinder when it reaches position *b*.

(*c*) Verify the results in part *b* by the direct application of Newton's second law.

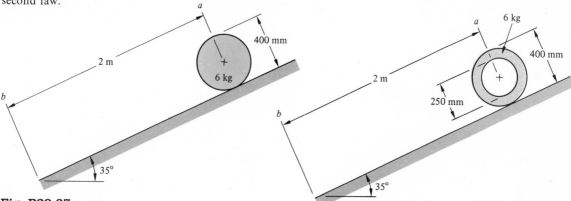

Fig. P20.37

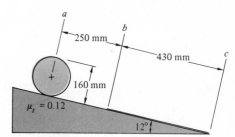

Fig. P20.38

20.38 Do the same as in Prob. 20.37 if the cylinder is hollow, as shown in Fig. P20.38.

20.39 Do the same as in Prob. 20.37, if the cylinder is replaced by a homogeneous sphere with the same outside diameter and mass.

20.40 A homogeneous cylinder is released from rest at position *a* in Fig. P20.40. It rolls without sliding until it reaches position *b*. Length *bc* of the inclined plane is contaminated with lubricant and, for the purpose of this problem, the coefficient of friction on this surface may be assumed to be zero.

(*a*) Find the angular velocity, and the velocity of the center, when the cylinder reaches position *b*.

(*b*) Do the same as in part *a*, when the cylinder reaches position *c*.

(*c*) Compare the results in parts *a* and *b* with the solution to Prob. 19.34, parts *c* and *d*.

Fig. P20.40

20.41 Figure 20.41 shows a cylinder of mass *m* and a track with the shape of a circular arc. The radius of the cylinder is *r*, and the radius of the track is *R*. The cylinder is released from rest at the position *β*.

(*a*) Find the angular velocity of the cylinder and the velocity of the center of this element, at position *b*, if the cylinder is assumed to roll without sliding.

(*b*) Do the same as part *a*, if the cylinder is assumed to slide without rolling.

(*c*) Find the normal acceleration of the center of the cylinder when it passes through position *b*, for the conditions of parts *a* and *b*.

(*d*) Find the numerical values for parts *a*, *b*, and *c* if $R = 200$ mm, $r = 25$ mm, and $β = 35°$.

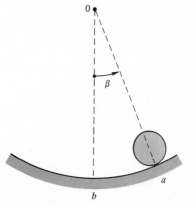

Fig. P20.41

20.42 A disk of diameter 250 mm and thickness 35 mm is made of steel, with $\rho = 7830 \text{ kg/m}^3$. The disk moves in general plane motion. The velocity diagram of the center of mass is shown in Fig. P20.42a, and the angular velocity diagram is shown in Fig. P20.42b. Find the maximum value of the kinetic energy of the disk in the time interval $0 \leq t \leq 10$ s.

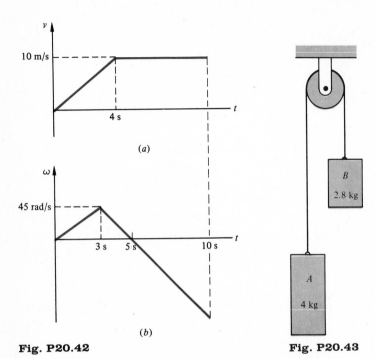

(a)

(b)

Fig. P20.42

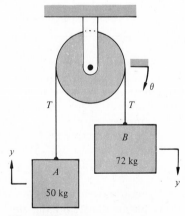

Fig. P20.43

20.43 At the instant shown in Fig. P20.43, block *A* has an upward velocity of 1.85 m/s. Find the additional upward motion of block *A* before this element comes to rest. The cable is inextensible, and all friction effects may be neglected.

20.44 Do the same as in Prob. 20.43, if a mass of 1 kg is added to block *B*.

20.45 Do the same as in Prob. 20.43, if a mass of 1 kg is added to block *A*.

20.46 The system of Example 19.8 is repeated in Fig. P20.46. Because of poor lubrication, the pulley must overcome a constant friction moment of 1.2 N·m as it rotates. Find the velocity of the blocks after block *B*, starting from rest, has moved downward 1 m.

Fig. P20.46

20.47 Fig. P20.47 shows a system of weights and pulleys. The cable is assumed not to slip on the pulleys. The masses and mass moments of inertia are $m_A = 20$ kg, $m_B = 14$ kg, $I_C = 0.005$ kg·m², and $I_D = 0.010$ kg·m².

(a) Find the velocities of the weights and pulleys when weight B, starting from rest, has moved upward 900 mm. Neglect the mass moments of inertia of the pulleys.

(b) Do the same as in part a, but include the mass moments of inertia of the pulleys.

(c) Compare the results in parts a and b with the solution to Prob. 19.43, parts b and c.

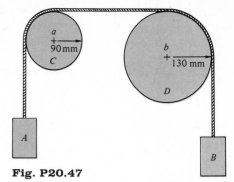

Fig. P20.47

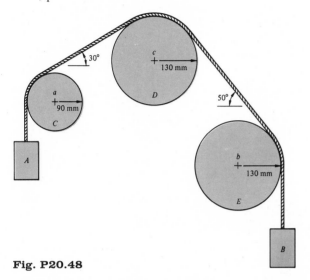

Fig. P20.48

20.48 (a) Do the same as in Prob. 20.47, for the system in Fig. P20.48.

(b) Compare the results in part a with the solution to Prob. 19.44. Pulleys D and E have the same mass properties.

20.49 The system of Example 19.9 is shown in Fig. P20.49. The diameter of the disk is 150 mm, the mass of the block is 600 g, and the mass moment of inertia of the disk about its center axis was found to be 2.76×10^{-3} kg·m².

(a) If the system is released from rest, find the angular velocity of the disk after the block has moved through a displacement of 1,400 mm.

(b) Verify the result in part a by using the value of angular acceleration $\alpha = 71.9$ rad/s² found in Example 19.9.

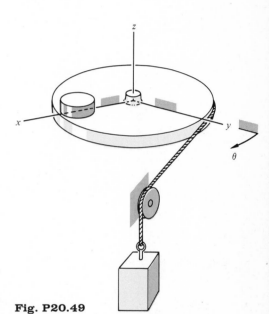

Fig. P20.49

20.50 The gears in Fig. P20.50 are steel, with $\gamma = 489$ lb/ft³, $d_1 = 4$ in, and $d_2 = 10$ in. The thickness of the gears is 1 in. An 8-lb weight is attached to the cable.

(a) Find the velocity of the weight after this element, starting from rest, has lowered through a distance of 20 in.

(b) Compare the result in part a with the solution to part b of Prob. 19.54.

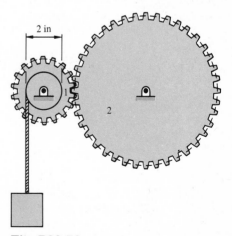

Fig. P20.50

20.51 (*a*) Do the same as in Prob. 20.50, if the gears and weight are arranged as shown in Fig. P20.51.

(*b*) Compare the results in part *a* with the solution to Prob. 19.55.

20.52 Fig. P20.52 shows a rack-and-pinion gear arrangement. The rack may be approximated as a steel rod of 0.5-in by 0.5-in square cross section, and the pinion may be approximated as a steel disk of 0.5 in thickness. All frictional effects may be neglected. The specific weight of steel is 489 lb/ft³. The system is released from rest in the position shown in the figure.

(*a*) Find the velocity of the rack at the position where the rack loses contact with the pinion.

(*b*) Do the same as in part *a*, if the pinion is assumed to have zero mass.

(*c*) Compare the results in parts *a* and *b* with the solution to Prob. 19.47, parts *c* and *d*.

20.53 (*a*) Do the same as in Prob. 20.52, if the pinion must overcome a constant friction moment of 1.2 in·lb.

(*b*) Compare the results in part *a* with the solution to Prob. 19.48.

20.54 Find the minimum required value of upward velocity of the rack, in the position shown in Fig. P20.52, for which the rack will just lose contact with the pinion. Neglect all friction effects.

20.55 The system shown in Fig. P20.55 is initially at rest. A second block of mass 3.5 kg is attached to block *B*. Find the angular velocity of the pulley when block *A* has moved through a distance of 1.75 m. Neglect mass of pulley.

20.56 Do the same as in Prob. 20.55, if the system is rearranged as shown in Fig. P20.56.

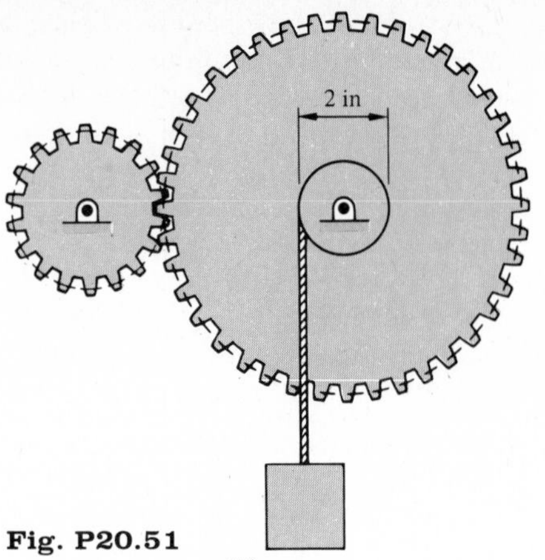

Fig. P20.51

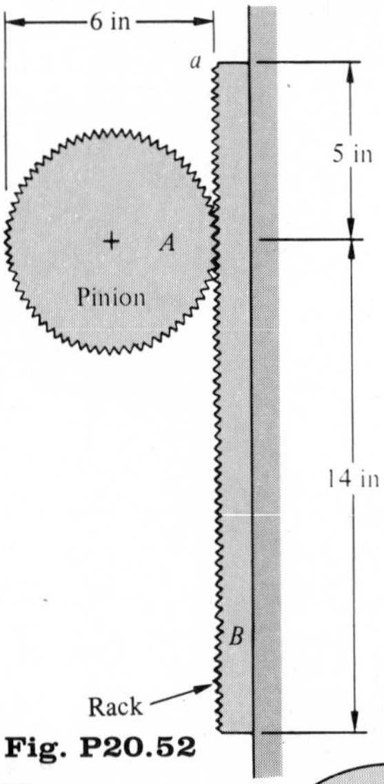

Fig. P20.52

Fig. P20.55

Fig. P20.56

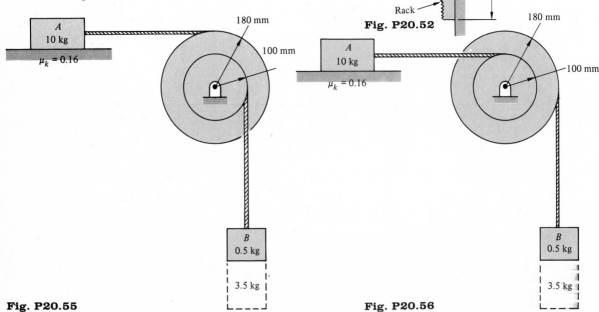

752

20.57 (*a*) Find the velocity of the blocks shown in Fig. P20.57 after these elements have moved through 2 m. The blocks are initially at rest. The mass of block *B* is 160 kg.

(*b*) Use the results from Prob. 16.44 to verify the result in part *a*.

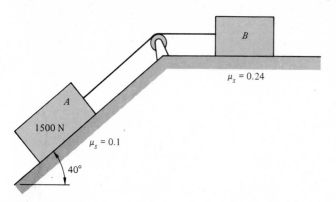

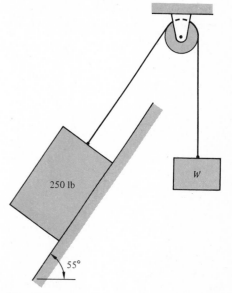

Fig. P20.57

20.58 The system in Fig. P20.58 is released from rest. $W = 100$ lb and the coefficient of kinetic friction between the block and the plane is 0.3.

(*a*) Find the distance through which the blocks must move to give these elements a velocity of 4 ft/s.

(*b*) Use the results in Prob. 16.42 to verify the result in part *a*.

Fig. P20.58

20.59 (*a*) Do the same as in Prob. 20.58, if $W = 300$ lb.
(*b*) Use the results in Prob. 16.42 to verify the result in part *a*.

20.60 For what range of values of weight of block *A* in Fig. P20.60 will the velocity of the blocks be less than, or equal to, 2 ft/s after the blocks have moved through a distance of 4 ft, starting from rest. Assume that $\mu_k \approx \mu_s$.

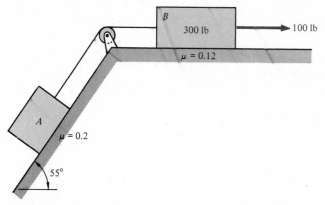

Fig. P20.60

20.61 The system of blocks in Fig. P20.61 is released from rest. The coefficient of kinetic friction on all sliding surfaces is 0.08. Find the velocity of block *B* after this element has moved through 20 in.

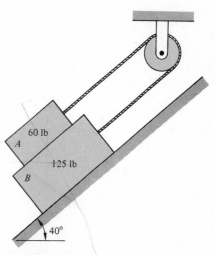

Fig. P20.61

20.62 A mass particle moves along a curved track that lies in a vertical plane, as shown in Fig. P20.62. The particle is assumed to not lose contact with the track.

(a) Find the magnitude, direction, and sense of the velocity of the particle at position b, if the particle has zero velocity at position a.

(b) Do the same as in part a, if the velocity of the particle at position a is 0.6 m/s.

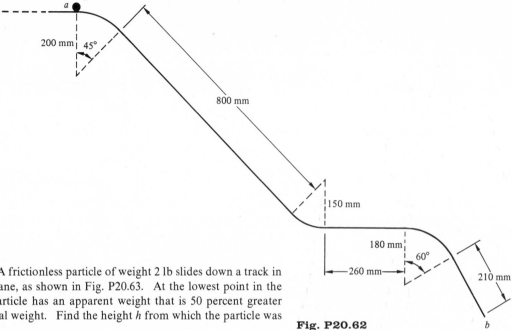

20.63 A frictionless particle of weight 2 lb slides down a track in a vertical plane, as shown in Fig. P20.63. At the lowest point in the track, the particle has an apparent weight that is 50 percent greater than its actual weight. Find the height h from which the particle was released.

Fig. P20.62

20.64 In the proposed system shown in Fig. P20.64 it is desired to have the small spherical mass particle, which is released from rest at position a, fall into an opening at position b.

(a) As one extreme condition, all friction effects may be neglected and it may be assumed that the particle slides, without rolling, along the track. Find the corresponding value of h.

(b) As the other extreme condition, it may be assumed that there is sufficient friction so that the particle rolls without sliding. Find the corresponding value of h.

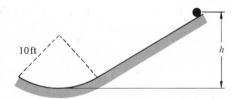

Fig. P20.63

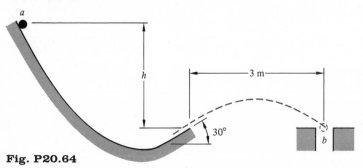

Fig. P20.64

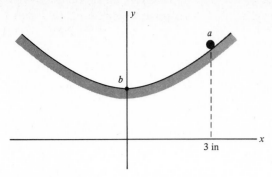

Fig. P20.65

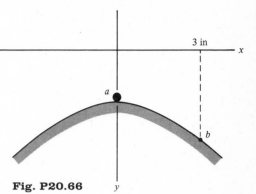

Fig. P20.66

20.65 The track of parabolic shape in Fig. P20.65 lies in a vertical plane, and is defined by $y = 5 + 0.3\,x^2$, where x and y are in inches. All friction effects may be neglected.
(*a*) Find the normal acceleration, in in/s², of the particle as it passes through position *b*.
(*b*) Do the same as in part *a*, if the particle has a velocity of 20 in/s as it passes through position *a*.

20.66 Do the same as in Prob. 20.65 if the track is inverted, as shown in Fig. P20.66. The particle is assumed to not lose contact with the track.

20.67 Figure P20.67 shows a man in an elevator. The weight of the man is 180 lb and the weight of the elevator cage is 1,450 lb. The elevator uses a 10-hp motor. If the overall efficiency of the elevator power system is 75 percent, find the maximum value of the constant speed with which the elevator can move upward.

20.68 An automobile weighs 4,000 lb. The coefficient of kinetic friction between the tires and the roadway is 0.6.
(*a*) Find the instantaneous power dissipation when the driver locks the brakes and starts to skid, when the vehicle is traveling at a speed of 60 mi/h.
(*b*) Find the energy expended in bringing the automobile to rest.

Fig. P20.67

20.69 Do the same as in Prob. 20.68, if the initial speed of the automobile is 70 mi/h.

20.70 Do the same as in Prob. 20.68, if the initial speed of the automobile is 80 mi/h.

20.71 (*a*) The block in Fig. P20.71 moves downward with a constant velocity of 7.5 m/s, and $\beta = 21.8°$. Find the power used to overcome the friction forces.
(*b*) The angle of the inclined surface is increased to 40°, and the block has a velocity of 7.5 m/s at the instant that it passes position *a*. Find the instantaneous power output when the block is at position *b*.

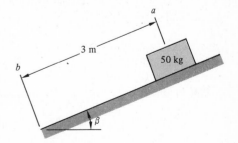

Fig. P20.71

20.72 Derive Eq. (20.191).

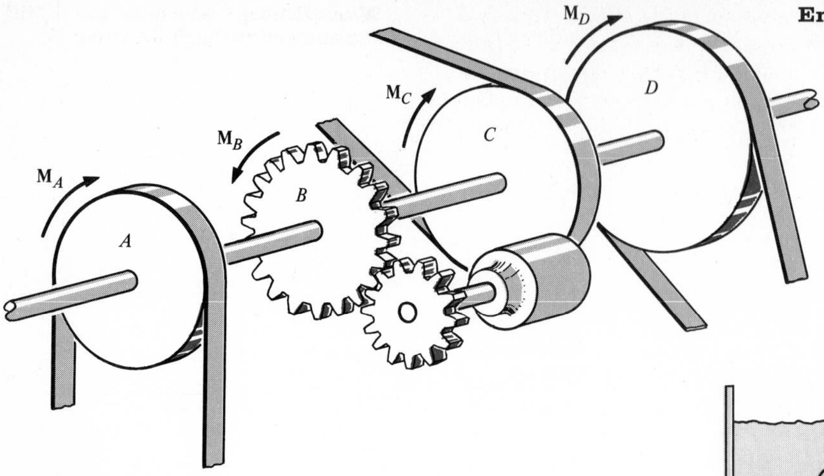

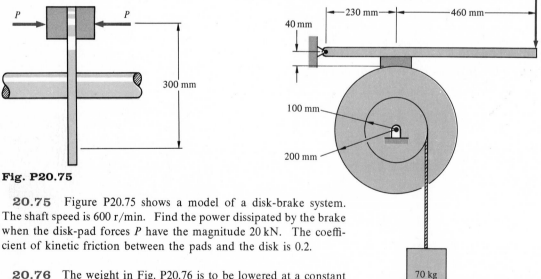

Fig. P20.73

20.73 The moment input M_B through gear B to the shaft in
Fig. P20.73 is 310 N·m. The shaft rotates at 1,500 r/min. The output moments are $M_A = 100$ N·m, $M_C = 80$ N·m, and $M_D =$
130 N·m. Find the power transmitted through sections AB, BC,
and CD of the shaft.

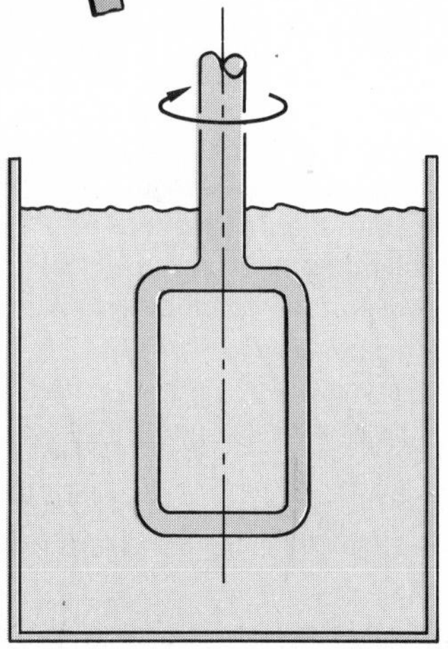

20.74 Figure P20.74 shows a stirrer blade used to agitate a thick
liquid solution. The blade rotates at 4 rad/s and overcomes a fluid
resistance of 250 ft·lb. If the motor is rated at 2 hp, find the efficiency of the motor.

Fig. P20.74

Fig. P20.75

20.75 Figure P20.75 shows a model of a disk-brake system.
The shaft speed is 600 r/min. Find the power dissipated by the brake
when the disk-pad forces P have the magnitude 20 kN. The coefficient of kinetic friction between the pads and the disk is 0.2.

20.76 The weight in Fig. P20.76 is to be lowered at a constant
speed of 3.7 m/s.
(a) Find the power dissipated at the brake shoe.
(b) Find the required value of the force P, if the coefficient of
kinetic friction between the brake shoe and the drum is 0.36.

Fig. P20.76

20.77 (*a*) The drum and weight system in Fig. P20.77 is released from rest. When the weight has lowered 3 ft, a force $P = 45$ lb is applied to the brake lever. Find how much farther the weight will lower before it comes to rest. The mass moment of inertia of the pulley is 0.61 lb·s²·in, and the coefficient of kinetic friction between the brake shoe and the drum is 0.4.

(*b*) Find the maximum value of the instantaneous power dissipation during the braking process.

Impulse-Momentum Methods for Particles and Rigid Bodies

21.1 INTRODUCTION

In the preceding chapters two methods for solving problems in dynamics have been used. The general characteristics of these methods are summarized here.

Direct Application of Newton's Second Law

In solving a problem by the direct application of Newton's second law, a necessary preliminary step is to draw a free-body diagram of the body under consideration. The resultant force, or moment, which acts on the body is then used in equations of the form

$$F = ma \tag{21.1}$$

for cases of translation or

$$T = I\alpha \tag{21.2}$$

for cases of rotation. These equations are solved, and the basic quantity found is the *acceleration* of the body. If the force or moment which acts on the body is *constant,* then the acceleration of the body will be *constant*. This value may then be used in known kinematic equations with the forms

$$v = v_0 + at \qquad \omega = \omega_0 + \alpha t \tag{21.3}$$

$$s = s_0 + v_0 t + \tfrac{1}{2}at^2$$
$$\theta = \theta_0 + \omega_0 t + \tfrac{1}{2}\alpha t^2$$

(21.4)

to relate the acceleration to the displacements, velocities, and times of the problem. The results of these computations are a *complete time history* of the motion of the body under consideration. The solution of problems in dynamics by the direct use of Newton's second law yields the maximum possible amount of information about the motion of the body.

Solutions Using Energy Methods

There are two distinct steps in solving problems in dynamics by using energy methods. One step is to express the *potential energy* of the body with respect to some arbitrarily chosen datum. The other is to express the velocity of the body in terms of coordinates describing the motion of the body. This velocity is then used to find the *kinetic energy* of the body. When the energy method is used, a free-body diagram of the body, and the time, never enter directly into a work-energy kinetic energy terms are then used in an equation which is a basic statement of conservation of energy. In using the energy method, the problem is described in terms of position coordinates, and velocities, at the endpoints of the time interval of interest. Thus, the solution obtained must be in terms of a displacement coordinate or a velocity. The acceleration of the body, and the time, never enter directly into a work-energy solution. If desired, these quantities may be found subsequently by using the kinematic equations describing the motion of the body. The work-energy method provides information about *only* the endpoints of the time interval under consideration. Thus, the solution is inherently incomplete, since it does not give a complete time history of the motion. In many problems, however, only the states of motion at these endpoints of the interval are of interest. The lack of a complete time history of motion is the characteristic which distinguishes work-energy solutions from solutions obtained by the direct application of Newton's second law.

In this chapter a third method of solving problems in dynamics will be presented. This technique is known as the *impulse-momentum method.* In order to show why this method is used, a simple problem will be posed, and it will be shown that this problem cannot be solved by either of the two general methods which have been used previously.

Figure 21.1 shows a sphere which is dropped from a height h onto a horizontal plate, and it is desired to find the maximum height to which the sphere will rebound. This problem may be divided into three regimes of motion. In the first regime, the

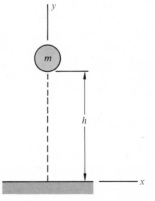

Fig. 21.1

sphere is in free fall until it contacts the plate. In the second, the sphere is in contact with the plate. In the third, the sphere moves upward with constant deceleration until the final height is reached.

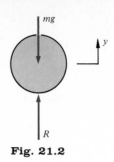

Fig. 21.2

The motion in the first and third regimes may be found readily by using either Newton's second law or the work-energy method. The free-body diagram of the sphere during the second regime is shown in Fig. 21.2, and R is the force exerted by the plane on the sphere. The equation of motion for this case is

$$R - mg = m\ddot{y} \tag{21.5}$$

From physical reasoning, it may be deduced that the reaction force R is some variable function of time. It follows from Eq. (21.5) that the acceleration is *not* constant. The symbol $\ddot{y}$, rather than a_y, is used to emphasize this effect. Both the reaction force R and the acceleration $\ddot{y}$ of the sphere are unknown. Thus, Eq. (21.5) is one equation in two unknowns, and this equation cannot be solved directly with the information given.

The thought may occur to the reader that a second, independent equation may be written that is a statement of conservation of energy, which would relate the kinetic energies, and thus the velocities, of the sphere before and after its contact with the plate. Unfortunately this cannot be done, since experimental evidence shows that the sphere will rebound to a height which is *less than* the height from which it was dropped. Thus, there is an energy loss of unknown magnitude in the problem.

This example typifies a class of problems in which one body impacts a second body. In this type of problem the impulse-momentum method finds its maximum utility. It will be seen in a subsequent section of this chapter that the problem considered above may be treated by the introduction of a term which is referred to as the coefficient of restitution.

21.2 IMPULSE OF A FORCE AND LINEAR MOMENTUM OF A PARTICLE

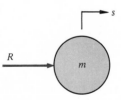

Fig. 21.3

Figure 21.3 shows a particle which moves in rectilinear translation and which is acted on by a resultant force R. The displacement coordinate of the particle is defined to be s, with the associated velocity and acceleration v and a. As before, the implication of particle motion is that there are no rotation effects.

Newton's second law may be written as

$$R = ma \tag{21.6}$$

Since

$$a = \frac{dv}{dt} \qquad (21.7)$$

Eq. (21.6) may be written as

$$R = m\frac{dv}{dt} \qquad (21.8)$$

Equation (21.8) is multiplied by dt and integrated, with the result

$$\int_1^2 R\,dt = \int_1^2 m\,dv = mv\Big|_1^2 = m(v_2 - v_1) \qquad (21.9)$$

where 1 and 2 designate the endpoints of the time interval of interest. The term on the left side of Eq. (21.9) is defined to be the *impulse* of the force R. The impulse of a force is a vector quantity which has the same direction as the force R. If R is a known function of time, this integral could be evaluated directly. In the general case, typified by the problem in Sec. 21.1, R is *not* known. For this case the quantity

$$I' = \int_1^2 R\,dt \qquad (21.10)$$

is a symbolic term which is used to represent the impulse I' of the force R. This integral is usually not evaluated directly in the solution of problems. It may be seen from Eq. (21.10) that the units of the impulse of a force are the product of force and time.

The numerical value of an impulse is not in itself a useful quantity. The force associated with the impulse is the desired quantity. In order to obtain the value of this force, it is necessary to know the duration of the impulse and the variation of the force of the impulse with respect to time. In the majority of actual problems, this latter information is not known, nor can it be obtained easily.

The two terms on the right side of Eq. (21.9) are the product of the mass of the particle and the velocity of this element. The product mv is defined to be the *linear momentum* of the particle, and this quantity is of fundamental importance in engineering dynamics. Since the linear momentum is expressed in terms of the velocity v, it follows that *linear momentum is a vector quantity*.

The numbers 1 and 2 designate the endpoints of the time interval of interest in the problem. The quantity $v_2 - v_1$ represents the *change in the velocity* of the particle, while the quantity $m(v_2 - v_1)$ represents the *change in the linear momentum* of the particle. The general conclusion may now be drawn from Eq. (21.9) that the effect of an impulse acting on a particle is to produce a change in the velocity of the particle. Equation

(21.9) is called the *impulse-momentum equation for a particle*.

It may be seen that the units of linear momentum are the product of mass and velocity. From consideration of Eq. (21.9) it follows that these units are the same as the units of impulse. The units of both of the above quantities are the product of force and time. These units are pound-seconds in USCS units and newton-seconds in SI units.

The impulse given by Eq. (21.10) may be interpreted as the area under the force-time curve of the resultant force acting on the particle. If this curve is known, the area under this curve may then be used directly to find the velocity *change* of the particle.

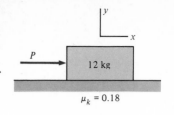

$\mu_k = 0.18$

(a)

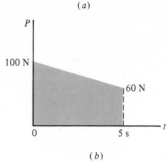

(b)

Fig. 21.4

Example 21.1 A block rests on a horizontal surface, as shown in Fig. 21.4a. It is acted on by an applied force P, and the variation of this force with time is shown in Fig. 21.4b. If the block is initially at rest, find the velocity of the block when $t = 5$ s.

Solution The free-body diagram of the block is shown in Fig. 21.5. The force-time diagram of the friction force is shown in Fig. 21.6. The force-time curve of the *resultant force* in the x direction which acts on the block is, then, the sum of the curves in Figs. 21.4b and 21.6, and this result is shown in Fig. 21.7.

The equation of impulse momentum now appears as

$$I' = \int_1^2 R \, dt = m(v_2 - v_1) \tag{21.11}$$

$$\frac{78.8 + 38.8}{2}(5) = 12(v_2 - 0) \tag{21.12}$$

$$294 = 12v_2 \qquad v_2 = 24.5 \text{ m/s} \tag{21.13}$$

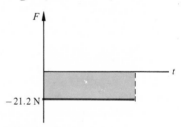

$12(9.81) = 118$ N

$F = 0.18(118) = 21.2$ N

118 N

Fig. 21.5

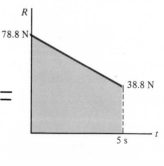

-21.2 N

Fig. 21.6

21.3 IMPULSE OF A CONSTANT FORCE

If the resultant force acting on the particle is constant, then the impulse of this force may be written as

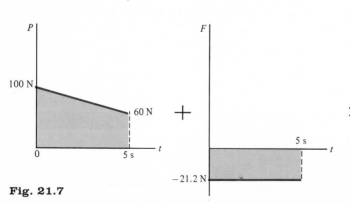

Fig. 21.7

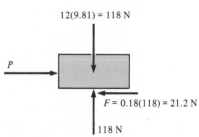

$$I' = \int_1^2 R\,dt = R \int_1^2 dt$$

$$= Rt \Big|_1^2 = R(t_2 - t_1)$$

(21.14)

This result is combined with Eq. (21.9) to obtain

$$R(t_2 - t_1) = m(v_2 - v_1) \qquad \text{constant resultant force}$$

(21.15)

Equation (21.15) is an elementary relationship between the times and velocities at the endpoints of the interval of interest. It should be noted that Eq. (21.15) is true *only if the resultant force which acts on the particle has a constant value.*

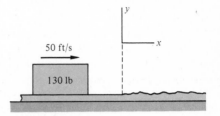

Fig. 21.8

Example 21.2 The system of Example 16.2 is repeated in Fig. 21.8. A block weighing 130 lb slides along a smooth, horizontal track with a velocity of 50 ft/s. At a certain point the smooth track joins a section of rough horizontal track. The coefficient of kinetic friction between the block and the rough track is 0.24. How long will it take the block to come to rest after it contacts the rough track?

Solution State 1 is defined to be when the block first contacts the rough horizontal track, and state 2 occurs when the block comes to rest. The constant force which acts on the block is the friction force, given by

$$F = -\mu_k N = -0.24(130) = -31.2\text{ lb} \qquad (21.16)$$

The minus sign is required in Eq. (21.16) since the friction force acts in a sense which is opposite to that of the motion. The remaining terms which are required are

$$t_1 = 0 \qquad v_1 = 50 \text{ ft/s} \qquad (21.17)$$

$$t_2 = t \qquad v_2 = 0 \qquad (21.18)$$

$$m = \frac{130}{32.2} = 4.04 \text{ lb·s}^2/\text{ft} \qquad (21.19)$$

The impulse-momentum equation, for constant force, now appears as

$$R(t_2 - t_1) = m(v_2 - v_1) \qquad (21.20)$$

$$-31.2(t - 0) = 4.04(0 - 50) \qquad t = 6.47 \text{ s} \qquad (21.21)$$

This is the result previously obtained in Eq. (16.27), where this same problem was solved by direct application of Newton's second law.

21.4 IMPACT

Impact is a term that describes the phenomenon of colliding physical bodies. Examples of impact problems abound in the physical world. Typical ones include a hammer driving a nail into a piece of wood, a ball dropped onto the ground, a bowling ball striking pins, and automobile bumpers contacting as a car maneuvers into a tight parking space.

The interactions which occur during impact are extremely complex and not fully understood. If the impacting velocity is sufficiently small, there will be no permanent deformation of the striking bodies; and these bodies, after impact, will be restored to their original shapes. If the velocity is greater than some critical, limiting value, there will be permanent deformation of one, or both, of the impacting bodies. A commonly seen example is the end of a cold chisel. The end of a new chisel is shown in Fig. 21.9a, while Fig. 21.9b shows the typical appearance of this end after considerable use.

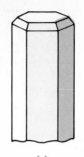

(b)

Fig. 21.9

A typical sequence of impact of one body with another body is shown in Fig. 21.10. For the purpose of this discussion, one body is assumed to be a sphere, and the second body is assumed to be a stationary horizontal plate. Figure 21.10a shows the sphere in its undeformed condition at the instant that it first makes contact with the plate. In the following time interval, shown in Fig. 21.10b, a period of deformation occurs in both bodies. The amount of deformation is a function of the velocity of impact and the materials and shapes of the impacting bodies. At the end of the period of deformation, the undeformed portion of the sphere has zero velocity, and the original potential energy of the sphere, due to elevation, has been expended in compressing portions of the two bodies.

Following the regime of deformation is a regime of restoration, or restitution. During this regime the energy (due to deformation) which is stored in the bodies is converted to kinetic energies, with associated velocities. If it is assumed that no permanent deformation occurs, the appearance of the sphere at the end of restitution is as shown in Fig. 21.10c. The original shape of the sphere is restored, and the sphere leaves the plate with an upward velocity v_1'. For an idealized case in which there are no permanent energy losses during the impact process, the magnitude of the rebound velocity v_1' would be equal to the magnitude of the striking velocity v_1. In actual cases of impact of physical bodies, *there is always an irreversible energy loss associated with the deformation and restitution phases of the impact*. Thus, the rebound velocity must obey the relationship

$$|v_1'| < |v_1| \qquad (21.22)$$

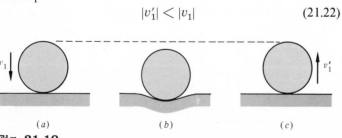

(a)   (b)   (c)

Fig. 21.10

The absolute value signs are used in Eq. (21.22) because the senses of v_1 and v_1' are opposite. A measure of the energy lost during impact, and the corresponding value of the rebound velocity, is given by a term called the *coefficient of restitution*. This term will be defined later in this chapter.

The following three effects characterize the impact problem in engineering dynamics.

1. The duration of the impact is much less than any other observed times in the problem. The case of dropping a sphere onto the horizontal plate may be simulated by dropping a ball onto the ground. It may be observed that the actual time that the ball is in contact with the ground is much less than either the time that the ball is falling toward the ground, or the time that the ball is rebounding away from the ground.

2. Because of the short time duration of the impact, *the impacting bodies are assumed to experience an instantaneous change in velocity, with no change in displacement.* In the problem of the sphere falling on the horizontal plate, shown in Fig. 21.1, the total impact phenomenon is assumed to occur at a *constant* value of displacement of the sphere given by $y = 0$. The velocity, by comparison, changes from a *downward* value of v_1 to an *upward* value of v_1' during the same infinitesimal time duration of the impact.

3. During the impact process, contact reaction forces *of extremely large magnitude* exist for very short time intervals. These forces are assumed to be much greater than any other forces, such as weight, spring, or friction forces, which act on the body.

In Example 21.7 a known problem from the theory of elasticity is solved for the time of impact and the magnitude of the impact force. These values of the time and force are then compared with other values of time and force in the problem, to confirm the statement in item 3 above.

As a consistent usage throughout this chapter, a *prime* will be used to designate a velocity after *impact*. Thus, if v_A and v_B are the velocities of two bodies before they impact each other, their velocities after impact would be written as v_A' and v_B'.

The principal use of solutions to problems of impact is to obtain a set of initial velocities for the regime of motion following the impact. This effect is illustrated in the later examples in this chapter.

21.5 CONSERVATION OF LINEAR MOMENTUM

Figure 21.11 shows two spheres which move in translation along the same axis. The spheres have the constant velocities

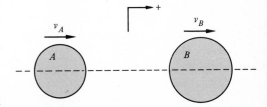

Fig. 21.11

v_A and v_B. It will be assumed that $v_A > v_B$, so that sphere A will eventually collide with sphere B. Figure 21.12 shows the free-body diagrams during the collision, or impact, of the two spheres. During this period of contact there exists a compressive force R between the two spheres and with it an associated impulse $I' = \int_1^2 R\, dt$. From Newton's third law, the impulses acting on the two spheres must have opposite senses. At the cessation of the impact process, the two spheres have the new velocities v_A' and v_B' shown in Fig. 21.13. All velocities in this problem are considered to be positive quantities if they act in the arbitrarily chosen positive sense shown in the figure.

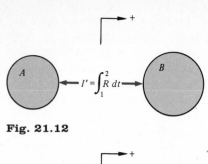

Fig. 21.12

The equations of impulse-momentum for each sphere are

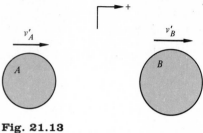

$$\text{Sphere } A \qquad -\int_1^2 R\, dt = m_A(v_A' - v_A) \qquad (21.23)$$

$$\text{Sphere } B \qquad \int_1^2 R\, dt = m_B(v_B' - v_B) \qquad (21.24)$$

Fig. 21.13

The minus sign is required in Eq. (21.23) to conform with the positive sense of motion shown in the figure. Equations (21.23) and (21.24) are added, with the result

$$0 = m_A(v_A' - v_A) + m_B(v_B' - v_B) \qquad (21.25)$$

This equation may be written in the form

$$m_A v_A + m_B v_B = m_A v_A' + m_B v_B' \qquad (21.26)$$

The left side of Eq. (21.26) is the combined initial momentum which the two spheres possessed before the impact, and the right side of the equation expresses the combined momentum of the two spheres after impact. The impulse which one sphere exerts on the other sphere during the time of impact is an internal force effect within the system of the two spheres. Equation (21.26) now leads to a conclusion of fundamental importance in dynamics. That is, for colliding bodies, in the absence of external forces, the total linear momentum of the system of bodies is constant. An alternate statement of this effect is that the *linear momentum of the system is conserved.*

In the problem illustrated in Fig. 21.11, a desired solution would be the values of the two velocities v_A' and v_B' of the spheres after impact. It may be seen that Eq. (21.26) is a single equation in these two unknowns. Thus, this equation by itself is not sufficient to solve the problem. In Sec. 21.6 a second independent equation, which relates the velocities before and after impact, will be developed in terms of the coefficient of restitution. With this latter equation, the complete solution may be obtained for the case of the two colliding spheres.

A very important observation may be made about Eq. (21.26). This equation may be used only to find the new velocities of the bodies after impact. It does not yield information about the duration of the impact or the magnitude of the impact forces.

21.6 COEFFICIENT OF RESTITUTION

When two physical bodies collide, there is a permanent *energy* loss as a result of effects occurring in the material during the deformation and restitution phases of the impact process. This energy loss manifests itself in lower values of velocity after impact than would have been the case had there been no energy loss.

In the initial condition *before* impact, as shown in Fig. 21.11, the relative velocity of the two spheres may be expressed as

$$v_r = v_A - v_B \qquad (21.27)$$

The relative velocity immediately after impact may be written as

$$v_r' = v_A' - v_B' \qquad (21.28)$$

A term which is a measure of the energy loss during impact will be introduced now. This quantity is referred to as the *coefficient of restitution,* designated by the symbol e, and defined as

$$e = -\frac{\text{relative velocity after impact}}{\text{relative velocity before impact}} \qquad (21.29)$$

$$= -\frac{v_r'}{v_r} = -\frac{v_A' - v_B'}{v_A - v_B} \qquad (21.30)$$

If the numerator and denominator of Eq. (21.30) are multiplied by -1, this equation may also be written in the form

$$e = -\frac{v_B' - v_A'}{v_B - v_A} \qquad (21.31)$$

Two limiting values of the coefficient of restitution will now be considered.

Plastic Impact

One extreme value of the coefficient of restitution occurs during *plastic impact*. In a plastic impact, the colliding bodies are assumed to physically adhere to each other and move with a common velocity after impact. For this case,

$$v_A' = v_B' \qquad (21.32)$$

and, from Eq. (21.30),

$$e = 0 \qquad (21.33)$$

The plastic impact case corresponds to the *maximum* energy loss which may occur between the two impacting bodies.

Elastic Impact

In an *elastic impact* the assumption is made that no permanent energy loss results from the impact process. Thus, all the energy is recovered, and elastic impact may be considered to be a theoretical limiting case. It can be shown that for the case of elastic impact $e = 1$. It then follows that the range of possible values of e is given by

$$0 \le e \le 1 \qquad (21.34)$$

If an impact is not elastic, it is referred to as *inelastic*. The actual value of the coefficient of restitution must be determined experimentally. In a given problem, a value may be estimated for this quantity.

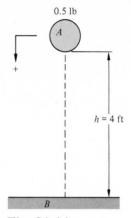

Fig. 21.14

Example 21.3 A ball weighing 0.5 lb is dropped onto the ground from a height of 4 ft, as shown in Fig. 21.14. Find the height to which the ball will rebound and the energy loss associated with the impact if the coefficient of restitution is assumed to be 0.85.

Solution The velocity v_A of the ball just before impact with the ground is

$$v_A = \sqrt{2gh} = \sqrt{2(32.2)(4)} = 16.0 \text{ ft/s} \qquad (21.35)$$

The ground is body B, and

$$v_A = 16.0 \text{ ft/s} \qquad v'_A = v'_A \qquad (21.36)$$

$$v_B = 0 \qquad v'_B = 0 \qquad (21.37)$$

The rebound velocity of the ball is found from

$$e = -\frac{v'_A - v'_B}{v_A - v_B} \qquad 0.85 = -\frac{v'_A - 0}{16.0 - 0} \qquad v'_A = -13.6 \frac{\text{ft}}{\text{s}} \qquad (21.38)$$

The minus sign in Eq. (21.38) indicates that the sense of the velocity is upward. The equation of impulse momentum is not required in this problem, since the velocity of the ground is zero throughout the impact process. Also, the above result is independent of the mass of the ball.

The final height h' attained by the ball after impact is found from

$$h' = \frac{(v'_A)^2}{2g} = \frac{(-13.6)^2}{2(32.2)} = 2.87 \text{ ft} \qquad (21.39)$$

The initial potential energy is

$$V_1 = mgh = 0.5(4) = 2 \text{ ft·lb} \qquad (21.40)$$

and the final potential energy is

$$V_2 = mgh' = 0.5(2.87) = 1.44 \text{ ft·lb} \qquad (21.41)$$

The permanent loss in energy may be stated in the form

$$\%D = \frac{V_1 - V_2}{V_1}(100) = \frac{2 - 1.44}{2}(100) = 28\% \qquad (21.42)$$

It may be seen that, due to the impact, there is a permanent loss of 28 percent of the initial energy in the system.

Fig. 21.15

Example 21.4 Figure 21.15 shows two prismatic rods which move along a common straight line on a surface. The masses of the two rods are equal, and the coefficient of kinetic friction between the rods and the surface is 0.28. Rod B is initially at rest.

a Find the velocities of the two rods after impact, in terms of v_A and e.

b Describe the velocities after impact if elastic impact, with $e = 1$, is assumed.

c Do the same as in part b if plastic impact, with $e = 0$, is assumed.

Fig. 21.16

Solution

a The configuration after impact is shown in Fig. 21.16. The impulse-momentum equation is

$$m_A v_A + m_B v_B = m_A v'_A + m_B v'_B \qquad (21.43)$$

$$m v_A + m(0) = m v'_A + m v'_B \qquad (21.44)$$

$$v'_A + v'_B = v_A \qquad (21.45)$$

The equation which relates the relative velocities before and after impact is

$$e = -\frac{v'_A - v'_B}{v_A - v_B} = -\frac{v'_A - v'_B}{v_A - 0} \qquad (21.46)$$

$$v'_A - v'_B = -e v_A \qquad (21.47)$$

Equations (21.45) and (21.47) are solved simultaneously, and the result is

$$v'_A = \frac{1 - e}{2} v_A \qquad v'_B = \frac{1 + e}{2} v_A \qquad (21.48)$$

b For the case of elastic impact, $e = 1$ and

$$v'_A = \frac{1 - 1}{2} v_A = 0 \qquad v'_B = \frac{1 + 1}{2} v_A = v_A \qquad (21.49)$$

For this case, it may be seen that the two rods *exchange* their velocities. After the impact, rod A is at rest and rod B has the original velocity of rod A.

An approximation of the above phenomenon may be observed with impacting billiard balls. This latter problem is not exactly the same as the problem of the impacting rods because of the rotation effects of the balls.

c For the case of plastic impact, $e = 0$ and

$$v'_A = \frac{1 - 0}{2} v_A = \frac{1}{2} v_A \qquad v'_B = \frac{1 + 0}{2} v_A = \frac{1}{2} v_A \qquad (21.50)$$

The two rods adhere to each other and move with a common velocity which is *one half* of the original impact velocity.

It may be seen that the friction forces do not enter into this problem. This is because of the earlier assumption that the magnitudes of forces such as weight, or friction, forces are negligible compared to the magnitudes of impact forces. These friction forces, however, would affect the motion of the rods after impact.

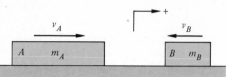

Example 21.5 Figure 21.17 shows two rods which move along a common line on a surface.

a Find the general expression for the velocities of the two rods after impact.

Fig. 21.17

b If $m_A = 2$ kg, $m_B = 1$ kg, $v_B = 3$ m/s, and $e = 0.65$, find the value of the initial velocity v_A which will cause rod A to be at rest after the impact.

c Find the magnitude of the impulse for the conditions of part b.

d Find the percent decrease in energy which corresponds to the impact in part b.

Solution

a The velocities of the two rods after impact are shown in Fig. 21.18. The equation of impulse momentum is

$$m_A v_A + m_B(-v_B) = m_A v_A' + m_B v_B' \qquad (21.51)$$

Fig. 21.18

and the equation which relates the relative velocities is

$$e = -\frac{v_A' - v_B'}{v_A - (-v_B)} \qquad (21.52)$$

Equations (21.51) and (21.52) are solved simultaneously, and the results are

$$v_A' = \frac{(m_A - em_B)v_A - (1 + e)m_B v_B}{m_A + m_B} \qquad (21.53)$$

$$v_B' = \frac{(1 + e)m_A v_A - (m_B - em_A)v_B}{m_A + m_B} \qquad (21.54)$$

b Using the values $m_A = 2$ kg, $m_B = 1$ kg, $v_B = 3$ m/s, and $e = 0.65$, with $v_A' = 0$, Eq. (21.53) appears as

$$v_A' = 0 = [2 - 0.65(1)]v_A - (1 + 0.65)(1)(3)$$
$$v_A = 3.67 \text{ m/s} \qquad (21.55)$$

The corresponding value of v_B' is found from Eq. (21.54) as

$$v_B' = \frac{(1 + 0.65)(2)(3.67) - 3[1 - 0.65(2)]}{2 + 1} = 4.34 \frac{\text{m}}{\text{s}} \qquad (21.56)$$

c The impulse which occurs during the impact is

$$I' = m_A(v_A' - v_A) = 2(0 - 3.67) = -7.34 \text{ N·s} \qquad (21.57)$$

The minus sign indicates that the sense of this impulse is to the left on rod A. From Newton's third law, it may be concluded that an impulse of the same magnitude acts to the right on rod B. It may be observed that the numerical value of the impulse has no particular useful application.

d The initial kinetic energy of the system is

$$T_1 = \tfrac{1}{2}m_A v_A^2 + \tfrac{1}{2}m_B v_B^2 \qquad (21.58)$$

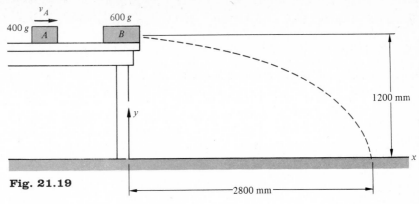

Fig. 21.19

$$= \tfrac{1}{2}(2)(3.67^2) + \tfrac{1}{2}(1)(3^2) = 18.0 \ \text{N·m} = 18.0 \ \text{J} \quad (21.59)$$

The kinetic energy after impact is

$$T_2 = \tfrac{1}{2}m_B(v_B')^2 = \tfrac{1}{2}(1)(4.34^2) = 9.42 \ \text{J} \quad (21.60)$$

The percent loss of energy is then

$$\%\text{D} = \frac{18.0 - 9.42}{18.0}(100) = 47.7\% \quad (21.61)$$

Example 21.6 A 600-g block rests on the edge of a table, as shown in Fig. 21.19. A second block, weighing 400 g and moving with velocity v_A, strikes the first block and causes the trajectory shown in the figure. The impact is assumed to be "nearly elastic," with an assumed value of the coefficient of restitution of 0.95. Find the initial velocity v_A and the final velocity v_A' of the striking block.

Solution The equation of motion of block B in the y direction is

$$y = y_0 + v_{0y}t - \tfrac{1}{2}gt^2 \quad (21.62)$$

The time t at which block B strikes the ground at $y = 0$ is found from

$$0 = 1.2 + 0 - \frac{1}{2}(9.81)t^2 \qquad t = 0.495 \ \text{s} \quad (21.63)$$

The equation of motion of block B in the x direction is

$$x = x_0 + v_{0x}t \quad (21.64)$$

The x component of the initial velocity of block B is found from

$$2.8 = 0 + v_{0x}(0.495) \qquad v_{0x} = 5.66 \ \frac{\text{m}}{\text{s}} \quad (21.65)$$

The above quantity is equal to v_B', the velocity of block B after the impact.

The impact phenomenon has the general form of that in Example 21.5. Equation (21.54) may thus be used directly, as

$$v_B' = \frac{(1 + e)m_A v_A - (m_B - em_A)v_B}{m_A + m_B} \quad (21.66)$$

$$5.66 = \frac{(1 + 0.95)(400/1,000)v_A - 0}{400/1,000 + 600/1,000} \qquad v_A = 7.26 \ \frac{\text{m}}{\text{s}} \quad (21.67)$$

771

The velocity v_A' may be found from Eq. (21.53) as

$$v_A' = \frac{(m_A - em_B)v_A - (1 + e)m_B v_B}{m_A + m_B} \tag{21.68}$$

$$= \frac{[400/1,000 - 0.95(600/1,000)](7.26) - 0}{400/1,000 + 600/1,000}$$

$$v_A' = -1.23 \,\frac{\text{m}}{\text{s}} \tag{21.69}$$

The minus sign in the above result indicates the block A moves leftward after the impact.

Example 21.7 The last example is a computation of an actual time of impact and the maximum value of the impact force for two colliding, metal spheres. The computation utilizes one of the few known solutions for the time and force in an impact problem.

Figure 21.20 shows two metal spheres which move toward each other along a rectilinear path. The solution, from the linear theory of elasticity,† is

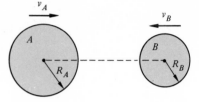

Fig. 21.20

$$x_r = \left(\frac{5}{4}\frac{v^2}{nn_1}\right)^{2/5} \tag{21.70}$$

$$v = v_A + v_B \qquad n_1 = \frac{m_A + m_B}{m_A m_B} \tag{21.71}$$

$$n = \sqrt{\frac{16}{9\pi^2}\frac{R_A R_B}{(K_A + K_B)^2(R_A + R_B)}} \tag{21.72}$$

$$K_A = \frac{1 - v_A^2}{\pi E_A} \qquad K_B = \frac{1 - v_B^2}{\pi E_B} \tag{21.73}$$

$$P_{\text{max}} = \sqrt{\frac{16 R_A R_B x_r^3}{9\pi^2(K_A + K_B)^2(R_A + R_B)}} \qquad t = \frac{2.94 x_r}{v} \tag{21.74}$$

In the above equations, x_r is the maximum distance through which the spheres approach each other during the impact, P_{max} is the maximum value of the impact force which corresponds to x_r, t is the time at which the maximum deformation of the bodies occurs, and v_A, v_B and E_A, E_B are material properties of the two spheres which are referred to as Poisson's ratio and the modulus of elasticity, respectively.

a If both spheres are of steel, with $v = 0.3$ and $E = 30 \times 10^6$ lb/in², find the time to reach the maximum value of impact force and the value of this force. Sphere A is 2 in in diameter, sphere B is 1 in in diameter, $v_A = 10$ ft/s, and $v_B = 5$ ft/s.

b Use the results of part a to verify the basic assumption of impact problems that extremely large forces act over very short time intervals.

Solution

a The specific weight of steel is $\gamma = 0.283$ lb/in³. The weights of the two spheres are

---

† Timoshenko and Goodier, *Theory of Elasticity*, McGraw-Hill, New York, 1951, pp. 383ff.

$$W_A = \tfrac{4}{3}\pi R_A^3 r = \tfrac{4}{3}\pi (1)^3 (0.283) = 1.19 \text{ lb} \qquad (21.75)$$

$$W_B = \tfrac{4}{3}\pi R_B^3 r = \tfrac{4}{3}\pi (0.5)^3 (0.283) = 0.148 \text{ lb} \qquad (21.76)$$

The remaining terms are found to be

$$K_A = K_B = \frac{1 - 0.3^2}{\pi (30 \times 10^6)} = 9.66 \times 10^{-9} \frac{\text{in}^2}{\text{lb}} \qquad (21.77)$$

$$n = \sqrt{\frac{16}{9\pi^2} \frac{1(0.5)}{[2(9.66 \times 10^{-9})]^2 (1 + 0.5)}} = 1.27 \times 10^7 \frac{\text{lb}}{\text{in}^{3/2}} \qquad (21.78)$$

$$n_1 = \frac{1/386(1.19 + 0.148)}{1/386^2 (1.19)0.148} = 2{,}930 \frac{\text{in}}{\text{lb·s}^2} \qquad (21.79)$$

$$v = (10 + 5)(12) = 180 \text{ in/s} \qquad (21.80)$$

$$x_r = \left[\frac{5}{4} \frac{(180)^2}{(1.27 \times 10^7)(2{,}930)} \right]^{2/5} = 4.12 \times 10^{-3} \text{ in} = 0.00412 \text{ in} \qquad (21.81)$$

$$t = 2.94 \frac{0.00412}{180} = 6.73 \times 10^{-5} \text{ s} = 0.0000673 \text{ s} = 67.3 \ \mu\text{s} \qquad (21.82)$$

$$P = \sqrt{\frac{16(1)(0.5)(0.00412)^3}{9\pi^2 [2(9.66 \times 10^{-9})]^2 (1 + 0.5)}} = 3{,}350 \text{ lb} \qquad (21.83)$$

b The time for the maximum deformation of the two spheres to occur is 0.0000673 s, or 67.3 μs. This time will be arbitrarily compared with the time t_0 for one of the spheres to travel through a distance equal to its own diameter. The times t_0 for the two spheres are

$$t_{0A} = \frac{2R_A}{v_A} = \frac{2(1)}{10(12)} = 0.0167 \text{ s} \qquad (21.84)$$

$$t_{0B} = \frac{2R_B}{v_B} = \frac{2(0.5)}{5(12)} = 0.0167 \text{ s} \qquad (21.85)$$

The above two times are seen to be equal. The factor ξ_t by which the above times are greater than the time to reach maximum deformation of the spheres is

$$\xi_t = \frac{0.0167}{0.0000673} = 248 \qquad (21.86)$$

The force at the time of maximum deformation of the two spheres is 3,350 lb. This force will be compared with the weight of the heavier of the two spheres. The factor ξ_f is defined to be the ratio of these two forces, and

$$\xi_f = \frac{3{,}350}{1.19} = 2{,}820 \qquad (21.87)$$

It may be seen from Eq. (21.87) that the peak value of the impact force is 2,820 times the magnitude of the weight force of the heavier sphere. Finally, the distance $x_r = 0.00412$ in through which the spheres approach each other during impact is only 0.4 percent of the diameter of the smaller sphere. This finding supports the basic assumption of impact problems that the displacements of the bodies do not change during impact.

21.7 DIRECT AND OBLIQUE, CENTRAL IMPACT

Figure 21.21 shows two bodies at the instant before impact. Points *a* and *b* are coincident points on the surfaces of the bodies at the location at which impact occurs. If the common normal line to the surfaces at points *a* and *b* also intersects the centers of mass of both bodies, the impact is referred to as *central impact*. In central impact, there is no tendency of the bodies to rotate. If this condition is not fulfilled, the impact is referred to as *eccentric impact*. In eccentric impact, one or both of the bodies will possess angular velocity after the impact. This section is concerned only with the case of central impact.

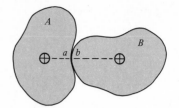

Fig. 21.21

If the velocities of the two bodies are *collinear* with the common normal line, the impact is described as *direct central impact*. All the examples considered in Sec. 21.6 were cases of direct central impact. If one or both of the velocities of the bodies are *not collinear* with the common normal line, the impact is referred to as *oblique central impact*. Figure 21.22 shows two bodies in a general configuration of oblique central impact. The initial velocities v_A and v_B, with the directions β_A and β_B, are known, and it is desired to find the magnitudes and directions of the velocities of the two bodies after impact.

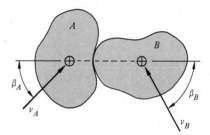

The free-body diagrams during impact of the two bodies are shown in Fig. 21.23. Because of the earlier assumption of *central impact,* the direction of the impulse I' which acts between the two bodies must be along the *x* axis. Thus, *there is no component of this impulse along the y axis*. The equation of impulse momentum in the *y* direction is written for each body, with the result

Fig. 21.22

$$0 = m_A(v'_{Ay} - v_{Ay}) \qquad v'_{Ay} = v_{Ay} \qquad (21.88)$$

$$0 = m_B(v'_{By} - v_{By}) \qquad v'_{By} = v_{By} \qquad (21.89)$$

The very significant conclusion is now arrived at that, in oblique central impact, *the components of the velocities of the two impacting bodies normal to the line of impact do not*

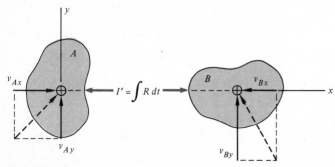

Fig. 21.23

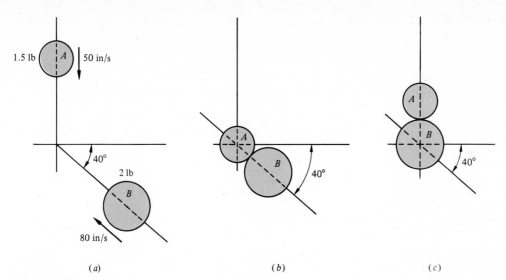

1.5 lb | A | 50 in/s

40°

2 lb

B

80 in/s

(a)

A

B

40°

(b)

A

B

40°

(c)

Fig. 21.24

change. For the case considered above, the x components of the velocities are then used as if the problem were one of direct central impact along the x axis.

Example 21.8 Two spheres approach each other with constant velocity along rectilinear paths, as shown in Fig. 21.24a. The coefficient of restitution is assumed to be 0.85.

a Find the magnitudes and directions of the velocities of the two spheres after impact, and the percent loss of energy, for the impact configuration shown in Fig. 21.24b.

b Do the same as in part a for the impact configuration shown in Fig. 21.24c.

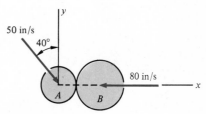

50 in/s

40°

80 in/s

A

B

y

x

Fig. 21.25

Solution

a The impact configuration for Fig. 21.24b is shown in Fig. 21.25. The components of initial velocity are

$$v_{Ax} = 50 \sin 40° = 32.1 \text{ in/s} \qquad v_{Bx} = -80 \text{ in/s} \quad (21.90)$$

$$v_{Ay} = -50 \cos 40° = -38.3 \text{ in/s} \qquad v_{By} = 0 \quad (21.91)$$

The components of velocity in the y direction are unchanged, so that

$$v'_{Ay} = v_{Ay} = -38.3 \text{ in/s} \qquad v'_{By} = v_{By} = 0 \quad (21.92)$$

The equation of impulse momentum in the x direction is

$$m_A v_{Ax} + m_B v_{Bx} = m_A v'_{Ax} + m_B v'_{Bx} \quad (21.93)$$

$$\frac{1.5}{g}(32.1) + \frac{2}{g}(-80) = \frac{1.5}{g}v'_{Ax} + \frac{2}{g}v'_{Bx} \quad (21.94)$$

The equation relating the relative velocities is

$$e = -\frac{v'_{Bx} - v'_{Ax}}{v_{Bx} - v_{Ax}} \qquad 0.85 = \frac{-(v'_{Bx} - v'_{Ax})}{-80 - 32.1} \quad (21.95)$$

775

Equations (21.94) and (21.95) are solved simultaneously, with the results

$$v'_{Ax} = -86.6 \text{ in/s} \qquad v'_{Bx} = 8.7 \text{ in/s} \qquad (21.96)$$

The magnitudes of the two velocities after impact are

$$v'_A = \sqrt{(v'_{Ax})^2 + (v'_{Ay})^2} = \sqrt{(-86.6)^2 + (-38.3)^2} = 94.7 \text{ in/s} \qquad (21.97)$$

$$v'_B = v'_{Bx} = 8.7 \text{ in/s} \qquad (21.98)$$

The orientations of the post impact velocities are shown in Fig. 21.26. The initial kinetic energy is

$$T_1 = \tfrac{1}{2}m_A v_A^2 + \tfrac{1}{2}m_B v_B^2 \qquad (21.99)$$

$$= \frac{1}{2}\left(\frac{1.5}{386}\right)(50^2) + \frac{1}{2}\left(\frac{2}{386}\right)(80^2) = 21.4 \text{ in·lb} \qquad (21.100)$$

The value of the kinetic energy after impact is

$$T_2 = \tfrac{1}{2}m_1(v'_A)^2 + \tfrac{1}{2}m_2(v'_B)^2 \qquad (21.101)$$

$$= \frac{1}{2}\left(\frac{1.5}{386}\right)(94.7^2) + \frac{1}{2}\left(\frac{2}{386}\right)(8.7^2) = 17.6 \text{ in·lb} \qquad (21.102)$$

The percent decrease in energy due to the impact is then

$$\%D = \frac{21.4 - 17.6}{21.4}(100) = 17.8\% \qquad (21.103)$$

b The impact configuration of Fig. 21.24c is redrawn in Fig. 21.27. The components of initial velocity are

$$v_{Ax} = 50 \text{ in/s} \qquad v_{Bx} = -80\sin 40° = -51.4 \text{ in/s} \qquad (21.104)$$

$$v_{Ay} = 0 \qquad v_{By} = -80\cos 40° = -61.3 \text{ in/s} \qquad (21.105)$$

The components of velocity in the y direction do not change, so that

$$v'_{Ay} = v_{Ay} = 0 \qquad v'_{By} = v_{By} = -61.3 \text{ in/s} \qquad (21.106)$$

The impulse-momentum equation in the x direction is

$$m_A v_{Ax} + m_B v_{Bx} = m_A v'_{Ax} + m_B v'_{Bx} \qquad (21.107)$$

$$\frac{1.5}{g}(50) + \frac{2}{g}(-51.4) = \frac{1.5}{g}v'_{Ax} + \frac{2}{g}v'_{Bx} \qquad (21.108)$$

The equation of relative velocities is

$$e = -\frac{v'_{Bx} - v'_{Ax}}{v_{Bx} - v_{Ax}} \qquad 0.85 = \frac{-(v'_{Bx} - v'_{Ax})}{-51.4 - 50} \qquad (21.109)$$

The above equations are solved simultaneously, with the results

$$v'_{Ax} = -57.3 \text{ in/s} \qquad v'_{Bx} = 28.9 \text{ in/s} \qquad (21.110)$$

The magnitudes of the velocities after impact are

$$v'_A = v'_{Bx} = -57.3 \text{ in/s} \qquad (21.111)$$

$$v'_B = \sqrt{(v'_{Bx})^2 + (v'_{By})^2} = \sqrt{28.9^2 + (-61.3)^2} = 67.8 \text{ in/s} \qquad (21.112)$$

The orientation of the velocities of the spheres after impact are shown in Fig. 21.28.

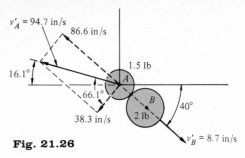

Fig. 21.26

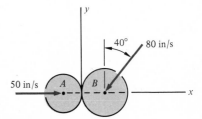

Fig. 21.27

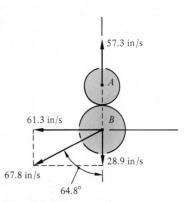

Fig. 21.28

The kinetic energy after impact is

$$T_2 = \tfrac{1}{2}m_A(v_A')^2 + \tfrac{1}{2}m_B(v_B')^2 \qquad (21.113)$$

$$= \frac{1}{2}\left(\frac{1.5}{386}\right)(57.3^2) + \frac{1}{2}\left(\frac{2}{386}\right)(67.8^2) = 18.3 \text{ in·lb} \quad (21.114)$$

The percent decrease in the initial energy, using the value in Eq. (21.100), is then

$$\%D = \frac{21.4 - 18.3}{21.4}(100) = 14.5\% \qquad (21.115)$$

The two spheres in this problem approach each other along the fixed directions shown in Fig. 21.24a. It may be seen from the above solutions that *the final velocities after impact are heavily dependent on the precise configuration in which the spheres strike each other.*

21.8 IMPULSIVE FORCES

A situation which is very similar to the case of impact is the problem of *impulsive forces.* Impulsive forces are forces of very large magnitude which occur for very short durations. The distinguishing characteristic between impulsive forces and impact forces is that *impulsive forces do not occur because of the impact of physical bodies.* These forces are typically caused by explosive effects, such as the firing of a bullet from a gun or the detonation process in an internal-combustion engine, when the fuel mixture in the cylinder ignites and exerts momentary forces of very large magnitudes on the face of the piston. Since impact is not present, there is no need for a quantity such as the coefficient of restitution. The equation which expresses the conservation of linear momentum is still valid, and this equation may be used directly to solve the problem.

Example 21.9 The rifle shown in Fig. 21.29 weighs 8 lb. It fires a bullet, weighing 0.8 oz, which leaves the rifle with a muzzle velocity of 2,000 ft/s. Find the recoil velocity of the rifle.

Fig. 21.29

Solution The initial velocities of the rifle and the bullet are zero. The model of the system when the rifle is fired is shown in Fig. 21.30. I' is the impulse which acts between the rifle and the bullet. This is an example of impulsive motion, and the equation of impulse momentum appears as

Fig. 21.30

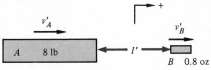

$$m_A v_A + m_B v_B = m_A v_A' + m_B v_B' \qquad (21.116)$$

$$0 + 0 = \frac{8}{g}v_A' + \frac{0.8(\frac{1}{16})}{g}(2{,}000) \qquad v_A' = -12.5 \text{ ft/s}$$
$$(21.117)$$

The minus sign in Eq. (21.117) indicates that the recoil velocity of the rifle is to the left.

21.9 ANGULAR MOMENTUM OF A RIGID BODY IN PLANE MOTION

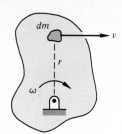

Figure 21.31 shows a rigid body which rotates about a fixed point with angular velocity ω. A typical mass element dm in the body has the velocity v shown in the figure. The *linear momentum* of this mass element is $dm\, v$. If this linear momentum of the mass element is multiplied by r, the distance from the linear momentum vector to the axis of rotation, the product is referred to as the *angular momentum*, or *moment of momentum*, of the particle. This latter quantity is designated by the symbol H, and

Fig. 21.31

$$dH = (v\, dm)r \qquad (21.118)$$

Equation (21.118) is now integrated over all the mass elements of the body, with the result

$$H = \int_0^H dH = \int_{\text{vol}} (v\, dm)r \qquad (21.119)$$

Since

$$v = r\omega \qquad (21.120)$$

Eq. (21.119) may be written as

$$H = \int_{\text{vol}} (r\omega\, dm)r = \int_{\text{vol}} r^2 \omega\, dm \qquad (21.121)$$

The angular velocity ω is the same for all mass elements of the body. Thus, this quantity may be moved outside the integral sign, and the result is

$$H = \omega \int_{\text{vol}} r^2\, dm \qquad (21.122)$$

This integral may now be identified as the *mass moment of inertia of the body about the fixed point*. This quantity is designated I, and the final form of the angular momentum of the body is

$$H = I\omega \qquad (21.123)$$

The angular momentum is a vector quantity which has the direction of the angular velocity vector. For the case of a rigid body which moves with plane motion, this direction will always be normal to the plane of the motion. The effect on the motion of the body when the *direction* of the angular momentum vector is allowed to change is considered in Chap. 22.

21.10 IMPULSE-MOMENTUM EQUATION FOR RIGID BODIES IN PLANE MOTION

The rigid body in Fig. 21.32 is acted on by the applied moment

Fig. 21.32

M, which is expressed as a moment about the fixed point. Newton's second law for rotation of the body about the fixed point is

$$M = I\alpha \qquad (21.124)$$

I is the mass moment of inertia of the body about the fixed point, and α, the angular acceleration of the body, may be expressed as

$$\alpha = \frac{d\omega}{dt} \qquad (21.125)$$

Equations (21.124) and (21.125) are combined and integrated over a time interval with the endpoints 1 and 2. The result is

$$\int_1^2 M\,dt = \int_1^2 I\,d\omega = I\int_1^2 d\omega \qquad (21.126)$$

$$= I(\omega_2 - \omega_1) = H_2 - H_1$$

The quantity $\int_1^2 M\,dt$ is the *impulse of the moment M.* It may be seen from Eq. (21.126) that the effect of this impulse is to give the rigid body a change in angular momentum, with a corresponding change in angular velocity. The magnitude of the impulse of the moment also may be identified as the area under the moment-time curve between times t_1 and t_2.

If the moment which acts on the rigid body is *constant,* then Eq. (21.126) reduces to the elementary form

$$M(t_2 - t_1) = I(\omega_2 - \omega_1) \qquad (21.127)$$

Example 21.10 The electric motor shown in Fig. 21.33a has the two-stage starting torque-time curve shown in Fig. 21.33b. The armature, and other rotating parts, of the motor may be approximated as a disk of mass 25 kg and diameter 400 mm.

a Find the steady-state angular velocity of the motor, in revolutions per minute, at the end of the startup phase of motion if no load is connected to the motor.

b A magnetic brake, which exerts a constant braking torque, is later used to stop the motor. If the motor is observed to come to rest in 2 s, find the value of the braking torque.

Solution
a The mass moment of inertia of the rotating parts is

$$I = \frac{1}{8}md^2 = \frac{1}{8}(25)\left(\frac{400}{1{,}000}\right)^2 = 0.5 \text{ kg·m}^2 \qquad (21.128)$$

The impulse of the starting torque is equal to the area A under the moment-time curve, given by

$$A = \frac{1}{2}(2)14 + \frac{14 + 16}{2}(8 - 2) = 104 \text{ N·s} \qquad (21.129)$$

The equation of impulse momentum then has the form

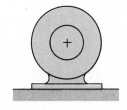

(a)

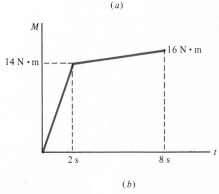

(b)

Fig. 21.33

$$\int_1^2 M\,dt = I(\omega_2 - \omega_1) \tag{21.130}$$

$$104 \text{ N·s} = (0.5 \text{ kg·m}^2)(\omega_2 - 0) \qquad \omega_2 = 208 \text{ rad/s} \tag{21.131}$$

$$\omega_2 = 208\left(\frac{60}{2\pi}\right) = 1{,}990\,\frac{\text{r}}{\text{min}} \tag{21.132}$$

b The braking of the motor occurs with a constant value of braking torque M_B. Thus,

$$M_B(t_2 - t_1) = I(\omega_2 - \omega_1) \tag{21.133}$$

By using $t_2 - t_1 = 2$ s, $\omega_1 = 208$ rad/s, and $\omega_2 = 0$, Eq. (21.133) appears as

$$M_B(2) = 0.5(0 - 208) \qquad M_B = -52 \text{ N·m} \tag{21.134}$$

The minus sign in Eq. (21.134) indicates that the sense of the braking torque is opposite to the sense of rotation.

21.11 IMPACT OF RIGID BODIES IN PLANE MOTION

For the case of impact of rigid bodies in plane motion, two independent effects occur.

Translation of the Center of Mass

For this case, the equation

$$I' = \int_1^2 R\,dt = m(v' - v) \tag{21.135}$$

may be written. I' is the impulse of the resultant force which acts on the body, and v and v' are the initial and final values, respectively, of the velocity of the *center of mass*.

Rotation of the Body about Its Center of Mass or about a Fixed Point

For this case, the equation

$$\int_1^2 M\,dt = I(\omega' - \omega) \tag{21.136}$$

may be written. The mass moment of inertia I is with respect to the center of mass, or the fixed point, as is appropriate in a particular problem, and the moment is with respect to the same point. This moment will be expressed in terms of the components of the impulse I', from Eq. (21.135), of the resultant force which acts on the body.

When Eqs. (21.135) and (21.136) are used, additional assumptions must be introduced which determine whether the impact is plastic or elastic and whether sliding motion is possible. These effects will be illustrated in the following examples. In all these examples it is assumed that the impacting bodies possess a common plane of symmetry in which act all the impulsive forces and moments. Thus, there is no tendency for the bodies to move out of the plane of motion after the impact.

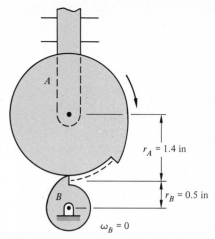

Example 21.11 Figure 21.34 shows two elements in a high-speed mechanism. Disk A rotates clockwise at 2,500 r/min, and disk B is stationary. The shaft of disk A is momentarily lowered into the position shown, so that the projection on this disk can strike the projection on disk B. After the impact, disk B has a counterclockwise angular velocity, and the shaft of disk A is raised to its original position.

a If the impact of the disks is assumed to be plastic, find the velocities of both disks after impact. $I_A = 6 \times 10^{-4}$ lb·s²·in and $I_B = 9.8 \times 10^{-6}$ lb·s²·in.

b Find the energy loss caused by the impact.

Fig. 21.34

Solution

a Figure 21.35 shows the tangential force impulse N' which acts on both disks and the two assumed positive senses of rotation. The equations of impulse momentum are

Disk A $\qquad -N'(1.4) = I_A(\omega'_A - \omega_A) \qquad$ (21.137)

Disk B $\qquad N'(0.5) = I_B(\omega'_B - \omega_B) \qquad$ (21.138)

N' is eliminated from Eqs. (21.137) and (21.138), with the result

$$\frac{I_A(\omega'_A - \omega_A)}{-1.4} = \frac{I_B(\omega'_B - \omega_B)}{0.5} \qquad (21.139)$$

Using $\omega_A = 2,500$ r/min $= 262$ rad/s and $\omega_B = 0$, we get

$$\frac{6 \times 10^{-4}(\omega'_A - 262)}{-1.4} = \frac{9.8 \times 10^{-6}\omega'_B}{0.5} \qquad (21.140)$$

$$\omega'_A - 262 = -0.0457\omega'_B \qquad (21.141)$$

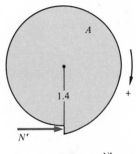

Fig. 21.35

Since plastic impact is assumed, the tangential velocity of the two disks at the point of contact must be the same after the impact. This kinematic relationship is

$$r_A\omega'_A = r_B\omega'_B \qquad 1.4\omega'_A = 0.5\omega'_B \qquad (21.142)$$

Eqs. (21.141) and (21.142) are solved simultaneously, and the final results are

$$\omega'_B = 650 \text{ rad/s} = 6,210 \text{ r/min} \qquad (21.143)$$

$$\omega'_A = \frac{0.5}{1.4}\omega'_2 = 232 \frac{\text{rad}}{\text{s}} = 2,220 \frac{\text{r}}{\text{min}} \qquad (21.144)$$

b The initial kinetic energy is

$$T_1 = \tfrac{1}{2}I_A\omega_A^2 = \tfrac{1}{2}(6 \times 10^{-4})(262^2) = 20.6 \text{ in·lb} \qquad (21.145)$$

The kinetic energy in the system after the impact is

$$T_2 = \tfrac{1}{2}I_A(\omega'_A)^2 + \tfrac{1}{2}I_B(\omega'_B)^2 \tag{21.146}$$

$$= \tfrac{1}{2}(6 \times 10^{-4})(232^2) + \tfrac{1}{2}(9.8 \times 10^{-6})(650^2) = 18.2 \text{ in} \cdot \text{lb} \tag{21.147}$$

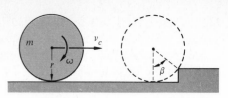

The percent loss of energy is

$$\%D = \frac{20.6 - 18.2}{20.6}(100) = 11.7\% \tag{21.148}$$

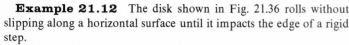

Fig. 21.36

Example 21.12 The disk shown in Fig. 21.36 rolls without slipping along a horizontal surface until it impacts the edge of a rigid step.

a Find the motion of the disk after impact and the energy loss, if plastic impact is assumed and the friction force between the disk and the edge is sufficiently large to avoid slipping. Find the numerical values if $v_c = 10$ m/s, $m = 5$ kg, $\beta = 30°$, and $r = 160$ mm.

b Find the necessary condition if slipping may not occur during the impact in part *a*.

c Do the same as in part *a* if slipping may occur during impact. Find the numerical values if $\mu_s = 0.05$.

d Do the same as in part *a* if the edge of the step is assumed to be frictionless.

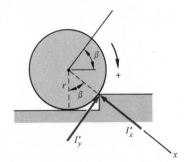

Solution a The configuration of the disk and the edge during impact is shown in Fig. 21.37. Since the disk initially rolls without slipping

Fig. 21.37

$$v_c = r\omega \tag{21.149}$$

The components I'_x and I'_y of the total impulse exerted by the edge on the disk are shown in the figure in their assumed *actual* senses. These quantities will be considered to be *positive* if they act in the positive coordinate senses. I'_x must be a compressive effect, and the sense of I'_y is chosen as shown, since this quantity is a friction force effect which must resist the initial angular velocity ω.

The equations of translational and rotational impulse momentum now appear as

$$-I'_x = m(v'_x - v_c \sin \beta) \tag{21.150}$$

$$I'_y = m(v'_y - v_c \cos \beta) \tag{21.151}$$

$$-I'_y r = I_0(\omega' - \omega) \tag{21.152}$$

Plastic impact is assumed, so that

$$v'_x = 0 \tag{21.153}$$

Since slipping may not occur during impact, the contact point between the disk and the edge is an instant center of rotation of the disk. Thus,

$$v'_y = r\omega' \tag{21.154}$$

I'_y is eliminated from Eqs. (21.151) and (21.152), and the result is used with Eqs. (21.149) and (21.154), together with $I = \tfrac{1}{2}mr^2$, to obtain

$$v'_y = \frac{v_c}{3}(1 + 2 \cos \beta) \tag{21.155}$$

782

The remaining two components of velocity after impact are

$$v_x' = 0 \qquad \omega' = \frac{v_y'}{r} = \frac{v_c}{3r}(1 + 2\cos\beta) \qquad (21.156)$$

The numerical values for part *a* are

$$v_c = 10 \text{ m/s} \qquad v_x' = 0 \qquad v_y' = \tfrac{10}{3}(1 + 2\cos 30°) = 9.11 \text{ m/s} \qquad (21.157)$$

$$\omega = \frac{v_c}{r} = \frac{10}{0.16} = 62.5 \frac{\text{rad}}{\text{s}} \qquad (21.158)$$

$$\omega' = \frac{v_y'}{r} = \frac{9.11}{0.16} = 56.9 \frac{\text{rad}}{\text{s}} \qquad (21.159)$$

The mass moment of inertia of the disk about its center is

$$I_0 = \tfrac{1}{2}mr^2 = \tfrac{1}{2}(5)(0.16)^2 = 0.064 \text{ kg·m}^2 \qquad (21.160)$$

The initial kinetic energy is

$$T_1 = \tfrac{1}{2}mv_c^2 + \tfrac{1}{2}I_0\omega^2 \qquad (21.161)$$

$$= \tfrac{1}{2}(5)(10^2) + \tfrac{1}{2}(0.064)(62.5^2) = 375 \text{ J} \qquad (21.162)$$

The kinetic energy after the impact is

$$T_2 = \tfrac{1}{2}m(v_y')^2 + \tfrac{1}{2}I_0(\omega')^2 \qquad (21.163)$$

$$= \tfrac{1}{2}(5)(9.11^2) + \tfrac{1}{2}(0.064)(56.9^2) = 311 \text{ J} \qquad (21.164)$$

The percent loss in energy due to the impact is

$$\%D = \frac{375 - 311}{375}(100) = 17.1\% \qquad (21.165)$$

b The impulse component I_y' in Fig. 21.37 is caused by the friction force exerted by the edge on the disk. The necessary condition, if slipping may not occur during impact, is

$$\mu_s I_x' > I_y' \qquad \mu_s > \frac{I_y'}{I_x'} \qquad (21.166)$$

where μ_s is the coefficient of static friction.
Using $v_x' = 0$ and v_y' from Eq. (21.155) in Eqs. (21.150) and (21.151), we get

$$I_x' = mv_c \sin\beta \qquad I_y' = \frac{mv_c}{3}(1 - \cos\beta) \qquad (21.167)$$

The limiting condition, Eq. (21.166), then has the form

$$\mu_s > \frac{I_y'}{I_x'} = \frac{(mv_c/3)(1 - \cos\beta)}{mv_c \sin\beta} = \frac{1 - \cos\beta}{3\sin\beta} \qquad (21.168)$$

It is interesting to note that the result above is independent of the mass and velocities and is a function only of angle β. The limiting value of μ_s, for $\beta = 30°$, is

$$\mu_s = \frac{1 - \cos 30°}{3\sin 30°} = 0.089 \qquad (21.169)$$

c For the case where slipping is assumed to occur during the plastic impact, Eqs. (21.150) through (21.153) are still valid. The condition of slipping is reflected in the equation

$$I'_y = \mu_s I'_x \tag{21.170}$$

The solution to this system of equations is

$$v'_x = 0 \qquad v'_y = v_c(\cos \beta + \mu_s \sin \beta) \qquad \omega' = \omega - \frac{rmv_c \,\mu_s \sin \beta}{I_0} \tag{21.171}$$

The numerical values, with $\mu_s = 0.05$, are

$$v'_x = 0 \qquad v'_y = 10(\cos 30° + 0.05 \sin 30°) = 8.91 \text{ m/s} \tag{21.172}$$

$$\omega' = 62.5 - \frac{(160/1{,}000)(5)(10)(0.05) \sin 30°}{0.064} = 59.4 \, \frac{\text{rad}}{\text{s}} \tag{21.173}$$

The kinetic energy after impact is

$$T_2 = \tfrac{1}{2}(5)(8.91^2) + \tfrac{1}{2}(0.064)(59.4^2) = 311 \text{ J} \tag{21.174}$$

d If the edge is frictionless,

$$I'_y = 0 \tag{21.175}$$

From Eq. (21.151),

$$v'_y - v_c \cos \beta = 0 \qquad v'_g = v_c \cos \beta = 10 \cos 30° = 8.66 \text{ m/s} \tag{21.176}$$

and, from Eq. (21.152),

$$0 = I_0(\omega' - \omega) \qquad \omega' = \omega = 62.5 \text{ rad/s} \tag{21.177}$$

The kinetic energy after impact is

$$T_2 = \tfrac{1}{2}(5)(8.66^2) + \tfrac{1}{2}(0.064)(62.5^2) = 312 \text{ J} \tag{21.178}$$

It may be seen that the above value for the kinetic energy after impact is the same as that in Eqs. (21.164) and (21.174), within three-significant-figure accuracy.

The very important conclusion may now be reached that *the energy loss is a function only of the impact phenomenon,* and not of the value of the friction force between the disk and the edge. The reason is that *the friction forces do not act through a distance and thus do not produce any work.* The velocities after impact for the three cases considered are summarized in Fig. 21.38. It may be seen that the case

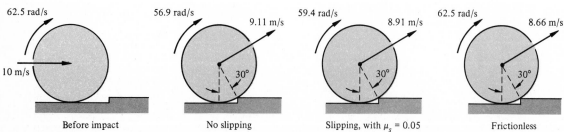

Before impact   No slipping   Slipping, with $\mu_s = 0.05$ Frictionless

Fig. 21.38

of no slipping produces the minimum change in translational velocity and the maximum change in rotational velocity. The frictionless case exhibits the opposite trend.

In the following two examples the subsequent motion of the disk, as it moves along a trajectory and then impacts the ground, will be studied.

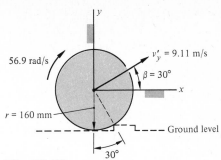

Fig. 21.39

Example 21.13 Find the complete time history of the motion of the disk of Example 21.12 from the time it leaves the edge of the step until it makes contact again with the ground. Assume that no slipping occurred during the impact with the edge.

Solution Figure 21.39 shows the configuration of the disk at the cessation of impact with the edge. A new set of xy coordinates, which are attached to the ground, are shown in the figure. These coordinates will be used as reference axes for the subsequent plane projectile motion of the disk.

The initial velocity components at $t = 0$ are

$$v_{0x} = v'_y \cos \beta = 9.11 \cos 30° = 7.89 \text{ m/s} \qquad (21.179)$$

$$v_{0y} = v'_y \sin \beta = 9.11 \sin 30° = 4.56 \text{ m/s} \qquad (21.180)$$

The total time of the flight is found from

$$y = y_0 + v_{0y}t - \tfrac{1}{2}gt^2 \qquad (21.181)$$

$$0 = 0 + 4.56t - \tfrac{1}{2}(9.81)t^2 \qquad t = 0, 0.931 \text{ s} \qquad (21.182)$$

The first solution corresponds to the initial time, and the total time of the flight is 0.931 s. The horizontal distance traveled by the disk is

$$x = v_{0x}t = 7.89(0.931) = 7.35 \text{ m} \qquad (21.183)$$

The maximum height attained by the disk is given by

$$v_y^2 = v_{0y}^2 - 2g(y - y_0) \qquad (21.184)$$

$$0 = 4.56^2 - 2(9.81)(y_{\max} - 0) \qquad y_{\max} = 1.06 \text{ m} \qquad (21.185)$$

Since all air resistance effects are neglected, there is no loss in kinetic energy. Thus, the magnitudes of the initial and final velocities are the same. The details of the trajectory motion are shown in Fig. 21.40. It also may be observed that there is no change in the angular velocity of the disk.

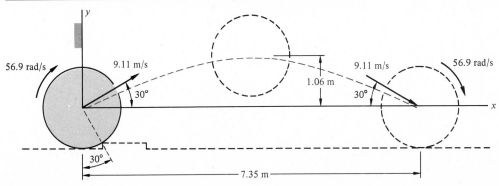

Fig. 21.40

785

Example 21.14 Find the velocity components of the disk of Example 21.13 after it impacts the ground following its free flight. Assume that the disk does not slip during impact and that the coefficient of restitution is 0.75. Find the magniude and direction of the rebound velocity and the energy loss due to impact.

Solution The impact configuration is shown in Fig. 21.41, together with a new position of the xy coordinates. The equations of impulse momentum are

$$I'_x = m(v'_x - v_c \cos \beta) \tag{21.186}$$

$$I'_y = m[v'_y - (-v_c \sin \beta)] \tag{21.187}$$

$$-I'_x r = I_0(\omega' - \omega) \tag{21.188}$$

The minus sign in the parentheses in Eq. (21.187) indicates that the y component of the initial velocity acts in the negative coordinate sense. The condition of no slipping requires that

$$v'_x = r\omega' \tag{21.189}$$

The coefficient of restitution is defined by Eq. (21.30) as

$$e = -\frac{v'_A - v'_B}{v_A - v_B} \tag{21.190}$$

The ground is assumed to be body B, and

$$v_B = 0 \qquad v'_B = 0 \tag{21.191}$$

The translational velocity of the disk in the y direction, before impact, is

$$v_A = -v_c \sin \beta \tag{21.192}$$

and the velocity of this element in the y direction, after impact, is

$$v'_A = v'_y \tag{21.193}$$

Equation (21.190) then has the form

$$e = -\frac{v'_y - 0}{-v_c \sin \beta - 0} \qquad v'_y = ev_c \sin \beta \tag{21.194}$$

Equations (21.186) through (21.189) and (21.194) are five equations in the five unknowns—v'_x, v'_y, ω', I'_x and I'_y.
    The solutions for the velocities after impact are

$$v'_x = \frac{rmv_c \cos \beta + I\omega}{rm + I/r} \qquad v'_y = ev_c \sin \beta \qquad \omega' = \frac{v'_x}{r} \tag{21.195}$$

With the numerical values

$$v_c = 9.11 \text{ m/s} \qquad \omega = 56.9 \text{ rad/s} \qquad \beta = 30° \qquad r = 160 \text{ mm} \tag{21.196}$$

$$m = 5 \text{ kg} \qquad I = 0.064 \text{ kg·m}^2 \qquad e = 0.75$$

The final values of the velocity components after impact are

$$v'_x = \frac{0.16(5)(9.11) \cos 30° + 0.064(56.9)}{0.16(5) + 0.064/0.16} = 8.29 \frac{\text{m}}{\text{s}} \tag{21.197}$$

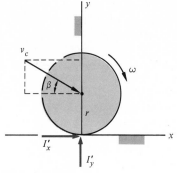

Fig. 21.41

$$v_y' = 0.75(9.11)\sin 30° = 3.42 \text{ m/s} \qquad \omega' = \frac{8.29}{0.16} = 51.8 \frac{\text{rad}}{\text{s}}$$
$$(21.198)$$

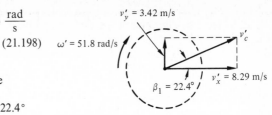

These velocities are shown in Fig. 21.42.

The magnitude and direction of the resultant velocity are

$$v' = \sqrt{8.29^2 + 3.42^2} = 8.97 \text{ m/s} \qquad \beta_1 = \tan^{-1}\frac{3.42}{8.29} = 22.4°$$
$$(21.199)$$

Fig. 21.42

The kinetic energy before impact is

$$T_1 = \tfrac{1}{2}mv_c^2 + \tfrac{1}{2}I_0\omega^2 = \tfrac{1}{2}(5)(9.11^2) + \tfrac{1}{2}(0.064)(56.9^2) = 311 \text{ J}$$
$$(21.200)$$

The kinetic energy after impact is

$$T_2 = \tfrac{1}{2}m(v')^2 + \tfrac{1}{2}I_0(\omega')^2 = \tfrac{1}{2}(5)(8.97^2) + \tfrac{1}{2}(0.064)(51.8^2) = 287 \text{ J}$$
$$(21.201)$$

The percent loss in energy is

$$\%D = \frac{311 - 287}{311}(100) = 7.7\% \qquad (21.202)$$

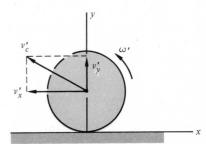

It may be seen that after impact both the translational and rotational velocities decrease. It is left as an exercise for the reader to verify that if $e = 1$, the energy loss would have been zero.

Fig. 21.43

In addition to being the particular initial conditions in the present problem, the configuration shown in Fig. 21.41 may be viewed as a general case of a spinning disk impacting a plane. An interesting result is obtained if ω is assumed to have a sense which is opposite that shown in the figure. If the magnitude ω is sufficiently large, Eq. (21.195) shows that (recalling that ω is now negative) v_x' may have a negative value. From Eq. (21.194), v_y' is always positive, and the direction of the rebound velocity v_c' for this case would be as shown in Fig. 21.43. The disk, after impact, would rebound in the general direction from which it had come. In addition, the angular velocity ω' after impact, following Eq. (21.195), would have the sense shown in the figure.

This effect may be demonstrated readily with a rubber ball. The ball is held between a person's thumb and middle finger and given an initial spin as it is tossed to the ground. The sense of the spin is such that the top surface of the ball moves toward the person. With a minimum amount of practice, it should be possible to catch the ball on the rebound!

Example 21.15 Figure 21.44 shows the hands of a ball player on a baseball bat. The bat is assumed to rotate counterclockwise in the plane, and the location of the player's hands is considered to be an instantaneous fixed point about which the bat rotates. The bat has angular velocity ω as it strikes the ball in the position shown in the figure, and the ball exerts the impulse I_x' on the bat. Show that, for certain locations of the impact of the ball on the bat, the player will feel no impulsive force reaction on his or her hands as the bat strikes the ball.

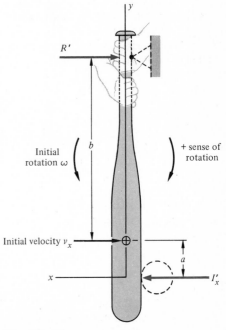

Fig. 21.44

Solution   The impulse of the ball on the bat is I'_x, as shown in the figure, and R' is the impulse exerted by the player's hands on the bat. The impulse I'_x occurs at the arbitrary distance a from the CM of the bat.

The equations of impulse momentum, for translation of the CM and rotation about this point, are

$$I'_x - R' = m[v'_x - (-v_x)] \qquad (21.203)$$

$$I'_x a + R'b = I_0[\omega' - (-\omega)] \qquad (21.204)$$

where I_0 is the mass moment of inertia of the bat about its center of mass. The translational and rotational velocities are related by

$$v_x = b\omega \qquad v'_x = b\omega' \qquad (21.205)$$

The above set of equations is solved for R', with the result

$$R' = \frac{(I_0 - abm)(\omega' + \omega)}{a + b} \qquad (21.206)$$

If $R' = 0$, the player will feel no force reaction on her or his hands. The necessary condition for this, from Eq. (21.206), is

$$I_0 - abm = 0 \qquad (21.207)$$

I_0 may be expressed in terms of the centroidal radius of gyration k_0 as

$$I_0 = k_0^2 m \qquad (21.208)$$

Using this result, equation (21.207) now appears as

$$k_0^2 m - abm = 0 \qquad a = \frac{k_0^2}{b} \qquad (21.209)$$

The location a defined by the above equation is the *center of percussion* of the bat. This term was defined in Sec. 19.8. It may be concluded that the maximum comfort of the player will be obtained if the ball is hit at the center of percussion of the bat.

21.12 SUMMARY

The impulse I' of a resultant force R which acts on a particle is

$$I' = \int_1^2 R\, dt \qquad (21.210)$$

The linear momentum mv of a particle is the product of the mass and the velocity of the particle. The linear momentum is a vector quantity. The impulse-momentum equation for a single particle is

$$I' = \int_1^2 R\, dt = m(v_2 - v_1) \qquad (21.211)$$

where 1 and 2 are the endpoints of the time interval of interest. The effect of an impulse acting on a particle is to change the velocity of the particle. The units of impulse and linear momentum are the product of force and time. The USCS units are pound-seconds, and the SI units are newton-seconds. The area under the force-time curve over a given time interval is equal to the change in linear momentum during this time interval. If the resultant force R which acts on the particle is constant, the impulse-momentum equation has the form

$$R(t_2 - t_1) = m(v_2 - v_1) \qquad (21.212)$$

Impact is a term which describes the phenomenon of colliding physical bodies. An irreversible energy loss is always associated with the impact of physical bodies. The impact problem has three characteristics:

1. The duration of the impact is much less than the other observed times in the problem.
2. Because of the short duration of the impact, the impacting bodies are assumed to experience an instantaneous change in velocity with no change in displacement.
3. During the impact process, reaction forces between the bodies, of extremely large magnitude, exist for very short intervals.

The principal use of solutions to problems of impact is to obtain a set of initial velocities for the regime of motion following the impact.

For colliding bodies in the absence of external forces, the total linear momentum of the system of bodies is constant. For two colliding bodies, the equation of conservation of linear momentum has the form

$$m_A v_A + m_B v_B = m_A v'_A + m_B v'_B \qquad (21.213)$$

where primes are used to designate velocities after impact.

The coefficient of restitution is defined by

$$e = -\frac{v'_A - v'_B}{v_A - v_B} \qquad (21.214)$$

In plastic impact, $e = 0$ and the colliding bodies adhere to each other. The case of plastic impact results in the maximum possible energy loss. The case of elastic impact, with $e = 1$, is a theoretical limiting case in which the energy loss is zero.

In central impact, the common normal line to the surfaces at the contact point passes through the centers of mass of both bodies. In central impact there is no tendency of the bodies to rotate. Direct central impact occurs if the velocities of the two bodies are collinear with the common normal line. If one or both of the velocities of the bodies are not collinear with the common normal line, the impact is referred to as oblique central impact. In oblique central impact, the components of the velocities of the two impacting bodies normal to the line of impact do not change during the impact.

Impulsive forces are forces of very large magnitude which exist for very short periods. The difference between impulsive forces and impact forces is that impulsive forces do not occur because of the impact of physical bodies. These forces are typically caused by explosive effects.

The angular momentum H of a body is a vector quantity defined by

$$H = I\omega \qquad (21.215)$$

where I is the mass moment of inertia about the reference point of interest. The rotational form of the equation of impulse momentum is

$$\int_1^2 M\,dt = H_2 - H_1 = I(\omega_2 - \omega_1) \qquad (21.216)$$

If the moment which acts on the rigid body is constant, the impulse-momentum equation has the form

$$M(t_2 - t_1) = I(\omega_2 - \omega_1) \qquad (21.217)$$

Two distinct effects occur in the case of impact of bodies in general plane motion, as described below.

1. Translation of the center of mass, with the equation of motion

$$I' = \int_1^2 R\,dt = m(v' - v) \qquad (21.218)$$

   where v and v' are the initial and final values, respectively, of the velocity of the center of mass.

2. Rotation of the body about its center of mass, or about a fixed point, with the equation of motion

$$\int_1^2 M\,dt = I(\omega' - \omega) \qquad (21.219)$$

   where ω and ω' are the initial and final values, respectively, of the angular velocities, and I is the mass moment of inertia about the center of mass, or about the fixed point.

PROBLEMS

21.1 The particle in Fig. P21.1 is acted on by the system of forces shown. It moves with rectilinear translation in a frictionless guide. At $t = 0$ the particle is at rest.
  (a) Find the velocity when $t = 2$ s.
  (b) Compare the result in part a with the solution to part b of Prob. 16.1.

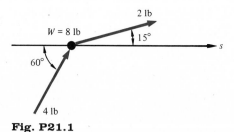

Fig. P21.1

21.2 An automobile moves along a straight roadway with a constant speed of 40 mi/h. Constant friction forces, exerted by the roadway on the tires of the automobile, act for 5 s until the automobile reaches a speed of 50 mi/h. The weight of the automobile is 3,600 lb.

(a) Find the required value of the constant friction forces which will produce this change of velocity.

(b) Compare the result in part a with the solution to part a of Problem 16.9.

21.3 (a) Do the same as in Prob. 21.2, if the speed of the car changes from 50 mi/h to 60 mi/h in 5 s.

(b) Compare the result in part a with the solution to Prob. 16.10.

21.4 The block in Fig. P21.4 is released from rest at $t = 0$.

(a) Find the velocity of the block at the end of 3 s.

(b) Compare the result in part a with the solution to part b of Prob. 16.33.

21.5 Do the same as in Prob. 21.4 if, at the instant shown in the figure, the block has a velocity of 6 ft/s up the plane.

21.6 Fig. P21.6a shows the time variation of a force which acts on the block shown in Fig. P21.6b. The block is initially at rest, and it may be assumed that $\mu_k \approx \mu_s$.

(a) If the surface is frictionless, find the velocity of the block at the end of 1 s, and at the end of 3 s.

(b) Do the same as in part a, if the coefficient of friction between the block and the plane is 0.15.

(c) At what time does the body, for the conditions of part b, start to move?

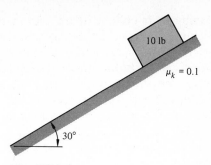

Fig. P21.4

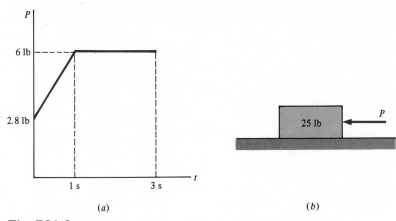

(a)

(b)

Fig. P21.6

21.7 Do the same as in parts a and b of Prob. 21.6 if, at $t = 0$, the block has a velocity of 15 ft/s to the right.

21.8 The block in Fig. P21.6b has a velocity v, to the right, at $t = 0$. For what value of v would the velocity of the block be zero at $t = 3$ s?

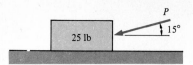

Fig. P21.9

21.9 Do the same as in Prob. 21.6, if the force P has the direction shown in Fig. P21.9.

21.10 Do the same as in Prob. 21.6, parts a and b, if the block moves along the incline shown in Fig. P21.10.

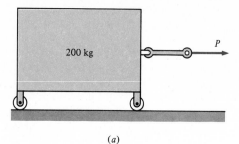

(a)

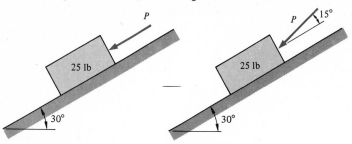

Fig. P21.10   **Fig. P21.11**

21.11 Do the same as in Prob. 21.6, parts a and b, for the arrangement of the block and force shown in Fig. P21.11.

21.12 Figure P21.12a shows a heavy cabinet. All friction effects, and the mass of the wheels, may be neglected. The time variation of the force which acts on the cabinet is shown in Fig. P21.12b.

(a) Find the time at which the velocity of the cabinet is 1.2 m/s to the right, if the cabinet is initially at rest.

(b) Do the same as part a, for a velocity of 1.2 m/s to the left.

21.13 Do the same as in Prob. 21.12, if the cabinet moves along the incline shown in Fig. P21.13.

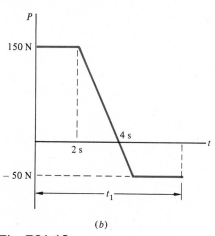

(b)

Fig. P21.12

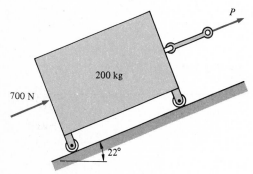

Fig. P21.13

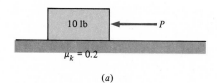

(a)

21.14 At $t = 0$ the block in Fig. P21.14a is moving to the left at 10 ft/s. The time variation of the force that acts on the block is shown in Fig. P21.14b.

(a) Find the value of P, if the block is to move leftward at 26 ft/s, when $t = 10$ s.

(b) Do the same as in part a, if the block is moving to the right at 10 ft/s at $t = 0$.

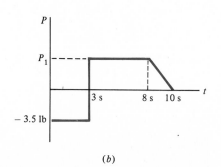

(b)

Fig. P21.14

21.15 A solid metal sphere of mass 0.6 kg is dropped onto a rigid surface from a height of 1.5 m, as shown in Fig. P21.15. The coefficient of restitution is 0.81.

(*a*) Find the maximum height attained by the sphere after the impact.

(*b*) Find the energy loss that occurs during the impact.

(*c*) Find the value of the impulse that occurs during the impact.

21.16 (*a*) To what height would the sphere in Prob. 21.15 rebound, if it impacted the ground with a velocity of 8 m/s?

(*b*) Find the energy loss for the motion of part *a*.

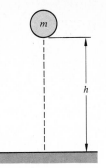

Fig. P21.15

21.17 A solid sphere is dropped from a height of 1800 mm onto a rigid surface. The maximum height of rebound of the sphere is 1,510 mm, and $m = 400$g.

(*a*) Find the value of the coefficient of restitution.

(*b*) Find the energy loss associated with the impact.

(*c*) Find the maximum height of the rebound after the sphere next impacts the rigid surface.

(*d*) Find the impulses of the two impacts.

21.18 Find the required value of the initial downward velocity of the sphere in Prob. 21.17, at the height 1,800 mm, if the rebound height is to be the same as the original height.

21.19 A ball is dropped onto a rigid floor, as shown in Fig. P21.19. The coefficient of restitution is 0.87.

(*a*) Find the maximum height attained by the ball after the first, second, and third impacts.

(*b*) Find the energy losses after the first, second, and third impacts.

21.20 Block *B* in Fig. P21.20 is initially at rest, and the plane surface is assumed to be frictionless.

(*a*) Find the velocities after impact. Also find the displacement of each block and the separation distance between the two blocks 2 s after impact, if elastic impact is assumed.

(*b*) Do the same as in part *a*, if a coefficient of restitution of 0.8 is assumed.

(*c*) Do the same as in part *a*, if a coefficient of restitution of 0.2 is assumed.

(*d*) Do the same as in part *a*, if plastic impact is assumed.

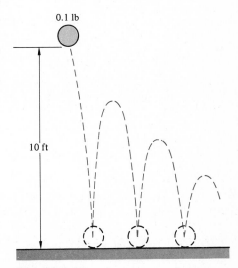

Fig. P21.19

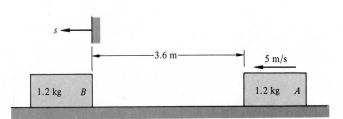

Fig. P21.20

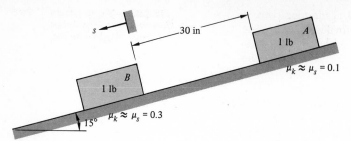

Fig. P21.21

21.21 At $t = 0$, both blocks are at rest in the position shown in Fig. P21.21. When the blocks collide, elastic impact is assumed.
(a) Find the time at which impact occurs.
(b) Find the velocities after impact.

21.22 Do the same as in Prob. 21.21, if the coefficient of restitution is assumed to be 0.8.

21.23 Do the same as in Prob. 21.21, if the coefficient of restitution is assumed to be 0.2.

21.24 Two blocks approach each other on a plane horizontal surface, as shown in Fig. P21.24. At $t = 0$ the separation distance between the blocks is 3 m. The surface is frictionless, and elastic impact is assumed. $m_A = 2$ kg, $m_B = 3$ kg, $v_A = 4$ m/s, and $v_B = 6.5$ m/s.
(a) Find the time of impact.
(b) Find the velocities after impact.
(c) Find the magnitude of the impulse.
(d) Find the time at which the separation distance between the blocks is 6 m.

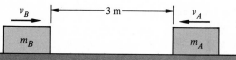

Fig. P21.24

21.25 Do the same as in Prob. 21.24, if $m_A = 2$ kg, $m_B = 3$ kg, $v_A = 6.5$ m/s, and $v_B = 4$ m/s.

21.26 Do the same as in Prob. 21.24, if $m_A = 2$ kg, $m_B = 3$ kg, $v_A = 6.5$ m/s, and $v_B = -4$ m/s.

21.27 (a) Do the same as in Prob. 21.24, if the coefficient of kinetic friction is 0.15.
(b) Find the separation distance between the blocks when these elements come to rest.

21.28 (a) Do the same as in Prob. 21.25, if the coefficient of kinetic friction is 0.15.
(b) Find the separation distance between the blocks when these elements come to rest.

21.29 (*a*) Do the same as in Prob. 21.24, if the coefficient of restitution is 0.8 and the coefficient of kinetic friction is 0.15.

(*b*) Find the separation distance between the blocks when these elements come to rest.

(*c*) Find the energy loss during the impact.

21.30 (*a*) Do the same as in Prob. 21.24, if the coefficient of restitution is 0.2 and the coefficient of kinetic friction is 0.15.

(*b*) Find the separation distance between the blocks when these elements come to rest.

(*c*) Find the energy loss during the impact.

21.31 At the instant shown in Fig. P21.31, block *B* is released with zero initial velocity. v_A is constant, and the blocks collide at a position 20 in from the original position of block *B*. The impact is assumed to be elastic. $W_A = 10$ lb and $W_B = 12$ lb.

(*a*) Find the velocities of the blocks after impact.

(*b*) Find the value of the impulse.

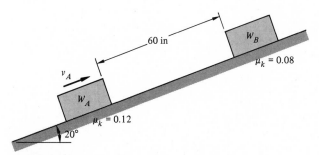

Fig. P21.31

21.32 (*a*) Do the same as in Prob. 21.31, if the coefficient of restitution is 0.8.

(*b*) Find the percent loss in energy due to the impact.

21.33 (*a*) Do the same as in Prob. 21.31, if the coefficient of restitution is 0.2.

(*b*) Find the percent loss in energy due to the impact.

Fig. P21.34

21.34 The two blocks in Fig. P21.34 approach each other at constant velocity. After impact, block *A* has a velocity of 3.1 m/s to the left.

(*a*) Find the value of the coefficient of restitution.

(*b*) Find the value of the impulse.

(*c*) Find the percent loss in energy during the impact.

21.35 (*a*) What value of initial velocity of block *B* in Prob. P21.34 will cause the velocity after impact of this block to be zero? (*b*) Find the corresponding value of the velocity of block *A* after impact.

21.36 Block *B* in Fig. P21.36 is initially at rest. Find the minimum required value of the velocity v_A, for the position of block *B* shown in the figure, that will push this block off the plane surface. The coefficient of kinetic friction between the blocks and the plane surface is 0.2, and the impact is assumed to be elastic. $W_A = 20$ lb and $W_B = 10$ lb.

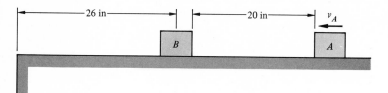

Fig. P21.36

21.37 Do the same as in Prob. 21.36, if $W_A = 10$ lb and $W_B = 20$ lb.

21.38 Do the same as in Prob. 21.36, if $e = 0.9$.

21.39 Do the same as in Prob. 21.36, if $e = 0.5$.

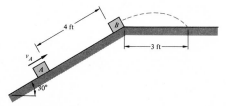

Fig. P21.40

21.40 Block *B* is initially at rest in Fig. P21.40. When it is struck by block *A*, it describes the trajectory shown in the figure. Both blocks weigh 2 lb. Find the required value of v_A, if the plane is frictionless and elastic impact is assumed.

21.41 Do the same as in Prob. 21.40, if $\mu_k = 0.1$ and the coefficient of restitution is 0.9.

21.42 Do the same as in Prob. 21.40, if $\mu_k = 0.25$ and the coefficient of restitution is 0.75.

21.43 In the position shown in Fig. P21.43, block *B* just contacts the spring. Block *A* impacts block *B* with a velocity of 8 ft/s. $W_A = 2$ lb and $W_B = 3$ lb.
(*a*) Find the maximum distance through which the spring is compressed, if the impact is elastic and the plane surface is frictionless.
(*b*) Do the same as in part *a*, if the impact is assumed to be plastic.
(*c*) Do the same as in part *a*, if $e = 0.9$ and $\mu_k = 0.1$.
(*d*) Do the same as part *a*, if $e = 0.5$ and $\mu_k = 0.25$.

Fig. P21.43

21.44 Block B in Fig. P21.44 is initially at rest on a spring. Block A is dropped, with zero initial velocity, and plastic impact between the two blocks is assumed. $m_A = 0.3$ kg and $m_B = 0.2$ kg.

(a) Find the maximum value of the deflection of the spring from the position shown in the figure.

(b) Do the same as part a if, at the instant of release, block A has a downward velocity of 2 m/s.

(c) Do the same as in part a if, at the instant of release, block A has an upward velocity of 2 m/s.

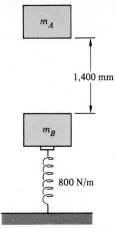

21.45 Particle A is released from rest in the position shown in Fig. P21.45. The mass of each particle is 100 g, the coefficient of restitution is 0.92, and all friction effects may be neglected.

(a) Find the velocity of particle B after the impact.

(b) Find the initial and final energies of the system of two particles.

Fig. P21.44

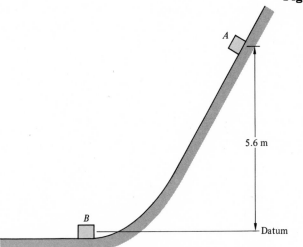

Fig. P21.45

21.46 Do the same as in Prob. 21.45, if the coefficient of restitution is 0.5.

21.47 Do the same as in Prob. 21.45 if, because of sliding friction effects, there is a 10 percent loss in energy as particle A slides down the track.

21.48 Do the same as in Prob. 21.47, for the condition of Prob. 21.46.

21.49 The simple pendulum in Fig. P21.49 is released from rest at position θ. Mass A moves down, and there is an inelastic impact with mass B. All friction effects may be neglected, and the mass of the string is negligible.

(a) Find the general expression for the velocity of mass B after impact.

(b) Find the numerical value of the result in part a, if $m = 150$ g, $l = 900$ mm, $e = 0.92$, and $\theta = 20°$.

(c) Find the percent loss of energy during the impact.

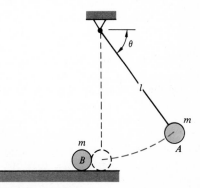

Fig. P21.49

21.50 Do the same as in Prob. 21.49, parts *b* and *c*, if *e* = 0.4.

21.51 A second pendulum is added to the system of Prob. 21.49, as shown in Fig. P21.51. Mass *A* is released from rest at the position θ. The impact is inelastic, all friction effects may be neglected, and the mass of the string is negligible. $l_1 = 680$ mm.

(*a*) Find the general expression for θ_1, corresponding to the maximum height which mass *B* attains.

(*b*) Find the numerical value of θ_1, using the data in Prob. 21.49.

(*c*) Find the position of mass *A* when mass *B* has the position θ_1 of part *b*.

(*d*) Find the percent loss of energy during the impact.

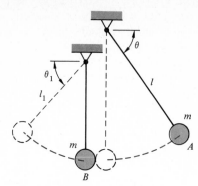

Fig. P21.51

21.52 The pendulum of Prob. 21.49 is arranged as shown in Fig. P21.52. Using the numerical data of Prob. 21.49, find the numerical values of *x* and *y* that define the trajectory of mass *B* after impact.

Fig. P21.52

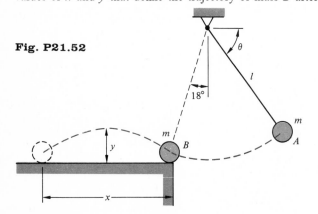

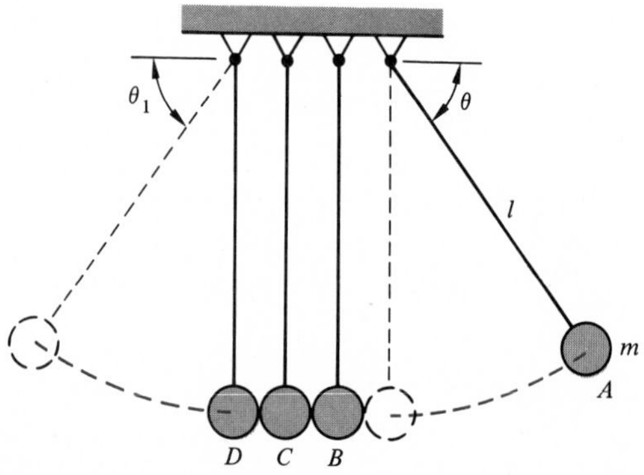

Fig. P21.53

21.53 All four pendulums in Fig. P21.53 are the same. Mass *A* is released from rest at position θ.

(*a*) Describe what occurs following the impact of mass *A* with mass *B*.

(*b*) Find the position θ_1 corresponding to the maximum elevation of mass *D*. Assume *e* = 0.95, and use the numerical data of Prob. 21.49.

(*c*) Do the same as in part *b*, for values of *e* of 0.85, 0.65, and 0.45.

21.54 Do the same as in Prob. 21.53, if pendulum system *C* is removed from the problem, so that mass *B* contacts mass *D* in the rest position.

21.55 Two metal spheres of equal diameter approach each other and experience direct central impact. Use the equations in Example 21.7 to find the time to reach the maximum value of impact force, and the value of this force, for the following cases.

(*a*) *d* = 1 in, v_A = 3 ft/s, v_B = 2 ft/s, steel, γ = 0.283 lb/in³, ν = 0.3, *E* = 30 × 10⁶ lb/in².

(*b*) The same as part *a*, except that sphere *A* is aluminum, with γ = 0.1 lb in³, ν = 0.3 and *E* = 10 × 10⁶ lb/in².

(*c*) The same as part *a*, except that sphere *A* is copper, with *r* = 0.323 lb/in³, ν = 0.3 and *E* = 17 × 10⁶ lb/in².

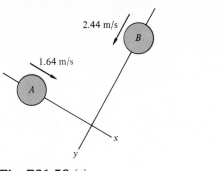

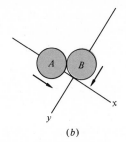

Fig. P21.56 (*a*)   (*b*)

21.56 Two identical spherical masses move along rectilinear paths with constant velocity, as shown in Fig. P21.56*a*.

(*a*) Find the magnitude and direction of the velocities of the spheres after impact, for the impact configuration shown in Fig. P21.63*b*. The impact is assumed to be elastic.

(*b*) Do the same as in part *a*, if $v_A = 2.44$ m/s and $v_B = 1.64$ m/s.

21.57 Do the same as in Fig. P21.56, for the impact configuration shown in P21.57.

Fig. P21.57

21.58 (*a*) Do the same as in Prob. 21.56, if the coefficient of restitution is 0.9.

(*b*) Find the percent energy loss associated with the impact.

21.59 Do the same as in Prob. 21.57, for the conditions of Prob. 21.58.

21.60 (*a*) Find the magnitude and direction of the velocities, after impact, of the two spheres shown in Fig. P21.60.

(*b*) Find the energy loss during the impact.
$W_A = 6$ lb, $W_B = 10.5$ lb, $v_A = 60$ in/s, $v_B = 72$ in/s, and $e = 0.84$.

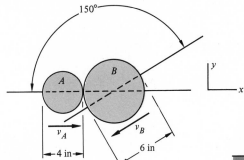

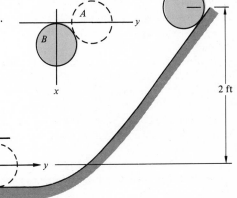

Fig. P21.60

Fig. P21.61

21.61 A sphere of weight $W_A = 1$ lb is released from rest in the position shown in Fig. P21.61, and impacts an identical sphere that is at rest. The track is frictionless, and the coefficient of restitution is 0.92.

(*a*) Find the magnitude, direction, and sense of the velocities of the two spheres after impact.

(*b*) Find the value of the impulse that occurs during the impact.

(*c*) Find the percent loss in energy due to the impact.

21.62 Do the same as in Prob. 21.61 if, at the instant of impact shown in Fig. P21.61, sphere B has a rightward velocity of 5 ft/s.

21.63 Sphere A in Fig. P21.63 moves with a constant velocity $v_A = 20$ in/s. Find the magnitude and direction of the velocities of spheres B and C after impact. The spheres have equal masses, and the impact is assumed to be elastic.

21.64 Do the same as in Prob. 21.63, if the coefficient of restitution is 0.85.

21.65 Do the same as in Prob. 21.63, for the configuration of the spheres shown in Fig. P21.65.

21.66 The device shown in Fig. P21.66 is called a ballistic pendulum. It is used to measure the velocity of a high-speed mass particle, such as a bullet. The box is filled with sand and supported by two thin inextensible cables. A bullet of mass m_A approaches the box with constant velocity v_A. When it strikes the sand-filled box of mass m_B, this element experiences a maximum increase in elevation given by h.

(a) Develop the general equation that relates h to the velocity of the bullet.

(b) Find the numerical value of h, if $m_A = 14$ g, $m_B = 5$ kg, and $v_A = 500$ m/s.

21.67 Figure P21.67 shows a model of an 8-in howitzer used on a naval battleship. The shell is 8 in in diameter and weighs 200 lb. The absolute velocity of the shell as it leaves the muzzle, is 2,200 ft/s. When the howitzer is fired, it is observed that the barrel has a recoil velocity of 60 ft/s.

(a) Find the weight of the howitzer barrel.

(b) Find the kinetic energy of the shell as it leaves the howitzer.

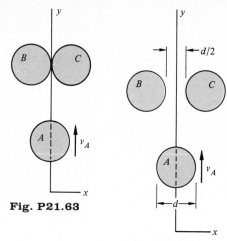

Fig. P21.63

Fig. P21.65

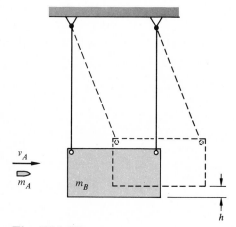

Fig. P21.66

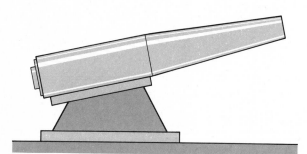

Fig. P21.67

21.68 Figure P21.68 shows an artillery cannon. It fires a 90-mm shell that weighs 4.41 lb. The muzzle velocity is 1,100 ft/s, and the weight of the cannon barrel is 160 lb. A nest of eight equal springs, each of stiffness k, is used to limit the recoil displacement. Find the value of k, if the displacement of the cannon barrel after firing must not exceed 10 in.

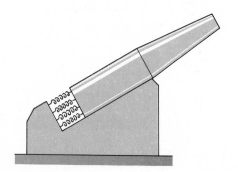

Fig. P21.68

21.69 The 4-kg disk shown in Fig. P21.69 is initially at rest at time $t = 0$. A force of 50 N is applied to the thin, inextensible cable wrapped around the disk.

(a) Find the angular velocity of the disk 4 s after the force is applied.

(b) Compare the result in part a with the solution to part b of Prob. 19.11.

21.70 (a) Do the same as in Prob. 21.69 if, at the time that the force is applied, the disk has a counterclockwise angular velocity of 30 rad/s.

(b) Compare the result in part a with the solution to Prob. 19.12.

21.71 (a) Do the same as in Prob. 21.69 if, in addition to the cable force, the disk is acted on by a counterclockwise couple of magnitude 2 N·m. The couple acts in the plane of the disk.

(b) Compare the result in part a with the solution to Prob. 19.13.

21.72 The impact of the two elements in the high-speed mechanism in Example 21.11 is assumed to be inelastic. A term e, which represents a coefficient of restitution effect, is assumed to have the form

$$e = -\left(\frac{r_A\omega_A' - r_B\omega_B'}{r_A\omega_A - r_B\omega_B}\right)$$

(a) Find the velocities of both disks after impact, and the energy loss during the impact, if $e = 0.9$.

(b) Do the same as in part a, if $e = 0.75$.

(c) Do the same as in part a, if $e = 0.5$.

21.73 A disk rolls along a plane surface, as shown in Fig. P21.73. Plastic impact is assumed, and the coefficient of friction between the disk and the edge of the step is 0.10. $W = 16$ lb, $r = 3$ in, and $\omega = 75$ rad/s.

(a) Find the translational and angular velocities of the disk after impact.

(b) Find the energy loss that occurs during impact.

(c) Find the horizontal distance through which the center of the disk moves before this element contacts the upper plane surface.

21.74 Do the same as in Prob. 21.73, if the coefficient of friction is 0.20.

21.75 The lower plane surface in Fig. P21.75 is lubricated, so that the coefficient of friction between it and the disk is effectively zero. The disk impacts the edge of the step with translational velocity v_C and zero angular velocity. Plastic impact is assumed, and the coefficient of friction between the disk and the edge of the step is 0.28. $r = 200$ mm, $m = 3$ kg, and $v_C = 6$ m/s.

(a) Find the translational and angular velocities of the disk after impact.

(b) Find the energy loss that occurs during impact.

(c) Find the horizontal distance through which the center of the disk moves, after impact, before this element contacts the upper plane surface.

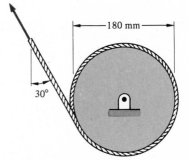

Fig. P21.69

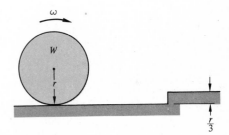

Fig. P21.73

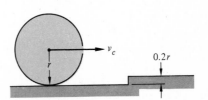

Fig. P21.75

21.76 (a) Find the general forms for the velocities of the disk in Example 21.12 after impact, if the impact is assumed to be inelastic, with a coefficient of restitution e, and the disk is assumed to not slip during the impact.

(b) Find the necessary condition for slipping not to occur during the impact.

(c) Do the same as in part a, if slipping may occur during impact. impact.

(d) Find the velocities of the disk, and the energy loss after impact. Use the numerical data of Example 21.12, together with $e = 0.6$ and $\mu_s = 0.04$.

(e) Do the same as in part d, if $e = 0.6$ and $\mu_s = 0.15$.

21.77 A solid, homogeneous sphere of mass m rolls along a plane surface and impacts a rigid step, as shown in Fig. P21.77. Find the limiting value of the coefficient of static friction between the edge of the step and the sphere that determines whether the sphere will slip during the impact.

21.78 Do the same as in Prob. 21.77, if the sphere of mass m is hollow, with an inside diameter 0.82 times the magnitude of the outside diameter.

21.79 (a) Find the velocities after impact of the disk in Example 21.14, if slipping during impact is assumed.

(b) Find the limiting value of the coefficient of static friction that determines whether slipping occurs.

(c) Find the numerical results for part a, using the data of Example 21.14, together with $e = 0.9$ and $\mu_s = 0.6$.

(d) Do the same as in part c, with $e = 0.6$.

21.80 Find the relationship between v_C and ω, of the disk in Example 21.14, if the direction of the rebound velocity is to be collinear with the direction of v_C.

21.81 A Yo-Yo consisting of a homogeneous disk of mass 1.4 kg is released from rest in the position shown in Fig. P21.81. When the center of the Yo-Yo is 1 m from the ground, the string is cut.

(a) Find the velocities of the disk after impact with the ground, if $e = 1$ and $\mu_s = 0.3$, and the radius is 50 mm.

(b) Do the same as in part a, if $e = 1$ and $\mu_s = 0.15$.

(c) Do the same as in part a, if $e = 0.5$ and $\mu_s = 0.3$.

(d) Do the same as in part a, if $e = 0.5$ and $\mu_s = 0.15$.

21.82 Do the same as in Example 21.14, for the case of a homogeneous sphere of mass m impacting the ground. Use the numerical constants of this problem.

21.83 Do the same as in Prob. 21.82, if the sphere of mass m is hollow, with an inside diameter 0.82 times the magnitude of the outside diameter.

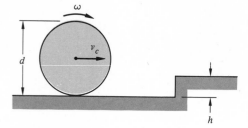

Fig. P21.77

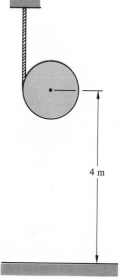

4 m

Fig. P21.81

21.84 The slender rod in Fig. P21.84 is released from rest. It rotates until it strikes a bumper. Find where the bumper should be placed to minimize the impulsive force experienced by the hinge pin.

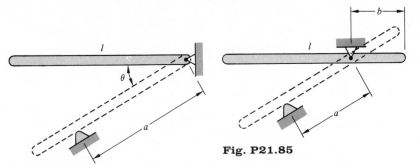

Fig. P21.85

Fig. P21.84

21.85 Do the same as in Prob. 21.84, for the arrangement of the rod shown in Fig. P21.85.

21.86 Figure P21.86 shows a storage canister with a hinged lid. In use, after material is removed from the canister, the lid is allowed to drop to the closed position. Two rubber stops, located distance *a* from the hinge, are to be used to cushion the closing action. Find the optimum spacing *a* for these stops that will result in the "smoothest" closing action.

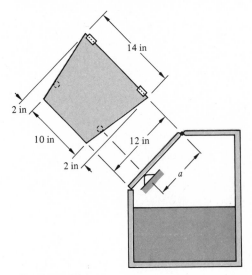

Fig. P21.86

Dynamics of Rigid Bodies in Three-Dimensional Motion– Dynamic Unbalance and Gyroscopic Moments

<h2 style="text-align:right">22</h2>

22.1 INTRODUCTION

In all the preceding chapters two general types of problems have been considered. In the first class of problem, the mass element was treated as a particle. A particle, *by definition,* is a physical element which has mass but whose dimensions are all vanishingly small. Thus, when the motion of a particle is analyzed, there are no rotation effects to be considered. A *complete* description of the motion of a particle consists of a description of its *translational* motion. This translational motion may be either rectilinear or curvilinear. If it is curvilinear, the path of the motion may lie in a plane, and this type of motion is referred to as *plane curvilinear motion.* If the curved path of the motion lies in three-dimensional space, the motion is referred to as *general curvilinear motion.* It was subsequently shown that the motion of the *center of mass of a rigid body,* which may be acted on by any type of force system, moves as a particle in translation. Thus, the entire body of knowledge of particle motion may be applied immediately to characterize the motion of the center of mass of a rigid body. This accounts, in retrospect, for the importance of the equations of particle motion.

The second general type of problem in dynamics is that of motion of a rigid body. A *rigid body* is defined to move with plane motion if all points in the body move in planes which are parallel to some fixed reference plane. In this case, the forces and moments which act on the body are also assumed to lie in a plane which is parallel to the fixed reference plane *and which passes through the center of mass of the body*. The most general description of the motion of a rigid body in plane motion characterizes the translational motion of the center of mass, and the rotation of the body with respect to this point.

In this chapter a three-dimensional description of motion of a rigid body will be considered. As might be anticipated, this problem is inherently more complex than that of plane motion. Only certain types of three-dimensional problems will be considered in this chapter, and the remaining classes of such problems are studied in advanced dynamics.

This chapter is divided into two major sections. The first section considers the case where the *axis* about which the rigid body rotates either is fixed in the inertial reference frame, or moves so that it is always parallel to its original location. An alternate description of this latter effect is that the axis about which the rigid body rotates can move with rectilinear or curvilinear translation *but cannot change its direction*. Readers should convince themselves that the description presented thus far also applies to the case of plane motion of a rigid body. The additional statement which distinguishes the three-dimensional problem from the case of plane motion is that, in the three-dimensional case, not all the forces, or moments, which act on the rigid body lie in planes which are normal to the axis of rotation and which pass through the center of mass of the body.

In the second class of rigid body motion, the body possesses complete axial symmetry with respect to an axis about which the body rotates. For this case, the *axis of rotation may have an arbitrary motion*. Familiar examples of this type of motion are a spinning top and a gyroscope. The analysis of the above two types of rigid-body dynamics problems may be extended to include the cases where impulsive forces act on the bodies or where impact of the bodies occurs.

There is a third class of problem in rigid body dynamics in which a rigid body of arbitrary shape can rotate about an axis which itself possesses any arbitrary motion. This type of motion is characterized by an airplane in flight, the motion of a spinning artillery shell along its trajectory, or the orbital motion of a space vehicle. The analysis of these types of problems is beyond the scope of this book, and they are studied extensively in texts in advanced dynamics.

22.2 REVIEW OF THE D'ALEMBERT, OR INERTIA, FORCE

The concept of the D'Alembert, or inertia, force was first introduced in Sec. 16.6. Since the following sections in this chapter make extensive use of inertia forces, a brief review of this theory will be presented.

Figure 22.1 shows a particle which is assumed to move with rectilinear translation along the s axis. The acceleration of the particle is a, and the positive sense of this term is the same as the positive sense of s.

The following three steps must be used when showing the inertia force which acts on a mass particle.

1. An arrow, which represents a vector and which has the *direction* and the *positive sense* of the acceleration of the particle, is first sketched on the particle. This positive sense may be that which is defined by the positive sense of a displacement coordinate, such as s, or it may be the sense of the *known actual acceleration*.

2. The *magnitude* of the vector represented by the arrow is defined to be the product of the mass, and the acceleration, of the particle.

3. A *minus sign* is placed in front of the magnitude which is written in step 2.

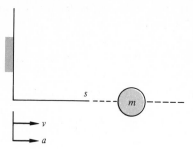

Fig. 22.1

These three steps, for the particle in Fig. 22.1, are shown in Fig. 22.2.

In the problem above, the quantity $-ma$ is the *inertia force acting on the particle*. When the inertia force is drawn on a mass particle, the original dynamics problem is transformed to a problem in *dynamic equilibrium*, which may be solved by using the equations of static equilibrium. The inertia force is a vector quantity. When a vector quantity is multiplied by -1, the *net* effect is to change the sense of the vector. Thus, in Fig. 22.2, step 3, the *actual* sense of the quantity ma is to the *left*. Since an applied force, acting to the right in the positive s-coordinate sense, would be required to produce a positive value of a, the leftward-acting force mentioned above may be thought of as a fictitious "applied force" which balances the

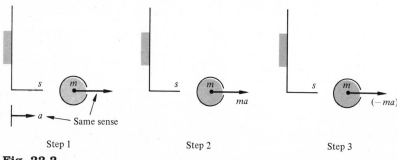

Step 1   Step 2   Step 3

Fig. 22.2

actual applied force and places the particle in a condition of *dynamic* equilibrium.

In the following sections of this chapter the inertia force will be required for a particle which travels in concentric circular paths about a fixed axis. Figure 22.3 shows the typical appearance of such a particle. The actual *sense* of the centripetal acceleration a_n is toward the axis of rotation, as shown in Fig. 22.3*a*, and

$$a_n = r\omega^2 \tag{22.1}$$

The inertia force, which is written in accordance with the rules presented above, is shown in Fig. 22.3*b*. If the minus sign is omitted from this force, the *sense* of the vector is reversed, and this construction is shown in Fig. 22.3*c*. The quantity $mr\omega^2$ is called the *centrifugal force,* and this force acts *radially outward* on the particle.

Throughout the remainder of this chapter the construction shown in Fig. 22.3*c* will represent the inertia force acting on a mass particle which rotates about a *fixed* axis.

22.3 DYNAMIC FORCES CAUSED BY ROTATING OFF-CENTER POINT MASSES— SOLUTION BY DIRECT USE OF INERTIA FORCES

Figure 22.4 shows a rigid shaft which rotates in fixed bearings *a* and *b* with constant angular velocity. Two point masses *m* are attached to thin rigid arms, of length *r*, which form part of the

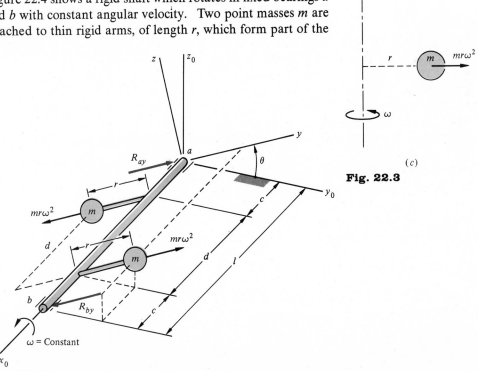

Fig. 22.3

Fig. 22.4

shaft. The $x_0 y_0 z_0$ coordinates are attached to the ground. The *xyz* coordinates are attached to the shaft *and thus possess the motion of the shaft*. The x and x_0 axes are collinear, and both arms lie in the xy plane. The centrifugal forces of the two masses, caused by the angular velocity of the shaft, are shown in the figure in their actual senses. It may be readily verified that the shaft assembly is in static equilibrium about the x axis for any position θ. The additional dynamic force effects at bearings a and b, caused by the rotating unbalance, will be found now. The mass of the arms is neglected in this analysis.

As the shaft rotates with the two off-center masses, the inertia forces produce a couple M_z, given by

$$M_z = Fd = (mr\omega^2)d \qquad (22.2)$$

This couple acts in the xy plane, about the z axis, and it is positive in the sense of the positive z axis. Since the xyz axes rotate with the shaft, it follows that the *couple produced by the unbalance forces also rotates with the shaft*. In order to have equilibrium of the shaft when it is rotating, the bearings must exert force reactions R_{ay} and R_{by} on the shaft, in the y direction, as shown in the figure.

In this problem the inertia forces are the applied forces acting on the shaft, and the resultant of these forces is a couple. The pair of reaction forces must thus constitute a couple, and the equilibrium requirements of the shaft are

$$\sum F_y = 0 \qquad R_{ay} - R_{by} = 0 \qquad R_{ay} = R_{by} = R \quad (22.3)$$

$$\sum M_z = 0 \qquad (mr\omega^2)d - Rl = 0 \qquad R = \frac{mrd\omega^2}{l} \quad (22.4)$$

The forces R are referred to as the *dynamic forces,* caused by the rotating unbalance, which are exerted by the bearings on the shaft. From Newton's third law, the shaft must exert forces R of the same magnitude and opposite sense on the bearings. It may be seen that these forces are independent of the dimension c and will vanish only if r, d, or ω^2 is zero.

The limiting case of no rotation of the shaft is $\omega = 0$. If $r = 0$, the mass center lies on the axis of rotation. If $d = 0$, there is no separation distance in the x direction between the masses, and the problem reduces to that of plane motion of a rigid body.

Two undesirable effects which are produced by a shaft rotating with unbalance will now be considered. Figure 22.5 shows the force R exerted by the shaft on bearing b. The z_0 axis is assumed to be normal to the ground. The components of R along the y_0 and z_0 axes are

$$F_{y_0} = R \cos\theta \qquad F_{z_0} = R \sin\theta \qquad (22.5)$$

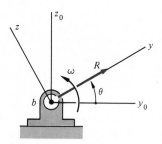

Fig. 22.5

The relationship between angular displacement and velocity, for constant angular acceleration, is

$$\theta = \theta_0 + \omega_0 t + \tfrac{1}{2}\alpha t^2 \qquad (22.6)$$

In the present problem,

$$\alpha = 0 \qquad \omega_0 = \omega = \text{const.} \qquad \theta_0 = 0 \qquad (22.7)$$

and therefore

$$\theta = \omega t \qquad (22.8)$$

Equation (22.5) is now written as

$$F_{y_0} = R \cos \omega t \qquad F_{z_0} = R \sin \omega t \qquad (22.9)$$

Both the sine and cosine functions are periodic. Thus $\sin \omega t$ and $\cos \omega t$, together with the forces F_{y_0} and F_{z_0}, vary periodically with time. This type of motion is referred to as *vibration*. The study of vibrations is a very important part of the synthesis and analysis of mechanical systems, and an introduction to mechanical vibrations is presented in Chap. 23.

It may be concluded from the above discussion that *any shaft which rotates with unbalance will exert pulsating forces on its bearing supports.*

The second major undesirable effect of rotating unbalance is that it causes increased forces to act on the internal material of the shaft. Figure 22.6 shows the shear and bending moment diagram of the shaft assembly. The maximum bending moments occur at the locations on the shaft of the unbalance. If the unbalance force is sufficiently large, the shaft may deform or fracture at these locations.

The techniques presented may be extended readily to cases where the unbalance masses have any orientation with respect to the axis of rotation. The inertia forces are shown as forces acting on the masses, and then the resulting configuration is solved as a three-dimensional statics problem in dynamic equilibrium. Only problems in which the unbalance masses lie in the same plane will be considered further in this chapter.

Example 22.1 The off-center masses on the shaft of Fig. 22.4 are repositioned, as shown in Fig. 22.7. Compare the dynamic forces exerted on the bearings with those found in the problem discussed above.

Solution The couple of the inertia force, from Eq. (22.2), is a function of the spacing of the unbalance masses with respect to each other. The couple of the dynamic reaction forces of the bearings on the shaft is a function of the constant length l of the shaft. Therefore it may be concluded that the dynamic forces on the bearings are the *same* as for the case of symmetrical placement of the unbalance masses on the shaft, given by Eq. (22.4) as

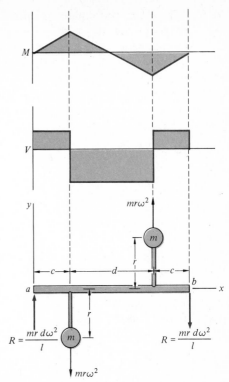

Fig. 22.6

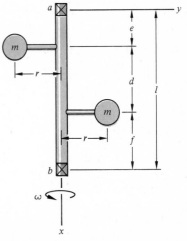

Fig. 22.7

809

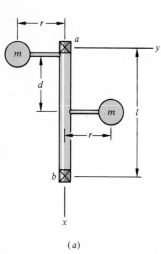

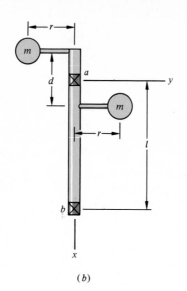

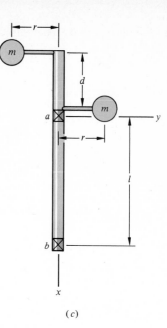

| (a) | (b) | (c) |

Fig. 22.8

$$R = \frac{mrd\omega^2}{l} \qquad (22.10)$$

Several other configurations which also have the *same* dynamic bearing forces are shown in Fig. 22.8.

Example 22.2 During the operation of the unbalanced shaft assembly in Fig. 22.4, the mass closest to the y axis suddenly becomes detached and flies away from the assembly.

a What is the subsequent effect on the dynamic forces acting on bearings a and b?

b Find the numerical values of these dynamic forces if $m = 100$ g, $r = 20$ mm, $c = 60$ mm, $d = 150$ mm, $l = 270$ mm, and $\omega = 1,500$ r/min.

Solution

a The shaft, with the remaining mass, is shown in Fig. 22.9. The equilibrium requirements are

$$\sum M_z = 0 \qquad (mr\omega^2)(c + d) - R_{by}l = 0 \qquad (22.11)$$

$$R_{by} = \frac{mr(c + d)\omega^2}{l} \qquad (22.12)$$

$$\sum F_y = 0 \qquad -R_{ay} + mr\omega^2 - R_{by} = 0 \qquad (22.13)$$

$$R_{ay} = \frac{mrc\omega^2}{l} \qquad (22.14)$$

In the original problem both dynamic bearing forces have the same magnitude, given by

$$R = \frac{mrd\omega^2}{l} \qquad (22.15)$$

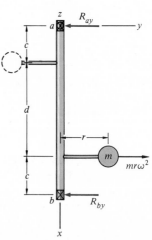

Fig. 22.9

810

From comparison of the above results and using the relationship

$$\frac{c+d}{l} > \frac{d}{l} \tag{22.16}$$

it may be concluded that the dynamic bearing force R_{by} *increases* after the mass is detached. The dynamic force R_{ay} will increase if $c > d$ and decrease if $c < d$.

b The angular velocity of the rotating assembly is

$$\omega = 1{,}500 \left(\frac{2\pi}{60}\right) = 157 \ \frac{\text{rad}}{\text{s}} \tag{22.17}$$

The original values of the dynamic bearing forces are

$$R = \frac{mrd\omega^2}{l} = \frac{(100/1{,}000)(20/1{,}000)(150/1{,}000)(157)^2}{(270/1{,}000)} = 27.4 \ \text{N} \tag{22.18}$$

The values of these bearing forces after one weight is detached are

$$R_{ay} = \frac{mrc\omega^2}{l} = \frac{100(20)60(157)^2}{270} \left(\frac{1}{1{,}000}\right)^2 = 11.0 \ \text{N} \tag{22.19}$$

$$R_{by} = \frac{mr(c+d)\omega^2}{l} = \frac{100(20)(60+150)(157)^2}{270} \left(\frac{1}{1{,}000}\right)^2 = 38.3 \ \text{N} \tag{22.20}$$

The percent increase in the value of the maximum dynamic force exerted on the bearings is

$$\%D = \frac{38.3 - 27.4}{27.4} (100) = 40\% \tag{22.21}$$

22.4 DYNAMIC FORCES CAUSED BY ROTATING OFF-CENTER SLENDER BODIES—SOLUTION BY INTEGRATION OF THE INERTIA FORCES ACTING ON THE MASS ELEMENTS

In the preceding examples the unbalance was in the form of a *discrete mass,* and this mass was treated as a particle. The technique used to solve these problems may be extended to the case of bodies with a continuous mass distribution. The inertia force acting on a typical differential mass element is found first. This force effect is then integrated over all the mass elements of the body to obtain the resultant force and the moment of all the inertia forces acting on the mass particles.

In Fig. 22.10 a thin rod of mass m is hinged to a vertical shaft which rotates with constant angular velocity ω. The lower end of the rod is attached to the center axis by an inextensible cable of negligible weight, so that angle β is constant. It is desired to find the tensile force in the cable.

As a first step, the magnitude, direction, and location of the

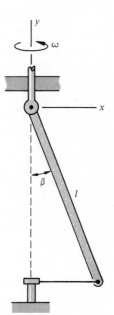

Fig. 22.10

resultant of the inertia forces acting on the rod will be determined.

A set of $x_1 y_1$ coordinates is positioned on the rod, as shown in Fig. 22.11. Since the rod is thin, all points on the mass element dm are at approximately the same radial distance from the axis of rotation. The differential centrifugal force dP is shown in the figure in its actual sense. Since all the centrifugal forces which act on the mass elements of the rod have directions normal to the center axis of rotation, it may be concluded that these forces comprise a *parallel-force system*. The mass per unit length of the rod is designated ρ_0, and

$$dP = dm(x_1 \sin \beta)\omega^2 = \rho_0(x_1 \sin \beta)\omega^2 dx_1 \quad (22.22)$$

The resultant magnitude P of the inertia force is then

$$P = \int dP = \int_0^l \rho_0(x_1 \sin \beta)\omega^2 \, dx_1 \quad (22.23)$$

$$= \rho_0(\sin \beta)\omega^2 \int_0^l x_1 \, dx_1 = \rho_0(\sin \beta)\omega^2 \frac{x_1^2}{2}\bigg|_0^l \quad (22.24)$$

$$= \rho_0 \frac{l^2}{2}\omega^2 \sin \beta \quad (22.25)$$

Since the mass m of the rod is

$$m = \rho_0 l \quad (22.26)$$

the final value of P is

$$P = m\left(\frac{l}{2}\sin \beta\right)\omega^2 \quad (22.27)$$

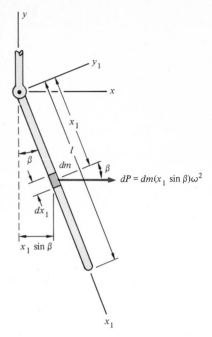

Fig. 22.11

The term $(l/2) \sin \beta$ may be recognized as the radial position of the center of mass of the rod. The *magnitude* of the total centrifugal force is thus the same value which would be obtained if all the mass were imagined to be "concentrated" at the center of mass and had the acceleration of this point. The resultant centrifugal force is shown in Fig. 22.12, and x_0 defines the location of the line of action of this resultant force. As will be seen in the following computation, this resultant force does *not* act through the center of mass of the rod.

The resultant moment M_p of the centrifugal forces about the hinge pin can be written as

$$M_p = (P \cos \beta)x_0 = \int_0^l (dP \cos \beta)x_1 \quad (22.28)$$

It may be observed that the forces $P \sin \beta$ and $dP \sin \beta$, in the x_1 direction, pass through the hinge pin and thus contribute no moment about this point.

Equations (22.22) and (22.27) are substituted into Eq. (22.28) to obtain

$$m\left(\frac{l}{2}\sin \beta\right)\omega^2 x_0 = \int_0^l [\rho_0(x_1 \sin \beta)\omega^2]x_1 \, dx_1 \quad (22.29)$$

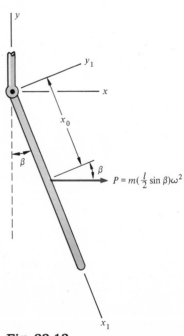

Fig. 22.12

$$m\frac{l}{2}x_0 = \rho_0 \int_0^l x_1^2\, dx_1 = \rho_0 \frac{x_1^3}{3}\bigg|_0^l = \frac{\rho_0 l^3}{3} \quad (22.30)$$

By using $m = \rho_0 l$, the final form of Eq. (22.30) is

$$x_0 = \tfrac{2}{3}l \quad (22.31)$$

This result has an interesting interpretation, since the coordinate $x_0 = \tfrac{2}{3}l$ locates the *center of percussion* of a slender rod which is hinged at its end. It may be recalled that the center of percussion is a point on a physical body, which is *never* coincident with the center of mass, about which the *resultant dynamic moment* is zero. It may also be observed that the location of the line of action of the resultant of the inertia forces acting on the rod is *independent of the rotational velocity ω.*

The free-body diagram of the slender rod is shown in Fig. 22.13. For moment equilibrium about the hinge,

$$\sum M_a = 0 \quad -m\left(\frac{l}{2}\sin\beta\right)\omega^2\left(\frac{2}{3}l\cos\beta\right)$$

$$+ W\left(\frac{l}{2}\sin\beta\right) + F_c(l\cos\beta) = 0 \quad (22.32)$$

$$F_c = \frac{W}{6}\left(\frac{2\omega^2 l \sin\beta}{g} - 3\tan\beta\right) \quad (22.33)$$

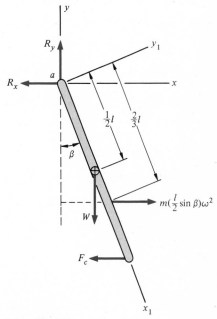

Fig. 22.13

F_c represents a cable tensile force, which is an inherently positive term. Thus, from Eq. (22.33) the magnitude of the angular velocity ω must satisfy

$$\frac{2\omega^2 l \sin\beta}{g} > 3\tan\beta = 3\frac{\sin\beta}{\cos\beta} \qquad \omega > \sqrt{\frac{3g}{2l\cos\beta}} \quad (22.34)$$

The remaining equilibrium requirements are

$$\sum F_x = 0 \quad -R_x + \frac{W}{g}\left(\frac{l}{2}\sin\beta\right)\omega^2 - F_c = 0 \quad (22.35)$$

Using F_c from Eq. (22.33), the final result is

$$R_x = \frac{W}{6}\left(\frac{\omega^2 l \sin\beta}{g} + 3\tan\beta\right) \quad (22.36)$$

$$\sum F_y = 0 \quad R_y = -W = 0 \quad R_y = W \quad (22.37)$$

The resultant force which acts on the hinge pin may then be found from

$$R = \sqrt{R_x^2 + R_y^2} \quad (22.38)$$

Example 22.3 Figure 22.14 shows a proposed design for a device which will indicate when the angular velocity of a rotating shaft reaches a limiting, minimum value. The drum spins about a fixed vertical axis. The arm has the shape of a quarter of a thin

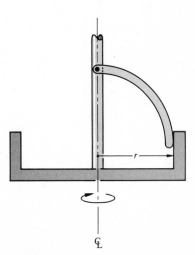

Fig. 22.14

circular ring, and it is hinged to the drum assembly at the axis of rotation. At sufficiently high speeds the centrifugal force which acts on the arm forces it against the drum.

a Find the magnitude and location of the resultant centrifugal force which acts on the arm.

b Derive a general expression for the angular velocity ω_0 at which the arm looses contact with the drum.

c Find the numerical value of ω_0 if $r = 1$ in.

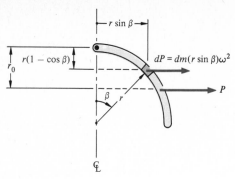

Fig. 22.15

Solution

a The centrifugal force which acts on a typical mass element of the arm is shown in Fig. 22.15. The magnitude of the resultant centrifugal force is

$$P = \int dP = \int dm (r \sin \beta) \omega^2 \qquad (22.39)$$

The mass per unit length of the arm is designated ρ_0, so that

$$dm = \rho_0 (r \, d\beta) \qquad (22.40)$$

Equation (22.39) now appears as

$$P = \int_0^{\pi/2} \rho_0 (r \, d\beta) r \sin \beta \omega^2 = \rho_0 r^2 \omega^2 \int_0^{\pi/2} \sin \beta \, d\beta \qquad (22.41)$$

$$= \rho_0 r^2 \omega^2 [-\cos \beta \,]_0^{\pi/2} = -\rho_0 r^2 \omega^2 [0 - 1] = \rho_0 r^2 \omega^2 \qquad (22.42)$$

The mass m of the quarter circular ring is

$$m = \frac{\rho_0 \pi r}{2} \qquad (22.43)$$

ρ_0 is eliminated between Eqs. (22.42) and (22.43), with the result

$$P = \frac{2 m r \omega^2}{\pi} \qquad (22.44)$$

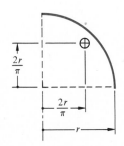

Fig. 22.16

Figure 22.16 shows a plane curve in the form of a quarter circle, and its centroidal coordinates. It may again be concluded, as in the preceding example, that the *magnitude* of the centrifugal force may be found by imagining all the mass to be concentrated at the center of mass, and to have the acceleration of this point.

The location of the resultant inertia force, following Fig. 22.15, is found from

$$P r_0 = \int dP \, r(1 - \cos \beta) = \int dm \, (r \sin \beta) \omega^2 r (1 - \cos \beta) \qquad (22.45)$$

Using $dm = \rho_0 r d\beta$, Eq. (22.45) can be written as

$$P r_0 = \rho_0 r^3 \omega^2 \int_0^{\pi/2} \sin \beta (1 - \cos \beta) \, d\beta \qquad (22.46)$$

$$= \rho_0 r^3 \omega^2 \left(\int_0^{\pi/2} \sin \beta \, d\beta - \int_0^{\pi/2} \sin \beta \cos \beta \, d\beta \right) \qquad (22.47)$$

$$= \rho_0 r^3 \omega^2 \left(-\cos \beta \, \Big|_0^{\pi/2} - \frac{\sin^2 \beta}{2} \, \Big|_0^{\pi/2} \right) \qquad (22.48)$$

$$= \rho_0 r^3 \omega^2 \left[-[0 - 1] - \left(\frac{1}{2} - 0 \right) \right] = \frac{\rho_0 r^3 \omega^2}{2} \qquad (22.49)$$

814

Using P from Eq. (22.42) in Eq. (22.49) results in

$$r_0 = \frac{\rho_0 r^3 \omega^2 / 2}{\rho_0 r^2 \omega^2} = \frac{r}{2} \qquad (22.50)$$

It is interesting to note that the resultant inertia force acts at exactly the midheight of the quarter circular arm.

b The free-body diagram of the arm is shown in Fig. 22.17, and N_1 is the compressive normal force between the arm and the drum. For moment equilibrium of the arm about the hinge pin

$$\sum M = 0 \qquad mg\frac{2r}{\pi} - \frac{2mr\omega^2}{\pi}\frac{r}{2} + N_1 r = 0 \qquad (22.51)$$

$$N_1 = \frac{m}{\pi}(r\omega^2 - 2g) \qquad (22.52)$$

The limiting condition when the arm loses contact with the drum occurs when $N_1 = 0$. The corresponding angular velocity ω_0 is found from

$$r\omega_0^2 - 2g = 0 \qquad \omega_0 = \sqrt{\frac{2g}{r}} \qquad (22.53)$$

It is interesting to note that this result is *completely independent* of the mass properties of the arm.

c The limiting value of ω_0 which corresponds to $r = 1$ in is

$$\omega_0 = \sqrt{\frac{2g}{r}} = \sqrt{\frac{2(386)}{1}} = 27.8 \ \frac{\text{rad}}{\text{s}} \qquad (22.54)$$

$$= 27.8 \left(\frac{60}{2\pi}\right) = 265 \ \frac{\text{r}}{\text{min}} \qquad (22.55)$$

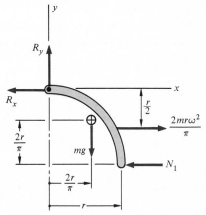

Fig. 22.17

22.5 MASS PRODUCT OF INERTIA OF THIN PLANE BODIES

In this chapter a general solution is presented for the dynamic forces which act when an unbalanced rigid body of arbitrary shape rotates about a fixed axis. Terms of central importance which appear in this solution are the *mass products of inertia* of the rigid body. This section is devoted to a preliminary consideration of the definition and techniques of computation of mass products of inertia.

Figure 22.18 shows a rigid body of arbitrary shape. A set of xyz coordinates is imagined to be attached to the body. The mass moments of inertia of the body about these three axes were presented earlier in Chap. 18 as

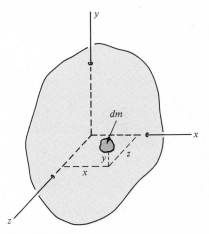

Fig. 22.18

$$I_x = \int_V (y^2 + z^2)\, dm$$

$$I_y = \int_V (z^2 + x^2)\, dm \qquad (22.56)$$

$$I_z = \int_V (x^2 + y^2)\, dm$$

where V is the volume of the body.

The three terms I_x, I_y, and I_z were shown to be combined properties of the mass distribution of the rigid body and of the *position* of the xyz coordinate axes with respect to the body. The additional physical interpretation was made that the magnitudes of the mass moments of inertia were measures of the resistance to angular acceleration about the respective axes. Finally, it was observed that the *mass moments of inertia are always positive qualities.*

There are three other mass-related terms which are properties of the mass distribution of the body and of the orientation of the body with respect to a set of coordinate axes. These terms are referred to as *products of inertia* and are defined by

$$I_{xy} = \int_V xy\, dm \qquad I_{yz} = \int_V yz\, dm \qquad I_{zx} = \int_V zx\, dm$$

$$(22.57)$$

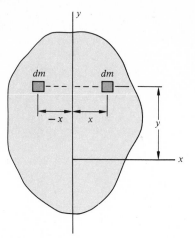

Fig. 22.19

By a judicious placement of the axes with respect to the body, one or more of the products of inertia may be made to vanish. Figure 22.19 shows a body referenced to the coordinate axes in such a way that the yz plane is a plane of symmetry of the body. For every mass element dm in the positive x region, there is a mirror-image mass element with the same y coordinate and an opposite-sense x coordinate. When all these elements are summed over the volume of the body, in accordance with Eq. (22.57), the result is

$$I_{xy} = 0 \qquad (22.58)$$

It is always possible to choose an orientation of the xyz axes with respect to the body in such a way that all three products of inertia are identically zero. If the products of inertia with respect to a set of coordinate axes are zero, these axes are referred to as *principal axes*. It may be observed from the definitions of the products of inertia that, unlike the mass moments of inertia, these terms may have *negative* as well as positive values. The physical interpretation of products of inertia is that *these quantities are a measure of the symmetry of placement of the xyz axes on the body.*

In Fig. 22.20 the rigid body is positioned with respect to two systems of *parallel* coordinate axes. The $x_0 y_0 z_0$ axes pass through the *center of mass* of the body, and d_x, d_y, d_z are the perpendicular separation distances between the two sets of coordinate axes. The center of mass of the body is located by x_c, y_c, and z_c. These centroidal coordinates are defined *relative to the xyz coordinate system.* Thus, they may have negative as well as positive values.

The moments and products of inertia about the centroidal axes are assumed to be known, and it is desired to find the corresponding values of these quantities about the xyz axes. It

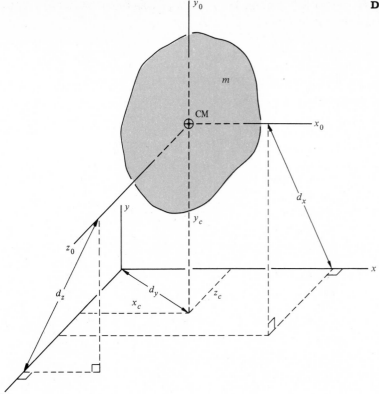

Fig. 22.20

was shown in Chap. 18 that the *parallel-axis,* or *transfer, theorems* for mass moments of inertia have the form

$$I_x = I_{0x} + md_x^2 \qquad I_y = I_{0y} + md_y^2 \qquad I_z = I_{0z} + md_z^2$$
$$(22.59)$$

where I_{0x}, I_{0y}, and I_{0z} are the mass moments of inertia about the centroidal axes, and I_x, I_y, and I_z are the mass moments of inertia about the x, y, and z axes. It can be shown that there exist similar transfer theorems for the products of inertia, with the forms

$$I_{xy} = I_{0,xy} + mx_c y_c \qquad (22.60)$$

$$I_{yz} = I_{0,yz} + my_c z_c \qquad (22.61)$$

$$I_{zx} = I_{0,zx} + mz_c x_c \qquad (22.62)$$

$I_{0,xy}$, $I_{0,yz}$, and $I_{0,zx}$ are the products of inertia about the centroidal axes, and I_{xy}, I_{yz}, and I_{zx} are the products of inertia about the parallel xyz axes.

The remainder of this section will be limited to the consideration of *slender,* or *thin, plane bodies.* The term *slender,* or *thin,* imply that the lateral, or thickness, dimension is much less than any other length dimensions of the body. The bodies will be assumed to lie in the *xy* plane, so that the *z* coordinate of any point on the thickness of the body satisfies the relationship

$$z \approx 0 \qquad (22.63)$$

With the above assumption the three products of inertia in Eq. (22.57) have the forms

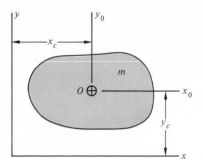

$$I_{xy} = \int_V xy \, dm \qquad I_{yz} = I_{zx} = 0 \qquad (22.64)$$

For the problems which will be considered subsequently, the reference axes *xy*, which are *parallel* to the centroidal coordinates $x_0 y_0$, will be assumed to lie in the *same* plane as these latter coordinates. Thus, $z_c = 0$. The general appearance of the slender, or thin, plane body and its orientation with respect to the coordinate axes are shown in Fig. 22.21.

Fig. 22.21

The transfer theorem for the product of inertia I_{xy} in the above problem has the form

$$I_{xy} = I_{0,xy} + mx_c y_c \qquad (22.65)$$

and

$$I_{yz} = I_{zx} = 0 \qquad (22.66)$$

Example 22.4 The slender rod shown in Fig. 22.22 lies in the $x_0 y_0$ plane, with the constant direction β. The $x_0 y_0$ axes pass through the center of mass of the rod.

a Find the product of inertia $I_{0,xy}$.
b Find the product of inertia I_{xy}.
c Find the numerical value for part *a* if the rod is made of white oak with a specific gravity of 0.77. The rod is 1 m in length, with a diameter of 25 mm, and $\beta = 20°$.

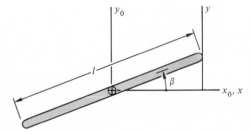

Fig. 22.22

Solution
a A set of $x_1 y_1$ axes is placed on the rod, as shown in Fig. 22.23. Since the rod is slender, the coordinates of the typical mass element are

$$x_0 = x_1 \cos \beta \qquad y_0 = x_1 \sin \beta \qquad (22.67)$$

The mass per unit length of the rod is ρ_0, so that

$$dm = \rho_0 \, dx_1 \qquad (22.68)$$

The product of inertia $I_{0,xy}$ of the rod is then

$$I_{0,xy} = \int_V x_0 y_0 \, dm = \int_{-l/2}^{l/2} (x_1 \cos \beta)(x_1 \sin \beta) \rho_0 \, dx_1 \qquad (22.69)$$

$$= \rho_0 \sin \beta \cos \beta \int_{-l/2}^{l/2} x_1^2 \, dx_1 = \frac{1}{2} \rho_0 \sin 2\beta \left(\frac{x_1^3}{3} \right) \Big|_{-l/2}^{l/2} \qquad (22.70)$$

$$= \frac{1}{2} \rho_0 \sin 2\beta \left[\left(\frac{l/2}{3} \right)^3 - \left(\frac{-l/2}{3} \right)^3 \right] = \frac{1}{24} ml^2 \sin 2\beta \qquad (22.71)$$

It may be observed that for $\theta = 0$ or $90°$, $I_{0,xy} = 0$. This is consist-

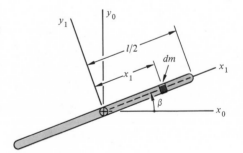

Fig. 22.23

ent with the fact that, for these orientations, the x_0 and y_0 axes are axes of symmetry of the rod.

b The product of inertia I_{xy}, following Eq. (22.65), may be written as

$$I_{xy} = I_{0,xy} + mx_cy_c \qquad (22.72)$$

Since $y_c = 0$, it follows that

$$I_{xy} = I_{0,xy} = \tfrac{1}{24}ml^2 \sin 2\beta \qquad (22.73)$$

c The density of the white oak rod, using 1,000 kg/m³ for standard water as the reference, is

$$\rho = 0.77(1,000) = 770 \text{ kg/m}^3 \qquad (22.74)$$

The mass of the rod is

$$m = \pi \frac{(25/1,000)^2}{4}(1)(770) = 0.378 \text{ kg} \qquad (22.75)$$

The centroidal product of inertia is then

$$I_{0,xy} = \tfrac{1}{24}ml^2 \sin 2\beta = \tfrac{1}{24}(0.378)(1)^2 \sin [2(20°)] = 0.0101 \text{ kg·m}^2 \qquad (22.76)$$

22.6 DYNAMIC FORCES CAUSED BY ROTATING UNBALANCE—GENERAL SOLUTION FOR UNBALANCED BODIES OF ARBITRARY SHAPE

Figure 22.24 shows a rigid body of arbitrary shape which rotates about a fixed axis. A general solution will now be developed for the *dynamic* bearing forces produced. By using

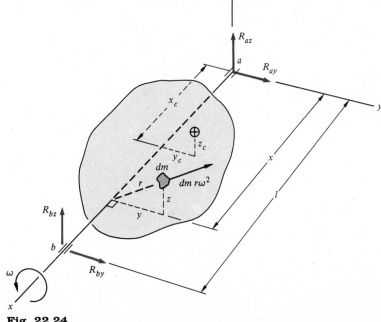

Fig. 22.24

this solution, the *necessary conditions* for perfect dynamic balance will be established. In the following analysis, the shaft and the attached rigid body are considered to be an integral assembly of total mass m, and the effect of the static weight of the assembly on the bearing forces is neglected.

The *xyz* axes are attached to the body, as shown in the figure, and rotate with this element. The origin of the coordinates is placed at one of the shaft bearings, designated a, and the x axis is the axis of rotation. The spacing of the two bearings is given by l, and the position coordinates of the center of mass of the assembly are given by x_c, y_c, and z_c. The y and z components of the bearing forces are assumed to act in the positive coordinate senses.

The typical mass element dm is acted on by the elementary centrifugal force $dP = (dm) r\omega^2$. This force and its components are shown in true view in Fig. 22.25. From this figure,

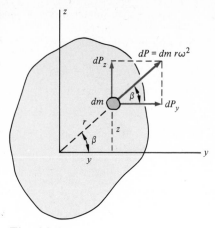

Fig. 22.25

$$dP_y = dP \cos \beta = (dm \, r\omega^2) \cos \beta \qquad (22.77)$$

$$dP_z = dP \sin \beta = (dm \, r\omega^2) \sin \beta \qquad (22.78)$$

Since

$$\sin \beta = \frac{z}{r} \qquad \cos \beta = \frac{y}{r} \qquad (22.79)$$

Eqs. (22.77) and (22.78) may be written as

$$dP_y = (dm \, r\omega^2)\frac{y}{r} = y\omega^2 \, dm \qquad (22.80)$$

$$dP_z = (dm \, r\omega^2)\frac{z}{r} = z\omega^2 \, dm \qquad (22.81)$$

The y and z components of the resultant centrifugal force acting on the rigid body are then

$$P_y = \int dP_y = \int_V y\omega^2 \, dm = \omega^2 \int_V y \, dm \qquad (22.82)$$

$$P_z = \int dP_z = \int_V z\omega^2 \, dm = \omega^2 \int_V z \, dm \qquad (22.83)$$

The centroidal coordinates y_c and z_c in Fig. 22.24 are defined by

$$y_c = \frac{\displaystyle\int_V y \, dm}{m} \qquad z_c = \frac{\displaystyle\int_V z \, dm}{m} \qquad (22.84)$$

where m is the total mass of the body. Thus,

$$\int_V y \, dm = my_c \qquad \int_V z \, dm = mz_c \qquad (22.85)$$

Equations (22.85) are substituted in Eqs. (22.82) and (22.83), with the result

$$P_y = my_c\omega^2 \qquad P_z = mz_c\omega^2 \qquad (22.86)$$

The requirements of force equilibrium are

$$\sum F_y = 0 \qquad R_{ay} + P_y + R_{by} = 0 \qquad (22.87)$$

$$R_{ay} + R_{by} = -P_y = -my_c\omega^2 \qquad (22.88)$$

$$\sum F_z = 0 \qquad R_{az} + P_z + R_{bz} = 0 \qquad (22.89)$$

$$R_{az} + R_{bz} = -P_z = -mz_c\omega^2 \qquad (22.90)$$

For moment equilibrium of the rigid body,

$$\sum M_y = 0 \qquad -\int_V (dP_z)x - R_{bz}l = 0 \qquad (22.91)$$

$$-\int_V (z\omega^2\, dm)x - R_{bz}l = 0 \qquad R_{bz} = \frac{-\omega^2 \int_V zx\, dm}{l} \qquad (22.92)$$

$$\sum M_z = 0 \qquad \int_V (dP_y)x + R_{by}l = 0 \qquad (22.93)$$

$$\int_V (y\omega^2\, dm)x + R_{by}l = 0 \qquad R_{by} = \frac{-\omega^2 \int_V xy\, dm}{l} \qquad (22.94)$$

The numerators in Eqs. (22.92) and (22.94) may be recognized as mass products of inertia, defined by

$$I_{xy} = \int_V xy\, dm \qquad I_{zx} = \int_V zx\, dm \qquad (22.95)$$

and the final forms for these force components are

$$R_{by} \quad \frac{-\omega^2 I_{xy}}{l} \qquad R_{bz} = \frac{-\omega^2 I_{zx}}{l} \qquad (22.96)$$

R_{ay}, R_{az}, R_{by}, and R_{bz} are the components of the *dynamic* force exerted on the shaft by the bearings. These terms, with opposite senses, are the dynamic forces exerted on the bearings by the shaft.

The rotating assembly consisting of the rigid body and the shaft is formally defined to be in *dynamic balance if the four force components above are identically zero for all values of ω.* This condition requires that

$$R_{by} = -\frac{\omega^2 I_{xy}}{l} = 0 \qquad \therefore I_{xy} = 0 \qquad (22.97)$$

$$R_{bz} = -\frac{\omega^2 I_{zx}}{l} = 0 \qquad \therefore I_{zx} = 0 \qquad (22.98)$$

$$R_{ay} + R_{by} = -my_c\omega^2 \qquad (22.99)$$

$$0 + 0 = -my_c\omega^2 \qquad \therefore y_c = 0 \qquad (22.100)$$

$$R_{az} + R_{bz} = -mz_c\omega^2 \qquad (22.101)$$

$$0 + 0 = -mz_c\omega^2 \qquad \therefore z_c = 0 \qquad (22.102)$$

The *necessary* condition for *static balance* of the assembly is that the center of mass be located on the axis of rotation. This requirement is given by

$$y_c = 0 \qquad z_c = 0 \qquad (22.103)$$

It may be seen that static balance is a *necessary,* but not *sufficient,* condition for dynamic balance. The additional requirement, following Eqs. (22.97) and (22.98), is that

$$I_{xy} = 0 \qquad I_{zx} = 0 \qquad (22.104)$$

The interpretation of these equations is that the *xyz axes must be principal axes of the body.*

In summary, for complete dynamic balance of a rotating mass assembly:

1. The center of mass of the assembly must lie on the axis of rotation.
2. The *xyz* axes which are attached to the body must be principal axes of the mass assembly.

The equations presented above are perfectly general results for the dynamic bearing forces which act on any rotating shaft-mass assembly that is supported by two bearings. As with any other general solution, the terms in the solution must be carefully interpreted in light of their original definition. The definitions which have been used in the present analysis are repeated now.

1. The *xyz* axes are *attached* to the body with the origin at one bearing, designated *a*, and the *x* axis coincident with the axis of rotation.
2. The remaining bearing is designated *b*.
3. The axial spacing between the bearings is designated *l*, measured in the positive *x* coordinate sense.
4. The centroidal coordinates and the products of inertia *are referenced to the axes which are attached to the body.*
5. The four components of the bearing forces exerted by the bearings on the shaft are considered to be *positive quantities* if they act in the positive coordinate senses.

If the bodies considered are slender, or thin, plane bodies which lie in the *xy* plane, the equations presented above have simplified forms. For the assumption of thin bodies,

$$z_c \approx 0 \qquad I_{yz} \approx 0 \qquad I_{zx} \approx 0 \qquad (22.105)$$

and the dynamic forces have the forms

$$R_{by} = -\frac{\omega^2 I_{xy}}{l} \qquad R_{bz} \approx 0 \qquad (22.106)$$

$$R_{ay} = \frac{\omega^2 I_{xy}}{l} - m y_c \omega^2 \qquad R_{az} \approx 0 \qquad (22.107)$$

It follows from these equations that the necessary and sufficient conditions for dynamic balance are

$$y_c = 0 \qquad I_{xy} = 0 \qquad (22.108)$$

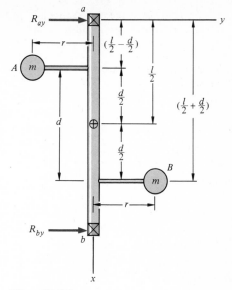

Fig. 22.26

Example 22.5 The system of Fig. 22.4 is redrawn in Fig. 22.26. Use the techniques presented above to find the dynamic forces which act on the shaft.

Solution Since the masses are assumed to be point masses,

$$I_{xy} = \int_V xy \, dm \approx x_A y_A m + x_B y_B m \qquad (22.109)$$

Using

$$x_A = \frac{l}{2} - \frac{d}{2} \qquad x_B = \frac{l}{2} + \frac{d}{2} \qquad y_A = -r \qquad y_B = r \quad (22.110)$$

we find the product of inertia I_{xy} to be

$$I_{xy} = \left(\frac{l}{2} - \frac{d}{2}\right)(-r)m + \left(\frac{l}{2} + \frac{d}{2}\right)rm = mrd \qquad (22.111)$$

By using Eq. (22.106), the dynamic force R_{by} is found as

$$R_{by} = \frac{-\omega^2 I_{xy}}{l} = \frac{-mrd\omega^2}{l} \qquad (22.112)$$

With $y_c = 0$, Eq. (22.107) appears as

$$R_{ay} + R_{by} = -m\omega^2 y_c = 0 \qquad R_{ay} = -R_{by} = \frac{mrd\omega^2}{l} \quad (22.113)$$

The minus sign on the result for R_{by} indicates that the actual sense of this force is to the left in Fig. 22.26.

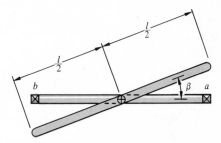

Fig. 22.27

Example 22.6 The slender, rigid rod shown in Fig. 22.27 is attached to a horizontal shaft at a fixed value of angle β.

   a Find the resultant inertial moment which acts on the rod, when the shaft rotates.
   b Use the result found in part a to find the dynamic bearing forces.
   c Use the general solution for the dynamic bearing forces to verify the result in part b.
   d Find the numerical value for part b if the white oak rod of Example 22.4 is used. The rotational speed is 340 r/min, and $\beta = 20°$. Find the factor by which the dynamic force at each bearing exceeds the static reaction force at the bearing when the rod assembly is stationary.

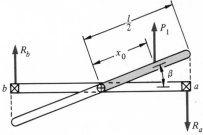

Fig. 22.28

Solution
   a The shaded portion of the rod seen in Fig. 22.28 is exactly the same configuration as a slender rod rotating with given inclination about a fixed axis. The magnitude, and the point of application, of the resultant centrifugal force which acts on half of the arm may be

found directly from the case shown in Fig. 22.10. Using Eqs. (22.27) and (22.31), with $l \rightarrow l/2$ and $m \rightarrow m/2$, we get

$$P = m\left(\frac{l}{2}\sin\beta\right)\omega^2 \Big|_{\substack{l\rightarrow l/2 \\ m\rightarrow m/2}} = \frac{m}{2}\left(\frac{l}{4}\sin\beta\right)\omega^2 = \frac{ml\omega^2 \sin\beta}{8} \quad (22.114)$$

$$x_0 = \frac{2}{3}l \Big|_{l\rightarrow l/2} = \frac{l}{3} \quad (22.115)$$

The dynamic moment due to the resultant centrifugal forces is

$$M = P(2x_0 \cos\beta) = \frac{ml\omega^2 \sin\beta}{8}\left[2\left(\frac{l}{3}\right)\cos\beta\right] = \frac{1}{24}ml^2\omega^2 \sin 2\beta$$
$$(22.116)$$

b Since the center of mass lies on the axis of rotation

$$R_a = R_b = R \quad (22.117)$$

and, for moment equilibrium,

$$\sum M = 0 \quad R(l\cos\beta) - \frac{1}{24}ml^2\omega^2 \sin 2\beta = 0$$
$$R = \frac{1}{12}ml\omega^2 \sin\beta \quad (22.118)$$

c The inclined slender rod is shown in Fig. 22.29, in its orientation with respect to the xy axes of Fig. 22.22. The product of inertia for this configuration was found in Example 22.4 as

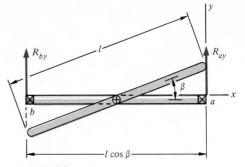

Fig. 22.29

$$I_{xy} = \frac{1}{24}ml^2 \sin 2\beta \quad (22.119)$$

The two bearing forces are shown in their functional positive senses. The general solutions for these two forces are given in Eqs. (22.106) and (22.107) as

$$R_{by} = \frac{-\omega^2 I_{xy}}{l} \quad R_{ay} + R_{by} = -my_c\omega^2 \quad (22.120)$$

In the derivation of these equations, the term l is the axial spacing between the two bearings, *measured along the positive x axis.* Thus, in this example,

$$l \rightarrow -l \cos\beta \quad (22.121)$$

The bearing force R_{by} is then found as

$$R_{by} = \frac{-\omega^2 I_{xy}}{l} = \frac{-\omega^2(\frac{1}{24})ml^2 2 \sin\beta \cos\beta}{-l\cos\beta} = \frac{1}{12}ml\omega^2 \sin\beta$$
$$(22.122)$$

The positive result for R_{by} indicates that this force acts upward on the left end of the shaft, in the view in Fig. 22.29.
    Since $y_c = 0$,

$$R_{ay} + R_{by} = -my_c\omega^2 = 0 \quad (22.123)$$
$$R_{ay} = -R_{by} = -\frac{1}{12}ml\omega^2 \sin\beta \quad (22.124)$$

The force R_{ay} acts downward on the right end of the shaft, as seen in Fig. 22.29.
    d The rotational velocity is

$$\omega = 340\left(\frac{2\pi}{60}\right) = 35.6 \frac{\text{rad}}{\text{s}} \quad (22.125)$$

Using $m = 0.378$ kg, $l = 1$ m, and $\beta = 20°$, we find the dynamic force at each bearing to be

$$R = \tfrac{1}{12}ml\omega^2 \sin \beta = \tfrac{1}{12}(0.378)(1)(35.6)^2 \sin 20° = 13.7 \text{ N} \quad (22.126)$$

The weight of the rod is

$$W = mg = 0.378(9.81) = 3.71 \text{ N} \quad (22.127)$$

When the rod assembly is stationary, the static reaction force at each bearing is $3.71/2 = 1.86$ N. The factor by which the magnitude of the dynamic bearing force exceeds the static bearing force is $13.7/1.86 = 7.37$.

Example 22.7 Figure 22.30 shows a stirring blade which is used in a paint manufacturing operation. The blade is formed of $\frac{3}{4}$-in-diameter steel rod. $\gamma = 0.283$ lb/in³, and the rotational velocity is 900 r/min. The two bearings at a and b have a maximum recommended radial load rating of 200 lb. Compare the dynamic forces which act on the bearings with the recommended load value.

Solution The xy axes are placed on the assembly as shown in Fig. 22.31. Since the rod lengths which comprise the stirrer blade are thin, the required term I_{xy} will be found by considering the stirrer blade to be a *composite plane curve*. The blade is subdivided into the three straight elements shown in Fig. 22.32. Centroidal axes, which are parallel to the xy axes, are placed on each of the elements. Since these axes are all principal axes, all centroidal products of inertia are identically zero. The term I_{xy} then has the form

$$I_{xy} = m_1 x_{c1} y_{c1} + m_2 x_{c2} y_{c2} + m_3 x_{c3} y_{c3} \quad (22.128)$$

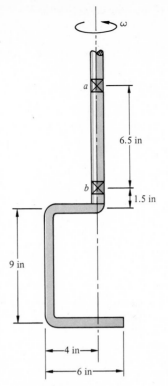

Fig. 22.30

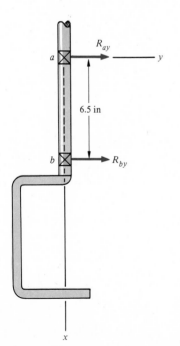

Fig. 22.31   **Fig. 22.32**

825

The mass density per unit length of the material, using $\gamma = 0.283$ lb/in³, is

$$\rho_0 = \rho A = \frac{0.283}{386}\left(\frac{\pi}{4}\right)(0.75^2) = 3.24 \times 10^{-4} \frac{\text{lb·s}^2}{\text{in}^2} \quad (22.129)$$

The computations are arranged in the tabular form shown in Table 22.1.

By using $\omega = 900(2\pi/60) = 94.2$ rad/s, the bearing force at b is

$$R_{by} = \frac{-\omega^2 I_{xy}}{l} = \frac{-94.2^2(-0.175)}{6.5} = 239 \text{ lb} \quad (22.130)$$

The bearing force at a is found from

$$R_{ay} + R_{by} = -m\omega^2 y_c \quad (22.131)$$

$$R_{ay} + 239 = -5.91 \times 10^{-3}(94.2)^2(-2.40)$$

$$R_{ay} = -113 \text{ lb} \quad (22.132)$$

It may be noted that the 239 lb magnitude of the force at bearing b exceeds the recommended bearing force of 200 lb by 20 percent.

Example 22.8 In order to reduce the stirring blade bearing forces in Example 22.7, it is proposed to modify this blade by the addition of the shaded length of rod shown in Fig. 22.33. Find the bearing forces for this new blade configuration, and compare them with the bearing forces in the original design.

Solution Since all the straight length elements of the blade are normal or parallel to the xy axes, all centroidal products of inertia of these lengths are zero. Thus

$$I_{xy} = m x_c y_c \quad (22.133)$$

where m is the mass of the entire blade, and x_c and y_c are the centroidal coordinates of the blade form.

The blade is divided into the four straight elements shown in Fig. 22.34. The centroidal coordinates of the plane curve shape of the blade are found by inspection to be

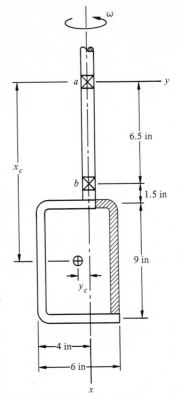

Fig. 22.33

			TABLE 22.1		
Elem.	x_{ci}	y_{ci}	$m_i = \rho_0 l_i$	$m_i x_{ci} y_{ci}$	$m_i y_{ci}$
1	8	−2	$3.24 \times 10^{-4}(4) = 1.30 \times 10^{-3}$	−0.0208	-2.60×10^{-3}
2	12.5	−3.63	$3.24 \times 10^{-4}(8.25) = 2.67 \times 10^{-3}$	−0.121	-9.69×10^{-3}
3	17	−1	$3.24 \times 10^{-4}(6) = 1.94 \times 10^{-3}$	−0.0330	-1.94×10^{-3}
Totals			$m = 5.91 \times 10^{-3} \dfrac{\text{lb·s}^2}{\text{in}}$	$I_{xy} = -0.175$	-1.42×10^{-2}
			$y_c = \dfrac{-1.42 \times 10^{-2}}{5.91 \times 10^{-3}} = -2.31 \text{ in}$		

$$x_c = 8 + 4.5 = 12.5 \text{ in} \qquad y_c = -1 \text{ in} \qquad (22.134)$$

The mass of the blade is

$$m = \rho_0 l = 3.24 \times 10^{-4}(6 + 8.25 + 6 + 8.25) = 9.23 \times 10^{-3} \frac{\text{lb} \cdot \text{s}^2}{\text{in}} \qquad (22.135)$$

The required product of inertia I_{xy} is then

$$I_{xy} = m x_c y_c = 9.23 \times 10^{-3}(12.5)(-1) = -0.115 \text{ lb} \cdot \text{s}^2 \cdot \text{in} \qquad (22.136)$$

The bearing forces are

$$R_{by} = \frac{-\omega^2 I_{xy}}{l} = \frac{-94.2^2(-0.115)}{6.5} = 157 \text{ lb} \qquad (22.137)$$

$$R_{ay} = -R_{by} - m\omega^2 y_c \qquad (22.138)$$

$$R_{ay} = -157 - 9.23 \times 10^{-3}(94.2^2)(-1) = -75.1 \text{ lb} \qquad (22.139)$$

The original bearing forces were

$$R_{by} = 239 \text{ lb} \qquad R_{ay} = -113 \text{ lb} \qquad (22.140)$$

It may be seen that the proposed blade modification reduces the magnitudes of both bearing forces.

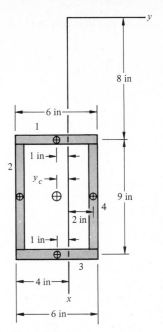

Fig. 22.34

Example 22.9 In a certain experimental configuration it is desired to apply a pulsating force to a bearing pedestal. A proposed technique is shown in Fig. 22.35. A diagonal hole is drilled through a steel cylinder. By careful speed regulation near the nominal operating speed, the desired value of force can be obtained. If the diameter of the drilled hole is 3 mm, find the nominal speed which will produce a pulsating force of magnitude 1.2 N. The density of steel is 7,830 kg/m^3.

Solution The cylinder is referenced to a set of xy axes as shown in Fig. 22.36. The product of inertia of the cylinder, considered to be a homogeneous, *solid* body, is designated $I_{xy,C}$. The product of inertia of the cylinder material *which would occupy the volume of the drilled hole* is called $I_{xy,H}$. The net product of inertia I_{xy} of the drilled cylinder is then

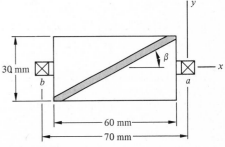

Fig. 22.35

$$I_{xy} = I_{xy,C} - I_{xy,H} \qquad (22.141)$$

Because of the symmetry of the cylinder with respect to the coordinate axes,

$$I_{xy,C} = 0 \qquad (22.142)$$

and thus

$$I_{xy} = -I_{xy,H} \qquad (22.143)$$

From consideration of Eq. (22.143) it may be seen that the effect of the drilled hole in the cylinder is the *same* as that of a slender steel rod at a fixed angle β with respect to the axis of rotation. This problem is similar to Example 22.6, where the dynamic moment, Eq. (22.116), has the form

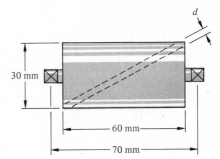

Fig. 22.36

$$M = \tfrac{1}{24}ml^2\omega^2 \sin 2\beta \qquad (22.144)$$

The term m in Eq. (22.144) is the mass of the material which occupies the hole.

From Fig. 22.36,

$$\tan \beta = \tfrac{30}{60} \qquad \beta = 26.6° \qquad \sin \beta = 0.448 \qquad (22.145)$$

The length l of the hole is

$$l = \sqrt{30^2 + 60^2} = 67.1 \text{ mm} \qquad (22.146)$$

The mass of material which occupies the hole is

$$m = \frac{\pi}{4}(3^2)(67.1)\text{mm}^3 \left(7,830 \ \frac{\text{kg}}{\text{m}^3}\right)\left(\frac{1 \text{ m}}{1,000 \text{ mm}}\right)^3 =$$
$$0.00371 \text{ kg} \quad (22.147)$$

Equation (22.144) now appears as

$$M = R\left(\frac{70}{1,000}\right) = \frac{1}{24}(0.00371)\left(\frac{67.1}{1,000}\right)^2 \omega^2 \sin [2(26.6°)] \quad (22.148)$$

$$7.96 \times 10^{-6}\omega^2 = R \qquad (22.149)$$

where ω is in radians per second and R is in newtons.

The value of ω which corresponds to a value of R of 1.2 N is then

$$7.96 \times 10^{-6}\omega^2 = 1.2 \qquad \omega = 388 \text{ rad/s} \qquad (22.150)$$

$$\omega = 388\left(\frac{60}{2\pi}\right) = 3,710 \ \frac{\text{r}}{\text{min}} \qquad (22.151)$$

It is left as an exercise for the reader to show that the dynamic forces which act on the bearings shown in Fig. 22.36 act up at bearing b and down at bearing a.

22.7 INDEPENDENCE OF DYNAMIC FORCES AND ANGULAR ACCELERATION OF ROTATING, UNBALANCED BODIES

The configuration of a rigid body of arbitrary shape which rotates about a fixed axis, Fig. 22.24, is repeated in Fig. 22.37. The assembly, consisting of the rigid body and the shaft, together with the inertia forces, is a three-dimensional problem in dynamic equilibrium. The necessary condition for equilibrium of this system is the satisfaction of six equations of equilibrium. In the earlier analysis for the dynamic bearing forces, the four equilibrium equations

$$\sum F_y = 0 \qquad \sum F_z = 0 \qquad \sum M_y = 0 \qquad \sum M_z = 0 \quad (22.152)$$

were used to find the values of the four dynamic bearing forces R_{ay}, R_{az}, R_{by}, and R_{bz}.

The remaining two equilibrium equations are

$$\sum F_x = 0 \qquad \sum M_x = 0 \qquad (22.153)$$

If no axial, or thrust, forces in the x direction act on the assembly, the first equation above is identically satisfied. If there are

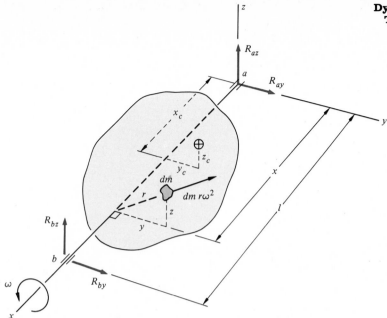

Fig. 22.37

axial forces, a typical example of which would be the axial component of the total force on a helical gear tooth, this equation would have the form

$$F_x = R_{ax} \text{ or } R_{bx} \qquad (22.154)$$

where F_x is the external axial force which acts on the gear tooth and R_{ax} or R_{bx} is the axial component of force at a bearing. The above forces are all *static* forces and thus do not contribute to the *dynamic* bearing force.

The final equation, $\Sigma M_x = 0$, is the rotational equation of motion about the fixed x axis. This equation may be written as

$$M = I_x \alpha \qquad (22.155)$$

where M is the resultant moment, about the x axis, which acts on the assembly, I_x is the mass moment of inertia of the assembly about the x axis, and α is the angular acceleration. Since Eq. (22.155) is the only equilibrium equation which includes the angular acceleration, and since this equation does *not* contain any of the bearing force components, it may be concluded that *the dynamic bearing forces due to rotating unbalance are independent of the angular acceleration of the rotating assembly.*

22.8 DYNAMIC BALANCING OF ROTORS

Figure 22.38 shows a rotor-shaft assembly which is supported by two bearings. The *xyz* axes are attached to the rotor, and the rotor is assumed to be in a general state of dynamic unbal-

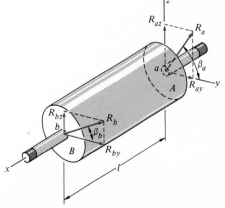

Fig. 22.38

ance. This means that at least one of the following conditions exists.

1. The center of mass does *not* lie on the axis of rotation, and thus the assembly is *not* in static balance about this axis.
2. The *xyz* axes are *not* principal axes of the body, and thus one or both of the products of inertia I_{xy} and I_{zx} are *not* zero.

The force components R_{ay}, R_{az}, R_{by}, and R_{bz} are forces caused by the dynamic unbalance. These forces are transmitted through the shaft to the bearings, where they manifest themselves as undesirable pulsating forces acting on the bearing supports.

The force components in the figure are assumed to be positive quantities if their actual senses are the same as the senses of the positive coordinate axes. The dynamic forces were derived in Sec. 22.6 and are repeated here:

$$R_{by} = \frac{-\omega^2 I_{xy}}{l} \qquad R_{bz} = \frac{-\omega^2 I_{zx}}{l} \qquad (22.156)$$

$$R_{ay} = -R_{by} - my_c\omega^2 \qquad (22.157)$$

$$R_{az} = -R_{bz} - mz_c\omega^2 \qquad (22.158)$$

In the above equations, l is used as the axial spacing between the *end faces* of the rotor.

The resultant forces at a and b are

$$R_a = \sqrt{R_{ay}^2 + R_{az}^2} \qquad R_b = \sqrt{R_{by}^2 + R_{bz}^2} \quad (22.159)$$

with the directions

$$\beta_a = \tan^{-1}\frac{R_{az}}{R_{ay}} \qquad \beta_b = \tan^{-1}\frac{R_{bz}}{R_{by}} \qquad (22.160)$$

From physical considerations, it may be concluded that one or more of the force components R_{ay}, R_{az}, R_{by}, R_{bz} must be negative.

It will now be shown that the rotor assembly in Fig. 22.38 may be put into *perfect dynamic balance* by the addition of correction weights to the rotor, *in two distinct parallel planes which are normal to the axis of rotation*. These planes will be chosen to be the two end planes A and B shown in the figure.

The true view of face A is shown in Fig. 22.39. A small mass m_a is attached to the end face of the rotor, along the line of action of R_a, at distance r_a from the center axis. If the magnitudes of m_a and r_a are chosen to satisfy

$$m_a r_a \omega^2 = R_a \qquad (22.161)$$

the resultant force on plane A will be exactly zero. The equivalent effect may be obtained by *drilling out* a portion of the rotor material, as shown in Fig. 22.40.

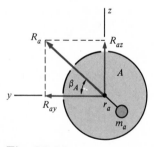

Fig. 22.39

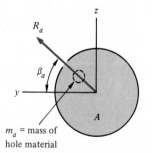

m_a = mass of hole material

Fig. 22.40

After the above correction, the rotor is acted on by only the force R_b shown in Fig. 22.38. A correction weight is now added to plane B, as shown in Fig. 22.41. If m_b and r_b satisfy

$$m_b r_b \omega^2 = R_b \qquad (22.162)$$

the net force on plane B will be zero. This correction also could be made by drilling a hole, shown as the dashed circle in Fig. 22.41, in face B of the rotor.

When the above two correction weights are added, the rotor is in perfect dynamic balance. The effect of the addition of the two correction weights is to *adjust the total mass distribution of the rotor,* so that the center of mass lies on the axis of rotation and the products of inertia in the xy and zx planes are identically zero.

Figure 22.42 shows a schematic setup for dynamically balancing a rotor. The rotor is mounted in a fixture which is connected to the ground by a hinge pin and a spring. Plane B is directly above the hinge pin, so that any resultant centrifugal forces which act in this plane are directly reacted out to the ground. The speed of the motor is varied until a condition is reached which is described as *resonance* of the spring-mounted fixture. This condition is characterized by large angular amplitudes of the spring-mounted frame, and this motion is caused by the rotating, unbalanced force in plane A. The rotating forces in plane B have no effect on this motion. An operator places balance weights on the rotor in plane A, by trial and error, until a condition is reached where the angular vibrational motion of the fixture ceases. At this condition, *the resultant dynamic force of the rotor, at the axial location of plane A, is identically zero.*

The rotor is then turned around in the fixture, so that planes A and B exchange their positions, and the process is repeated. At the conclusion of the above operation, the rotor is dynamically balanced.

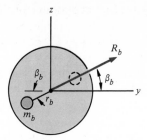

Fig. 22.41

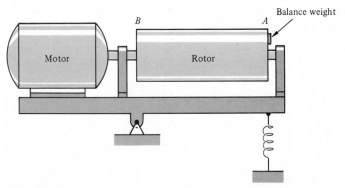

Fig. 22.42

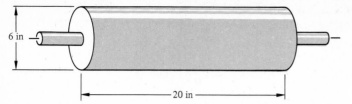

Fig. 22.43

Example 22.10 The cylindrical rotor shown in Fig. 22.43 has
a radial unbalance force of 360 lb in the plane of each end face when
it rotates at 1,400 r/min. It is proposed to dynamically balance the
rotor by drilling $\frac{3}{8}$-in-diameter holes in the end faces, on a 4-in-
diameter circle, and inserting lead plugs flush with these faces.

  a Find the required depth of these balancing holes.

  b Find the required depth if drilled holes alone, at positions which
are 180° from that required in part *a*, are used.

  The densities of lead and steel are 710 and 489 lb/ft³, respectively,
and the drilled holes may be assumed to have the shape of a right
circular cylinder.

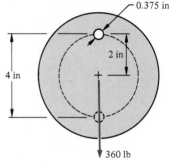

Fig. 22.44

Solution

  a The balancing holes for the lead plugs are shown in Fig. 22.44.
The mass density of the plug-hole combination is the difference
between the densities of the lead and the steel. The rotational
velocity is

$$\omega = 1{,}400\left(\frac{2\pi}{60}\right) = 147\ \frac{\text{rad}}{\text{s}} \qquad (22.163)$$

and the required depth l of the holes is found from

$$F = mr\omega^2 \qquad 360 = \frac{\pi}{4}(0.375)^2 l\left(\frac{710-489}{1{,}728}\right)(2)(147)^2$$

$$l = 0.590\ \text{in} \qquad (22.164)$$

  b For the hole alone, the density of steel is used directly, and the
required hole depth is found from

$$F = mr\omega^2 \qquad 360 = \frac{\pi}{4}(0.375)^2 l\left(\frac{489}{1{,}728}\right)(2)(147)^2 \qquad l = 0.267\ \text{in}$$

$$(22.165)$$

The position of this hole is shown as the dashed circle in Fig. 22.44.

22.9 CRITICAL SPEED OF A SHAFT
WITH AN UNBALANCED ROTOR

The problem considered in this section is inherently a problem
in plane vibrational motion of a rigid body. It is included in
this chapter, however, because it is primarily a problem of
rotating unbalance.

  In all the previous examples in this chapter of an unbalanced mass rotating about a fixed axis, the assumption was made that the shaft on which the mass is mounted is infinitely stiff, so that all effects of shaft deflection could be neglected. In this section that assumption is relaxed, and the problem of a rotating thin, unbalanced disk on a *flexible* shaft will be briefly considered.

Figure 22.45 shows the disk. Point c is the *geometric center* of the circular area which represents the disk. This point is assumed to be coincident with the center axis of the shaft and bearings when the assembly is not rotating. Because of the assumed inhomogeneity of the material, lack of perfect roundness, and lack of perfect parallelism of the two flat faces of the disk, the center of mass of the disk is assumed not to be precisely at the geometric center, but rather at a small distance e from this point.

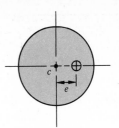

Fig. 22.45

Figure 22.46 shows a greatly exaggerated view of the shaft and disk when the shaft rotates. The lateral stiffness of the shaft in the y direction is designated k, with the units of force per unit length. This term is found by using beam deflection theory, and this subject is studied in detail in strength, or mechanics, of materials. For the purposes of the present problem, k is assumed to be a known constant.

When the shaft and disk assembly rotates, the disk, neglecting its static weight, is acted on by only two forces. These forces are the inertia force due to rotation, which acts through the center of the mass, and the force exerted by the shaft on the disk. Since only two forces act on the disk, this system of forces comprises a *collinear-force system*. The free-body diagram of the disk is shown in Fig. 22.47, and the inertia force is drawn in the figure as a centrifugal force. The points 0, c, and the CM are assumed to lie on the same straight line. For equilibrium,

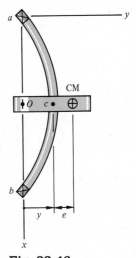

$$\sum F_y = 0 \qquad m(y + e)\omega^2 - ky = 0 \qquad (22.166)$$

$$y = \frac{m\omega^2 e}{k - m\omega^2} = \frac{\omega^2 e}{k/m - \omega^2} \qquad (22.167)$$

Fig. 22.46

From inspection of Eq. (22.167) it may be seen that, when $\omega^2 \rightarrow k/m$, the denominator approaches zero and y may have very large values. A limiting value of ω, designated ω_0, is defined by

$$\omega_0 = \sqrt{\frac{k}{m}} \qquad (22.168)$$

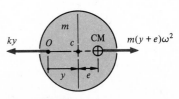

This value of angular velocity is referred to as the *critical speed* of the disk-shaft assembly. If the assembly were run at this speed, the shaft would experience large values of lateral displacement which would result in early failure of this element.

Fig. 22.47

By using the above result, Eq. (22.167) may be written as

$$y = \frac{\omega^2 e}{\omega_0^2 - \omega^2} = \frac{e}{(\omega_0/\omega)^2 - 1} \qquad (22.169)$$

Two distinct cases will now be considered, depending on whether $\omega < \omega_0$ or $\omega > \omega_0$. If $\omega < \omega_0$, the motion is described as *operation below the critical speed*. From Eq. (22.169), $y > 0$ and the configuration during rotation is as shown in Fig. 22.48. For this case, the disk is described as rotating with the "heavy side" out, since the geometric center of the disk is between the centerline of the bearings and the center of mass. If $\omega \ll \omega_0$, $y \approx 0$.

When $\omega > \omega_0$, the operation is referred to as *operation above the critical speed*. The first conclusion, which follows from Eq. (22.169), is that $y < 0$. The general configuration for this regime of operation has the appearance shown in Fig. 22.49. For this case the disk rotates with the "heavy side" in, since the center of mass of disk lies between the geometric center of the disk and the centerline of the bearings.

At very high rotational speeds a limiting condition is reached. For $\omega \gg \omega_0$,

$$\frac{\omega_0^2}{\omega^2} \to 0 \qquad (22.170)$$

and, from Eq. (22.169),

$$y \to -e \qquad (22.171)$$

For this limiting case the disk tends to "rotate about its center of mass" in such a way that *the center of mass lies on the centerline of the bearings*. This operation is shown in Fig. 22.50.

Example 22.11 Figure 22.51 shows a 50-lb steel disk mounted on a shaft. Due to manufacturing tolerances, the eccentricity e is 0.010 in. From an earlier calculation, $k = 18,000$ lb/in.

a For what ranges of rotational speed, in revolutions per minute, will the maximum lateral deflection of the shaft not exceed 0.015 in?

b Find the dynamic bearing forces which correspond to the above value of shaft deflection.

Solution

a The critical speed is

$$\omega_0 = \sqrt{\frac{k}{m}} = \sqrt{\frac{18,000}{50/386}} = 373 \frac{\text{rad}}{\text{s}} = 3,560 \frac{\text{r}}{\text{min}} \qquad (22.172)$$

For operation below the critical speed, y is positive. Using Eq. (22.169), we get

$$y = \frac{e}{(\omega_0/\omega)^2 - 1} \qquad 0.015 = \frac{0.010}{(\omega_0/\omega)^2 - 1} \qquad \frac{\omega_0}{\omega} = 1.29 \qquad (22.173)$$

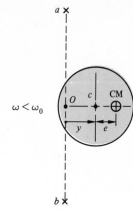

Fig. 22.48 $\omega < \omega_0$

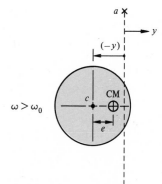

Fig. 22.49 $\omega > \omega_0$

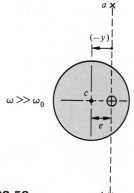

Fig. 22.50 $\omega \gg \omega_0$

834

$$\omega = \frac{\omega_0}{1.29} = \frac{3{,}560}{1.29} = 2{,}760 \ \frac{r}{min} \qquad (22.174)$$

For speeds above the critical speed, y is *negative*. Thus, using Eq. (22.169), we have

$$-0.015 = \frac{0.010}{(\omega_0/\omega)^2 - 1} \qquad \frac{\omega_0}{\omega} = 0.577 \qquad (22.175)$$

$$\omega = \frac{\omega_0}{0.577} = \frac{3{,}560}{0.577} = 6{,}170 \ \frac{r}{min} \qquad (22.176)$$

If the rotational speed is in either of the ranges

$$\omega < 2{,}760 \ r/min \qquad \omega > 6{,}170 \ r/min \qquad (22.177)$$

the lateral shaft deflection will not exceed 0.015 in.

b For a lateral shaft deflection of 0.015 in, the force exerted by the disk on the shaft is

$$F = ky = 18{,}000(0.015) = 270 \ lb \qquad (22.178)$$

The dynamic bearing forces are then

$$R = \frac{F}{2} = \frac{270}{2} = 135 \ lb \qquad (22.179)$$

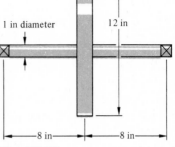

Fig. 22.51

22.10 DERIVATIVE OF A VECTOR WITH CONSTANT MAGNITUDE AND CHANGING DIRECTION

In Sec. 22.11 it will be necessary to take a time derivative of a vector. As a preliminary step, the problem of finding the time derivative of a vector with constant magnitude and changing direction will be considered.

Figure 22.52 shows a vector **A**. This vector has a *constant magnitude A*, and it is constrained to move in the xy plane as it rotates about the z axis. It is desired to find the quantity $d\mathbf{A}/dt$.

The position of vector **A** at time t, designated $\mathbf{A}(t)$, is shown in Fig. 22.53. The *direction* of this vector rotates with the angular velocity ω_1, so that at a later time $t + \Delta t$ the vector $\mathbf{A}(t + \Delta t)$ has the new position shown in the figure. The change $\Delta \mathbf{A}$, by definition, is

$$\Delta \mathbf{A} = \mathbf{A}(t + \Delta t) - \mathbf{A}(t) \qquad (22.180)$$

as seen in the figure.

The first time derivative of **A** is defined to be

$$\frac{d\mathbf{A}}{dt} = \lim_{\Delta t \to 0} \frac{\Delta \mathbf{A}}{\Delta t} \qquad (22.181)$$

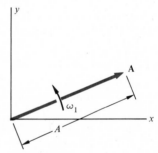

Fig. 22.52

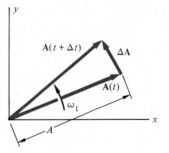

Fig. 22.53

The *direction* of this vector is that of the vector $\Delta \mathbf{A}$. This direction, in the limit, is *perpendicular to the directon of* **A**. The *sense* of $d\mathbf{A}/dt$ is the same as that obtained by imagining the vector **A** to be rotated 90° in the same sense as its angular velocity.

Finally, the *magnitude* of Δ**A** is found, in the limit, as

$$\lim_{\Delta t \to 0} |\Delta \mathbf{A}| = \lim_{\Delta t \to 0} A(\omega_1 \Delta t) \qquad (22.182)$$

These results are now combined to obtain

$$\frac{d\mathbf{A}}{dt} = \lim_{\Delta t \to 0} \frac{\Delta \mathbf{A}}{\Delta t} = \lim_{\Delta t \to 0} \mathbf{i}_A \frac{A\omega_1 \Delta t}{\Delta t} = (A\omega_1)\mathbf{i}_A \quad (22.183)$$

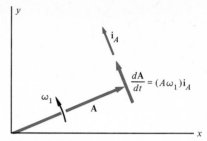

Fig. 22.54

where $\mathbf{i}_A$ is a unit vector with the direction and sense shown in Fig. 22.54.

The very important conclusion now arrived at is that the *time derivative* of a vector of *constant magnitude* has *a direction which is normal to the direction of the original vector.*

22.11 MOMENT EFFECTS DUE TO CHANGE IN DIRECTION OF AN AXIS OF ROTATION—THE GYROSCOPIC MOMENT

In all the preceding examples in this chapter, the axis about which the body rotates is *fixed* in space. In this section, the effect which takes place when this axis of rotation is allowed to *change its direction* will be investigated.

As a preliminary consideration, Fig. 22.55 shows a piece of equipment which is commonly found in physics laboratories. It consists of a bicycle wheel and tire, with a pair of handles attached at the axis of the wheel. A person grips the handles, and the wheel is set into spinning motion. If the person holding the handles attempts to change the direction of the axis of the handles, it appears that an "invisible hand" opposes this change. A substantial force resists the attempt to rotate the axis of the handles from its original position, and the spinning bicycle wheel appears to be "built in" in space. The above physical phenomenon is an example of a *gyroscopic moment*. The theory which explains this effect will now be presented.

Figure 22.56 shows a symmetrical disk which spins with a constant angular velocity ω about its axis of symmetry *aa*. The mass moment of inertia of the disk about this axis is designated *I*. The *angular momentum* **H** of the disk was defined in Chap. 21 to be

$$\mathbf{H} = I\boldsymbol{\omega} \qquad (22.184)$$

where I is the mass moment of inertia about the center axis of the disk, and ω is the angular velocity. The *angular momentum,* as the product of a scalar quantity I and a vector quantity ω, is a *vector quantity.*

If the angular velocity is represented by the double-headed arrow shown in Fig. 22.57*a*, then the angular momentum **H**

Fig. 22.55

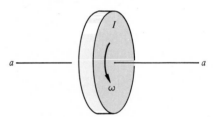

Fig. 22.56

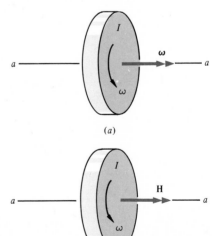

(*a*)

(*b*)

Fig. 22.57

may be represented by the double-headed arrow shown in Fig. 22.57b.

Newton's second law for rotational motion was shown earlier to have the form

$$M = I\alpha = I\frac{d\omega}{dt} \qquad (22.185)$$

Since I is a constant in this problem, the right side of Eq. (22.185) may be written as

$$I\frac{d\omega}{dt} = \frac{d}{dt}(I\omega) = \frac{dH}{dt} \qquad (22.186)$$

Since both M and H are vector quantities, Eqs. (22.185) and (22.186) may be written in boldface vector notation as

$$\mathbf{M} = \frac{d\mathbf{H}}{dt} \qquad (22.187)$$

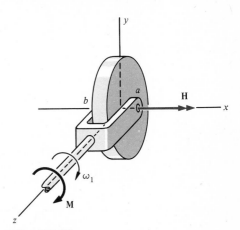

Fig. 22.58

Since $\mathbf{H}$ in the present problem is a vector of constant magnitude, it follows that the right-hand side of Eq. (22.187) represents the operation of finding a time derivative of a vector of constant magnitude. This problem was solved in Sec. 22.10, and the results which were obtained there may be used directly.

A spinning disk, with a shaft and bearing arrangement, is shown in Fig. 22.58. The spin axis is initially collinear with the x axis, and the spacing between bearings a and b is l. A moment of constant magnitude $\mathbf{M}$ is applied to the clevis rod, as shown in the figure, which causes this rod to have an angular velocity ω_1. It is desired to find the magnitude, direction, and sense of the bearing forces exerted by bearings a and b on the shaft.

The change in the momentum vector $\mathbf{H}$, due to the imposed rotation ω_1, is shown in Fig. 22.59. The moment $\mathbf{M}$ required to produce this change in momentum is found from

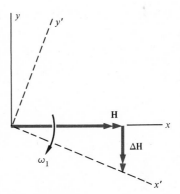

Fig. 22.59

$$\mathbf{M} = \frac{d\mathbf{H}}{dt} \qquad (22.188)$$

By comparison of this equation with Eq. (22.183) it follows that

$$M = \frac{dH}{dt} = I\omega\omega_1 \qquad (22.189)$$

Figure 22.60 shows a top view of the disk. The moment M given above is the required external moment acting on the disk to give the motion ω_1. This moment must be equal to the couple of the two forces R, shown in Fig. 22.161, which act on the shaft, so that

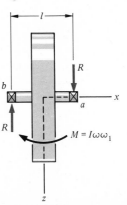

Fig. 22.60

$$Rl = M = I\omega\omega_1 \qquad R = \frac{I\omega\omega_1}{l} \qquad (22.190)$$

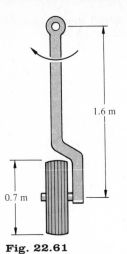

1.6 m

0.7 m

Fig. 22.61

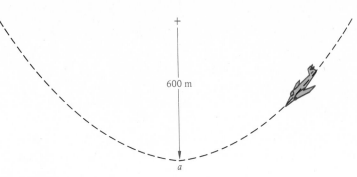

600 m

a

Fig. 22.62

Example 22.12   Figure 22.61 shows an aircraft landing gear just after the wheel leaves the runway during takeoff.   The velocity of the aircraft is 200 km/h, and the retraction angular velocity of the arm is 0.2 rad/s.   The wheel may be approximated as a disk of mass 20 kg and diameter 0.7 m.   Find the gyroscopic moment which tends to twist the landing gear arm.

Solution   The mass moment of inertia of the wheel is

$$I = \tfrac{1}{8}md^2 = \tfrac{1}{8}(20)(0.7)^2 = 1.23 \text{ kg·m}^2 \qquad (22.191)$$

The angular velocity of the wheel is found from

$$\omega = \frac{v}{r} = \frac{200(1000)}{3,600(0.35)} = 159 \; \frac{\text{rad}}{\text{s}} \qquad (22.192)$$

The gyroscopic moment is then

$$M = I\omega\omega_1 = 1.23(159)(0.2) = 39.1 \text{ N·m} \qquad (22.193)$$

Example 22.13   The system of Example 16.9 is repeated in Fig. 22.62.   The fighter plane is in a power dive.   The speed of the plane is 960 km/h, and the minimum radius of curvature of the flight path occurs at point *a* as the pilot pulls out of the dive.   A representation of the compressor and turbine rotors of the jet engine is shown in Fig. 22.63.   Find the magnitude of the dynamic bearing forces caused by the gyroscopic moment as the plane passes point *a*.   The engine speed is 15,000 r/min, and the specific weight of steel is 0.283 lb/in³.

Solution   The mass moment of inertia of each disk about its center axis is of the form

$$I = \tfrac{1}{8}md^2 \qquad (22.194)$$

The moment of inertia of the entire rotating assembly of the jet engine is

$$I = 8\left[\frac{1}{8}\frac{\pi(15)^2}{4}(2)\left(\frac{0.283}{386}\right)(15)^2\right] + 2\left[\frac{1}{8}\frac{\pi(24)^2}{4}(1.75)\left(\frac{0.283}{386}\right)(24)^2\right]$$
$$= 142 \text{ lb·s}^2\text{·in} \quad (22.195)$$

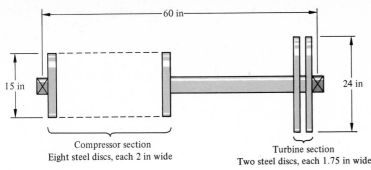

60 in

15 in

24 in

Compressor section
Eight steel discs, each 2 in wide

Turbine section
Two steel discs, each 1.75 in wide

Fig. 22.63

The angular velocity of the aircraft as it passes point a is given by

$$\omega_1 = \frac{v}{r} = \frac{960(1000)}{3600(600)} = 0.445 \ \frac{\text{rad}}{\text{s}} \qquad (22.196)$$

The speed of rotation of the engine is

$$\omega = 15{,}000 \left(\frac{2\pi}{60} \right) = 1{,}570 \ \frac{\text{rad}}{\text{s}} \qquad (22.197)$$

The gyroscopic moment then has the value

$$M = I\omega\omega_1 = 142(1{,}570)(0.445) = 99{,}200 \ \text{in·lb} \qquad (22.198)$$

Since the gyroscopic moment is a pure couple effect, the dynamic bearing reaction forces are equal, with the magnitude

$$R = \frac{M}{l} = \frac{99{,}200}{60} = 1650 \ \text{lb} \qquad (22.199)$$

22.12 SUMMARY

An unbalanced rigid body which rotates about a fixed axis exerts pulsating, or time-varying, forces on the bearings supporting the shaft. In addition, the rotating unbalance causes increased forces in the internal material of the shaft.

The problem of rotating unbalance may be solved with the direct use of inertia forces and the equations of dynamic equilibrium. This problem also may be solved in terms of the centroidal coordinates and the mass products of inertia of the rotating mass assembly. The particular problem to be solved usually dictates which method is more convenient.

Mass products of inertia are a measure of the symmetry of placement of a set of coordinate axes on a body. These quantities may be positive or negative, and they have the basic units of mass times length squared. For a thin plane body which lies in the xy plane

$$I_{xy} = \int_V xy \, dm \qquad (22.200)$$

The parallel-axis, or transfer, theorem for the thin plane body is

$$I_{xy} = I_{0,xy} + mx_c y_c \qquad (22.201)$$

where $I_{0,xy}$ is the centroidal product of inertia, m is the mass, and x_c and y_c are the centroidal coordinates of the body, measured in the xyz coordinate system.

The necessary and sufficient conditions for the complete dynamic balance of a rotating mass assembly are that

1. The center of mass of the assembly must lie on the axis of rotation.
2. The axis of rotation and the two rectangular coordinate axes normal to this axis must be principal axes of the body.

If the rotating mass is a thin plane body which lies in the xy plane, the dynamic forces exerted by the bearings on the shaft have the forms

$$R_{by} = \frac{-\omega^2 I_{xy}}{l} \qquad R_{ay} = \frac{\omega^2 I_{xy}}{l} - my_c\omega^2 \qquad (22.202)$$

where ω is the angular velocity, I_{xy} is the mass product of inertia, y_c is the displacement of the center of mass from the axis of rotation, and l is the axial separation distance between bearings a and b.

Any rotating mass assembly may be put into a condition of perfect balance by the addition of correction weights, or by the removal of material, in two distinct parallel planes which are normal to the axis of rotation. The dynamic forces due to rotating unbalance are completely independent of the angular acceleration of the rotating assembly.

The critical speed of a thin, rigid disk on a flexible shaft is

$$\omega_0 = \sqrt{\frac{k}{m}} \qquad (22.203)$$

where m is the mass of the disk and k is the lateral stiffness of the shaft. The deflection y of the geometric center of the disk from the center axis of the bearings is

$$y = \frac{e}{(\omega_0/\omega)^2 - 1} \qquad (22.204)$$

where ω is the angular velocity and e is the eccentricity of the disk, defined to be the distance between the geometric center of the disk and the center of mass of this element. If $\omega \to \omega_0$, the shaft will experience very large lateral deflection. If $\omega \ll \omega_0$, $y \approx 0$. If $\omega \gg \omega_0$, the disk tends to rotate about its center of mass.

A gyroscopic moment occurs when the axis of rotation of a rigid body with angular velocity changes its direction in space. The magnitude of the gyroscopic moment is given by

$$M = I\omega\omega_1 \qquad\qquad (22.205)$$

where I is the mass moment of inertia of the body, ω is the spin angular velocity, and ω_1 is the angular velocity of the axis of rotation. The gyroscopic moment acts about an axis which is normal to the axis of spin of the body.

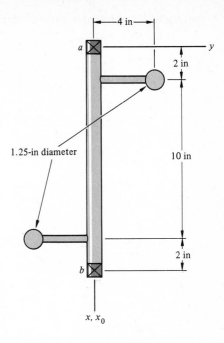

Problems

22.1 The assembly shown in Fig. P22.1 rotates at 1,000 r/min. The two spherical masses are steel, with $\gamma = 0.283$ lb/in^3, and these elements may be considered to be point masses attached to massless arms. At $t = 0$, the two masses lie in the x_o, y_o plane.
  (a) Find the magnitude of the dynamic bearing forces.
  (b) Find the z_o and y_o components of the dynamic forces exerted by the shaft on the bearings at $t = 0.95$ s.
  (c) Find the maximum value of the bending moment in the shaft.

22.2 Do the same as in Prob. 22.1 if, at $t = 0$, the upper mass in the figure suddenly becomes detached and flies away from the assembly.

22.3 The assembly in Fig. P22.1 is initially at rest. A couple about the x axis, of magnitude 0.5 in·lb, is applied to the shaft at $t = 0$. Find the magnitude of the dynamic bearing forces when $t = 5$ s.

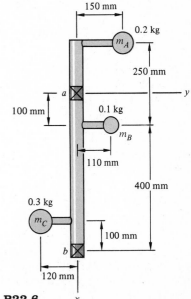

22.4 Figure P22.4 shows the construction of the bearings that support the shaft in Fig. P22.1. The maximum force in the y_o direction that the pair of mounting bolts may be subjected to is 800 lb. Find the maximum permissible speed of the shaft.

Fig. P22.1

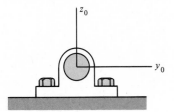

Fig. P22.4

22.5 Do the same as in Prob. 22.4, but allow for the possibility of one of the masses becoming detached as the assembly rotates.

22.6 The assembly shown in Fig. P22.6 rotates at 50 rad/s. Find the dynamic forces at bearings a and b.

22.7 (a) Do the same as in Prob. 22.6, if mass m_A becomes detached and flies away from the assembly.
  (b) Do the same as in part a, if mass m_B becomes detached.
  (c) Do the same as in part a, if mass m_C becomes detached.

Fig. P22.6

841

22.8 Do Prob. 22.6 by using the general solutions given by Eqs. (22.106) and (22.107).

22.9 Do Prob. 22.7 by using the general solutions given by Eqs. (22.106) and (22.107).

22.10 The form shown in Fig. P22.10 is fabricated from 0.5-in steel plate, with $\gamma = 0.283$ lb/in³. The ends are fitted to bearings at a and b, and the assembly rotates about the center axis of the 20-in length. Find the dynamic bearing forces by integration of the inertia forces acting on the mass elements.

22.11 Do the same as in Prob. 22.10, if the center axis of the 20-in length is displaced 0.050 in from the centerline of the two bearings.

22.12 Do Prob. 22.10 by using the general solutions given by Eqs. (22.106) and (22.107). Consider the two projections on the shaft to be slender rod elements.

22.13 Do Prob. 22.11 by using the general solutions given by Eqs. (22.106) and (22.107).

22.14 The rotating assembly of Prob. 22.10 is to be put into perfect dynamic balance by welding onto the assembly the additional two arms shown in Fig. P22.14. Find the required lengths of these two arms. The mass of the weld material may be neglected.

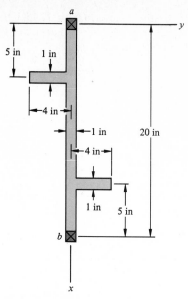

Fig. P22.10

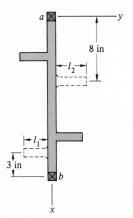

Fig. P22.14

22.15 The thin rod of mass 1.5 kg in Fig. P22.15 is hinged to a vertical shaft that rotates with constant angular velocity ω. The lower end of the rod is attached to the center axis by an inextensible cable of negligible weight.

(a) Find the tensile force in the cable, and the resultant force that acts on the hinge pin, when $\omega = 1,000$ r/min.

(b) Find the limiting value of ω for which the cable will experience a tensile force.

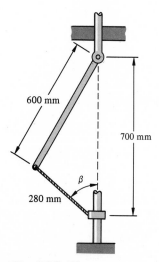

Fig. P22.15

22.16 Do the same as in Prob. 22.15, if the rod is replaced by the simple pendulum of mass 1.5 kg shown in Fig. P22.16. The mass of the pendulum rod may be neglected.

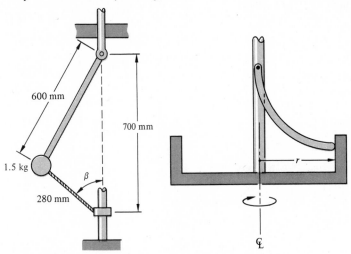

Fig. P22.16   **Fig. P22.17**

22.17 The device in Example 22.3 is modified to the arrangement shown in Fig. P22.17. The weight of the arm is 0.025 lb.

(*a*) Find the general expression for the limiting value ω_0 of the angular velocity at which the arm looses contact with the drum.

(*b*) Find the numerical value of ω_0, if $r = 1$ in.

(*c*) Find the normal force exerted by the curved arm on the drum, and the hinge pin force, when $\omega = 600$ r/min.

22.18 The two arms in Fig. P22.18 are hinged to the rotating member and connected to each other by an inextensible, weightless cable. The arms each have a weight of 0.2 lb/in.

(*a*) Find the tensile force in the cable when the assembly rotates at 850 r/min.

(*b*) Find the minimum value of the rotational speed for which the cable force will be tensile.

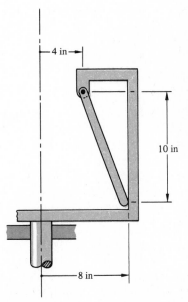

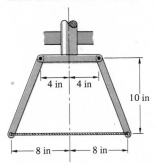

Fig. P22.18

22.19 Figure P22.19 shows a view of a cylindrical drum that rotates about a fixed axis. How could the results obtained in Prob. 22.18 be used to find the speed at which the hinged arm loses contact with the curved surface of the drum?

Fig. P22.19

22.20 A slender rod of mass 1.4 kg is hinged to the center shaft of a cylindrical drum, as shown in Fig. P22.20. The drum rotates about a fixed vertical axis with a speed of 290 r/min.

(a) Find the hinge-pin force and the compressive normal force exerted by the rod on the drum.

(b) Find the limiting speed at which the rod loses contact with the drum.

22.21 Find the maximum value of the speed at which the assembly in Prob. 22.20 may be operated without causing failure of the hinge pin. The hinge-pin force that causes this element to shear is estimated to be 32 N.

22.22 The hinged rod in Prob. 22.20 is replaced by the simple pendulum arrangement shown in Fig. P22.22. Find the required value of h, if the mass is to lose contact with the drum at the same rotational speed at which the rod in Prob. 22.20 loses contact with the drum.

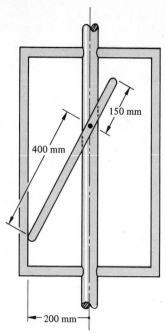

Fig. P22.20

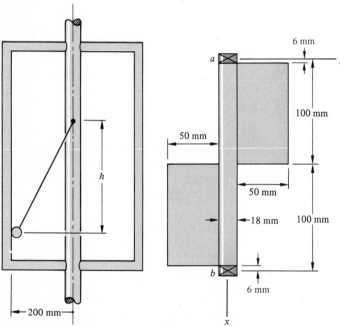

Fig. P22.22   **Fig. P22.23**

22.23 Two thin, rectangular brass plates are soldered to a shaft, as shown in Fig. P22.23. The thickness of the plates is 4 mm and the density of brass is 8,550 kg/m³.

(a) Find the dynamic bearing forces when the assembly rotates at 200 r/min.

(b) How would the results in part a change if one of the plates became detached from the shaft?

22.24 The stirring blade in Fig. P22.24 is formed of thin bronze rod of 8-mm diameter. The density of bronze is 8,800 kg/m³. Find the dynamic forces that act on the bearings at a and b when the shaft rotates at 440 r/min.

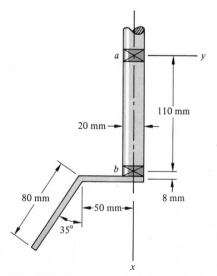

Fig. P22.24

844

22.25 The plane blade shape in Fig. P22.25 is formed of 0.5-in-diameter steel rod. The specific weight of steel is 489 lb/ft³. Find the maximum permissible value of the rotational speed, if the dynamic bearing force is not to exceed 12 lb.

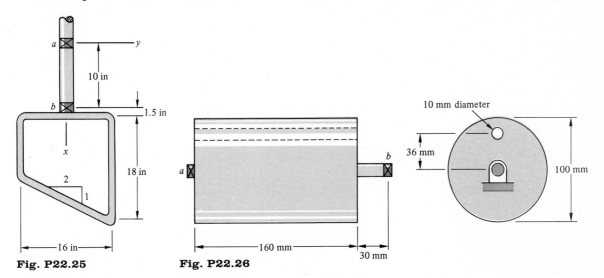

Fig. P22.25   **Fig. P22.26**

22.26 A hole is drilled in a bronze cylinder, as shown in Fig. P22.26. Find the dynamic forces exerted on bearings a and b when the cylinder rotates at 3,250 r/min. The density of bronze is 8,800 kg/m³.

22.27 Do the same as in Prob. 22.26, if the orientation of the drilled hole is as shown in Fig. P22.27. The volume of the hole may be approximated as a right circular cylinder of height d_1.

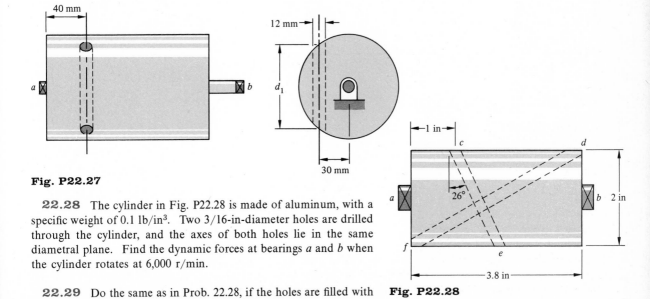

Fig. P22.27

22.28 The cylinder in Fig. P22.28 is made of aluminum, with a specific weight of 0.1 lb/in³. Two 3/16-in-diameter holes are drilled through the cylinder, and the axes of both holes lie in the same diametral plane. Find the dynamic forces at bearings a and b when the cylinder rotates at 6,000 r/min.

22.29 Do the same as in Prob. 22.28, if the holes are filled with lead, with a specific weight of 710 lb/ft³.

Fig. P22.28

22.30 Figure P22.30 shows a cross-sectional view of a hollow cylinder supported by bearings at *a* and *b*. A hole with a 0.200-in diameter is located at *c*, and a second hole, with a 0.284-in diameter, is located at *d*. The centerlines of both holes lie in the same plane.

(*a*) Find the dynamic bearing forces when the cylinder rotates at 1,725 r/min.

(*b*) It is desired to have bearing *a* experience no dynamic force. To accomplish this, a third hole is to be drilled in the cylinder along a circumferential circle 1.6 in from bearing *a*. Find the required diameter of the hole.

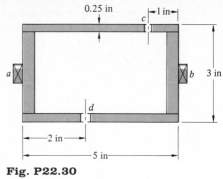

Fig. P22.30

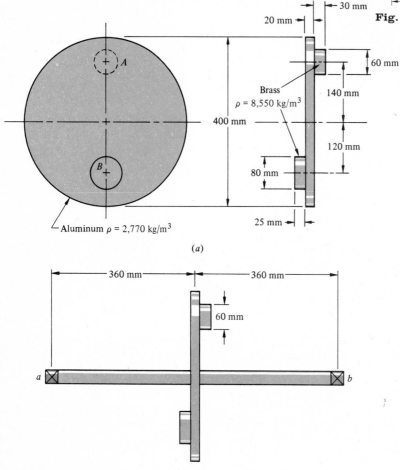

(*a*)

(*b*)

Fig. P22.31

22.31 The disk assembly in Fig. P22.31*a* is mounted on a shaft, as shown in Fig. P22.31*b*.

(*a*) Find the dynamic bearing forces when the unit rotates with a speed of 3,400 r/min.

(*b*) Do the same as in part *a* if, because of a faulty mounting procedure, the center of the disk is displaced 2 mm, along the diameter *AB*, from the bearing centerline.

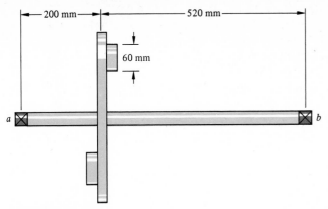

Fig. P22.32

22.32 Do the same as in Prob. 22.31, if the disk assembly is mounted as shown in Fig. P22.32.

22.33 Figure P22.33 shows a cross-sectional view of a cylindrical rotor made of steel, with a specific weight of 489 lb/ft^3. The center-lines of both holes and the center axis of the rotor lie in a common plane. Find the maximum permissible value of the angular velocity, if the dynamic bearing forces must not exceed 6 lb.

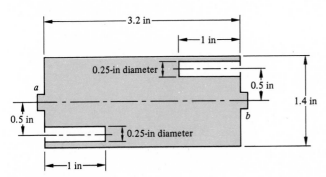

Fig. P22.33

22.34 The rotor in Fig. P22.33 is initially at rest. A couple of magnitude 0.1 in-lb, about the *ab* axis, is applied to the rotor. For what length of time may this couple act on the rotor, if the dynamic bearing forces are not to exceed 6 lb?

22.35 The part shown in Fig. P22.35 is fabricated from steel, with a density of 7,830 kg/m^3. The part is to be chucked in a lathe for a facing operation on the flat face of the element that supports the two cylindrical stubs.

(*a*) Find the dynamic force exerted on the lathe chuck, if the 28-mm diameter is chucked and the part rotates about the x_1 axis at 740 r/min.

(*b*) Do the same as in part *a*, if the 20-mm diameter is chucked and the part rotates about the *x* axis at 740 r/min.

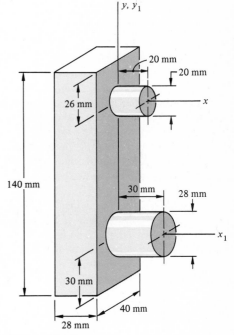

Fig. P22.35

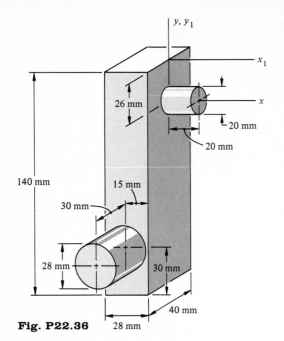

Fig. P22.36

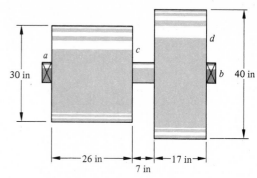

Fig. P22.37

22.36 Do the same as in Prob. 22.35, if the part is modified to the shape shown in Fig. P22.36.

22.37 Figure P22.37 shows a shaft, with two heavy metal rotors, that rotates at 2,200 r/min. During the dynamic balancing of the assembly, correction weights were welded on faces c and d. A steel disk 1 in thick and 1.2 in in diameter was welded to face c, on a mean diameter of 26.4 in. On face d, a steel disk 0.75 in thick and 1 in in diameter, on a mean diameter of 36.8 in, was welded on. Find the values of the dynamic bearing forces that existed before the correction weights were added. The specific weight of steel is 489 lb/ft³, and the mass of the welds may be neglected.

22.38 The four disks in Fig. P22.38 are 200 mm in diameter and 25 mm thick. Disks B and C have 30-mm-diameter holes on a 120-mm-diameter circle. The assembly is to be dynamically balanced by drilling holes, on 110-mm-diameter circles, in disks A and B. Find the required diameters of the holes, and the positions θ_A and θ_D, if all four disks are steel, with $\rho = 7,830$ kg/m³.

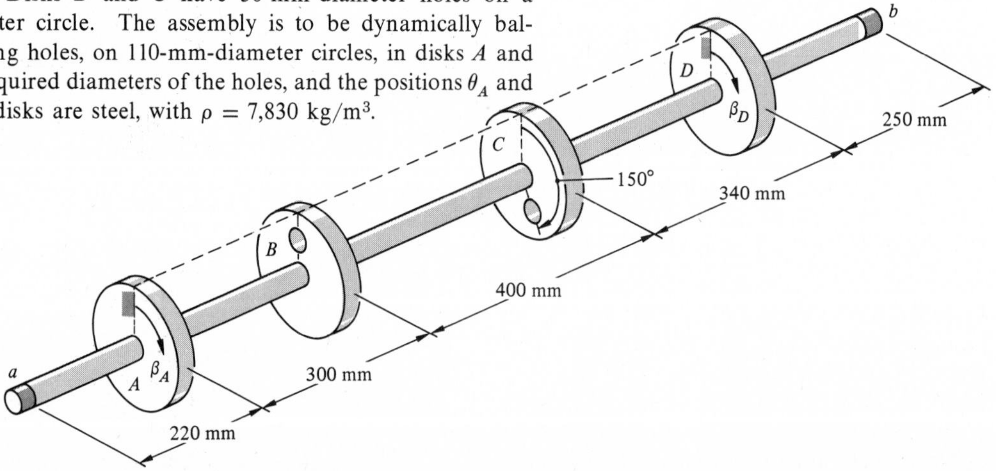

Fig. P22.38

22.39 Do the same as in Prob. 22.38 if disk B is aluminum, with $\rho_B = 2{,}770 \text{ kg/m}^3$, disk C is bronze, with $\rho_C = 8{,}800 \text{ kg/m}^3$, and disks A and D are steel.

22.40 Do the same as in Prob. 22.38 if disk A is aluminum, disk D is bronze, and disks B and C are steel.

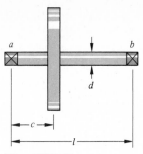

Fig. P22.41

22.41 Figure P22.41 shows a shaft on which is mounted a rotor of mass m. The lateral stiffness of the shaft at the location of the rotor is given by $k = 3EIl/[c^2(l - c)^2]$, where E, the modulus of elasticity, is a property of the shaft material, with the units lb/in^2; and I is the area moment of inertia of the cross section area of the shaft, given by $I = \pi d^4/64$, where d is the diameter of the shaft. For the system in Fig. P22.41, $W = 22 \text{ lb}$, $c = 6 \text{ in}$, $l = 18 \text{ in}$, and $d = 1 \text{ in}$. The shaft is steel, with $E = 30 \times 10^6 \text{ lb/in}^2$.
(a) Find the critical speed of the shaft.
(b) When the unit operates at 3,200 r/min, the lateral deflection of the shaft at the location of the rotor is 0.020 in. Find the eccentricity of the rotor.
(c) Find the lateral deflection of the shaft at the location of the rotor when the unit operates at 5,800 r/min.
(d) Find the dynamic bearing forces corresponding to the speeds in parts b and c.

22.42 Do the same as in parts a, c and d of Prob. 22.41, if the rotor is mounted on a shaft of diameter 1.5 in. Assume the same eccentricity as in Prob. 22.41.

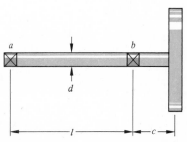

Fig. P22.43

22.43 Figure P22.43 shows a shaft with an overhung rotor. The lateral stiffness of the shaft at the location of the rotor is given by $k = 3EI/[c^2(l + c)]$. In a certain system, $l = 600 \text{ mm}$, $c = 100 \text{ mm}$, $d = 32 \text{ mm}$, $m = 14 \text{ kg}$, $E = 207 \text{ GPa}$, and the eccentricity is 0.4 mm.
(a) Find the critical speed of the shaft.
(b) Find the shaft deflection at the location of the rotor, and the dynamic bearing forces, when the speed of the unit is 2,400 r/min.
(c) Do the same as in part b, if the speed is 3,200 r/min.
(d) Do the same as in part b, if the speed is 5,000 r/min.

22.44 The unit in Prob. 22.43 is to operate at 3,200 r/min.
(a) For what range of values of c will the dynamic shaft deflection at the location of the rotor not exceed 1 mm?
(b) For what range of values of c will the dynamic bearing forces not exceed 50 N?

22.45 A rotor is mounted on a shaft supported by the yoke arrangement shown in Fig. P22.45. The weight of the rotor is 4 lb and the centroidal radius of gyration is 1.25 in. The speed of the rotor is $\omega = 2{,}000$ r/min and the speed of the yoke is $\omega_1 = 100$ r/min. Find the magnitude, direction, and sense of the dynamic forces exerted on the bearings.

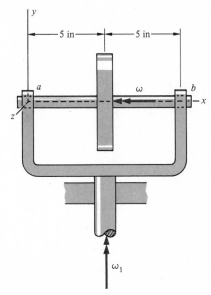

Fig. P22.45

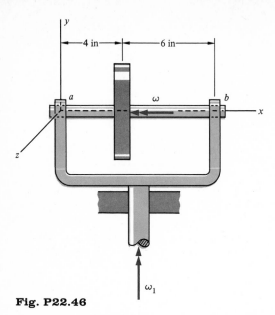

Fig. P22.46

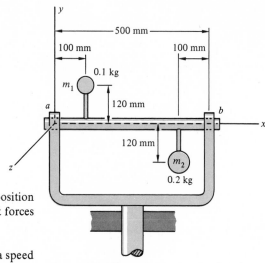

Fig. P22.47

22.46 Do the same as in Prob. 22.45, if the rotor has the position shown in Fig. P22.46. Only bearing *a* in Fig. P22.46 can resist forces in the *x* direction.

22.47 The yoke arrangement in Fig. P22.47 rotates with a speed of 22 rad/s, and the shaft rotates at 100 rad/s. Find the maximum and minimum values of the dynamic forces at bearings *a* and *b*. Only bearing *b* can resist forces in the *x* direction.

22.48 Do the same as in Prob. 22.47, if m_1 becomes detached from the assembly.

22.49 Do the same as in Prob. 22.47, if m_2 becomes detached from the assembly.

22.50 An automobile travels around a horizontal circular track, of diameter 800 ft, at a constant speed of 60 mi/h. The outer diameter of the tires is 30 in. Each wheel-tire assembly weighs 50 lb and has a centroidal radius of gyration of 8 in.
(*a*) Find the gyroscopic moment acting on each wheel.
(*b*) Each front wheel is mounted on two bearings which are 6 in apart. Find the values of the gyroscopic forces which act on these bearings.

23

Mechanical Vibration with One Degree of Freedom

23.1 INTRODUCTION

In this chapter the subject of vibration analysis is introduced. The distinguishing characteristic of this type of dynamic motion is *time periodicity,* or *repetition,* of a pattern of displacement of a mass element. The study of vibration is a broad and encompassing field. An understanding of the nature of vibration phenomena is a necessary prerequisite to the analysis and synthesis of mechanical systems in which periodic motion effects are present.

23.2 NATURAL FREQUENCY OF UNDAMPED FREE VIBRATION

Figure 23.1 shows a mass m which is attached to a helical spring. The mass is assumed to move in rectilinear translation along a vertical axis, and the spring is assumed to exhibit the linear force-deflection relationship shown in Fig. 23.2*a*. The stiffness of the spring is designated k, with the units of force per unit length, and

$$k = \frac{P}{\delta} \qquad (23.1)$$

It may be seen that k is the slope of the load-deflection curve of the spring. It is assumed that there is no dissipation of energy as the mass vibrates. A system which exhibits this characteristic is referred to as an *undamped system.*

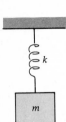

Fig. 23.1

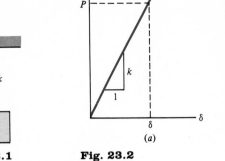

(a)   (b)

Fig. 23.2

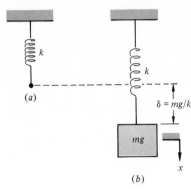

Fig. 23.3

The mass is placed on the spring, as shown in Fig. 23.3. This latter element is allowed to extend through the displacement $\delta = mg/k$, so that the spring force is just equal to the weight force mg of the mass. In this position, Fig. 23.3b, the resultant of all the forces acting on the mass is zero. *The displacement coordinate x of the mass is always measured from this position of equilibrium.*

Only one coordinate, in this case the displacement x, is required to completely define the position of the mass. A system in which the displacement configuration can be completely defined by one coordinate is referred to as a *system with one degree of freedom.* The motion of the mass which occurs when this element is displaced *from its equilibrium position* will now be found.

The mass is imagined to be displaced in the positive coordinate sense, as shown in Fig. 23.4. The static weight of the mass is reacted out by the initial spring force when the mass is in the equilibrium position, and the mass of the spring is neglected. Thus, only the unbalanced spring force $F_s = -kx$ acts on the mass shown in Fig. 23.4. The equation of motion is

Fig. 23.4

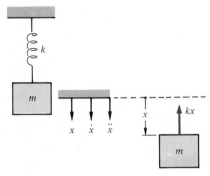

$$F_s = -kx = m\ddot{x} \qquad (23.2)$$

The double-dot notation is used on the acceleration term to emphasize that this quantity is a variable function of time. The minus sign is required in Eq. (23.2) because the spring force acts in a sense which is *opposite* to that of the positive acceleration. Equation (23.2) has two very significant characteristics:

1. The *magnitude* of the resultant force F_s which acts on the mass is *directly proportional to the displacement* of the mass from its equilibrium position.
2. The *sense* of the resultant force which acts on the mass is such as to *oppose* the motion. If x in Eq. (23.2) is positive, the acceleration $\ddot{x}$ is negative and the velocity $\dot{x}$ is decreasing, so that the mass is slowing down as it moves

farther from the equilibrium position. If x is negative, the acceleration is positive. Since the corresponding position of the mass is in the negative x region, the mass slows down as it moves farther from the equilibrium position and speeds up as it moves closer to this position. Thus, the sense of the resultant force always tends to restore the mass to the equilibrium position.

Equation (23.2) may be written in the form

$$m\ddot{x} + kx = 0 \qquad (23.3)$$

This expression is a classical equation of fundamental importance in mathematical physics. It is referred to as a second-order, linear differential equation with constant coefficients. It is of second order because the highest ordered derivative is $\ddot{x}$. It is linear because the coefficients m and k, which are constants in this particular case, are not functions of x or of its derivatives. From the theory of ordinary differential equations, the solution to Eq. (23.3) may be shown to have the form

$$x = A_1 \sin \omega_n t + A_2 \cos \omega_n t \qquad (23.4)$$

where

$$\omega_n = \sqrt{\frac{k}{m}} \qquad (23.5)$$

The time-varying periodic displacement x given by Eq. (23.4) is referred to as the *amplitude of free vibration* of the system consisting of the mass and the spring. A_1 and A_2 are two constants of integration that are to be determined from the initial conditions of the problem. The quantity ω_n has a very special significance, and this term is referred to as the *natural frequency* of the system consisting of the spring and mass. Both the sine and cosine functions are periodic; they repeat themselves each time the argument $\omega_n t$ increases by 2π rad. From Eq. (23.5) it may be seen that ω_n has the basic units of radians per second. In vibration problems, it is usually more convenient to present the results in terms of the number of cycles f_n of vibration per second. The basic frequency unit in USCS and SI units is the hertz, designated Hz, which is a frequency of 1 cycle/s. The relationship between the natural frequency ω_n in terms of radians per second and the natural frequency f_n in terms of cycles per second is given by

$$\frac{\omega_n}{2\pi} = f_n \text{ Hz} \qquad 2\pi f_n = \omega_n \frac{\text{rad}}{\text{s}} \qquad (23.6)$$

The time to complete one cycle of motion is defined to be the *natural period*, with the symbol τ_n. It follows that

$$\tau_n = \frac{1}{f_n} \qquad (23.7)$$

where τ_n is in seconds.

Example 23.1 Figure 23.5 shows a spring mass system.
a Find the natural frequency and natural period of the system.
b Find the percent change in the frequency if the weight of the mass is increased by 25 percent.

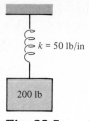

$k = 50$ lb/in

200 lb

Fig. 23.5

Solution
a Using Eq. (23.5), we get

$$\omega_n = \sqrt{\frac{k}{m}} = \sqrt{\frac{50(386)}{200}} = 9.82 \; \frac{\text{rad}}{\text{s}} \qquad f_n = \frac{\omega_n}{2\pi} = \frac{9.82}{2\pi} = 1.56 \text{ Hz}$$

(23.8)

and

$$\tau = \frac{1}{f_n} = \frac{1}{1.56} = 0.641 \text{ s} \qquad (23.9)$$

b When the weight of the mass is increased by 25 percent, to 250 lb,

$$\omega_n = \sqrt{\frac{k}{m}} = \sqrt{\frac{50(386)}{250}} = 8.79 \; \frac{\text{rad}}{\text{s}} \qquad (23.10)$$

The percent decrease in the frequency is then

$$\%D = \frac{8.79 - 9.82}{9.82}(100) = -10.5\% \qquad (23.11)$$

The mass in Fig. 23.4 is assumed to be set into motion by displacing it by the amount x_0 from the initial position and releasing it with zero initial velocity. The mathematical statements of these initial conditions are

$$t = 0 \qquad x = x_0 = \text{const.} \qquad \dot{x} = 0 \qquad (23.12)$$

The velocity of the mass is the first time derivative of Eq. (23.4), given by

$$\dot{x} = A_1\omega_n \cos \omega_n t - A_2\omega_n \sin \omega_n t \qquad (23.13)$$

Using the conditions $t = 0$ and $\dot{x} = 0$ in Eq. (23.13), we have

$$0 = A_1\omega_n \qquad A_1 = 0 \qquad (23.14)$$

This result is used in Eq. (23.4), together with the initial condition $t = 0$, $x = x_0$, to obtain

$$A_2 = x_0 \qquad (23.15)$$

The formal statement of the motion is then

$$x = x_0 \cos \omega_n t \qquad (23.16)$$

Equation (23.16) describes the *free vibrational motion* of the mass with the *natural frequency* ω_n. This motion is also referred to as *simple harmonic motion,* because of the pure sinusoidal variation of the displacement with respect to time. It may be seen from this equation that the maximum amplitude of the motion is the same as the initial displacement of the system.

If Eq. (23.16) is differentiated twice with respect to time, then the velocity and acceleration are

$$\dot{x} = -x_0\omega_n \sin \omega_n t \qquad \ddot{x} = -x_0\omega_n^2 \cos \omega_n t \qquad (23.17)$$

The variations of the displacement, velocity, and acceleration, for one cycle of motion, are shown in Fig. 23.6, together with the positions of the mass at the quarter points of the cycle.

It may be seen that the extreme values of velocity occur when the mass passes through the equilibrium position. The extreme values of acceleration occur when the deflection of the spring is maximum, at which time the velocity is zero. These effects characterize the *free vibration of a system with one degree of freedom*.

When the system vibrates, a time-varying force is transmitted

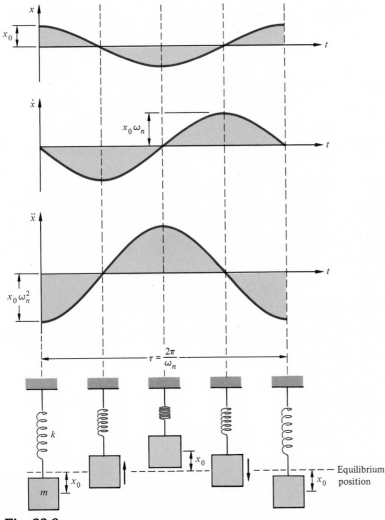

Fig. 23.6

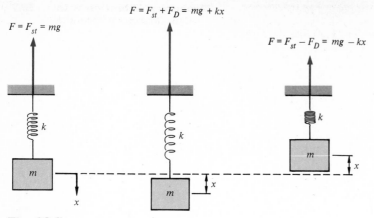

Fig. 23.7

through the spring to the foundation. When the mass is in the *equilibrium position*, the static weight force F_{st}, given by

$$F_{st} = mg \qquad (23.18)$$

is transmitted to the foundation. During vibration, an additional *dynamic force* F_D is transmitted through the spring. The magnitude of this dynamic force is given by

$$F_D = kx \qquad (23.19)$$

where x, the amplitude of free vibration, is given by an equation of the form of Eq. (23.4). The total force F transmitted through the spring to the foundation is then

$$F = F_{st} + F_D = mg + kx \qquad (23.20)$$

The above effect is shown in Fig. 23.7. The *maximum value* of the total force transmitted to the foundation is

$$F_m = mg + kx_m \qquad (23.21)$$

where x_m is the maximum value of the displacement of the mass during the free vibration.

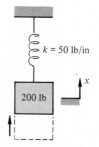

Fig. 23.8

Example 23.2 The spring mass system of Example 23.1 is shown in Fig. 23.8. At $t = 0$, the mass is impacted by a second mass, shown as the dashed outline in the figure. The effect of this is to give the mass on the spring an initial velocity. The initial conditions for this problem are

$$t = 0 \qquad x = 0 \qquad \dot{x} = \dot{x}_0 = \text{const.} \qquad (23.22)$$

  a Find the equation of free vibrational motion of the system.
  b If $\dot{x}_0 = 30$ in/s, find the maximum value of the amplitude of free vibration and the maximum value of the acceleration of the mass.
  c Find the maximum value of the force exerted by the vibrating mass on the supporting foundation.

Solution

a The general solution for free vibration, Eq. (23.4), has the form

$$x = A_1 \sin \omega_n t + A_2 \cos \omega_n t \qquad (23.23)$$

Using the conditions $t = 0$ and $x = 0$

$$0 = A_2 \qquad (23.24)$$

The velocity of the mass is given by Eq. (23.13) as

$$\dot{x} = A_1 \omega_n \cos \omega_n t - A_2 \omega_n \sin \omega_n t \qquad (23.25)$$

Using $t = 0$, $\dot{x} = \dot{x}_0$, in Eq. (23.25) results in

$$\dot{x}_0 = A_1 \omega_n \qquad A_1 = \frac{\dot{x}_0}{\omega_n} \qquad (23.26)$$

The motion of free vibration is then

$$x = \frac{\dot{x}_0}{\omega_n} \sin \omega_n t \qquad (23.27)$$

b The natural frequency of the system, from Eq. (23.8), is 9.82 rad/s. Using Eq. (23.27), the maximum value of the displacement of the mass is

$$x_m = \frac{\dot{x}_0}{\omega_n} = \frac{30}{9.82} = 3.05 \text{ in} \qquad (23.28)$$

The acceleration is the second time derivative of Eq. (23.27), with the form

$$\ddot{x} = -\dot{x}_0 \omega_n \sin \omega_n t \qquad (23.29)$$

The magnitude of the maximum acceleration is

$$\ddot{x}_m = \dot{x}_0 \omega_n = 30(9.82) = 295 \text{ in/s}^2 \qquad (23.30)$$

c The maximum value of the dynamic force F_D exerted on the foundation by the spring is

$$F_{D,m} = k x_m = 50(3.05) = 153 \text{ lb} \qquad (23.31)$$

The maximum value of the total force transmitted to the foundation, from Eq. (23.21), is

$$F_m = mg + k x_m = 200 + 153 = 353 \text{ lb} \qquad (23.32)$$

From Eq. (23.5), the frequency of motion, or natural frequency, has the form

$$\omega_n = \sqrt{\frac{k}{m}} \qquad (23.33)$$

In a given problem, k and m are known quantities. Thus, the resulting natural frequency ω_n of the system *has a fixed value which is independent of the initial displacement or velocity of the mass*. A vibrational system which exhibits this characteristic is referred to as a *linear system*. The spring constant k is a measure of the *stiffness* of the system, while the magnitude of m

is a measure of the *mass*, or inertia, of the system. Thus, as a general conclusion, increasing the stiffness (or decreasing the mass) of a vibrating system has the effect of *increasing* the natural frequency. Since the mass is usually a fixed quantity in a given problem, it is generally the stiffness of the system which is adjusted if the natural frequency does not have a desired value. It may also be observed from Eq. (23.33) that the natural frequency of the system is defined by the *ratio* of k and m. Thus, changing both terms by a common factor has no effect on the natural frequency.

The differential equation of free vibration of a spring mass system with one degree of freedom has the form, given by Eq. (23.3), of

$$m\ddot{x} + kx = 0 \qquad (23.34)$$

and the natural frequency is expressed by

$$\omega_n = \sqrt{\frac{k}{m}} \qquad (23.35)$$

If the equation of motion of any system with one degree of freedom is of the form

$$a\ddot{\xi} + b\xi = 0 \qquad (23.36)$$

where ξ is the displacement coordinate, $\ddot{\xi}$ is the acceleration, and a and b are known constants, then the natural frequency may be found by inspection. Comparison of Eq. (23.36) with Eq. (23.34) reveals that both equations have identical mathematical forms, and thus

$$\omega_n = \sqrt{\frac{b}{a}} \qquad (23.37)$$

The above technique of solution will be used in several of the following examples.

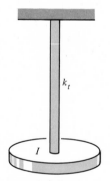

Fig. 23.9

Example 23.3   Figure 23.9 shows a device which is referred to as a torsional pendulum. A disk with mass moment of inertia I about its center axis is mounted on a shaft which has a torsional stiffness k_t, expressed in the units of moment divided by angular deflection.

a Find the natural frequency of the system in terms of k_t and I.

b Find the numerical value of the natural frequency. The steel disk is 50 mm thick, with a diameter of 300 mm, and $k_t = 4{,}600$ N·m/rad. The density of steel is 7,830 kg/m³.

Solution

a The single displacement coordinate is chosen to be θ, the rotation of the disk in its own plane. The disk is displaced in the positive coordinate sense, and the restoring moment which acts on the disk is shown in Fig. 23.10.

The equation of motion is

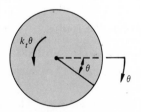

Fig. 23.10

$$-k_t\theta = I\ddot{\theta} \qquad I\ddot{\theta} + k_t\theta = 0 \qquad (23.38)$$

Eq. (23.38) has the form of Eq. (23.36), and thus

$$\omega_n = \sqrt{\frac{k_t}{I}} \qquad (23.39)$$

b The mass of the disk is

$$m = \frac{\pi(300)^2}{4}(50) \text{ mm}^3(7{,}830 \text{ kg/m}^3)\left(\frac{1 \text{ m}}{1{,}000 \text{ mm}}\right)^3 = 27.7 \text{ kg} \qquad (23.40)$$

The mass moment of inertia is

$$I = \frac{1}{8}md^2 = \frac{1}{8}(27.7)\left(\frac{300}{1{,}000}\right)^2 = 0.312 \text{ kg·m}^2 \qquad (23.41)$$

The natural frequency is then

$$\omega_n = \sqrt{\frac{k_t}{I}} = \sqrt{\frac{4{,}600}{0.312}} = 121 \frac{\text{rad}}{\text{s}} = 19.3 \text{ Hz} \qquad (23.42)$$

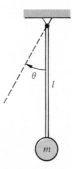

Fig. 23.11

23.3 NATURAL FREQUENCY OF UNDAMPED FREE VIBRATION OF A ROTATIONAL SYSTEM WITH SMALL ANGULAR DISPLACEMENTS

Figure 23.11 shows a device which is referred to as a simple pendulum. The mass of the rigid rod is neglected, and the mass of the pendulum bob is assumed to be a point mass which is constrained to move only in the plane of the figure. Angle θ is chosen to be the single coordinate which is required to fully define the position of the pendulum.

The rod is displaced in the positive coordinate sense, as shown in Fig. 23.12. Newton's second law for rotational motion about the hinge pin has the form

$$-mg(l\sin\theta) = I\ddot{\theta} \qquad I = ml^2 \qquad (23.43)$$

$$l\ddot{\theta} + g\sin\theta = 0 \qquad (23.44)$$

Equation (23.44) is *not* in the standard form of Eq. (23.36) because of the presence of the function $\sin\theta$. If, however, it is assumed that the angular displacement of the rod is limited to small values, then

$$\sin\theta \approx \theta \qquad (23.45)$$

and Eq. (23.44) has the form

$$l\ddot{\theta} + g\theta = 0 \qquad (23.46)$$

Now Eq. (23.46) is now in the standard form, and

$$\omega_n = \sqrt{\frac{g}{l}} \qquad (23.47)$$

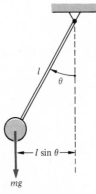

Fig. 23.12

TABLE 23.1					
$\theta,°$	$\sin \theta$	θ, rad	$\theta,°$	$\sin \theta$	θ, rad
2	0.03490	0.03491	10	0.1736	0.1745
4	0.06976	0.06981	12	0.2079	0.2094
6	0.1045	0.1047	14	0.2419	0.2443
8	0.1392	0.1396	16	0.2756	0.2793

It may be seen that the frequency of a simple pendulum *is independent of the mass* and is a function of only the pendulum length. A major use of the simple pendulum is to regulate time in mechanical clocks.

The small-angle approximation used above is not as restrictive as it might appear at first. Table 23.1 shows a comparison of θ and $\sin \theta$ for angles up to 16°. For $\theta = 16°$, the percent difference between θ and $\sin \theta$ is only 1.3 percent. It should also be noted that a value of $\theta = 16°$ corresponds to a total range of angular motion of 32°.

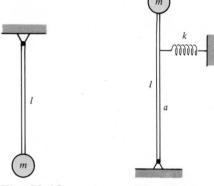

Fig. 23.13   Fig. 23.14

Example 23.4 Find the required length of the pendulum rod in Fig. 23.13, in meters, if the natural period is to be 1 s.

Solution Using Eq. (23.7), we have

$$T_n = \frac{1}{f_n} = \frac{2\pi}{\omega_n} = 1 \text{ s} \qquad \omega_n = 2\pi = \sqrt{\frac{g}{l}} \qquad (23.48)$$

$$(2\pi)^2 = \frac{g}{l} \qquad l = \frac{g}{4\pi^2} = \frac{9.81}{4\pi^2} = 0.248 \text{ m} \qquad (23.49)$$

Example 23.5 Figure 23.14 shows an inverted simple pendulum.

a Find the general expression for the natural frequency if small angular deflection is assumed.

b What relationship must exist among the four parameters m, k, l, and a if simple harmonic motion of the pendulum is to occur?

c Discuss the motion if $mg = 6$ lb, $l = 36$ in, $a = 18$ in, and $k = 0.5$ lb/in.

Solution

a The rod is displaced in the positive coordinate sense, as shown in Fig. 23.15. The equation of motion, for the small-angle approximation, is

$$mg(l\theta) - (ka\theta)a = ml^2\ddot{\theta} \qquad (23.50)$$

$$ml^2\ddot{\theta} + (ka^2 - mgl)\theta = 0 \qquad (23.51)$$

This equation is in the form of Eq. (23.36), and thus

$$\omega_n = \sqrt{\frac{ka^2 - mgl}{ml^2}} \qquad (23.52)$$

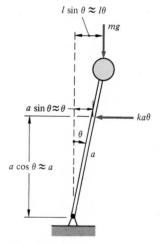

Fig. 23.15

b For Eq. (23.52) to have a real solution, the quantity inside the radical must be positive. Thus, a necessary condition for ω_n to exist is that

$$ka^2 > mgl \qquad (23.53)$$

If the above inequality is not satisfied, the pendulum, when displaced from the equilibrium position, will continue to move clockwise and will not return to the equilibrium position.

c Using the given numerical values, the inequality appears as

$$0.5(18)^2 \overset{?}{>} 6(36) \qquad 162 \not> 216 \qquad (23.54)$$

This result indicates that vibrational motion of the system will *not* occur.

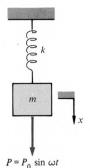

$P = P_0 \sin \omega t$
Fig. 23.16

23.4 UNDAMPED FORCED VIBRATION

The mass in the system with one degree of freedom shown in Fig. 23.16 is acted on by a time-varying force $P_0 \sin \omega t$. P_0 is the *constant* value of the peak magnitude of this driving force, and ω is the frequency of the force. The mass is imagined to be displaced in the positive coordinate sense, and the free-body diagram of this element is shown in Fig. 23.17. The equation of motion of the mass is

$$P_0 \sin \omega t - kx = m\ddot{x} \qquad (23.55)$$

$$m\ddot{x} + kx = P_0 \sin \omega t \qquad (23.56)$$

From the theory of differential equations it can be shown that the complete solution to Eq. (23.56) is

$$x = x_c + x_p \qquad (23.57)$$

where x_c satisfies the equation

$$m\ddot{x}_c + kx_c = 0 \qquad (23.58)$$

and x_p satisfies the equation

$$m\ddot{x}_p + kx_p = P_0 \sin \omega t \qquad (23.59)$$

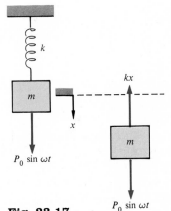

Fig. 23.17

The solution to Eq. (23.58) is given by Eq. (23.4) as

$$x_c = A_1 \sin \omega_n t + A_2 \cos \omega_n t \qquad (23.60)$$

The right side of Eq. (23.59) contains the function $\sin \omega t$. The theory of differential equations dictates that an assumed form of solution for x_p must contain this function and all its possible derivatives. Thus, x_p is chosen in the form

$$x_p = A \sin \omega t + B \cos \omega t \qquad (23.61)$$

This equation is substituted into Eq. (23.59), and the terms A and B are found† to be

---

†The verification of these results is required in Prob. 23.26.

$$A = \frac{P_0}{k - m\omega^2} = \frac{P_0/k}{1 - (\omega/\omega_n)^2} \qquad B = 0 \qquad (23.62)$$

The complete solution for the motion of a mass with one degree of freedom which is acted on by the force $P_0 \sin \omega t$ is

$$x = \underbrace{A_1 \sin \omega_n t + A_2 \cos \omega_n t}_{\text{Transient solution}} + \underbrace{\frac{P_0/k}{1 - (\omega/\omega_n)^2} \sin \omega t}_{\text{steady-state solution}} \qquad (23.63)$$

The first two terms in Eq. (23.63) contain the two constants of integration A_1 and A_2. These two values are found from the initial conditions of the problem at $t = 0$. This part of the solution is referred to as the *transient* motion, and this motion eventually dies out. The last term in Eq. (23.63) is referred to as *steady-state* motion. It may be seen that this function is fully defined and that it is *not* a function of the manner in which the system was set into motion. It may be seen that the steady-state solution has the same functional time variation, given by $\sin \omega t$, as the exciting force $P_0 \sin \omega t$. The maximum value of the amplitude of the steady-state motion is designated x_m, with the form

$$x_m = \frac{P_0/k}{1 - (\omega/\omega_n)^2} \qquad (23.64)$$

The remainder of this section will be devoted to a study of Eq. (23.64).

For a prescribed value of the driving frequency ω, the amplitude x_m has a constant value. If, however, ω is allowed to take on different values, then this amplitude of forced vibration may be viewed as a function of frequency. The quantity ω/ω_n is the ratio of the driving frequency to the natural frequency, and this term is designated the *frequency ratio*. The variation of the maximum steady-state amplitude with frequency ratio, given by Eq. (23.64), is shown in Fig. 23.18. It may be seen that, for excitation frequencies which are near the natural frequency, $\omega/\omega_n \to 1$ and $x_m \to \pm\infty$. The condition $\omega/\omega_n = 1$ is defined to be *resonance*.

For very low values of driving frequency, $\omega/\omega_n \approx 0$ and $x_m \approx P_0/k$, which is the displacement that would be obtained if the force P_0 were applied quasi-statically to the mass. At large values of excitation frequencies, $\omega/\omega_n \to \infty$ and $x_m \to 0$. For this limiting condition, *the mass tends to remain motionless in space*.

One final observation may be made about the forced motion of the undamped system with one degree of freedom. The driving force is of the form

$$P = P_0 \sin \omega t \qquad (23.65)$$

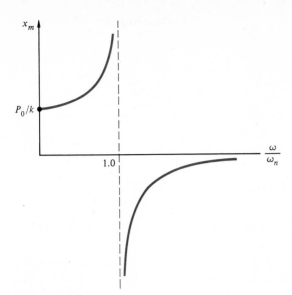

Fig. 23.18

while the resulting steady-state displacement has the form

$$x = x_m \sin \omega t \qquad x_m = \frac{P_0/k}{1 - (\omega/\omega_n)^2} \qquad (23.66)$$

If P and x have the same sign, then the motion is described as being *in phase* with the applied force, since both quantities reach their *positive maximum values* at the same time. If P and x have opposite signs, then the motion is *out of phase* with the applied force. It may be observed from Eq. (23.64) that x_m will be positive or negative depending on whether the frequency ratio ω/ω_n is less than, or greater than, 1. If $\omega/\omega_n < 1$, the system operates *below* resonance and the displacement of the mass is *in phase* with the driving force. If $\omega/\omega_n > 1$, the system operates above resonance and the displacement of the mass is *out of phase* with the applied force.

23.5 NATURAL FREQUENCY OF FREE VIBRATION WITH VISCOUS DAMPING

The solution for the undamped free vibration of the spring mass system with one degree of freedom shown in Fig. 23.19 was found in Eq. (23.4) to have the form

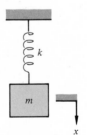

Fig. 23.19

$$x = A_1 \sin \omega_n t + A_2 \cos \omega_n t \qquad (23.67)$$

The terms A_1 and A_2 are constants which are determined from the initial conditions of displacement, or velocity, that set the mass into motion. Physical observations indicate that the motion of the mass will eventually die out and that this element will come to rest, at some time after the onset of motion. It may be seen from Eq. (23.67), however, that there is no range of values of time t for which the displacement x remains identically zero. Therefore the solution given by Eq. (23.67) must be viewed as an approximation to the actual motion. In order to improve the accuracy of the model, the concept of *damping* will now be introduced.

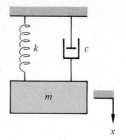

Figure 23.20 shows the original spring mass system, with the addition of an element which is referred to as a *viscous damper*, or *dashpot*. *The sole function of a viscous damper is to dissipate energy.* The force F_d exerted by the viscous damper on the mass is assumed to have the form

Fig. 23.20

$$F_d = -c\dot{x} \qquad (23.68)$$

where c is the *damping constant* and $\dot{x}$ is the velocity of the mass. The force F_d is considered to be positive if it acts in the positive x coordinate sense. The damper force given above *always acts in a sense which opposes the velocity of the mass.* Units of the damping constant are force-divided by velocity. Further discussion of viscous damping is found in Chap. 24.

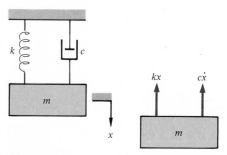

The block is assumed to be displaced from its equilibrium position, in the positive coordinate sense, as shown in Fig. 23.21. The symbolic damper force $c\dot{x}$ is drawn on the free-body diagram in a sense which opposes motion. If the mass moves downward, $\dot{x}$ is positive and the force $c\dot{x}$ acts upward. If the block moves upward, the term $\dot{x}$ is negative and the force $c\dot{x}$ acts downward. It may be seen that the mathematical form given in Eq. (23.68) for the damping force *automatically adjusts the sense of this force.* This is the principal reason for the assumption of a viscous damping force in vibration problems.

Fig. 23.21

The equation of motion has the form

$$-kx - c\dot{x} = m\ddot{x} \qquad m\ddot{x} + c\dot{x} + kx = 0 \qquad (23.69)$$

Equation (23.69) is a linear, second-order differential equation with constant coefficients.

With the substitutions

$$c_c = 2\sqrt{km} = 2m\omega_n \qquad \omega_n = \sqrt{\frac{k}{m}} \qquad (23.70)$$

$$\zeta = \frac{c}{c_c} = \frac{c}{2\sqrt{km}} = \frac{c}{2m\omega_n} \qquad (23.71)$$

and, if $0 \le \zeta < 1$, the solution to Eq. (23.69) can be shown to have the form

$$x = e^{-\zeta\omega_n t}(A_1 \sin \sqrt{1 - \zeta^2}\omega_n t + A_2 \cos \sqrt{1 - \zeta^2}\omega_n t) \qquad (23.72)$$

Equation (23.72) represents periodic motion with amplitude

which *decreases* with increasing time. The quantity ζ is the *damping ratio,* and the term c_c is referred to as the *critical damping constant.* If $\zeta = 1$, then $c = c_c$ and this is a limiting maximum condition of damping at which the motion just ceases to be periodic. If $\zeta > 1$, the mass will return to the equilibrium position after an initial displacement, but the motion will not be periodic.

It may be seen from Eq. (23.72) that the *damped natural frequency* ω_{nd} has the form

$$\omega_{nd} = \sqrt{1 - \zeta^2}\,\omega_n \tag{23.73}$$

It follows from Eq. (23.73) that

$$\omega_{nd} < \omega_n \tag{23.74}$$

For small values of ζ, which characterize most problems in engineering vibrations, the approximation is usually made that

$$\omega_{nd} \approx \omega_n \tag{23.75}$$

The velocity of the mass, from Eq. (23.72) and by using the product rule of differentiation

$$\frac{d}{dt}(uv) = u\frac{dv}{dt} + v\frac{du}{dt} \tag{23.76}$$

may be shown† to be

$$\dot{x} = e^{-\zeta\omega_n t}[(A_1\sqrt{1-\zeta^2} - A_2\zeta)\omega_n \cos\sqrt{1-\zeta^2}\omega_n t$$
$$-(A_2\sqrt{1-\zeta^2} + A_1\zeta)\omega_n \sin\sqrt{1-\zeta^2}\omega_n t] \tag{23.77}$$

Example 23.6 Find the error introduced by the assumption that the damped and undamped natural frequencies are equal, for $\zeta = 0.1$, 0.25, and 0.5.

Solution The frequencies are related by

$$\omega_{nd} = \sqrt{1 - \zeta^2}\,\omega_n \tag{23.78}$$

The percent difference between the frequencies may be written as

$$\%D = \frac{\omega_n - \omega_{nd}}{\omega_n}(100) = \frac{\omega_n - \sqrt{1-\zeta^2}\omega_n}{\omega_n}(100) \tag{23.79}$$

$$\%D = (1 - \sqrt{1-\zeta^2})(100) \tag{23.80}$$

For the values of this example

$$\zeta = 0.1 \quad \%D = (1 - \sqrt{1-0.1^2})(100) = 0.5\% \tag{23.81}$$

$$\zeta = 0.25 \quad \%D = (1 - \sqrt{1-0.25^2})(100) = 3.2\% \tag{23.82}$$

$$\zeta = 0.50 \quad \%D = (1 - \sqrt{1-0.5^2})(100) = 13.4\% \tag{23.83}$$

---

†The verification of this result is required in Prob. 23.45.

Example 23.7 The spring mass system shown in Fig. 23.21 is set into motion with the initial conditions

$$t = 0 \qquad x = x_0 = \text{const.} \qquad \dot{x} = 0 \qquad (23.84)$$

a Find the general form for the motion of free vibration.
b If $m = 90$ kg, $k = 8,750$ N/m, $\zeta = 0.1$, and $x_0 = 40$ mm, find the displacement at the end of one, two, and three cycles.

Solution

a Using Eqs. (23.72) and (23.77), together with Eq. (23.84), we get

$$x_0 = e^0(A_2) \qquad A_2 = x_0 \qquad (23.85)$$

$$0 = e^0(A_1 \sqrt{1 - \zeta^2} - A_2\zeta)\omega_n \qquad (23.86)$$

$$A_1 = \frac{A_2\zeta}{\sqrt{1 - \zeta^2}} = \frac{x_0\zeta}{\sqrt{1 - \zeta^2}} \qquad (23.87)$$

The general solution for the displacement has the form

$$x = x_0 e^{-\zeta\omega_n t}\left(\frac{\zeta}{\sqrt{1 - \zeta^2}} \sin \sqrt{1 - \zeta^2}\omega_n t + \cos \sqrt{1 - \zeta^2}\omega_n t\right)$$

$$(23.88)$$

Equation (23.88) represents a periodic motion with decreasing amplitude, as shown in Fig. 23.22.
b For the given numerical values,

$$\omega_n = \sqrt{\frac{8,750}{90}} = 9.86 \frac{\text{rad}}{\text{s}} = 1.57 \text{ Hz} \qquad (23.89)$$

$$\omega_{nd} = \sqrt{1 - \zeta^2}\omega_n = \sqrt{1 - 0.1^2}(9.86) = 9.81 \frac{\text{rad}}{\text{s}} = 1.56 \text{ Hz}$$

$$(23.90)$$

$$\tau_{nd} = \frac{1}{1.56} = 0.641 \text{ s} \qquad (23.91)$$

The sine and cosine functions in Eq. (23.88) repeat themselves at the end of each cycle. Thus, at the end of one cycle, $t = \tau_{nd}$ and

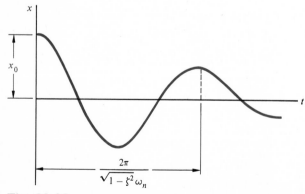

Fig. 23.22

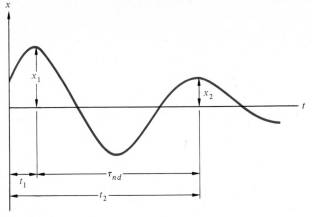

Fig. 23.23

$$x = x_0 e^{-\zeta \omega_n \tau_{nd}}(1 + 0) \qquad (23.92)$$

$$= 40(e^{-0.1(9.86)(0.641)}) = 21.3 \text{ mm} \qquad (23.93)$$

At the end of two cycles, $t = 2\tau_{nd}$ and

$$x = 40(e^{-0.1(9.86)[2(0.641)]}) = 11.3 \text{ mm} \qquad (23.94)$$

At the end of three cycles,

$$x = 40(e^{-0.1(9.86)[3(0.641)]}) = 6.01 \text{ mm} \qquad (23.95)$$

It may be observed that at the end of three cycles the amplitude of motion is reduced to $6.01/40 = 15$ percent of its initial value.

23.6 THE LOGARITHMIC DECREMENT

The *log decrement* δ is defined to be the natural logarithm of the ratio of two successive peak amplitudes of free vibration. Figure 23.23 shows the two amplitudes. The function in parentheses in Eq. (23.72) has the same value each time the argument of the sine and cosine function is increased by 2π. By using this equation, δ may be written as

$$\delta = \ln \frac{x_1}{x_2} = \ln \frac{e^{-\zeta \omega_n t_1}}{e^{-\zeta \omega_n (t_1 + \tau_{nd})}} = \ln e^{\zeta \omega_n \tau_{nd}} = \zeta \omega_n \tau_{nd}$$

$$(23.96)$$

The natural period of the damped free vibration is

$$\tau_{nd} = \frac{2\pi}{\sqrt{1 - \zeta^2}\omega_n} \qquad (23.97)$$

and thus

$$\delta = \frac{2\pi\zeta}{\sqrt{1 - \zeta^2}} \qquad (23.98)$$

δ is a quantity which may be determined experimentally and used in Eq. (23.98) to find the actual value of the damping ratio ζ.

Example 23.8 Use Eq. (23.98) to find the displacement at the end of the first cycle of motion in Example 23.7.

Solution The log decrement is

$$\delta = \frac{2\pi(0.1)}{\sqrt{1 - 0.1^2}} = 0.631 = \ln \frac{x_1}{x_2} \qquad (23.99)$$

The displacement x_1 is taken to be the initial displacement $x_0 = 40$ mm. Displacement x_2 at the end of one cycle is then found from

$$0.631 = \ln \frac{40}{x_2} \qquad e^{0.631} = \frac{40}{x_2} \qquad x_2 = 21.3 \text{ mm} \qquad (23.100)$$

The value confirms the value found in Eq. (23.93).

Example 23.9 Find the value of the displacement of the mass in Example 23.7 at the end of eight cycles of motion.

Solution If the displacement at $t = 0$ is taken as x_1, then the displacement at the end of eight cycles is x_9. The ratio of these two displacements may be written as

$$\frac{x_1}{x_9} = \frac{x_1}{x_2} \cdot \frac{x_2}{x_3} \cdot \frac{x_3}{x_4} \cdots \frac{x_8}{x_9} \qquad (23.101)$$

Eight equal factors

Each of the eight equal factors on the right side of Eq. (23.101) is the ratio of two successive amplitudes, and each of these ratios must satisfy equations of the form

$$\delta = \ln \frac{x_1}{x_2} \qquad \frac{x_1}{x_2} = e^\delta \qquad (23.102)$$

Equation (23.101) now appears as

$$\frac{x_1}{x_9} = (e^\delta)^8 = e^{8\delta} = e^{8(0.631)} = 156 = \frac{40}{x_9} \qquad x_9 = 0.26 \text{ mm}$$

$$(23.103)$$

23.7 FORCED VIBRATION WITH VISCOUS DAMPING

The spring mass system with a viscous damper is now acted on by a sinusoidally varying force $P_0 \sin \omega t$, as shown in Fig. 23.24a. The block is imagined to be displaced in the positive coordinate sense, as shown in Fig. 23.24b, and the equation of motion is

$$P_0 \sin \omega t - kx - c\dot{x} = m\ddot{x} \qquad (23.104)$$

$$m\ddot{x} + c\dot{x} + kx = P_0 \sin \omega t \qquad (23.105)$$

Equation (23.105) is a linear, second-order differential equation

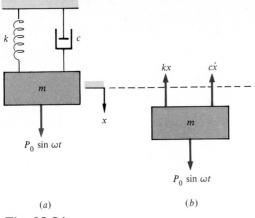

(a)

Fig. 23.24

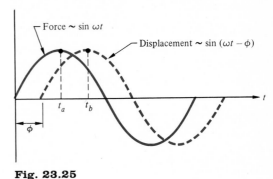

(b)

Fig. 23.25

with constant coefficients. The complete solution to this equation has the form

$$x = x_c + x_p \qquad (23.106)$$

The transient part of the solution is x_c, given by Eq. (23.72). The steady-state part is assumed to have the form

$$x_p = x_m \sin(\omega t - \phi) \qquad (23.107)$$

where x_m, the maximum steady-state displacement, and the angle ϕ are constants to be determined. It may be seen from Eq. (23.107) that the frequency of the motion is ω, the same frequency as the driving force. From the structure of Eq. (23.107) it may be concluded that ϕ is *a phase angle by which the displacement x_p lags the applied force $P_0 \sin \omega t$ in time.* This effect is shown graphically in Fig. 23.25. The *maximum value of displacement* occurs at the time t_b, which is later than the time t_a of the *maximum value of the driving force.*

The remainder of this section considers the *steady-state* motion of the mass. If Eq. (23.107) is substituted into Eq. (23.105), it can be shown† that

$$x_m = \frac{P_0}{\sqrt{(k - m\omega^2)^2 + (c\omega)^2}} \qquad \phi = \tan^{-1}\frac{c\omega}{k - m\omega^2}$$
$$(23.108)$$

The *static deflection* x_{st} is defined to be the displacement which the mass would experience if a constant force P_0 were applied to it, or

$$x_{st} = \frac{P_0}{k} \qquad (23.109)$$

†The verification of this result is required in Prob. 23.46.

A dimensionless ratio is now formed, by using Eqs. (23.108) and (23.109), with the result

$$\frac{x_m}{x_{st}} = \frac{1}{\sqrt{[1 - (\omega/\omega_n)^2]^2 + [2\zeta(\omega/\omega_n)]^2}} \qquad (23.110)$$

Equation (23.110) may be thought of as a "dynamic magnification factor" by which the static deflection of the spring is increased because of the vibrational motion. It may be seen that this equation is a function of only the frequency ratio ω/ω_n and the damping ratio ζ. The phase angle ϕ in Eq. (23.108) may be written in the nondimensional form

$$\phi = \tan^{-1} \frac{2\zeta(\omega/\omega_n)}{1 - (\omega/\omega_n)^2} \qquad (23.111)$$

The variation of the magnitude of x_m/x_{st} and ϕ with the frequency ratio, for several values of ζ, is shown in Fig. 23.26.

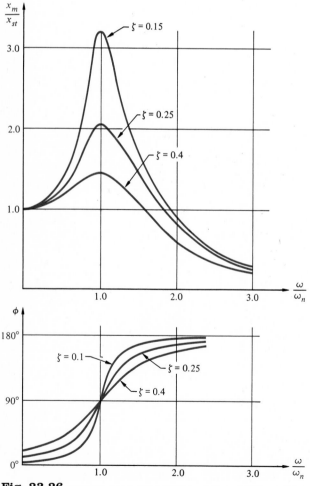

Fig. 23.26

It may be seen that the amplitude in the neighborhood of the resonant frequency $\omega/\omega_n = 1$ is very sensitive to the amount of damping in the system. Also, the phase angle continually increases as the frequency ratio increases and reaches a limiting value of $180°$ as $\omega/\omega_n \to \infty$.

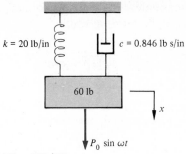

Fig. 23.27

Example 23.10 The spring-mass-damper system shown in Fig. 23.27 is acted on by a force $P_0 \sin \omega t$. The peak magnitude P_0 of the driving force is 40 lb. The driving frequency has low and high values of 1.40 and 4.50 Hz, respectively.

a Find the values of the maximum dynamic deflections x_m of the mass for the low- and high-frequency operations.

b If the damper is assumed to be accidentally disconnected from the mass, find the percent increase in the dynamic displacements for low- and high-frequency operations.

Solutions

a The undamped natural frequency is

$$\omega_n = \sqrt{\frac{k}{m}} = \sqrt{\frac{20(386)}{60}} = 11.3 \ \frac{\text{rad}}{\text{s}} = 1.80 \ \text{Hz} \quad (23.112)$$

and the critical damping coefficient is

$$c_c = 2m\omega_n = 2\left(\frac{60}{386}\right)(11.3) = 3.51 \ \frac{\text{lb·s}}{\text{in}}$$
$$(23.113)$$

The damping ratio is

$$\zeta = \frac{c}{c_c} = \frac{0.846}{3.51} = 0.241 \quad (23.114)$$

The displacement magnification ratio, for the low-frequency ratio of $\omega/\omega_n = 1.40/1.80 = 0.778$, is

$$\frac{x_m}{x_{st}} = \frac{x_m}{P_0/k} = \frac{1}{\sqrt{[1 - (\omega/\omega_n)^2]^2 + [2\zeta(\omega/\omega_n)]^2}} \quad (23.115)$$

$$\frac{x_m}{40/20} = \frac{1}{\sqrt{(1 - 0.778^2)^2 + [2(0.241)0.778]^2}} \quad (23.116)$$

$$x_m = 3.67 \ \text{in} \quad \text{low frequency} \quad (23.117)$$

At the high-frequency ratio of $\omega/\omega_n = 4.50/1.80 = 2.5$,

$$\frac{x_m}{40/20} = \frac{1}{\sqrt{(1 - 2.5^2)^2 + [2(0.241)(2.5)]^2}} \quad (23.118)$$

$$x_m = 0.371 \ \text{in} \quad \text{high frequency} \quad (23.119)$$

It may be seen, from comparison of Eqs. (23.117) and (23.119), that the maximum displacements of the mass at the low and high frequencies differ by a factor of approximately ten.

b When the damper is disconnected, the dynamic displacement is given by Eq. (23.64) as

$$x_m = \frac{P_0/k}{1 - (\omega/\omega_n)^2} \quad (23.120)$$

At the low frequency,

$$x_m = \frac{40/20}{1 - 0.778^2} \qquad x_m = 5.07 \text{ in} \qquad (23.121)$$

The percent increase of this result over the value in Eq. (23.117) is

$$\%D = \frac{5.07 - 3.67}{3.67} 100 = 38.1\% \qquad (23.122)$$

For the high-frequency operation,

$$x_m = \frac{40/20}{1 - 2.5^2} \qquad x_m = -0.381 \text{ in} \qquad (23.123)$$

The minus sign in Eq. (23.123) represents the 180° phase shift, for $\omega/\omega_n > 1$, in the undamped case. The percent increase, in magnitude, over the result in Eq. (23.119) is

$$\%D = \frac{0.381 - 0.371}{0.371}(100) = 2.7\% \qquad (23.124)$$

It may be observed that, at the higher frequency, the damping has a negligible effect on the amplitude of the displacement.

As the mass in Fig. 23.27 vibrates, because of the forcing function $P_0 \sin \omega t$, forces are transmitted to the foundation through the spring and damper elements. The magnitudes of these forces will now be found, and it will be shown subsequently that the *extreme values of the spring and damper forces do not occur at the same time.*

The displacement of the mass, from Eq. (23.107), is

$$x = x_m \sin (\omega t - \phi) \qquad (23.125)$$

where x_m is the *maximum* value of the amplitude of the mass. The spring force acting on the foundation has the form

$$F_s = kx = kx_m \sin (\omega t - \phi) \qquad (23.126)$$

The viscous damper force is defined in terms of the velocity of the vibrational motion of the mass. The first time derivative of Eq. (23.125) is

$$\dot{x} = x_m \omega \cos (\omega t - \phi) \qquad (23.127)$$

and the magnitude of the damper force acting on the foundation is written as

$$F_d = c\dot{x} = c\omega x_m \cos (\omega t - \phi) \qquad (23.128)$$

It should be noted that F_d given by Eq. (23.128) differs from Eq. (23.68) by a factor of -1. This is because Eq. (23.68) defines the damper force acting on the mass, while Eq. (23.128) is the Newton's third law reaction effect of the same force, transmitted through the damper element, acting on the foundation. From consideration of Eqs. (23.126) and (23.128), it may be concluded that the maximum values of the spring and damper forces occur at different times. The extreme values of the spring force occur when

$$\sin(\omega t - \phi) = \pm 1 \qquad (23.129)$$

The first value of the argument which satisfies Eq. (23.129) is

$$\omega t - \phi = \frac{\pi}{2} \qquad \omega t = \phi + \frac{\pi}{2} \qquad (23.130)$$

The maximum values of the damper forces occur when

$$\cos(\omega t - \phi) = \pm 1 \qquad (23.131)$$

The first argument which satisfies Eq. (23.131) is

$$\omega t - \phi = 0 \qquad \omega t = \phi \qquad (23.132)$$

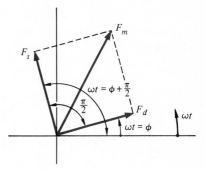

This effect is shown in Fig. 23.28, which shows a pair of rotating vectors that represent the spring and damper forces. Angle ωt is measured in the plane of the figure, and ϕ is the constant phase angle given by Eq. (23.111). The maximum value of the damper force occurs when $\omega t = \phi$. The corresponding position, in time, of the maximum value of the spring force is found from Eq. (23.130) as $\omega t = \phi + \pi/2$. At a later time the two vectors shown in the figure will have rotated counterclockwise through the same angle since t, and therefore ωt, will have increased. The significant observation is, however, that these two vectors will still have the *same* relative position in time with respect to each other. Thus the spring and damper forces may be viewed as two rectangular components of the total dynamic force acting on the mass, or on the foundation. The maximum value F_m of the resultant force is

Fig. 23.28

$$F_m = \sqrt{F_{s,m}^2 + F_{d,m}^2} \qquad (23.133)$$

By using the results in Eqs. (23.126) and (23.128), Eq. (23.133) has the form

$$F_m = \sqrt{(kx_m)^2 + (c\omega x_m)^2} = x_m\sqrt{k^2 + (c\omega)^2} \qquad (23.134)$$

The total force transmitted to the foundation is the sum of F_m, from Eq. (23.134), and the static weight force of the mass.

A dimensionless ratio called the *transmissibility* is now defined as

$$\text{TR} = \frac{F_m}{P_0} \qquad (23.135)$$

This quantity may be viewed as the *dynamic magnification factor* by which the maximum driving force amplitude P_0 is altered as its effect passes through the mass, and the spring and damper, to the foundation. The concept of transmissibility has an extremely important technical significance in the field of vibration isolation. If the transmissibility is unity, it means that the full effect of the maximum value P_0 of the driving force is felt by the foundation. For this case, the spring and damper could be removed and the mass attached directly to the foundation, as shown in Fig. 23.29. The case of TR = 1 may be viewed as a limiting reference against which other values of TR are compared. If the transmissibility is greater than 1, the presence of the spring and damper in the system results in a larger force transmission to the foundation than would be the case if these elements were absent. The usual objective in a problem in vibration isolation is to minimize the transmissibility.

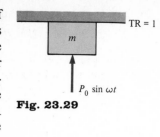

Fig. 23.29

By using the results in Eq. (23.110) for x_m, together with Eqs. (23.134) and (23.135), the transmissibility may be written in the nondimensional form

$$\text{TR} = \frac{\sqrt{1 + [2\zeta(\omega/\omega_n)]^2}}{\sqrt{[1 - (\omega/\omega_n)^2]^2 + [2\zeta(\omega/\omega_n)]^2}} \qquad (23.136)$$

This equation is plotted in Fig. 23.30. It may be seen that when the driving frequency is in the neighborhood of the natural frequency of the system, so that $\omega/\omega_n \approx 1$, the TR may have very large values. For this regime of operation, the magnitude of TR is extremely sensitive to the value of damping. An unusual condition occurs if the frequency ratio $\omega/\omega_n = \sqrt{2}$. For this case the transmissibility is 1 for all

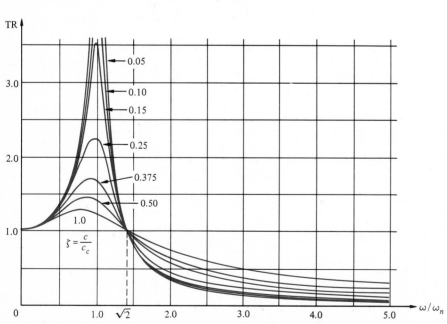

Fig. 23.30

874

values of ζ. Finally, it may be seen that damping *decreases* the transmitted force if $\omega/\omega_n < \sqrt{2}$ and *increases* this force if $\omega/\omega_n > \sqrt{2}$.

Example 23.11 The system of Example 23.10 is repeated in Fig. 23.31. The peak magnitude of the driving force is 40 lb. The driving frequency has low and high values of 1.40 and 4.50 Hz, respectively.

a Find the maximum values of the spring force, the damper force, the total force transmitted to the foundation, and the transmissibility, for the low- and high-frequency operations.

b If the damper is assumed to be removed from the system, find the values of the maximum spring force transmitted to the foundation, and the transmissibility, for the low- and high-frequency operations.

c Compare the results for parts *a* and *b*.

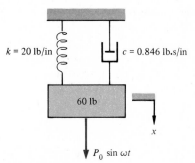

$k = 20$ lb/in $c = 0.846$ lb.s/in

60 lb

x

$P_0 \sin \omega t$

Fig. 23.31

Solution

a For the low-frequency operation,

$$\omega = 1.40(2\pi) = 8.80 \text{ rad/s} \qquad (23.137)$$

The required values of the forces, using Eq. (23.117), are

$$F_s = kx_m = 20(3.67) = 73.4 \text{ lb} \qquad (23.138)$$

$$F_d = c\omega x_m = 0.846(8.80)(3.67) = 27.3 \text{ lb} \qquad (23.139)$$

$$F_m = \sqrt{F_s^2 + F_d^2} = \sqrt{73.4^2 + 27.3^2} = 78.3 \text{ lb} \qquad (23.140)$$

By using Eq. (23.135), the transmissibility is

$$\text{TR} = \frac{F_m}{P_0} = \frac{78.3}{40} = 1.96 \qquad (23.141)$$

For the high-frequency operation,

$$\omega = 4.50(2\pi) = 28.3 \text{ rad/s} \qquad (23.142)$$

Using the magnitude of x_m from Eq. (23.119), the maximum forces have the values

$$F_s = kx_m = 20(0.371) = 7.42 \text{ lb} \qquad (23.143)$$

$$F_d = c\omega x_m = 0.846(28.3)(0.371) = 8.88 \text{ lb} \qquad (23.144)$$

$$F_m = \sqrt{F_s^2 + F_d^2} = \sqrt{7.42^2 + 8.88^2} = 11.6 \text{ lb} \qquad (23.145)$$

The transmissibility

$$\text{TR} = \frac{F_m}{P_0} = \frac{11.6}{40} = 0.290 \qquad (23.146)$$

b When the damper is removed for the low-frequency operation, using Eq. (23.121), the maximum value of the spring force transmitted to the floor is

$$F_s = F_m = kx_m = 20(5.07) = 101 \text{ lb} \qquad (23.147)$$

The corresponding value of the transmissibility is

$$\text{TR} = \frac{101}{40} = 2.53 \qquad (23.148)$$

	Damped Case					Undamped Case		
	x_m	F_s	F_d	F_m	TR	x_m	$F_s = F_m$	TR
Low Frequency	3.67	73.4	27.3	78.3	1.96	5.07	101	2.53
High Frequency	0.37	7.4	8.9	11.6	0.29	0.38	7.6	0.19

TABLE 23.2

For the high-frequency operation, from Eq. (23.123),

$$F_s = F_m = kx_m = 20(0.381) = 7.62 \text{ lb} \qquad (23.149)$$

$$\text{TR} = \frac{7.62}{40} = 0.191 \qquad (23.150)$$

c The results above are displayed in Table 23.2. It may be seen that, at the low frequency and with the damper included, the magnitude of the applied force $P_0 = 40$ lb is increased by a factor of almost 2 as it is transmitted to the foundation. If the damper is absent, this increase is by a factor of 2.5. At the high frequency the damper force is slightly greater than the spring force. Both forces are small, however, and the total dynamic force transmitted to the foundation is only 29 percent of the magnitude of the applied force. The most effective vibration isolation at the higher frequency would occur with the damper removed. For this case, only 19 percent of the applied force would be transmitted to the foundation. It should be recalled that in *all* the cases above, the *total* force transmitted to the foundation must be increased by the addition of the static weight force.

23.8 SUMMARY

A vibration is a time-varying motion of a mass element. In a system with one degree of freedom only one coordinate is required to completely define the position of the single mass element in the system.

The displacement of the mass in a vibration problem is measured from the equilibrium position of the mass on the spring. In the equilibrium position, the resultant force which acts on the mass is zero. In a linear spring mass system the spring constant k has a constant value. The magnitude of the resultant force which acts on the mass is directly proportional to the displacement of this element from the equilibrium position. The sense of this force always opposes the motion and tends to return the mass to the equilibrium position.

The general solution for undamped, free vibrational motion is

$$x = A_1 \sin \omega_n t + A_2 \cos \omega_n t \qquad (23.151)$$

where A_1 and A_2 are constants of integration which are defined by the initial conditions of the particular problem. The natural frequency of undamped, free vibration is given by an equation of the form

$$\omega_n = \sqrt{\frac{k}{m}} \qquad (23.152)$$

where k is the stiffness and m is the mass. The basic units of ω_n are radians per second. The natural frequency f_n in hertz is related to the natural frequency ω_n in radians per second by

$$f_n = \frac{1}{2\pi}\omega_n \qquad (23.153)$$

The natural period τ_n is the time required to complete one cycle of vibration, and

$$\tau_n = \frac{1}{f_n} \qquad (23.154)$$

The natural frequency is an intrinsic characteristic of the system, and it is independent of the way in which the system is set into motion. The motion represented by Eq. (23.151) is referred to as simple harmonic motion.

If the equation of motion of any linear spring mass system with one degree of freedom is of the form

$$a\ddot{\xi} + b\xi = 0 \qquad (23.155)$$

where ξ is the displacement coordinate, $\ddot{\xi}$ is the acceleration, and a and b are known constants, then the natural frequency may be found directly as

$$\omega_n = \sqrt{\frac{b}{a}} \qquad (23.156)$$

For steady-state forced vibration in the absence of damping, the maximum displacement of the mass is

$$x_m = \frac{P_0/k}{1 - (\omega/\omega_n)^2} \qquad (23.157)$$

Resonance is defined to occur when $\omega/\omega_n = 1$. If the forcing frequency ω is less than the natural frequency ω_n, the displacement is in phase with the driving force. If this frequency is greater than the natural frequency, then the force and displacement are out of phase with each other. For large values of the frequency ratio, $\omega/\omega_n \to \infty$ and the mass tends to remain motionless in space.

The maximum value of the dynamic force transmitted to the foundation in the undamped case is

$$F_d = kx_m = \frac{P_0}{1 - (\omega/\omega_n)^2} \qquad (23.158)$$

The maximum value of the total force transmitted to the foundation is

$$F_m = mg + kx_m \qquad (23.159)$$

where mg is the static weight of the mass. The force exerted by a viscous damper has the form

$$F_d = -c\dot{x} \qquad (23.160)$$

where c is the damping constant and $\dot{x}$ is the velocity of the mass. A viscous damper always opposes motion and thus dissipates energy.

The general solution for free vibrational motion with viscous damping is

$$x = e^{-\zeta\omega_n t}(A_1 \sin \sqrt{1 - \zeta^2}\omega_n t + A_2 \cos \sqrt{1 - \zeta^2}\omega_n t)$$
$$(23.161)$$

where ζ is the damping ratio, A_1 and A_2 are constants of integration which are determined from the initial conditions of the problem, and

$$\omega_n = \sqrt{\frac{k}{m}} \qquad c_c = 2\sqrt{km} = 2m\omega_n \qquad (23.162)$$

$$\zeta = \frac{c}{c_c} = \frac{c}{2\sqrt{km}} = \frac{c}{2m\omega_n} \qquad (23.163)$$

The damped natural frequency is given by

$$\omega_{nd} = \sqrt{1 - \zeta^2}\omega_n \qquad (23.164)$$

If the damping in a system is small,

$$\omega_{nd} \approx \omega_n \qquad (23.165)$$

The log decrement δ is defined to be the natural logarithm of the ratio of two successive peak amplitudes of free vibration. The log decrement and the damping ratio are related by

$$\delta = \frac{2\pi\zeta}{\sqrt{1 - \zeta^2}} \qquad (23.166)$$

δ is a quantity which may be determined experimentally and used with Eq. (23.166) to find the value of the damping ratio ζ.

In steady-state forced vibration of a system with viscous damping, the displacement lags the driving force in time. This displacement has the form

$$x = x_m \sin (\omega t - \phi) \qquad (23.167)$$

where ω is the driving frequency and ϕ is the phase angle in time between the displacement and the force. The maximum value of the displacement due to forced vibration is x_m, given by

$$x_m = \frac{P_0}{\sqrt{(k - m\omega^2)^2 + (c\omega)^2}} \qquad (23.168)$$

The ratio of the dynamic and static displacements is

$$\frac{x_m}{x_{st}} = \frac{1}{\sqrt{[1 - (\omega/\omega_n)^2]^2 + [2\zeta(\omega/\omega_n)]^2}} \qquad (23.169)$$

where

$$x_{st} = \frac{P_0}{k} \qquad (23.170)$$

The maximum value of the spring force transmitted to the foundation is

$$F_s = kx_m \qquad (23.171)$$

The maximum value of the damper force transmitted to the foundation is

$$F_d = c\omega x_m \qquad (23.172)$$

The maximum values of the spring and damper forces occur at different times during the cycle. The maximum value of the resultant dynamic force transmitted to the foundation is

$$F_m = \sqrt{F_{s,m}^2 + F_{d,m}^2} \qquad (23.173)$$

The transmissibility TR is the magnification factor by which the magnitude of the driving force is altered as it passes through the mass, and the spring and damper, to the foundation, with the form

$$TR = \frac{\sqrt{1 + [2\zeta(\omega/\omega_n)]^2}}{\sqrt{[1 - (\omega/\omega_n)^2]^2 + [2\zeta(\omega/\omega_n)]^2}} \qquad (23.174)$$

The maximum value of the total force transmitted to the foundation is

$$F_{t,m} = mg + F_m \qquad (23.175)$$

where mg is the static weight of the mass, and F_m is given by Eq. (23.173).

PROBLEMS

23.1 The spring mass system shown in Fig. P23.1 has a frequency of free vibration of 4 Hz.

(a) Find the value of k.

(b) Find the new values of the frequency of free vibration and the natural period, if a 2 kg mass is attached to the 8 kg mass shown in the figure.

23.2 Find the required value of the weight W in Fig. P23.2, if the period of free vibration is to be 0.12 s.

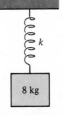

Fig. P23.1

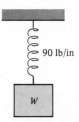

Fig. P23.2

23.3 It is desired to construct a single degree of freedom system that will have a natural period of 3 s. The weight to be supported is 250 kg.

(*a*) Find the required value of the spring constant.

(*b*) Discuss the initial deflection of the spring when the weight is attached to this element.

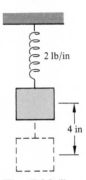

23.4 The force-deflection relationship of the spring in Fig. P23.4*a* is shown in Fig. P23.4*b*. Find the natural frequency and natural period of the system.

(*a*)   (*b*)

Fig. P23.4

23.5 When a weight of mass 1.8 kg is attached to a spring of initial length 150 mm, the spring extends 22 mm. Find the natural frequency of the spring mass system.

23.6 The mass in Fig. P23.6 is supported by a helical spring that has 20 coils. The spring constant of a helical spring is inversely proportional to the number of coils in the spring. Find the percent increase in the natural frequency if 5 coils are removed from the spring.

Fig. P23.6

23.7 The mass in Fig. P23.7 is displaced 4 in from its equilibrium position and released with zero initial velocity. The mass is 6 lb.

(*a*) Find the time for the mass to return to its initial position.

(*b*) Find the maximum values of velocity that the mass experiences and the corresponding times.

(*c*) Find the maximum values of acceleration that the mass experiences and the corresponding times.

(*d*) Find the maximum value of the dynamic force transmitted to the foundation.

(*e*) Find the maximum value of the total force transmitted to the foundation.

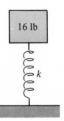

23.8 A spring mass system has a natural frequency of 3 Hz. When the spring constant is increased by 900 N/m, the frequency changes by 35 percent. Find the mass of the system and the original value of the spring constant.

Fig. P23.7

23.9 The mass in Fig. P23.9 is displaced 2 in from the equilibrium position and released with zero initial velocity. The maximum value of the total force transmitted to the foundation is 26 lb.

(*a*) Find the value of the spring constant *k*.

(*b*) Find the natural frequency of the system.

(*c*) Find the maximum values of the velocity and acceleration of the mass.

Fig. P23.9

23.10 Block *A* shown in Fig. P23.10 is in equilibrium on a frictionless plane in the position shown. A second, identical block strikes block *A* with a velocity *v*. Direct central impact is assumed, with no energy loss.

(*a*) Find the maximum value of the displacement of the spring.

(*b*) Find the maximum values of the velocity and acceleration of block *A*.

Fig. P23.10

880

(c) Find the maximum value of the total force transmitted to the foundation.

(d) Find the numerical values for parts a through c, if $k = 45 \text{ lb/in}$, $W = 18 \text{ lb}$, and $v = 60 \text{ in/s}$.

23.11 Do the same as in Prob. 23.10, if the coefficient of restitution is 0.5.

23.12 Do the same as in Prob. 23.10, if plastic impact is assumed.

23.13 The mass in Fig. P23.13 is initially at rest and is impacted by a second mass, shown as the dashed outline in the figure. Subsequent to the impact, the first mass achieves a maximum displacement of 50 mm.

(a) Find the initial velocity of the mass connected to the spring.

(b) Find the maximum value of the acceleration of the mass connected to the spring.

(c) Find the maximum value of the dynamic force transmitted to the foundation.

23.14 Figure P23.14 shows a homogeneous cylinder of mass m, which is partially submerged in liquid of mass density ρ.

(a) Show that if the cylinder is displaced vertically from its equilibrium position and released, it will perform simple harmonic motion.

(b) Find the general solution for the natural frequency, in terms of k, m, and ρ.

(c) Find the numerical value of the result in part b, if $k = 1350 \text{ N/m}$, $m = 7 \text{ kg}$, and the liquid is water, with a density of $1,000 \text{ kg/m}^3$.

(d) Find the system natural frequency, when the liquid is absent from the problem.

23.15 Figure P23.15 shows a manometer U tube filled with a frictionless liquid. The cross-section area of the tube is A, and the liquid in the tube has a mass density of ρ.

(a) Show that, if the liquid is displaced from the equilibrium position shown in the figure and released, it will move with simple harmonic motion.

(b) Verify that the natural frequency of the motion is $\sqrt{2\,g/l}$.

23.16 The 0.5-in-thick disk in Fig. P23.16 is made of steel, with a specific weight of 0.283 lb/in^3. It is restrained by a torsional spring of stiffness 510 in $\cdot$ lb/rad. Two circular holes of diameter d are to be drilled in the disk, to adjust the natural frequency of the system to 18.5 Hz.

(a) Find the required value of d.

(b) Find the value of the natural frequency if four such holes, instead of two, on the same mean diameter circle are drilled in the disk.

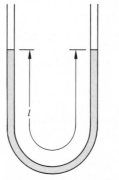

Fig. P23.13

Fig. P23.14

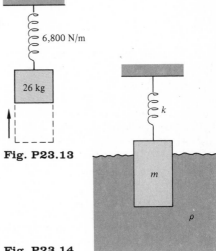

Fig. P23.15

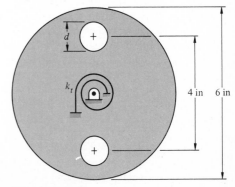

Fig. P23.16

23.17 Figure P23.17 shows a disk, of mass 4 kg, connected to a helical spring. The disk is given a small angular displacement and released with zero initial velocity.

(a) Find the required value of the spring constant, if the natural period of vibration is to be 0.26 s.

(b) Find the maximum value of the spring force transmitted to the foundation, if the initial displacement of the disk is 8°.

23.18 (a) Do the same as in part a of Prob. 23.17, if the disk is restrained by a torsional spring instead of a helical spring, as shown in Fig. P23.18.

(b) Find the maximum value of the dynamic moment transmitted to the foundation, if the initial displacement of the disk is 8°.

23.19 A torsional pendulum, of the type shown in Fig. 23.9, is displaced 15° from its equilibrium position and released with zero initial velocity. It vibrates with a natural frequency of 6 Hz. The disk is 250 mm in diameter and 30 mm thick, with a density of 7,830 kg/m³. Find the maximum value of the dynamic moment exerted on the foundation.

23.20 A spring is to be added to the simple pendulum system shown in Fig. P23.20. $k = 20$ lb/in, $W = 12$ lb and $l = 40$ in. State where the spring should be placed to double the original pendulum natural frequency.

23.21 Figure P23.21 shows a pendulum arrangement. The mass of the rod may be neglected.

(a) Find the natural frequency of the system.

(b) What is the "spring constant" of the system?

(c) Discuss the stability requirements of the system.

(d) Find the magnitude of m_A if the natural period is to be 2 s. $m_B = 0.72$ kg, $b = 250$ mm, and $a = 65$ mm.

23.22 The system in Fig. P23.22 is in equilibrium in the position shown, and the mass of the rod may be neglected.

(a) Find the natural frequency of the system.

(b) Find the numerical value of the result in part a, if $k = 2,000$ N/m, $m = 1.4$ kg, $l = 1$ m, and $a = 0.72$ m.

23.23 The pendulum-type arrangement in Prob. 23.22 is replaced by the slender rod of mass m shown in Fig. P23.23. The rod is in equilibrium in the position shown.

(a) Find the natural frequency of the system.

(b) Find the numerical value of the result in part a, if $k = 2,000$ N/m, $m = 1.4$ kg, $l = 1$ m, and $a = 0.72$ m.

(c) Compare the result in part b with the solution to Prob. 23.22, and discuss.

23.24 The system in Fig. P23.24 is in equilibrium in the position shown. The masses of the two arms may be neglected.

(a) Find the natural frequency of the system.

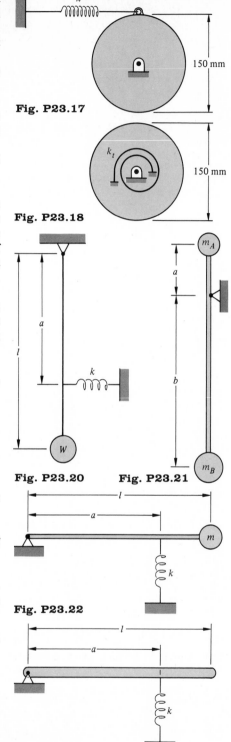

Fig. P23.17

Fig. P23.18

Fig. P23.20   **Fig. P23.21**

Fig. P23.22

Fig. P23.23

(b) Find the numerical value for part a, if $m_A g = 1.2$ lb, $m_B g = 0.8$ lb, $l_1 = 10$ in, $l_2 = 14$ in, $a = 9$ in, and $k = 7.4$ lb/in.

(c) Is there any relation among the magnitudes of m_A, m_B, l_1, l_2 and a for which the arm arrangement will not vibrate?

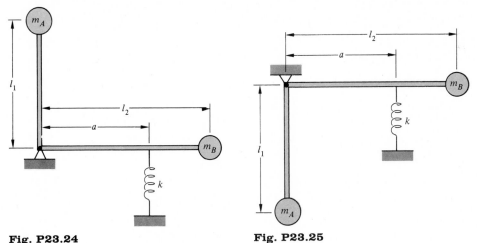

Fig. P23.24   **Fig. P23.25**

23.25 Do the same as in Prob. 23.24 if the system is inverted, as shown in Fig. P23.25.

23.26 Part of the solution for the forced vibration motion of the system in Fig. 23.16 has the assumed form, given in Eq. (23.61), of $x_p = A \sin \omega t + B \cos \omega t$. Verify that when this result is substituted into Eq. (23.59), the results are those given by Eq. (23.62).

23.27 (a) Find the maximum steady-state amplitude of the single degree of freedom system shown in Fig. P23.27, if $P_o = 6$ lb and $\omega = 1.5$ Hz.

(b) Find the maximum value of the dynamic force transmitted to the foundation, for the conditions of part a.

(c) Find the maximum value of the total force transmitted to the foundation, for the conditions of part a.

(d) Do the same as in parts a through c, if $P_o = 6$ lb and $\omega = 3.5$ Hz.

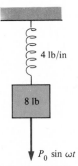

Fig. P23.27

23.28 For what range of values of the frequency ratio ω/ω_n will the maximum value of the steady-state amplitude of the system in Fig. P23.27 not exceed 1.72 in? Use $P_o = 6$ lb.

23.29 For what range of values of the frequency ratio ω/ω_n will the maximum value of the steady-state amplitude of the system in Fig. P23.27 not exceed 0.64 in? Use $P_o = 6$ lb.

23.30 The single-degree-of-freedom system shown in Fig. P23.30 is to experience an amplitude of steady-state motion that is no greater than 16 mm. Find the range of permissible values of k, if $P_o = 8$ N and $\omega = 5$ Hz.

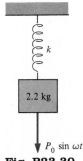

Fig. P23.30

23.31 Do the same as in Prob. 23.30, if the driving frequency is 12 Hz.

23.32 Do the same as in Prob. 23.30, if the driving frequency may have any value between 5 and 12 Hz.

23.33 The amplitude of the steady-state motion of the system shown in Fig. P23.33 is not to exceed 20 mm. If $P_0 = 26$ N and $\omega = 4$ Hz, find the permissible range of values of the weight of the mass m.

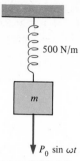

500 N/m

m

$P_0 \sin \omega t$

Fig. P23.33

23.34 Do the same as in Prob. 23.33, if the driving frequency is 7.6 Hz.

23.35 A single-degree-of-freedom system is excited by a force $P_0 \sin \omega t$. When the frequency ratio is 0.8, the maximum value of the steady-state amplitude of the block is 0.183 in. What will the maximum value of the steady-state amplitude be if the frequency ratio is doubled?

23.36 A mass connected to a helical spring moves in a vertical direction. The mass is acted on by a force $P_0 \sin \omega t$, where $P_0 = 25$ lb and $\omega = 45$ rad/s. During this operation, the maximum value of the force exerted on the foundation is 75 lb, and the magnitude of the mass is 0.104 lb $\cdot$ s^2/in. Find the value of the stiffness of the spring.

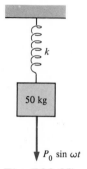

k

50 kg

$P_0 \sin \omega t$

Fig. P23.37

23.37 For what values of k will the spring in Fig. P23.37 reduce the dynamic force transmitted to the foundation? $P_0 = 75$ N and $\omega = 32$ Hz.

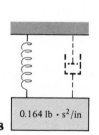

0.164 lb $\cdot$ s^2/in

Fig. P23.38

23.38 The spring mass system in Fig. P23.38 has a natural frequency of 3.8 Hz. A viscous damper with a damping constant of 1.42 lb $\cdot$ s/in is added to the system.
(a) Find the damped natural frequency and the damped natural period.
(b) Find the value of the damping ratio.

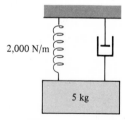

2,000 N/m

5 kg

Fig. P23.39

23.39 The single degree of freedom system shown in Fig. P23.39 has a damping ratio of 0.14.
(a) Find the value of the damping constant.
(b) Find the value of the damped natural frequency.

23.40 When the 10-kg mass in Fig. P23.40 is attached to the spring, the end of this element moves through a distance of 60 mm.
(a) Find the undamped and damped natural periods of the system.
(b) Find the value of the damping ratio.

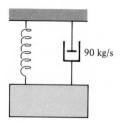

90 kg/s

Fig. P23.40

23.41 The natural frequency of a single-degree-of-freedom spring mass system changes from 26 to 20 Hz when a viscous damper is added to the system. The mass is 16.8 kg.
(a) Find the value of the damping constant.
(b) Find the value of the damping ratio.

23.42 (*a*) Find the ratio of two successive amplitudes of free vibration of the system shown in Fig. P23.42.

(*b*) Find the value of the log decrement.

(*c*) The mass is displaced 2.8 in from the equilibrium position and released with zero initial velocity. Find the displacement at the end of 12 cycles of vibration.

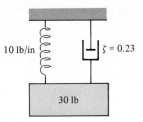

Fig. P23.42

23.43 Figure P23.43 shows a spring mass system with a viscous damper. The mass is displaced 60 mm from the equilibrium position and released with zero initial velocity. At the end of five complete cycles, the amplitude of the motion is 18 mm.

(*a*) Find the value of the log decrement.

(*b*) Find the amplitude at the end of seven complete cycles of motion.

(*c*) Find the value of the damping ratio.

(*d*) Find the value of the damping constant.

23.44 The mass in Fig. P23.44 is displaced 3 in from the equilibrium position and released with zero initial velocity at $t = 0$.

(*a*) Find the displacement of the mass when $t = 0.27$ s.

(*b*) Find the magnitude and sense of the velocity of the mass when $t = 0.27$ s.

(*c*) Find the displacement of the mass at the end of 2.5 cycles of vibration.

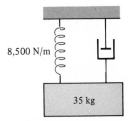

Fig. P23.43

23.45 Take the first derivative of Eq. (23.72) and verify the result in Eq. (23.77).

23.46 Show that when Eq. (23.107) is substituted into Eq. (23.105) the result is Eq. (23.108).

23.47 The damped single-degree-of-freedom system shown in Fig. P23.47 is acted upon by a disturbing force with a peak amplitude of 120 lb. The frequency of this force is twice the undamped frequency of the system. $W = 80$ lb.

(*a*) Find the maximum value of the amplitude of the steady-state motion.

(*b*) Find the phase angle that corresponds to part *a*.

(*c*) Do the same as in parts *a* and *b*, if the disturbing frequency is reduced to a value that is 80 percent of the undamped frequency.

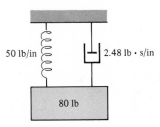

Fig. P23.44

23.48 Do the same as in Prob. 23.27 if a damper, with a damping ratio of 0.18, is added to the system.

23.49 Do the same as in Prob. 23.30 if a damper, with a damping ratio of 0.3, is added to the system.

23.50 Do the same as in Prob. 23.33 if a damper, with a damping ratio of 0.1, is added to the system.

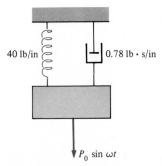

Fig. P23.47

23.51 The value of P_0 in the system shown in Fig. P23.51 is 110 N, and the frequency ratio is 0.72.

(a) Find the maximum value of the spring force.

(b) Find the maximum value of the damper force.

(c) Find the maximum value of the force transmitted to the foundation.

23.52 Do the same as in Prob. 23.51, for a frequency ratio of 1.90.

23.53 Find the time interval between the time when the spring force in Prob. 23.51 reaches its maximum positive value and the time when the damper force reaches its maximum positive value.

23.54 Do the same as in Prob. 23.53, for the condition of Prob. 23.52.

23.55 (a) Find the transmissibility of the system shown in Fig. P23.55. The amplitude of the driving force is 8.6 lb and the frequency ratio is 1.78.

(b) Find the maximum value of the dynamic force transmitted to the foundation.

23.56 (a) Find for what values of ω/ω_n the transmissibility of the system in Prob. 23.55 will not exceed 0.28.

(b) Find the corresponding values of the phase angle.

23.57 (a) Determine the values of ω/ω_n for which the transmissibility of the system in Prob. 23.55 will not exceed 1.35.

(b) Find the corresponding values of the phase angle.

23.58 The maximum value of the dynamic force transmitted to the foundation of the system shown in Fig. P23.58 may not exceed 200 N.

(a) Find the maximum permissible value of the amplitude P_0 of the disturbing force, if the frequency ratio is 0.25.

(b) Do the same as in part a, if the frequency ratio is 0.75.

(c) Do the same as in part a, if the frequency ratio is 1.25.

23.59 Do the same as in Prob. 23.58, if the damping ratio is decreased to 0.12.

23.60 When the system in Fig. P23.60 operates at 2.5 Hz, the maximum value of the spring force is 3 lb.

(a) Find the maximum value of the force transmitted by the damper to the foundation.

(b) Find the maximum value of the spring force if the damper becomes accidently disconnected from the mass.

23.61 The amplitude, at resonance, of the maximum displacement of a forced single-degree-of-freedom system is twice the value of maximum displacement at a frequency 25 percent greater than the resonant frequency. Find the value of the damping ratio.

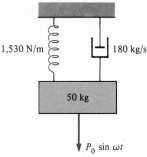

Fig. P23.51

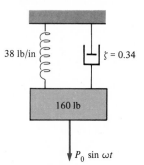

Fig. P23.55

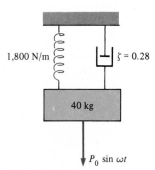

Fig. P23.58

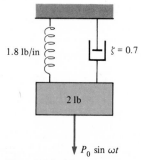

Fig. P23.60

24

Rectilinear Motion of a Body with Resisting, or Drag, Forces

24.1 INTRODUCTION

In Chaps. 15 and 16 the kinematics and dynamics of a particle in rectilinear motion were studied. Figure 24.1 shows the typical appearance of such a particle. The particle is constrained to move along the x axis in rectilinear motion. F_x is the component of the *resultant* force, in the x direction, of all the forces acting on the particle. Newton's second law for this problem has the elementary form

Fig. 24.1

$$F_x = m\ddot{x} \qquad (24.1)$$

In the previous treatment of this problem, the case was considered where the magnitude of the resultant force had a *constant* value. For this case, from Eq. (24.1) the acceleration has a constant value. The equations which relate the displacement, velocity, acceleration, and time were then found to be

$$v = v_0 + at \qquad x = x_0 + v_0 t + \tfrac{1}{2}at^2$$
$$v^2 = v_0^2 + 2a(x - x_0) \qquad (24.2)$$

where v_0 and x_0 are the initial velocity and displacement, respectively, at $t = 0$. It should be emphasized that these equations are true *only* for the case where the particle is acted by a resultant force of *constant* magnitude which produces a *constant* acceleration. In many actual problems the resultant

887

force which acts on a body is constant, so that the above set of equations finds widespread application in the solution of practical engineering problems.

It was subsequently shown in Chap. 19 that the center of mass of a rigid body moves as a particle in translation which is acted on by the resultant of all the forces acting on the body. Thus, in the following discussion, *all the results apply equally to particles, and to the centers of mass of rigid bodies, in translation.* The analysis of the rectilinear motion of a particle will now be extended to include the cases where the particle is acted on by resisting, or drag, forces. As a preliminary consideration, the resultant force which acts on a particle may be envisioned to consist of forces of two general types. The first type has the same sense as the velocity and may be thought of as an effect which "assists" motion, with the net effect of increasing the velocity of the particle. Typical examples of this type of force are the weight force of a falling body and a cable tensile force which acts on a body. The second type of force that may act on a body has a sense which is opposite to that of the velocity and may be thought of as a force which "opposes" motion, with the effect of decreasing the magnitude of the velocity. One type of force in this latter category is referred to as a *dissipative force.* Dissipative forces always transform a part of the kinetic energy of the particle, through frictional dissipative effects, to heat energy, with an unrecoverable decrease in the velocity. Typical examples include friction forces which exist when one body slides along the surface of a second body, and the drag forces which act on a body, such as an automobile, airplane, or boat, as it moves through a fluid medium.

It is interesting to note that a particular force in a given problem may act so as to either assist or oppose motion. In the case of a body which is projected upward from the ground, for example, the same weight force *opposes* motion during the ascent of the body and *assists* the motion during descent of the body. In the following analysis a very important consideration will be whether a force tends to assist, or to oppose, the motion.

For convenience the resisting, or drag, forces which act on a body may be separated into three groups:

1. Drag force is a constant.
2. Drag force is directly proportional to velocity.
3. Drag force is directly proportional to velocity squared.

The motion caused by each type of drag force will now be investigated.

24.2 CONSTANT DRAG FORCE

A common example of rectilinear motion of a particle with constant drag force is the sliding Coulomb friction. Here, the general form of the resisting force F_D is

$$F_D = -\mu_k N = \text{const.} \qquad (24.3)$$

where N is the normal contact force between the sliding surfaces and μ_k is the coefficient of kinetic friction. The particle is assumed to move in the positive sense of the x axis, and the drag force F_D is defined to act in this positive sense. Thus, the minus sign in Eq. (24.3) indicates that this sliding friction drag force *always acts to oppose the motion*.

Several examples in Chap. 16 illustrated the techniques of solution for the motion of particles which are acted on by *constant* drag forces. It may finally be observed that since the drag force is constant, the resulting acceleration (in this case, actually a deceleration) of the particle must also be constant.

24.3 DRAG FORCE DIRECTLY PROPORTIONAL TO VELOCITY—LINEAR RESISTANCE LAW

The general term used to describe the case where the drag force is directly proportional to the velocity is *viscous resistance*. This type of motion is observed both where surfaces which move with low velocity relative to one another are separated by a thin layer of lubricant, and in the motion of submerged bodies at very low velocities in a viscous fluid, such as when very fine particles in a container of liquid settle slowly to the bottom. The concept of a viscous resisting force is also used extensively in vibration analysis to characterize the dissipative effect of an element which is referred to as a *viscous damper*. The concept of a viscous damper was used in Chap. 23 to represent the dissipative effects in a vibration system with one degree of freedom.

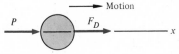

Fig. 24.2

Figure 24.2 shows the forces acting on a particle in rectilinear translation with viscous drag forces. P is a constant external force which acts on the particle, in the sense of the motion. In the following analysis, a necessary condition is that $P > 0$. The viscous drag force F_D is written as

$$F_D = -cv \qquad (24.4)$$

where $v = dx/dt$ is the velocity of the particle and c is a constant. It may be observed from Eq. (24.4) that the mathematical structure of force F_D is such that it *automatically* adjusts the sense of the drag force to oppose the velocity. If v is positive, so that the particle moves to the right in Fig. 24.2, then F_D is negative and acts to the left. If v is negative, which characterizes leftward motion of the particle, then force F_D is positive and acts to the right on the particle, to oppose its motion. This characteristic of the viscous drag force of automatically adjusting its sense finds widespread application in the solution of problems of oscillatory motion about an equilibrium position.

The equation of motion of the particle in Fig. 24.2 is

$$\Sigma F_x = ma_x \qquad P + F_D = m\frac{dv}{dt} \qquad P - cv = m\frac{dv}{dt}$$

$$(24.5)$$

$$\frac{dv}{dt} = \frac{P}{m} - \frac{cv}{m} \qquad (24.6)$$

With the notations

$$\xi = \frac{P}{m} > 0 \qquad \eta = \frac{c}{m} \qquad (24.7)$$

the equation of motion may be written as

$$\frac{dv}{dt} = \xi - \eta v \qquad (24.8)$$

An immediate conclusion may be drawn from Eq. (24.8). When the right side of this equation is equal to zero,

$$\frac{dv}{dt} = 0 \qquad v = \text{const.} = v_T \qquad (24.9)$$

This limiting value of constant velocity v_T of the particle is called the *terminal velocity*. This quantity is found by setting the right side of Eq. (24.8) equal to zero, with the result

$$\xi - \eta v_T = 0 \qquad (24.10)$$

$$v_T = \frac{\xi}{\eta} = \frac{P/m}{c/m} = \frac{P}{c} \qquad (24.11)$$

When the particle reaches its terminal velocity, the resultant force which acts on it is identically zero, since the magnitude of the applied force P is exactly equal to the magnitude of the viscous drag force cv_T. It may also be concluded from Eq. (24.10) that the range of velocities in the problem must satisfy $v < \frac{\xi}{\eta}$. It is left as an exercise for the reader to show that, if this latter inequality is not true, the viscous drag forces would increase the velocity of the particle.

The initial conditions for all examples in this section are that at $t = 0$, $v = v_0$ and $x = x_0$. At the end of the time interval of consideration, the motion is described by x, v, and t.

Equation 24.8) may be written in the form

$$dt = \frac{dv}{\xi - \eta v} \qquad (24.12)$$

Equation (24.12) is integrated, with the result

$$\int_0^t dt = \int_{v_0}^v \frac{dv}{\xi - \eta v} \qquad (24.13)$$

This equation has the form

$$\int_1^2 \frac{du}{u} = \ln u \Big|_1^2 \qquad (24.14)$$

and it may be written as

$$\int_0^t dt = \frac{1}{-\eta} \int_{v_0}^v \frac{-\eta\, dv}{\xi - \eta v} \qquad (24.15)$$

$$t = \Big|_0^t = \frac{-1}{\eta} \ln (\xi - \eta v) \Big|_{v_0}^v \qquad (24.16)$$

$$t = -\frac{1}{\eta} \Big[\ln (\xi - \eta v) - \ln (\xi - \eta v_0) \Big] \qquad (24.17)$$

$$= -\frac{1}{\eta} \ln \Big[\frac{\xi - \eta v}{\xi - \eta v_0} \Big] \qquad (24.18)$$

$$e^{-\eta t} = \frac{\xi - \eta v}{\xi - \eta v_0} \qquad (24.19)$$

This equation is solved for v, with the result

$$v = \frac{\xi}{\eta} - \Big(\frac{\xi}{\eta} - v_0 \Big) e^{-\eta t} \qquad (24.20)$$

By using $v_T = \xi/\eta$ from Eq. (24.11), Eq. (24.20) has the final form

$$v = v_T - (v_T - v_0) e^{-\eta t} \qquad (24.21)$$

The velocity and displacement of a particle in rectilinear translation obey the fundamental relationship

$$v = \frac{dx}{dt} \qquad dx = v\, dt \qquad (24.22)$$

$$\int_0^x dx = \int_0^t v\, dt \qquad (24.23)$$

Equation (24.21) is now used in the right side of Eq. (24.23) to obtain

$$\int_0^x dx = \int_0^t \Big[v_T - (v_T - v_0) e^{-\eta t} \Big] dt \qquad (24.24)$$

$$x \Big|_0^x = \Big[v_T t - \Big(\frac{1}{-\eta} \Big)(v_T - v_0) e^{-\eta t} \Big]_0^t \qquad (24.25)$$

$$x = v_T t + \frac{1}{\eta} (v_0 - v_T)(1 - e^{-\eta t}) \qquad (24.26)$$

If the particle is acted on by only the viscous drag force, then the above equations have simpler forms. For this case,

$$P = 0 \qquad v_T = \frac{P}{c} = 0 \qquad (24.27)$$

and the velocity and displacement are given by

$$v = v_0 e^{-\eta t} \qquad x = \frac{v_0}{\eta}(1 - e^{-\eta t}) \qquad (24.28)$$

An interesting consequence of the assumption of viscous drag force may be observed in the above equations. From Eqs. (24.28), it may be concluded that theoretically it takes infinite time for the particle to attain zero velocity. The corresponding displacement x_m of the particle, by comparison, is finite and is found to be

$$\lim_{t \to \infty} x = \lim_{t \to \infty} \frac{v_0}{\eta}(1 - e^{-\eta t}) = \frac{v_0}{\eta} = x_m \qquad (24.29)$$

The apparent inconsistency of the above mathematical results with the physically observed motion of bodies may be explained as follows. At very small values of velocity of the particle, the constant sliding Coulomb friction drag forces, which were neglected in this analysis of the particle motion, predominate over the viscous drag forces. It is these sliding friction forces which eventually bring the body to rest.

The results for the case where the applied constant force has the same sense as the velocity are summarized here.

$$v_T = \frac{P}{c} \qquad \eta = \frac{c}{m} \qquad (24.30)$$

$$v = v_T - (v_T - v_0)\, e^{-\eta t} \qquad (24.31)$$

$$x = v_T t + \frac{1}{\eta}(v_0 - v_T)(1 - e^{-\eta t}) \qquad (24.32)$$

$$v = v_0 e^{-\eta t} \qquad\qquad P = 0 \qquad (24.33)$$

$$x = \frac{v_0}{\eta}(1 - e^{-\eta t}) \qquad \left.\right\} \quad \therefore v_T = 0 \qquad (24.34)$$

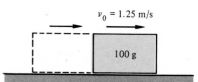

Fig. 24.3

Example 24.1 A 100-g steel block rests on a plane horizontal surface, shown in Fig. 24.3, which is coated with a thick oil. A second block, shown in the dashed outline in the figure, impacts the steel block and causes it to move rightward with an initial velocity of 1.25 m/s. The drag force on the block is assumed to be viscous and from an earlier measurement the constant c was found to have the value 0.350 N·s/m.

a Find the distance through which the block moves before coming to rest.

b Find the time at which the velocity of the block is reduced to 50 percent of its initial value.

c Do the same as in part b for a reduction of the velocity to 1 percent of its initial value.

d Find the maximum value of the drag force which acts on the body.

e Find the total energy loss during the sliding motion of the block.

Solution

a The block starts with an initial velocity $v_0 = 1.25$ m/s and later comes to rest. The constant η is

$$\eta = \frac{c}{m} = \frac{0.350}{0.1} = 3.50 \ s^{-1} \qquad (24.35)$$

The total distance x_m through which the block moves before coming to rest, using Eq. (24.29), is

$$x_m = \frac{v_0}{\eta} = \frac{1.25}{3.5} = 0.357 \ m \qquad (24.36)$$

b Equation (24.28) may be written in the form

$$\frac{v}{v_0} = e^{-\eta t} = e^{-3.5t} \qquad (24.37)$$

When the velocity of the block is 50 percent of its initial value,

$$\frac{v}{v_0} = 0.50 = e^{-3.5t} \qquad \ln 0.50 = -3.5t \qquad (24.38)$$

$$t = \frac{-\ln 0.50}{3.5} = 0.198 \ s \qquad (24.39)$$

c When the velocity of the block is 1 percent of its original value

$$\frac{v}{v_0} = 0.01 = e^{-3.5t} \qquad t = 1.32 \ s \qquad (24.40)$$

d The velocity of the block decreases monotonically from the initial maximum velocity v_0 to zero velocity. The maximum value of the drag force, from Eq. (24.4), occurs at maximum velocity, so that

$$F_{D,\max} = -cv_{\max} = -cv_0 = -0.350 \ (1.25) = -0.438 \ N \quad (24.41)$$

e The initial energy of the system is the kinetic energy of the block, given by

$$T_1 = \tfrac{1}{2} m v_0^2 = \tfrac{1}{2} (0.1)(1.25)^2 = 0.0781 \ N \cdot m = 0.0781 \ J \ (24.42)$$

When the block comes to rest, the energy of the system is zero. Thus, the total energy loss is 0.0781 J, and this quantity represents the work done in overcoming the viscous friction forces.

Example 24.2 The plane surface in the Example 24.1 is now inclined as shown in Fig. 24.4. The block is released from rest at the top of the incline, and at a later time it moves with a constant velocity of 1.25 m/s. It is assumed that the plane has sufficient length to allow the terminal velocity to be attained.

a Find the required value of the angle β.

b Find the time and the displacement of the block when the velocity of this element has reached 50 percent, 90 percent, and 99 percent of the value of the terminal velocity.

c If the block had been set into motion with an initial velocity, would the result for part *a* have been different?

Solution

a The free-body diagram of the block, when this element moves

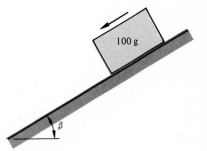

Fig. 24.4

with its constant terminal velocity, is shown in Fig. 24.5. For force
equilibrium of the block,

$$\Sigma F_x = 0 \qquad mg \sin \beta - cv_T = 0 \qquad (24.43)$$

$$0.1 (9.81) \sin \beta - 0.350 (1.25) = 0 \qquad (24.44)$$

$$\sin \beta = 0.446 \qquad (24.45)$$

$$\beta = 26.5° \qquad (24.46)$$

b The velocity of the block, using Eq. (24.31) with $v_0 = 0$, is

$$v = v_T (1 - e^{-\eta t}) \qquad \frac{v}{v_T} = 1 - e^{-\eta t} \qquad (24.47)$$

The displacement of the block, from Eq. (24.32) with $v_0 = 0$, is

$$x = v_T \left[t - \frac{1}{\eta} (1 - e^{-\eta t}) \right] \qquad (24.48)$$

η has the value 3.50 s^{-1} given by Eq. (24.35). When the velocity of the
block has reached 50 percent of its terminal value,

$$\frac{v}{v_T} = 0.50 = 1 - e^{-3.50t} \qquad t = 0.198 \text{ S} \qquad (24.49)$$

$$x = 1.25[0.198 - 1/3.50(1 - e^{-3.50(0.198)})] \qquad (24.50)$$

$$= 0.0690 \text{ m} = 69 \text{ mm} \qquad (24.51)$$

By using the above equations, it can be shown that when the block
reaches 90 percent of its terminal velocity,

$$t = 0.658 \text{ s} \qquad x = 0.501 \text{ m} = 501 \text{ mm} \qquad (24.52)$$

At 99 percent of the terminal velocity, the values are

$$t = 1.32 \text{ s} \qquad x = 1.30 \text{ m} = 1,300 \text{ mm} \qquad (24.53)$$

c It may be seen from Eq. (24.43) that β is a function of only mg, c,
and v_T. Since none of these three terms is a function of the initial
velocity v_0, it follows that the value of β is *independent* of the initial
velocity. Setting the block into motion with an initial velocity would,
however, change the value of t and x found in part b.

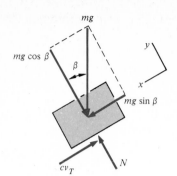

Fig. 24.5

24.4 DRAG FORCE PROPORTIONAL TO VELOCITY SQUARED—QUADRATIC RESISTANCE LAW

Figure 24.6 shows a body which moves through a fluid medium
such as air or water. The movement of the body through the
fluid creates an unbalanced pressure distribution on the surface
of the body, which tends to oppose the motion of this element.
In addition, there are internal friction effects within the fluid
because it was deformed from its original shape by the passage
of the body. There are also frictional drag forces on the solid
boundary, or "skin," of the body which is in contact with the
fluid. The force F_D, shown in the figure, is the force required to

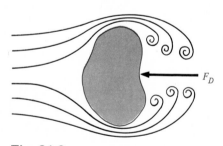

Fig. 24.6

overcome *all* these resisting forces as the body moves through the fluid.

In the following discussion, it will be assumed that *the major component of the total drag force is due to the pressure effects.* The physical problems which closely correspond to this assumption would be either bodies with plane (or slightly curved) surfaces which are normal to the direction of the velocity of the body or bodies which have sharp edges where the fluid loses contact with the body. Examples of bodies where the pressure effects are *not* the major contribution to drag force are plane (or slightly curved) surfaces in which the fluid flow is along the surface and pointed slender bodies whose axes are parallel to the velocity of the body. Typical examples of such shapes are airplane wings, boat hulls, and other "streamlined" shapes. The determination of the drag forces on such bodies is beyond the scope of this book, and this subject is treated in texts on fluid mechanics.

All the following analysis is for the case where the body moves with respect to a stationary fluid. These results also may be applied to the case where the body is stationary and the fluid moves relative to it, as in a wind tunnel. It must be emphasized that all the following results are valid *only for velocities which are less than the speed of sound,* so that the flow field is subsonic. For sea-level air at 60°F, this limiting sonic velocity is approximately 1,120 ft/s.

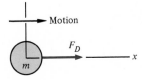

Fig. 24.7

Figure 24.7 shows a body which moves in a fluid medium and experiences a force resistance primarily due to a pressure difference over the surface area of the body. The particle is constrained to move *only along the positive x axis, with a positive velocity v.* Thus, the body shown in Fig. 24.7 may move only *to the right* in the figure. The drag force which acts on the particle is designated F_D, and this quantity is defined to be positive if it acts in the positive x-coordinate sense.

It is shown in texts in fluid mechanics and aerodynamics that the drag force may be expressed in the functional form

$$F_D = -C_D(\tfrac{1}{2}\rho v^2)A \qquad (24.54)$$

In this expression A is the projected area of the body on a plane which is normal to the direction of motion. The term $\frac{1}{2}\rho v^2$, where ρ is the mass density of the fluid and v is the velocity of the body, is referred to as the *dynamic pressure,* and this quantity is used extensively in fluid mechanics. For the purposes of this discussion, this term will be considered to be merely a defined quantity, having no other particular significance. The term C_D is called the *drag coefficient,* and for other than very small values of the velocity, this term may be assumed to be constant. On the basis of this assumption and from consideration of Eq. (24.54), it may be seen that the drag force is propor-

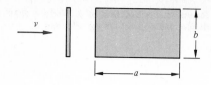

TABLE 24.1

Rectangular Plate

a/b	C_D
1	1.16
4	1.17
8	1.23
25	1.57
50	1.76
∞	2.00

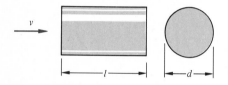

Cylinder

l/d	C_D
1	0.91
2	0.85
4	0.87
7	0.99

Circular Disk

$C_D = 1.11$ for all d

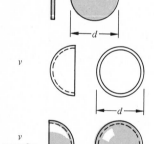

Open, Hemispherical
Shell

$C_D = 0.41$ for all d

Open, Hemispherical
Shell, or Parachute

$C_D = 1.35$ for all d

tional to the velocity squared. This force-velocity relationship is referred to as the *quadratic resistance law*. Table 24.1 shows typical values of the drag coefficient for bodies of simple geometry.

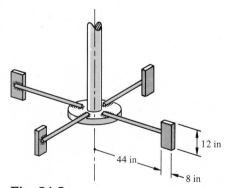

Fig. 24.8

Example 24.3   Figure 24.8 shows a stirring apparatus which is used in a chemical manufacturing operation. The paddle assembly consists of four vertical steel blades which rotate about a fixed vertical axis. The entire assembly is submerged in a large tank which contains a chemical solution with a specific gravity of 1.08. Estimate the power required to drive the paddle wheel at a constant speed of 30 r/min.

Solution Each blade will be analyzed as a rectangular plane, whose direction is normal to the direction of motion, which moves through a fluid medium. It is assumed that the disturbance produced in the fluid by any one blade has no effect on the flow field about the remaining blades. From Table 24.1 the value of the drag coefficient is estimated to be $C_D = 1.16$.

The velocity of each blade will be taken as the average velocity at the midpoint of the blade. Thus,

$$v = r\omega = \frac{44 + 4}{12}(30)\left(\frac{2\pi}{60}\right) = 12.6 \frac{\text{ft}}{\text{s}} \qquad (24.55)$$

The total drag force which acts on each blade is then

$$F_D = C_D\left(\frac{1}{2}\rho v^2\right)A \qquad (24.56)$$

Using 62.4 lb/ft³ as the specific weight of standard water, we get

$$F_D = 1.16\left\{\frac{1}{2}\left[\frac{1.08(62.4)}{32.2}(12.6)^2\right]\right\}\frac{12(8)}{(12)^2} = 128\ \text{lb} \quad (24.57)$$

The torque transmitted to the shaft by the force which acts on each blade is

$$M = 128(4) = 512\ \text{ft·lb per blade} \qquad (24.58)$$

The total power required to drive the four-bladed paddle assembly is then

$$P = 4\,M\omega = \frac{4(512)[30(2\pi)/60]}{550} = 11.7\ \text{hp} \qquad (24.59)$$

Example 24.4 Figure 24.9 shows a device, referred to as a cup anenometer, which is used to measure wind velocity. If the anenometer shaft is held stationary, with the orientation of the wind direction shown in Fig. 24.10, estimate the torque, in inch-ounces, exerted by the wind forces on the shaft. The wind velocity is 35 mi/h, and standard air at 14.7 lb/in² absolute and 60°F, with a specific weight of 0.07637 lb/ft³, is assumed.

Solution The three cups are designated A, B, and C, as shown in Fig. 24.11. Cup A behaves as an open hemispherical shell, and the drag coefficient for this shape, from Table 24.1, is $C_D = 1.35$. The velocity of the wind stream past the anenometer is

$$v = \left(35\,\frac{\text{mi}}{\text{h}}\right)\left(\frac{5{,}280\ \text{ft/mi}}{3{,}600\ \text{s/h}}\right) = 51.3\ \text{ft/s} \qquad (24.60)$$

The force F_A which acts on cup A is

$$F_A = C_D(\tfrac{1}{2}\rho v^2)A \qquad (24.61)$$

$$= 1.35\left[\frac{1}{2}\left(\frac{0.07637}{32.2}\right)(51.3)^2\right]\frac{\pi(1.25)^2}{4(144)}$$

$$= 0.0359\ \text{lb} = 0.574\ \text{oz} \qquad (24.62)$$

The velocity of the wind stream passing cups B and C is resolved into

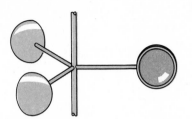

Fig. 24.9

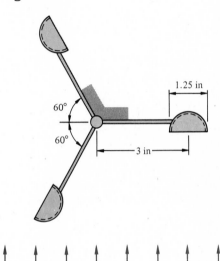

Fig. 24.10

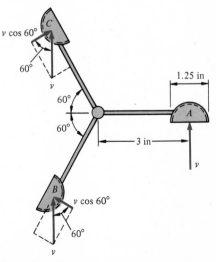

Fig. 24.11

components along the arms and normal to these directions. The drag forces caused by the components of the wind velocity along the arm are assumed to offer a negligible contribution to the torque which acts on the shaft.

Cups B and C are assumed to act as hemispherical shells with their convex sides exposed to the flow. From Table 24.1, $C_D = 0.41$ and

$$v = 51.3 \cos 60° = 25.7 \text{ ft/s} \qquad (24.63)$$

The drag forces are then

$$F_B = F_C = C_D(\tfrac{1}{2}\rho v^2)A \qquad (24.64)$$

$$= 0.41 \left[\frac{1}{2} \left(\frac{0.07637}{32.2} \right) (25.7)^2 \right] \frac{\pi(1.25)^2}{4(144)}$$

$$= 0.00274 \text{ lb} = 0.0438 \text{ oz} \qquad (24.65)$$

The torque exerted by the three cup forces on the shaft is

$$M = 0.574(3) + 2\,[0.0441(3)] = 1.99 \text{ in} \cdot \text{oz} \qquad (24.66)$$

24.5 QUADRATIC RESISTANCE LAW—APPLIED CONSTANT FORCE WITH SAME SENSE AS VELOCITY

In deriving the forms for the velocity and displacement for the case of a body which is acted on by quadratic resisting forces, a distinction must be made between applied forces which *assist* the motion and those which *oppose* the motion. The case will first be considered where the external applied force assists the motion. The free-body diagram for this case is shown in Fig. 24.12. The applied force P has a *constant* magnitude, and the drag force F_D is given by Eq. (24.54). The equation of motion is

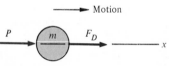

Fig. 24.12

$$P + F_D = m\frac{dv}{dt} \qquad (24.67)$$

$$P - C_D\left(\frac{1}{2}\rho v^2\right)A = m\frac{dv}{dt} \qquad (24.68)$$

$$\frac{dv}{dt} = \frac{P}{m} - \frac{C_D\rho A}{2m}v^2 \qquad (24.69)$$

Using the notations

$$\xi = \frac{P}{m} \qquad \zeta = \frac{C_D\rho A}{2m} \qquad (24.70)$$

we find that Eq. (24.69) has the form

$$\frac{dv}{dt} = \xi - \zeta v^2 \qquad (24.71)$$

The terminal velocity v_T is attained when the right side of Eq. (24.71) is equal to zero, or

$$\xi - \zeta v_T^2 = 0 \qquad v_T = \sqrt{\frac{\xi}{\zeta}} \qquad (24.72)$$

When the body reaches its terminal velocity, the resultant force acting on it is zero, since the applied force P is exactly balanced by the quadratic resisting force $C_D(\frac{1}{2}\rho v_T^2)A$.

Equation (24.71) may be written in the form

$$dt = \frac{dv}{\xi - \zeta v^2} = \frac{dv}{\xi[1 - (\zeta/\xi)v^2]} = \frac{dv}{\xi[1 - (v/v_T)^2]} \qquad (24.73)$$

At the beginning of the time interval of interest, $t = 0$ and $v = v_0$, and v and t are the values at the end of this interval. Equation (24.73) is now integrated, with the result

$$\int_0^t dt = \frac{1}{\xi} \int_{v_0}^v \frac{dv}{1 - (v/v_T)^2} \qquad (24.74)$$

Equation (24.74) is of the form

$$\int \frac{du}{1 - u^2} = \tanh^{-1} u + \text{const.} \qquad u < 1 \qquad (24.75)$$

where $\tanh^{-1} u$ is the inverse hyperbolic tangent and $\tanh u$ is defined by

$$\tanh u = \frac{e^u - e^{-u}}{e^u + e^{-u}} \qquad (24.76)$$

A plot of $\tanh u$, for positive u, is shown in Fig. 24.13. It may be seen that for large values of u, $\tanh u \to 1$.

Now the substitution

$$u = \frac{v}{v_T} \qquad du = \frac{1}{v_T} dv \qquad (24.77)$$

is made. Since, from physical considerations $v < v_T$, it follows that $u < 1$.

Equation (24.74) may now be written as

$$\int_0^t dt = \frac{v_T}{\xi} \int_{v_0}^v \frac{(1/v_T)\, dv}{1 - (v/v_T)^2} \qquad (24.78)$$

$$t \Big|_0^t = \frac{v_T}{\xi} \tanh^{-1} \frac{v}{v_T} \Big|_{v_0}^v \qquad (24.79)$$

$$t = \frac{v_T}{\xi} \left(\tanh^{-1} \frac{v}{v_T} - \tanh^{-1} \frac{v_0}{v_T} \right) \qquad v < v_T \quad (24.80)$$

Equation (24.80) may be solved for v, with the result

$$v = v_T \tanh \left(\frac{\xi t}{v_T} + \tanh^{-1} \frac{v_0}{v_T} \right) \qquad v < v_T \quad (24.81)$$

The displacement of the body is found from

$$dx = v\, dt \qquad (24.82)$$

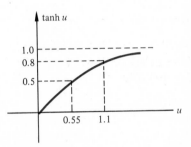

Fig. 24.13

Using Eq. (24.73), we get

$$dx = \frac{v \, dv}{\xi[1 - (v/v_T)^2]} \qquad (24.83)$$

$$\int_0^x dx = \frac{1}{\xi} \int_{v_0}^v \frac{v \, dv}{1 - (v/v_T)^2} \qquad (24.84)$$

Equation (24.84) is in the form

$$\int \frac{du}{u} = \ln u + \text{const.} \qquad (24.85)$$

and it may be written as

$$\int_0^x dx = \frac{v_T^2}{\xi(-2)} \int_{v_0}^v \frac{(-2) \, v \, dv}{v_T^2 - v^2} \qquad (24.86)$$

$$x \Big|_0^x = \frac{-v_T^2}{2\xi} \ln (v_T^2 - v^2) \Big|_{v_0}^v \qquad (24.87)$$

$$x = -\frac{v_T^2}{2\xi} [\ln (v_T^2 - v^2) - \ln (v_T^2 - v_0^2)] \qquad (24.88)$$

$$= \frac{v_T^2}{2\xi} \ln \frac{v_T^2 - v_0^2}{v_T^2 - v^2} \qquad v < v_T \qquad (24.89)$$

If the body starts from rest, with $v_0 = 0$, the velocity and displacement have the simplified forms

$$v = v_T \tanh \frac{\xi t}{v_T} \qquad (24.90)$$

$$x = \frac{v_T^2}{2\xi} \ln \frac{v_T^2}{v_T^2 - v^2} \qquad (24.91)$$

Equations (24.90) relates the time t of motion to the velocity v, while Eq. (24.91) relates the displacement x to the velocity v. If v is eliminated between these two equations, it can be shown that the result is

$$x = \frac{v_T^2}{2\xi} \ln \left(\cosh \frac{\xi t}{v_T} \right) \qquad (24.92)$$

The results for the case where the applied constant force has the same sense as the velocity are summarized here:

$$v_T = \sqrt{\frac{\xi}{\zeta}} \qquad \xi = \frac{P}{m} \qquad \xi = \frac{C_D \rho A}{2m} \qquad (24.93)$$

$$v = v_T \tanh \left(\frac{\xi t}{v_T} + \tanh^{-1} \frac{v_0}{v_T} \right) \qquad v_0 \neq 0 \qquad (24.94)$$

$$x = \frac{v_T^2}{2\xi} \ln \frac{v_T^2 - v_0^2}{v_T^2 - v^2} \qquad\qquad v_0 \neq 0 \qquad (24.95)$$

$$v = v_T \tanh \frac{\xi t}{v_T} \qquad\qquad v_0 = 0 \qquad (24.96)$$

$$x = \frac{v_T^2}{2\xi} \ln \frac{v_T^2}{v_T^2 - v^2} \qquad\qquad v_0 = 0 \qquad (24.97)$$

Example 24.5 Figure 24.14 shows a parachutist in free flight in the absence of any cross winds. The weight of the person is 225 lb, and the weight of the chute and rigging is 25 lb.

a Find the terminal velocity of the parachutist. Assume standard air at 14.7 psia and 60°F, with a specific weight of 0.07637 lb/ft³.

b Do the same as in part *a* if a person of slight build, who weighs 100 lb, uses the rig.

Fig. 24.14

Solution **a** The weight W of the person and the parachute is a force which assists the motion, so that

$$P = W \qquad (24.98)$$

and

$$\xi = \frac{P}{m} = \frac{W}{W/g} = g = 32.2 \frac{\text{ft}}{\text{s}} \qquad (24.99)$$

The projected area of the parachute is

$$A = \frac{\pi (20)^2}{4} = 314 \text{ ft}^2 \qquad (24.100)$$

The value of the drag coefficient, from Table 24.1, is 1.35, and

$$\zeta = \frac{C_D \rho A}{2m} = \frac{1.35 \, (0.07637/32.2)(314)}{2(250/32.2)} = 0.0647 \text{ ft}^{-1} \quad (24.101)$$

The terminal velocity then has the value

$$v_T = \sqrt{\frac{\xi}{\zeta}} = \sqrt{\frac{32.2}{0.0647}} = 22.3 \frac{\text{ft}}{\text{s}} = 15.2 \frac{\text{mi}}{\text{h}} \qquad (24.102)$$

b With a chutist of weight 100 lb, the total weight of the assembly is 125 lb. Thus

$$\zeta = \frac{C_D \rho A}{2m} = \frac{1.35 \, (0.07637/32.2)(314)}{2 \, (125/32.2)} = 0.129 \text{ ft}^{-1} \quad (24.103)$$

$$v_T = \sqrt{\frac{\xi}{\zeta}} = \sqrt{\frac{32.2}{0.129}} = 15.8 \frac{\text{ft}}{\text{s}} = 10.8 \frac{\text{mi}}{\text{h}} \qquad (24.104)$$

The terminal velocity of the heavier person is greater than that of the person of slight build by

$$\%D = \frac{22.3 - 15.8}{15.8} (100) = 41\% \qquad (24.105)$$

If one contemplates sky diving, this result argues strongly for the benefits of not being overweight!

24.6 QUADRATIC RESISTANCE LAW—APPLIED CONSTANT FORCE WITH SENSE OPPOSITE THAT OF VELOCITY

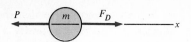

Fig. 24.15

Figure 24.15 shows the free-body diagram for the case where the constant applied force P opposes the motion of the body. The drag force, as before, is positive when it acts in the positive coordinate sense, with the functional form given by Eq. (24.54) as

$$F_D = -C_D \left(\tfrac{1}{2}\rho v^2\right)A \qquad (24.106)$$

The equation of motion is

$$-P + F_D = m\frac{dv}{dt} \qquad (24.107)$$

$$-P - C_D \left(\tfrac{1}{2}\rho v^2\right)A = m\frac{dv}{dt} \qquad (24.108)$$

$$\frac{dv}{dt} = -\frac{P}{m} - \frac{C_D\rho A}{2m}v^2 \qquad (24.109)$$

By using the quantities ξ and ζ, defined earlier as

$$\xi = \frac{P}{m} \qquad \zeta = \frac{C_D\rho A}{2m} \qquad (24.110)$$

Eq. (24.109) appears as

$$\frac{dv}{dt} = -\xi - \zeta v^2 \qquad (24.111)$$

Inspection of Eq. (24.111) leads to a very significant conclusion for the case where the applied force opposes the motion. Since the right side of the equation is *always* negative, and never zero, it follows that

1. The rate of change of the velocity is always negative, so that the velocity may only decrease from some initial value.

2. A terminal velocity *does not exist for* this type of problem. The parameters ξ and ζ were related to each other earlier, in Eq. (24.72), by

$$v_T = \sqrt{\frac{\xi}{\zeta}} \qquad (24.112)$$

For the case where the applied force assists motion, the quantity v_T had the interpretation of a terminal velocity. Although a terminal velocity does not exist in the present problem, Eq. (24.112) will be used in the form

$$v_T^* = \sqrt{\frac{\xi}{\zeta}} \qquad (24.113)$$

902

The asterisk is used to emphasize that the quantity v_T^* is not a terminal velocity, but rather a quantity which is defined by the above equation. By using this result, Eq. (24.111) may be written as

$$dt = \frac{-dv}{\xi[1 + (v/v_T^*)^2]} \qquad (24.114)$$

$$\int_0^t dt = -\frac{1}{\xi} \int_{v_0}^v \frac{dv}{1 + (v/v_T^*)^2} \qquad (24.115)$$

Equation (24.115) of the form

$$\int \frac{du}{a + bu^2} = \frac{1}{\sqrt{ab}} \tan^{-1} \sqrt{\frac{b}{a}} u + \text{const.} \qquad a > 0, \ b > 0$$

$$(24.116)$$

With the substitutions

$$a = 1 > 0 \qquad b = \frac{1}{(v_T^*)^2} > 0 \qquad u = v \qquad du = dv \quad (24.117)$$

Eq. (24.115) may be integrated directly, with the result

$$t \Big|_0^t = -\frac{1}{\xi} \left(\frac{1}{1/v_T^*} \right) \tan^{-1} \sqrt{\frac{1}{(v_T^*)^2}} v \Big|_{v_0}^v \qquad (24.118)$$

$$t = \frac{v_T^*}{\xi} \left(\tan^{-1} \frac{v_0}{v_T^*} - \tan^{-1} \frac{v}{v_T^*} \right) \qquad (24.119)$$

This equation may be solved for v:

$$v = v_T^* \tan \left(\tan^{-1} \frac{v_0}{v_T^*} - \frac{\xi t}{v_T^*} \right) \qquad (24.120)$$

When the body comes to rest, $v = 0$ and the corresponding time t_m may be found from the above equation as

$$t_m = \frac{v_T^*}{\xi} \tan^{-1} \frac{v_0}{v_T^*} \qquad (24.121)$$

The displacement is found by using Eq. (24.114), together with

$$dx = v \, dt \qquad (24.122)$$

in the form

$$dx = \frac{-v \, dv}{\xi[1 + (v/v_T^*)^2]} \qquad (24.123)$$

Equation (24.124) is in the form of Eq. (24.85), and

$$\int_0^x dx = -\frac{1}{\xi} \int_{v_0}^v \frac{v \, dv}{1 + (v/v_T^*)^2} = -\frac{1}{\xi} \frac{(v_T^*)^2}{2} \int_{v_0}^v \frac{[2/(v_T^*)^2] v \, dv}{1 + (v/v_T^*)^2}$$

$$(24.124)$$

$$x \bigg|_0^x = -\frac{(v_T^*)^2}{2\xi} \ln\left[1 + \left(\frac{v}{v_T^*}\right)^2\right]_{v_0}^v \tag{24.125}$$

$$x = -\frac{(v_T^*)^2}{2\xi}\left\{\ln\left[1 + \left(\frac{v}{v_T^*}\right)^2\right] - \ln\left[1 + \left(\frac{v_0}{v_T^*}\right)^2\right]\right\} \tag{24.126}$$

$$= \frac{(v_T^*)^2}{2\xi} \ln\frac{(v_T^*)^2 + v_0^2}{(v_T^*)^2 + v^2} \tag{24.127}$$

When the body comes to rest, $v = 0$ and the corresponding displacement x_m is found from Eq. (24.127) as

$$x_m = \frac{(v_T^*)^2}{2\xi} \ln\frac{(v_T^*)^2 + v_0^2}{(v_T^*)^2} \tag{24.128}$$

The results for the case where the applied constant force has a sense opposite that of the velocity are summarized here:

$$v_T^* = \sqrt{\frac{\xi}{\zeta}} \qquad \xi = \frac{P}{m} \qquad \zeta = \frac{C_D \rho A}{2m} \tag{24.129}$$

$$v = v_T^* \tan\left(\tan^{-1}\frac{v_0}{v_T^*} - \frac{\xi t}{v_T^*}\right) \tag{24.130}$$

$$x = \frac{(v_T^*)^2}{2\xi} \ln\frac{(v_T^*)^2 + v_0^2}{(v_T^*)^2 + v^2} \tag{24.131}$$

The time and displacement when the body comes to rest are

$$t_m = \frac{v_T^*}{\xi} \tan^{-1}\frac{v_0}{v_T^*} \tag{24.132}$$

$$x_m = \frac{(v_T^*)^2}{2\xi} \ln\frac{(v_T^*)^2 + v_0^2}{(v_T^*)^2} \tag{24.133}$$

Example 24.6 A ball is projected vertically upward from the ground with an initial velocity of 70 ft/s. The ball is 2.5 in in diameter and weighs 0.1 lb, and standard air of 14.7 psia and 60°F is assumed.

a Estimate the maximum height which the ball attains, and the corresponding time.

b Do the same as in part a for the case where the drag force is assumed to be zero.

c Estimate the time for the ball to fall from the maximum height to the ground, and the velocity with which it strikes the ground.

d Do the same as in part c for the case where the drag force is assumed to be zero.

e Find the values of the drag force and the resultant force on the ball at the instant of launch and when the ball strikes the earth.

f Find the total energy expended in overcoming the viscous drag forces.

Solution
a The drag force effects on the ball will be assumed to be the same

as those of a hemispherical shell whose convex side is in the sense of motion. Thus, from Table 24.1,

$$C_D = 0.41 \tag{24.134}$$

Additional terms which are required are

$$\xi = g = 32.2 \text{ ft/s}^2 \tag{24.135}$$

$$\zeta = \frac{C_D \rho A}{2m} \tag{24.136}$$

$$= \frac{0.41\,(0.07637/g)\,\pi\,(2.5)^2/[4(144)]}{2\,(0.1/g)} = 5.34 \times 10^{-3} \text{ ft}^{-1} \tag{24.137}$$

$$v_T = v_T^* = \sqrt{\frac{\xi}{\zeta}} = \sqrt{\frac{32.2}{5.34 \times 10^{-3}}} = 77.7\,\frac{\text{ft}}{\text{s}} \tag{24.138}$$

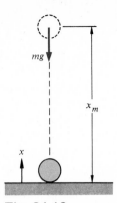

Fig. 24.16

Figure 24.16 shows the ascent phase of the flight, and the weight force opposes the motion. Using Eq. (24.133), we find the maximum height attained is

$$x_m = \frac{(v_T^*)^2}{2\xi} \ln \frac{(v_T^*)^2 + v_0^2}{(v_T^*)^2} \tag{24.139}$$

$$= \frac{77.7^2}{2(32.2)} \ln \frac{77.7^2 + 70^2}{77.7^2} = 55.7 \text{ ft} \tag{24.140}$$

The time to reach this height is found from Eq. (24.132) as

$$t_m = \frac{v_T^*}{\xi} \tan^{-1} \frac{v_0}{v_T} = \frac{77.7}{32.2} \tan^{-1} \frac{70}{77.7} = 1.77 \text{ s} \tag{24.141}$$

b For the ideal case, where the drag force is absent,

$$v^2 = v_0^2 + 2ax \qquad 0 = v_0^2 - 2gx_m \tag{24.142}$$

$$0 = 70^2 - 2\,(32.2)\,x_m \qquad x_m = 76.1 \text{ ft} \tag{24.143}$$

The time required to reach this height is found from

$$v = v_0 + at \qquad 0 = v_0 - gt_m \tag{24.144}$$

$$0 = 70 - 32.2\,t_m \qquad t_m = 2.17 \text{ s} \tag{24.145}$$

Comparison of this result with Eq. (24.141) reveals that the actual time of flight during ascent is less than the theoretical time. Because of the drag forces, the ball attains a height which is only $(55.7/76.1)100 = 73.2$ percent of the height theoretically possible.

c As the ball returns from the maximum height to the ground, the weight force assists the motion. The ball starts this regime of motion with zero initial velocity. Using Eq. (24.91), we have

$$x = \frac{v_T^2}{2\xi} \ln\left(\cosh \frac{\xi t}{v_T}\right) \tag{24.146}$$

$$55.7 = \frac{77.7^2}{2(32.2)} \ln\left(\cosh \frac{32.2t}{77.7}\right) \tag{24.147}$$

$$\ln\left(\cosh \frac{32.2t}{77.7}\right) = 0.594 \tag{24.148}$$

$$\cosh \frac{32.2t}{77.7} = e^{0.594} = 1.81 \tag{24.149}$$

$$\frac{32.2t}{77.7} = 1.20 \qquad t = 2.90 \text{ s} \qquad (24.150)$$

The velocity with which the ball strikes the ground is found from Eq. (24.96) as

$$v = v_T \tanh \frac{\xi t}{v_T} = 77.7 \tanh \frac{32.2(2.90)}{77.7} = 64.8 \frac{\text{ft}}{\text{s}} \qquad (24.151)$$

The percent difference between the initial launch velocity and the velocity when the ball returns to the ground is

$$\%D = \frac{70 - 64.8}{70}(100) = 7.4\% \qquad (24.152)$$

d For the case where the drag forces are absent, the descent time is the *same* as the ascent time, given by Eq. (24.145) as 2.17 s. The velocity with which the ball strikes the ground is the same as the initial velocity of 70 ft/s with which the ball leaves the ground.
e The drag force on the ball, from Eq. (24.54), is

$$F_D = C_D \left(\frac{1}{2}\rho v^2 \right) A = 0.41 \left[\frac{1}{2}\left(\frac{0.07637}{32.2} v^2 \right) \right] \frac{\pi(2.5)^2}{4(144)} = 1.66 \times 10^{-5} v^2$$
$$(24.153)$$

where F_D is in pounds and v is in feet per second. At the instant of launch

$$v = v_0 = 70 \text{ ft/s} \qquad F_D = 1.66 \times 10^{-5}(70)^2 = 0.0813 \text{ lb} \quad (24.154)$$

when the ball strikes the ground,

$$v = 64.8 \text{ ft/s} \qquad F_D = 1.66 \times 10^{-5}(64.8)^2 = 0.0697 \text{ lb} \quad (24.155)$$

The free-body diagrams for the above two configurations are shown in Fig. 24.17.

f The ground is taken as the datum for potential energy. When the ball leaves the ground, it has zero potential energy and an initial kinetic energy given by

$$T_1 = \frac{1}{2}mv_0^2 = \frac{1}{2}\left(\frac{0.1}{32.2} \right)70^2 = 7.61 \text{ ft} \cdot \text{lb} \qquad (24.156)$$

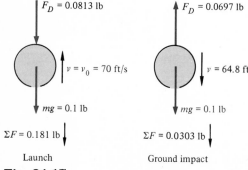

Launch   Ground impact

Fig. 24.17

When the ball contacts the ground, it again has zero potential energy, and its kinetic energy is

$$T_2 = \frac{1}{2}mv_f^2 = \frac{1}{2}\left(\frac{0.1}{32.2}\right)(64.8)^2 = 6.52 \text{ ft·lb} \qquad (24.157)$$

The difference

$$\Delta T = 7.61 - 6.52 = 1.09 \text{ ft·lb} \qquad (24.158)$$

is the energy expended in overcoming the drag forces on the ball. The permanent percent loss of the initial energy is

$$\%D = \frac{1.09}{7.61}(100) = 14.3\% \qquad (24.159)$$

24.7 SUMMARY

The sole effect of a drag force which acts on a body is to transform a part of the kinetic energy of the body to heat energy, with an unrecoverable decrease in velocity.

If the motion of the body is resisted by sliding Coulomb friction forces as the first body slides relative to a second body, then the drag force may be assumed to be a constant, with the form

$$F_D = -\mu_k N \qquad (24.160)$$

where N is the normal contact force between the sliding surfaces and μ_k is the coefficient of kinetic friction. In Eq. (24.160) F_D is positive in the same sense as the velocity, and the minus sign indicates that the drag force opposes the motion.

If viscous resistance to motion is assumed, the form of the drag force is

$$F_D = -cv \qquad (24.161)$$

where c is a constant. This type of motion is observed (1) where surfaces which move with low relative velocity relative to one another are separated by a thin layer of lubricant and (2) in the motion of submerged bodies at very low velocities. The minus sign in Eq. (24.162) automatically adjusts the sense of the drag force to oppose the motion.

If the predominant drag force effect is due to differences in pressure acting on the body, a quadratic resistance law may be assumed, and the drag force has the form

$$F_D = - C_D\left(\frac{1}{2}\rho v^2\right)A \qquad (24.169)$$

where A is the projected area of the body on a plane which is normal to the direction of the motion, ρ is the mass density of the fluid medium through which the body moves, and C_D is the drag coefficient. A quadratic resistance law may be assumed if the body has plane (or slightly curved) surfaces which are normal to the direction of motion or has sharp edges where the fluid loses contact with the body.

When the body reaches a terminal velocity, the resultant force which acts on it is zero.

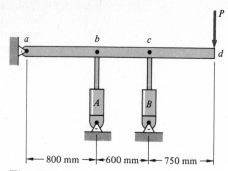

Fig. P24.1

PROBLEMS

24.1 The rigid arm in Fig. P24.1 is connected to two viscous dampers. $c_A = 0.70\ \text{N} \cdot \text{s/m}$ and $c_B = 0.58\ \text{N} \cdot \text{s/m}$. A force P is applied to the arm and end d moves downward with an initial velocity of 4 m/s.

(a) Find the initial force in each damper.

(b) Find the value of force P and the hinge-pin force.

24.2 Find the initial velocity of end d of the arm in Fig. P24.1, if a vertical force of 250 N is applied to the arm at point c.

24.3 (a) A vertical force is to be applied to the arm in Fig. P24.1. How far from the hinge pin should this force be applied, if the initial value of the hinge pin force is to be zero?

(b) Find the initial forces in dampers A and B, if a 400 N force is applied at the location found in part a.

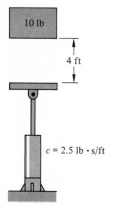

Fig. P24.4

24.4 Figure P24.4 shows a model of a proposed shock-absorbing device. A weight falls vertically and imparts an initial velocity to a platform. The platform is connected to the ground by a telescoping cylinder arrangement which is filled with oil. Plastic impact between the weight and the platform is assumed, and the resisting force exerted by the cylinder rod is assumed to be viscous.

(a) Find the initial velocity of the platform.

(b) Find the velocity and displacement of the platform at the end of 1, 2, and 3 s.

(c) Find the energy dissipated by the cylinder at the times in part b.

(d) Find the maximum height from which the weight may be dropped onto the platform, if the maximum strength of the platform pin is 90 lb.

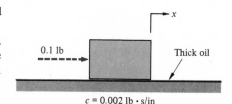

Fig. P24.5

24.5 The 0.25-lb block shown in Fig. P24.5 is at rest on a horizontal plane coated with a thick oil. The drag force on the block is assumed to be viscous. At $t = 0$, the horizontal force shown in the figure is applied to the block. This force is removed 1.8 s later.

(a) Find the velocity and displacement of the block at the instant that the force is removed.

(b) Find the additional distance through which the block moves before it comes to rest.

(c) Find the maximum value of the drag force that acts on the block.

(d) Find the total energy loss during the motion of the block.

24.6 The block and plane in Fig. P24.5 are thoroughly cleaned of the oil. An experimental measurement of the coefficient of kinetic friction yields a value of 0.08 for this quantity. Do the same as in Prob. 24.5, assuming the drag force to be constant.

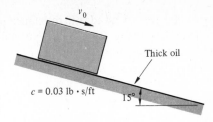

24.7 The inclined plane surface in Fig. P24.7 is coated with a heavy lubricant, and viscous resistance is assumed. At $t = 0$ the 5-lb block is given an initial velocity $v_o = 8$ ft/s down the plane.
(a) Find the value of the terminal velocity.
(b) Find the velocity and displacement of the block when $t = 2.6$ s.
(c) Find the energy loss at the time in part b.
(d) Find the maximum value of the drag force.
(e) Find the time when the velocity of the block has reached 98 percent of the value of the terminal velocity.

Fig. P24.7

24.8 Figure P24.8 shows a spherical body submerged in a liquid. It is shown in texts in fluid mechanics that if the velocity of the body is sufficiently small, the drag force is given by Stoke's law as $F_D = -3\pi\mu\, vd$, where v is the velocity and μ, a property of the liquid, is the absolute viscosity. The units of this latter quantity are the product of force and time divided by area. It can be shown that Stoke's law is valid if $(vd\,\rho/\mu) < 1$, where ρ is the mass density of the liquid. Find the viscous drag force constant for a sphere that moves with Stoke's law motion.

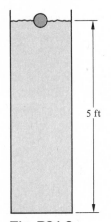

Fig. P24.8

24.9 Figure P24.9 shows a tall cylindrical tank filled with a heavy oil with a specific gravity of 0.92 and an absolute viscosity of 0.01 lb·s/ft². A steel sphere, of specific weight 0.283 lb/in³, is released from rest at the surface at $t = 0$. $d = 0.125$ in.
(a) Find the terminal velocity of the sphere.
(b) Find the value of the velocity and displacement of the sphere at $t = 1$ s.
(c) Estimate the time at which the sphere strikes the bottom of the tank, and the corresponding value of the velocity.

24.10 Do the same as in Prob. 24.9 if the sphere is aluminum, with a specific weight of 0.1 lb/in³.

24.11 Do the same as in Prob. 24.9 if the sphere is lead, with a specific weight of 0.411 lb/in³.

24.12 Figure P24.12 shows two spheres that are released from rest at the same instant at the free surface of the column of liquid shown in Fig. P24.9. Sphere A is bronze, with $d_A = 0.4$ in and $\gamma_A = 0.318$ lb/in³. Sphere B is magnesium, with $\gamma_B = 0.0659$ lb/in³. Find the required value of the diameter of sphere B, if the two spheres are to strike the bottom at the same instant.

Fig. P24.9

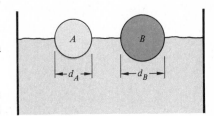

Fig. P24.12

Note: Where required in the following problems, standard air has a specific weight of 0.07637 lb/ft³ and a density of 1.22 kg/m³.

24.13 Figure P24.13 shows a temporary wall at a construction site. A wind with a velocity of 50 km/h and the direction shown in the figure acts on the wall. Find the resultant force that acts on the wall.

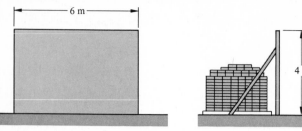

Fig. P24.13

24.14 A large cylindrical storage tank is transported on a flatbed trailer, as shown in Fig. P24.14.

(*a*) Estimate the value of the drag force of the atmosphere on the tank when the truck travels at 25 mi/h.

(*b*) Find the power loss caused by the drag force in part *a*.

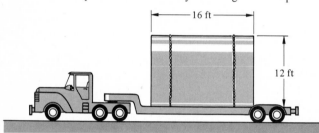

Fig. P24.14

24.15 Figure P24.15 shows a stirring blade arrangement used to agitate a water soluble chemical solution. The constant power input into the system is 3,400 W.

(*a*) Estimate the angular velocity of the shaft.

(*b*) Estimate the force exerted on each of the disk-shaped parts of the blade.

24.16 The packing crate with a uniform mass distribution shown in Fig. P24.16 rests on a rough ground surface. The crate is exposed to a wind of constant velocity *v* with the direction shown in the figure. Estimate the value of *v* that will cause tipping motion of the crate to be impending. The crate is 25 kg

24.17 Figure P24.17 shows a light-weight, high-speed elevator for a high-rise building. The floor of the elevator has the form of a square with 3.5 m sides. The total mass of the elevator and passengers is 1,700 kg. The elevator shaftway has unobstructed sides for free circulation of air.

(*a*) Estimate the drag force when the elevator moves upward at 15 m/s.

(*b*) Find the corresponding value of the cable force.

(*c*) Find the power required to overcome the drag force.

(*d*) Find the total power required to raise the elevator.

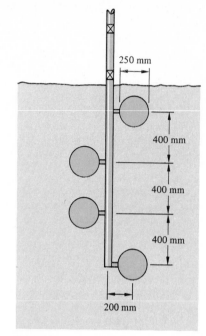

Fig. P24.15

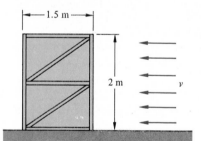

Fig. P24.16

Fig. P24.17

24.18 The 3,000 lb van shown in Fig. P24.18 travels along a horizontal roadway with constant speed. The frontal area is 36 ft². $W = 2,600$ lb.

(a) Estimate the drag force, and the power required to overcome this force, when the van travels at 30 mi/h.

(b) Do the same as in part a, for a speed of 50 mi/h.

(c) Do the same as in part a, for a speed of 70 m/h.

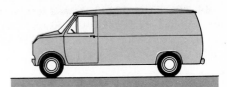

Fig. P24.18

24.19 The van of Prob. P24.18 rolls down the incline shown in Fig. P24.19.

(a) Find for what value of β the van would move at a constant speed of 20 mi/h.

(b) Find the power dissipation that corresponds to the condition in part a.

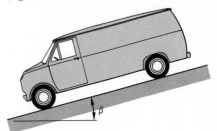

Fig. P24.19

24.20 Figure P24.20 shows a proposed device to stir liquid in a very shallow tank. The wheels rotate at 5 r/min and the length of each blade is 5 ft. The liquid is carbon tetrachloride, with a specific weight of 99.5 lb/ft³. Estimate the power required to operate the unit.

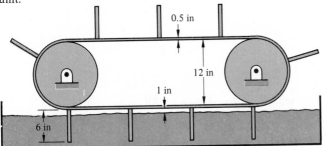

Fig. P24.20

24.21 Figure P24.21 shows a steel boat anchor with a mass of 25 kg. The anchor is released at the surface of a lake with zero initial velocity, and the depth of the lake is 10 m. Assume that the line attached to the anchor offers no resistance as this latter element sinks into the water. Diameter is 300 mm.

(a) Find the velocity and displacement of the anchor at the end of 1, 2, and 3 s.

(b) Find the time at which the anchor strikes the bottom of the lake.

(c) Find the maximum value of the drag force that acts on the anchor during its descent.

Fig. P24.21

24.22 Do the same as in Prob. 24.21 if the anchor, with the same dimensions, is made of lead with a density of 11,400 kg/m³.

24.23 Figure P24.23 shows a diving bell on the floor of the ocean. The bell has a spherical shape, is 8 ft in diameter, and weighs 40 tons.

(a) Find the cable force required to raise the bell at the rate of 10 ft/min.

(b) Find the value of the drag force.

(c) Find the power required for the condition of part a.

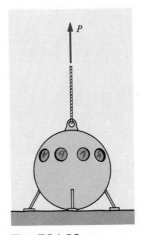

Fig. P24.23

24.24 Do the same as in Prob. 24.23, if the diving bell is to be raised at the rate of 25 ft/min.

24.25 Find the force in the cable that supports the diving bell in Prob. 24.23, as this element is lowered at a rate of 80 ft/min.

24.26 A man tosses a beach ball vertically upward. The ball leaves the man's hand at a position 2 m above the ground. The ball reaches a maximum height of 6 m above the ground. The man subsequently catches the ball when this element is 1.5 m above the ground. The mass of the ball is 0.14 kg and the diameter is 100 mm.
  (a) Find the time at which the maximum height is reached.
  (b) Find the total time of the flight.
  (c) Find the velocity of the ball when the man catches it.

24.27 A child drops the beach ball of prob. 24.26 from a motel balcony which is 8 m above the ground. Simultaneously, another child drops a small pebble from the same balcony. Estimate the time interval between the time when the ball strikes the ground and the time when the pebble strikes the ground.

24.28 Do the same as in Prob. 24.26 if the ball is filled with sea water with a density of 1,030 kg/m³.

24.29 A full can of soda rolls off a boat deck and is assumed to strike the surface of a lake, at $t = 0$, in the position shown in Fig. P24.29. The weight of the empty soda can is 0.14 lb, and the can is assumed to move with rectilinear translation as it sinks into the water.
  (a) Estimate the velocity and displacement of the can of soda at $t = 1$, 2, and 3 s.
  (b) Find the maximum value of the drag force in the time interval $0 \le t \le 3$s.

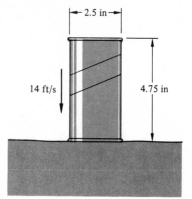

Fig. P24.29

Appendix

Multiplication Factor	Prefix	Symbol	Multiplication Factor	Prefix	Symbol
$1\ 000\ 000\ 000\ 000\ 000\ 000 = 10^{18}$ $1\ 000\ 000\ 000\ 000\ 000 = 10^{15}$	exa peta	E P	$0.1 = 10^{-1}$ $0.01 = 10^{-2}$ $0.001 = 10^{-3}$	deci* centi* milli	d c m
$1\ 000\ 000\ 000\ 000 = 10^{12}$ $1\ 000\ 000\ 000 = 10^{9}$ $1\ 000\ 000 = 10^{6}$	tera giga mega	T G M	$0.000\ 001 = 10^{-6}$ $0.000\ 000\ 001 = 10^{-9}$ $0.000\ 000\ 000\ 001 = 10^{-12}$	micro nano pico	μ n p
$1\ 000 = 10^{3}$ $100 = 10^{2}$ $10 = 10^{1}$	kilo hecto deka	k h da	$0.000\ 000\ 000\ 000\ 001 = 10^{-15}$ $0.000\ 000\ 000\ 000\ 000\ 001 = 10^{-18}$	femto atto	f a

TYPICAL CONVERSION FACTORS BETWEEN USCS AND SI UNITS

To Convert From	To	Multiply By
foot (ft)	meter (m)	$3.048\ 000\text{*E}-01$
ft^2	meter^2 (m^2)	$9.290\quad\text{E}-02$
ft^3	meter^3 (m^3)	$2.832\quad\text{E}-02$
ft^4	meter^4 (m^4)	$8.631\quad\text{E}-03$
ft/min	meter per second (m/s)	$5.080\quad\text{*E}-03$
ft/s	meter per second (m/s)	$3.048\quad\text{*E}-01$
ft/s^2	meter per second^2 (m/s^2)	$3.048\quad\text{*E}-01$
inch (in)	meter (m)	$2.540\quad\text{*E}-02$
in^2	meter^2 (m^2)	$6.452\quad\text{*E}-04$
in^3	meter^3 (m^3)	$1.639\quad\text{E}-05$
in^4	meter^4 (m^4)	$4.162\quad\text{E}-07$
kip (1000 lb)	newton (N)	$4.448\quad\text{E}+03$
kip/in^2 (ksi)	pascal (Pa)	$6.895\quad\text{E}+06$
mile (mi)	meter (m)	$1.609\quad\text{*E}+03$
mi^2	meter^2 (m^2)	$2.589\quad\text{E}+06$
pound (lb)	newton (N)	$4.448\quad\text{E}+00$
lb·ft	newton meter (N·m)	$1.356\quad\text{E}+00$
lb·ft/in	newton meter per meter (N·m/m)	$5.338\quad\text{E}+01$
lb·in	newton meter (N·m)	$1.130\quad\text{E}-01$
lb·in/in	newton meter per meter (N·m/m)	$4.448\quad\text{E}+00$
lb/ft	newton per meter (N/m)	$1.459\quad\text{E}+01$
lb/ft^2	pascal (Pa)	$4.788\quad\text{E}+01$
lb/in	newton per meter (N/m)	$1.751\quad\text{E}+02$
lb/in^2 (psi)	pascal (Pa)	$6.895\quad\text{E}+03$
slug	kilogram (kg)	$1.459\quad\text{E}+01$
slug/ft^3	kilogram per meter^3 (kg/m^3)	$5.154\quad\text{E}+02$
yard (yd)	meter (m)	$9.144\quad\text{*E}-01$
yd^2	meter^2 (m^2)	$8.361\quad\text{E}-01$
yd^3	meter^3 (m^3)	$7.646\ 549\ \text{E}-01$

* The standard usage of SI units discourages the use of *centi* and *deci* prefixes in technical work.

List of Symbols

a	Radius of a circle, scalar points, lengths, multiplier, acceleration
$\mathbf{A}$	General vector quantity
A	Magnitude of $\mathbf{A}$; area, mass element
$\mathbf{a}$	Acceleration
$\mathbf{a}_{ab}$	Relative acceleration
$\mathbf{a}_c$	Acceleration of the center of mass (CM)
a_n	Normal acceleration
a_t	Tangential acceleration
a_x, a_y, a_z	xyz components of acceleration
$b, c, d, \ldots$	Points, lengths
$\mathbf{B}, \mathbf{C}, \ldots$	General vector quantities
$B, C, \ldots$	Magnitudes of $\mathbf{B}, \mathbf{C}, \ldots$, mass elements
B_x, B_y, B_z	xyz components of $\mathbf{B}$
C_D	Drag coefficient
d_x, d_y	Separation distances between xy axes and centroidal x_0, y_0 axes
d_x, d_y, d_z	Lengths
$\mathbf{F}, \mathbf{F}_1, \mathbf{F}_2, \ldots$	Forces
$F, F_1, F_2, \ldots$	Magnitudes of $\mathbf{F}, \mathbf{F}_1, \mathbf{F}_2, \ldots$
F_D	Drag force
F_n	Normal component of force
F_t	Tangential component of force
F_x, F_y, F_z	xyz components of $\mathbf{F}$
$F_{x'}, F_{y'}$	Components of $\mathbf{F}$ along x' and y' axes
$F_{\min}$	Minimum value of $\mathbf{F}$
$F_{\max}$	Maximum value of $\mathbf{F}$
g	Acceleration of gravity
i	$1, 2, 3, \ldots$
I_x, I_y, I_z	Moment of inertia of a plane area, curve, or mass about xyz axes
I_{0x}, I_{0y}, I_{0z}	Centroidal moment of inertia of a plane area, curve, or mass above $x_0 y_0 z_0$ axes
J	Polar moment of inertia of a plane area or curve
J_0	Centroidal polar moment of inertia of a plane area or curve
k_x, k_y, k_z	Radii of gyration
l	Length of a straight or curved line
m	Mass
$\mathbf{M}$	Moment, or couple
M	Magnitudes of $\mathbf{M}$
$M_a, M_b, \ldots$	Moments about points $a, b, \ldots$
M_0	Applied moment
n	Number of forces in system

$N, N_a, N_b, \ldots$	Compressive normal reaction forces
P	Force
$\mathbf{P}, \mathbf{P}_1, \mathbf{P}_2$	Forces
$P, P_1, P_2, \ldots$	Magnitude of $\mathbf{P}, \mathbf{P}_1, \mathbf{P}_2$
$\mathbf{R}\ \mathbf{r}$	Position vector
S	Displacement
$\mathbf{S}$	Displacement
$\mathbf{S}_{ab}$	Relative displacement
SG	Specific gravity
t	Thickness of a plate
T	Force
M	Torque, or moment
v	Velocity
$\mathbf{v}$	Velocity
$\mathbf{v}_{ab}$	Relative velocity
v_x, v_y, v_z	xyz components of velocity
v_{0x}, v_{0y}	xy components of initial velocity
W	Weight
x, y, z	Coordinate axes
x', y'	Coordinate axes
x_c, y_c, z_c	Coordinates of centroid of a body
x_0, y_0	Coordinate axes through the centroid
α	Angular acceleration
β	Angle
γ	Specific weight, angle
θ	Angular displacement
ρ	Mass density, radius of curvature
μ_s	Coefficient of static friction
μ_k	Coefficient of kinetic friction
ω	Angular velocity

Index

Index

Answers to Odd-Numbered Problems

Note: All solutions are computed using three significant figures. The maximum error to be expected when using three significant figures is 1 percent, and all comparisons should be made in accordance with this criterion. In certain problems, final values are obtained from a sequence of several discrete calculations. Errors may accumulate in these types of problems, so the maximum error in the final answer may be several times greater than the value of 1 percent.

Chapter 15

15.1 (a) $v = 32$ m/s, $a = 0$ (b) $t = 0$:
$S = -50$ m, $v = 32$ m/s, $a = 0$; $t = 4$ s: $s = 78$ m,
$v = 32$ m/s, $a = 0$ (c) $v_{avg} = 32$ m/s, $a_{avg} = 0$
(d) None   (e) $t = 1.56$ s, $v = 32$ m/s, $a = 0$
15.3 (a) $v = 4t + 9$ ft/s, $a = 4$ ft/s^2 (b) $t = 0$:
$s = 10$ ft, $v = 9$ ft/s, $a = 4$ ft/s^2, $t = 4$ s: $s = 78$ ft,
$v = 25$ ft/s, $a = 4$ ft/s^2 (c) $v_{avg} = 17$ ft/s,
$a_{avg} = 4$ ft/s^2 (d) None   (e) None
15.5 (a) $v = 0.5e^{-0.5t}$ m/s,
$a = -0.25e^{-0.5t}$ m/s^2 (b) $t = 0$: $s = 0$,
$v = 0.5$ m/s, $a = -0.25$ m/s^2; $t = 4$ s: $s = 0.865$ m,
$v = 0.0677$ m/s, $a = -0.0338$ m/s^2
(c) $v_{avg} = 0.216$ m/s, $a_{avg} = 0.108$ m/s^2
(d) None   (e) $t = 0$, $v = 0.5$ m/s, $a = -0.25$ m/s^2
15.7 (a) $a = -2.06$ ft/s^2, $b = 29.3$ ft/s
(c) $v = -4.12t + 29.3$ ft/s, $a = -4.12$ ft/s^2
(d) $v_{avg} = -10$ ft/s   (e) No
15.9 (a) $a = 52$ ft/s^2, $b = -108$ ft/s
(c) $v = 104t - 108$ ft/s, $a = 104$ ft/s^2
(d) $v_{avg} = 100$ ft/s   (e) $t = 2$ s, $s = 0$
15.11 (a) $t = 2$ s: $v = 24$ m/s, $s = 24$ m; $t = 4$ s:
$v = 48$ m/s, $s = 96$ m   (b) $v_{avg, 0-2} = 12$ m/s,
$v_{avg, 2-4} = 36$ m/s, $v_{avg, 0-4} = 22.5$ m/s,
$a_{avg, 0-2} = a_{avg, 2-4} = a_{avg, 0-4} = 12$ m/s^2 (c) $t = 0$,
$v = 0$, $a = 12$ m/s^2
15.13 (a) $t = 2$ s: $v = 0.4$ m/s, $s = 0.267$ m,
$t = 4$ s: $v = 1.6$ m/s, $s = 2.13$ m
(b) $v_{avg, 0-2} = 0.134$ m/s, $v_{avg, 2-4} = 0.932$ m/s,
$v_{avg, 0-4} = 0.533$ m/s, $a_{avg, 0-2} = 0.2$ m/s^2,
$a_{avg, 2-4} = 0.6$ m/s^2, $a_{avg, 0-4} = 0.4$ m/s^2 (c) $t = 0$,
$v = a = 0$
15.15 (a) $t = 2$ s: $v = 2$ ft/s, $s = 2.67$ ft; $t = 4$ s:
$v = 0$, $s = 5.34$ ft

(b) $v_{avg, 0-2} = v_{avg, 2-4} = v_{avg, 0-4} = 1.34$ ft/s,
$a_{avg, 0-2} = 1$ ft/s^2, $a_{avg, 2-4} = -1$ ft/s^2, $a_{avg, 0-4} = 0$
(c) $t = 0$, $v = 0$, $a = 2$ ft/s^2
15.17 (a) $t = 2$ s: $v = -46$ m/s, $s = -44$ m;
$t = 4$ s: $v = -104$ m/s, $s = -192$ m
(b) $v_{avg, 0-2} = -22$ m/s, $v_{avg, 2-4} = -74$ m/s,
$v_{avg, 0-4} = -48$ m/s, $a_{avg, 0-2} = -23$ m/s^2,
$a_{avg, 2-4} = -29$ m/s^2, $a_{avg, 0-4} = -26$ m/s^2
(c) $t = 0$, $v = 0$, $a = -20$ m/s^2
15.19 (a) $t = 2$ s: $v = -9.6$ in/s, $s = -6.4$ in;
$t = 4$ s: $v = -28.8$ in/s, $s = -44.8$ in
(b) $v_{avg, 0-2} = -3.2$ in/s, $v_{avg, 2-4} = -19.2$ in/s,
$v_{avg, 0-4} = -11.2$ in/s, $a_{avg, 0-2} = -4.6$ in/s^2,
$a_{avg, 2-4} = -9.6$ in/s^2, $a_{avg, 0-4} = -7.2$ in/s^2
15.21 (b) $a_m = 22$ m/s^2 (c) 33 m
(d) $s = 33$ m   (e) $v_{avg} = 11$ m/s, $a_{avg} = 7.33$ m/s^2
15.23 (b) $a_m = -0.8$ m/s^2 (c) 60 m
(d) $s = -60$ m   (e) $v_{avg} = -4$ m/s,
$a_{avg} = -0.533$ m/s^2
15.25 (b) $a_m = 2.2$ ft/s^2 (c) 1,760 ft
(d) $s = 0$ (e) $v_{avg} = 0$, $a_{avg} = 0$
15.27 (b) $v_m = 34$ m/s, $s_m = 150$ m
(c) $v_{avg} = 25$ m/s, $a_{avg} = 2$ m/s^2
15.29 (b) $v_m = 56$ in/s, $s_m = 139$ in
(c) $v_{avg} = 17.4$ in/s, $a_{avg} = 7$ in/s^2
15.31 (b) $v_m = -72$ in/s, $s_m = -453$ in
(c) $v_{avg} = -54.6$ in/s, $a_{avg} = 7$ in/s^2
15.33 (b) $v_m = 4.8$ m/s, $s_m = 12.8$ m
(c) $v_{avg} = 3.2$ m/s, $a_{avg} = 0.4$ m/s^2
15.35 (b) $v_m = -12$ m/s, $s_m = -54$ m
(c) $v_{avg} = -9$ m/s, $a_{avg} = -2$ m/s^2
15.37 (b) $v_m = -22$ m/s, $s_m = -114$ m
(c) $v_{avg} = -19$ m/s, $a_{avg} = -2$ m/s^2
15.39 (a) $t_1 = 8$ s   (b) $a_m = 20$ in/s^2
15.41 (a) $t_1 = 2.46$ s   (b) $v_{avg} = 1.54$ m/s,
$a_{avg} = 1.06$ m/s^2
15.43 (a) 6.6 s   (b) $s = 892$ in   (c) 923 in
15.45 (a) $a_1 = -49.6$ m/s^2 (b) $v_m = 20$ m/s
15.47 (a) $t = 1.08$ s, $s = 5.27$ m   (b) $t = 2.17$ s,
$s = 7.04$ m
15.49 (a) 18.4 mi/h   (b) 650 ft
(c) $t = 8.57$ s, $s = 367$ ft
15.51 (a) $t = 9.80$ s, $s_A = 164$ m, $s_B = 136$ m
(b) $v_A = 60$ km/h, $v_B = 50$ km/h, $v_{AB} = 110$ km/h
15.53 (a) $t = 7.14$ s, $s_A = 160$ m, $s_B = 140$ m
(b) $v_A = 101$ km/h, $v_B = 91.1$ km/h, $v_{AB} = 192$ km/h
15.55 (a) $t = 13.2$ s, $s_A = 168$ m, $s_B = 131$ m
(b) $v_A = 31.6$ km/h, $v_B = 21.5$ km/h,
$v_{AB} = 53.1$ km/h

15.57 $a_A = -0.521$ m/s^2
15.59 (a) 15 s   (b) 725 ft   (c) 65.6 mi/h
(d) 14.3 mi/h
15.61 4.96 s, 82.8 m
15.63 (a) 175 ft   (b) 518 ft
15.65 242 ft
15.67 302 ft
15.69 (a) $v_0 = 76.1$ ft/s   (b) 2.36 s   (c) 4.72 s
15.71 (a) Second ball   (b) 0.42 s
15.73 138 ft above ground
15.75 135 ft above ground
15.77 3.05 ft
15.79 (a) 15.3 ft, 0.802 s   (b) 65.6 ft to right,
5 ft down   (c) 48.5 ft/s   (d) 1.78 s
15.81 27,400 ft
15.83 (a) 14.0 s   (b) 8,180 ft
(c) 777 ft/s $\searrow$41.2°
15.85 16.5°
15.87 1,420 m
15.89 1,650 m
15.91 $y = (v_{0y}/v_{0x})x - (g/2v_{0x}^2)x^2$
15.93 (a) 309° counterclockwise from a,
$v_x = 1.51$ ft/s, $v_y = -1.87$ ft/s   (b) $a_n = 1.44$ ft/s^2,
$a_t = 0$ (c) $a_x = 1.12$ ft/s^2, $a_y = 0.906$ ft/s^2
15.95 (a) $v_x = 1.58$ m/s, $v_y = 0.575$ m/s
(b) $a = 2.84$ m/s^2 75.7°$\searrow$
15.97 (a) $v_x = -1.93$ m/s, $v_y = -0.701$ m/s
(b) $a = 4.21$ m/s^2 66.2°$\searrow$
15.99 Origin: $a_n = 3,030$ ft/s^2 $\angle$82.4°; point a:
$a_n = 1,210$ ft/s^2 47.0°$\searrow$; point b: $a_n = 553$ ft/s^2
34.2°$\searrow$
15.101 $s_{AB} = 1,460$ m 59.0°$\nearrow$, $v_{AB} = 75$ m/s
$\searrow$53.1°, $a_{AB} = 4.29$ m/s^2 $\angle$62.2°
15.103 (a) $s_{AB} = 1,050$ ft 20°$\searrow$, $v_{AB} = 80.2$ ft/s
$\angle$80.4°, $a_{AB} = 4$ ft/s^2 $\angle$30°   (b) $s_{AB,x} = 987$ ft,
$s_{AB,y} = -359$ ft, $v_{AB,x} = -13.4$ ft/s,
$v_{AB,y} = -79.1$ ft/s, $a_{AB,x} = -3.46$ ft/s^2,
$a_{AB,y} = -2$ ft/s^2
15.105 (a) $v_r = 4.84$ knots $\angle$51.7°
(b) 3,160 ft
15.107 (a) $s_{ab} = 0.7$ m, downward, $v_{ab} = 36$ m/s,
to the left   (b) $s_{ab} = 3.1$ m, upward, $v_{ab} = 16$ m/s,
to the right   (c) $s_{ab} = 2.71$ m 17.4°$\searrow$,
$v_{ab} = 22.7$ m/s $\angle$27.6°   (d) $s_{ab} = 2.83$ m 19.0°$\searrow$,
$v_{ab} = 21.0$ m/s 68.6°$\searrow$
15.109 $v_{BA} = 25.9$ ft/s $\searrow$22.5°

Chapter 16

16.1 (a) 15.8 ft/s^2 (b) $v = 31.7$ ft/s, $s = 31.6$ ft
16.3 (a) 31.9 ft/s^2 (b) $v = 63.8$ ft/s, $s = 63.8$ ft
16.5 (a) 16.1 ft/s^2 (b) $v = 32.2$ ft/s, $s = 32.2$ ft
16.7 (a) -6.84 m/s^2 (b) $v = -13.7$ m/s,
$s = -13.7$ m
16.9 (a) 326 lb   (b) 330 ft
16.11 (a) 820 lb   (b) 143 ft
16.13 $a = 0.445$ m/s^2, $s = 164$ ft
16.15 (a) 1,030 lb   (b) 1,010 lb

16.17 (a) 2.44 m/s^2 (b) 516 N
16.19 (a) 3.03 m/s^2 (b) 475 N, 340 N
16.21 3,590 N
16.23 9.66 ft/s^2, 1 slug
16.25 0 ft/s^2, 1.86 slug
16.27 7.37 s
16.29 (a) $a = g \tan \theta$ (b) 0.345 N
16.31 (a) 0.0159   (b) 100 in
16.33 (a) 13.3 ft/s^2 (b) 39.9 ft/s
16.35 240 N
16.37 513 N
16.39 11.8 m
16.41 3.22 m/s^2
16.43 3.06 ft/s^2, W moves downward
16.45 77.3 kg
16.47 (a) 5.93 ft/s^2 (b) 0.451 lb
16.49 751 N
16.51 (a) 2.35 m/s^2 (b) 136 N
16.53 (a) 11.3°   (b) 32.2 ft/s^2
16.55 (a) 12.7 m/s^2 (b) 19.4 m/s^2
(c) 32.1 m/s^2
16.57 8.04 ft/s^2, up and to the right
16.59 2.62 m/s
16.61 Speed: 2.08; string force: 1.23
16.63 2.05 m/s
16.65 (a) 679 mm   (b) 0.788 mN
16.67 (a) $v = \sqrt{rg/\mu_s}$ (b) 10.4 ft/s
16.69 (a) $W_a = 0.898$ W, $W_b = 1.10$ W
(b) 189 km/h
16.71 44.8 mi/h
16.73 1.92 m/s^2
16.75 2.97 mN
16.77 3.64 mN
16.79 (a) 0.12 N   (b) Along length cd

Chapter 17

17.1 (a) $\theta = 1.9$ rad, $\dot{\theta} = 1.9$ rad/s, $\ddot{\theta} = 0$
(b) $t = 1$ s: $\theta = 3.8$ rad, $\dot{\theta} = 1.9$ rad/s, $\ddot{\theta} = 0$; $t = 2$ s:
$\theta = 5.7$ rad, $\dot{\theta} = 1.9$ rad/s, $\ddot{\theta} = 0$ (c) 3.31 s
17.3 (a) $\theta = 2$ rad, $\dot{\theta} = 1$ rad/s, $\ddot{\theta} = 2$ rad/s^2
(b) $t = 1$ s: $\theta = 4$ rad, $\dot{\theta} = 3$ rad/s, $\ddot{\theta} = 2$ rad/s^2;
$t = 2$ s: $\theta = 8$ rad, $\dot{\theta} = 5$ rad/s, $\ddot{\theta} = 2$ rad/s^2
(c) 2.06 s
17.5 (a) $a = -1/s^2$, $b = 4/s$, $c = -1.2$
(b) $\theta = -1.2$ rad, $\omega = -4$ rad/s, $\alpha = 2$ rad/s^2
17.7 (a) $a = 5/s^2$, $b = -15/s$, $c = 11.3$
(b) $\theta = 31.3$ rad, $\omega = 25$ rad/s, $\alpha = 10$ rad/s^2
17.9 (a) $t = 1$ s: $\omega = -0.3$ rad/s, $\theta = -0.1$ rad;
$t = 3$ s: $\omega = -2.7$ rad/s, $\theta = -2.7$ rad
(b) $\omega_{\text{avg}} = -1.3$ rad/s, $\alpha_{\text{avg}} = -1.2$ rad/s^2
(c) $\Delta\omega = -2.4$ rad/s
17.11 (a) $t = 1$ s: $\omega = 3.5$ rad/s, $\theta = 2$ rad;
$t = 3$ s: $\omega = 1.5$ rad/s, $\theta = 9$ rad
(b) $\omega_{\text{avg}} = 3.5$ rad/s, $\alpha_{\text{avg}} = -1$ rad/s^2
(c) $\Delta\omega = -2$ rad/s
17.13 (b) -25 rad/s^2 (c) -150 rad
(d) $\omega_{\text{avg}} = -37.5$ rad/s, $\alpha_{\text{avg}} = -12.5$ rad/s^2

17.15 (b) 1.8 rad/s^2 (c) 0   (d) $\omega_{\text{avg}} = 0$, $\alpha_{\text{avg}} = 0$

17.17 (b) $\omega_m = 330$ rad/s, $\theta_m = 2{,}180$ rad

17.19 (b) $\omega_m = -28.4$ rad/s, $\theta_m = 53.6$ rad

17.21 (b) $\omega_m = -73.4$ rad/s, $\theta_m = -340$ rad

17.23 (b) $\omega_m = -110$ rad/s, $\theta_m = -1{,}090$ rad

17.25 15.7 s

17.27 (a) -3.2 rad/s^2 (b) 294 r   (c) 0.246 s

17.29 (a) 5.8 s   (b) 174 r

17.31 (a) $v_a = 3.51$ m/s 52°⬊, $v_b = 1.46$ m/s 52°⬊, $a_a = 22.8$ m/s^2 ⬊38°, $a_b = 9.51$ m/s^2 ⬊38°   (b) $v_{ax} = -2.16$ m/s, $v_{ay} = 2.77$ m/s, $v_{bx} = -0.899$ m/s, $v_{by} = 1.15$ m/s, $a_{ax} = 18.0$ m/s^2, $a_{ay} = 14.0$ m/s^2, $a_{bx} = 7.49$ m/s^2, $a_{by} = 5.85$ m/s^2

17.33 (a) $v_a = 5.40$ m/s ⬋52°, $v_b = 2.25$ m/s ⬋52°, $a_a = 54.2$ m/s^2 ⬊42.6°, $a_b = 22.6$ m/s^2 ⬊42.6°   (b) $v_{ax} = 3.32$ m/s, $v_{ay} = -4.26$ m/s, $v_{bx} = 1.39$ m/s, $v_{by} = -1.77$ m/s, $a_{ax} = 39.9$ m/s^2, $a_{ay} = 36.7$ m/s^2, $a_{bx} = 16.6$ m/s^2, $a_{by} = 15.3$ m/s^2

17.35 (a) $a_{nb} = 9.33$ ft/s^2, $a_{tb} = 19.8$ ft/s^2 (b) 11.3 rad/s, 27.0 rad/s^2 (c) $a_b = 95.4$ ft/s^2 12°⬊   (d) Speeding up

17.37 (a) $\omega = 3.88$ rad/s, $a_n = 19.6$ m/s^2 (b) $\theta = 60°$ (c) $a_x = -8.49$ m/s^2, $a_y = 4.9$ m/s^2

17.39 (a) $v_A = 4$ m/s, $v_B = 10$ m/s, $v_C = 13.5$ m/s, $a_A = -0.96$ m/s^2, $a_B = -2.4$ m/s^2, $a_C = -3.24$ m/s^2 (b) $v_{AB} = -6$ m/s upward, $v_{BC} = 3.5$ m/s upward, $v_{AC} = 9.5$ m/s upward, $a_{AB} = 1.44$ m/s^2 downward, $a_{BC} = 0.84$ m/s^2 downward, $a_{AC} = 2.28$ m/s^2 downward

17.41 (a) $v_A = -4$ m/s, $v_B = 10$ m/s, $v_C = 13.5$ m/s, $a_A = 0.96$ m/s^2, $a_B = -2.4$ m/s^2, $a_C = -3.24$ m/s^2 (b) $v_{AB} = 14$ m/s upward, $v_{BC} = 3.5$ m/s upward, $v_{AC} = 17.5$ m/s upward, $a_{AB} = 3.36$ m/s^2 downward, $a_{BC} = 0.84$ m/s^2 downward, $a_{AC} = 4.2$ m/s^2 downward

17.43 (a) $v_A = 4$ m/s, $v_B = -10$ m/s, $v_C = 13.5$ m/s, $a_A = -0.96$ m/s^2, $a_B = 2.4$ m/s^2, $a_C = -3.24$ m/s^2 (b) $v_{AB} = 14$ m/s downward, $v_{BC} = 23.5$ m/s upward, $v_{AC} = 9.5$ m/s upward, $a_{AB} = 3.36$ m/s^2 upward, $a_{BC} = 5.64$ m/s^2 downward, $a_{AC} = 2.28$ m/s^2 downward

17.45 (a) $x = -30$ in, $y = 28$ in, $\theta = -30°$ (b) 44.7 in/s 26.6°⬊   (c) $-60°$/s

17.47 (a) $x = -12.3$ in, $y = 18.4$ in, $\theta = 9.04°$ (b) 28.8 in/s 51.6°⬊   (c) $-5.42°$/s

17.49 (a) $IC - a$: 366 mm; $IC - b$: 105 mm   (b) $\omega = 27.3$ rad/s   (c) $v_b = 2.87$ m/s, $v_c = 6.42$ m/s

17.51 (a) 5.56 rad/s   (b) 2.07 m/s

17.53 $v_A = v_B = 11.5$ m/s

17.55 $v_a = 14.8$ m/s, $v_b = 6$ m/s

17.57 $\omega = 3.33$ rad/min, $\alpha = 1.67$ rad/min^2, $v = 2$ ft/min, $a = 1$ ft/min^2

17.59 $\omega = 262$ rad/s, $v = 78.5$ in/s, $a = 4{,}740$ in/s^2

17.61 $\omega = 401$ rad/s, $v = 36.7$ in/s,

$a = 1{,}040$ in/s^2

17.63 (a) 0.236 s, 42.5 in/s   (b) 42.5 rad/s, 180 rad/s^2 (c) $v = 42.5$ in/s upward, $a = 1{,}820$ in/s^2 ⬊5.68°

17.65 (a) 55.5 in/s 30°⬊, 2,570 in/s^2 58.9°⬋   (c) 103 in/s 80°⬊, 8,840 in/s 10°⬋

17.67 (a) $v_a = 10$ m/s downward, $a_a = 2{,}000$ m/s^2 to the right, $v_d = 10$ m/s to the right, $a_d = 3{,}000$ m/s^2 upward   (b) $v_{ax} = 0$, $v_{ay} = -10$ m/s, $a_{ax} = 2{,}000$ m/s^2, $a_{ay} = 0$, $v_{dx} = 10$ m/s, $v_{dy} = 0$, $a_{dx} = 0$, $a_{dy} = 3{,}000$ m/s^2 (c) $v_a = 10$ m/s 29°⬋, $a_a = 2{,}000$ m/s^2 ⬋61°, $v_d = 10$ m/s ⬈89°, $a_d = 3{,}000$ m/s^2 1°⬊

17.69 (a) $v_a = 10.2$ m/s downward, $a_{na} = 2{,}080$ m/s^2, $a_{ta} = 6$ m/s^2, $v_d = 10.2$ m/s to the right, $a_{nd} = 3{,}120$ m/s^2, $a_{td} = 6$ m/s^2 (b) $v_{ax} = 0$, $v_{ay} = -10.2$ m/s, $a_{ax} = 2{,}080$ m/s^2, $a_{ay} = -6$ m/s^2, $v_{dx} = 10.2$ m/s, $v_{dy} = 0$, $a_{dx} = 6$ m/s^2, $a_{dy} = 3{,}120$ m/s^2 (c) $v_a = 16$ m/s ⬈47°, $a_a = 5{,}120$ m/s^2 43°⬊, $v_d = 16$ m/s 25.4°⬋, $a_d = 7{,}690$ m/s^2 ⬋64.6°

17.71 (a) $v_a = 2.84$ m/s, $a_a = 1.2$ m/s^2, $v_b = 2.84$ m/s, $a_b = 101$ m/s^2 (b) $v_{ab} = 5.21$ m/s, $a_{ab} = 102$ m/s^2

17.73 $v_a = v_b = v_c = v_d = 118$ ft/s ⬈12°, $a_a = a_b = a_c = a_d = 2{,}390$ ft/s^2 ⬋60°

17.75 (a) $0.111 \le \omega_2/\omega_1 \le 1\frac{1}{12}$ (b) 752 in/s^2

17.77 $\omega = v/r$

17.79 $v_a = 130$ ft/s, $v_b = 132$ ft/s, $v_c = 108$ ft/s, $a_a = 3{,}480$ ft/s^2, $a_b = 3{,}480$ ft/s^2, $a_c = 3{,}480$ ft/s^2

Chapter 18

18.1 (a) 2.56 in   (b) 2.4 percent

18.3 (a) 1.04 ft   (b) 4 percent

18.5 11.3 in

18.7 21.8 in above base

18.9 (a) $I_x = 0.00116$ kg·m^2, $I_y = 0.00139$ kg·m^2, $I_z = 0.00255$ kg·m^2 (b) $m = 0.277$ kg, $k_x = 64.6$ mm, $k_y = 70.9$ mm, $k_z = 95.9$ mm   (c) $I_{0x} = 0.000401$ kg·m^2, $I_{0y} = 0.000475$ kg·m^2, $I_{0z} = 0.000876$ kg·m^2 (d) $k_{0x} = 38.0$ mm, $k_{0y} = 41.4$ mm, $k_{0z} = 56.2$ mm

18.11 (a) $I_x = 0.0484$ lb·s^2·in, $I_y = 0.335$ lb·s^2·in, $I_z = 0.385$ lb·s^2·in   (b) $m = 0.0104$ lb·s^2/in, $k_x = 2.15$ in, $k_y = 5.67$ in, $k_z = 6.07$ in   (c) $I_{0x} = 0.0138$ lb·s^2·in, $I_{0y} = 0.0885$ lb·s^2·in, $I_{0z} = 0.102$ lb·s^2·in   (d) $k_{0x} = 1.15$ in, $k_{0y} = 2.91$ in, $k_{0z} = 3.13$ in

18.13 (a) $I_x = 26.3$ lb·s^2·in, $I_y = 102$ lb·s^2·in, $I_z = 128$ lb·s^2·in   (b) $m = 0.340$ lb·s^2·in, $k_x = 8.79$ in, $k_y = 17.3$ in, $k_z = 19.4$ in   (c) $I_{0x} = 7.13$ lb·s^2·in, $I_{0y} = 22.1$ lb·s^2·in, $I_{0z} = 29.3$ lb·s^2·in   (d) $k_{0x} = 4.58$ in, $k_{0y} = 8.06$ in, $k_{0z} = 9.28$ in

18.15 (a) $I_x = 0.926$ lb·s^2·in, $I_y = 0.0776$ lb·s^2·in   (b) $m = 0.0145$ lb·s^2·in,

$k_x = 7.99$ in   (c) $I_{0x} = 0.310$ lb·s²·in
(d) $k_{0x} = 4.62$ in
18.17   (a) $I_x = 16.5$ kg·m², $I_y = 18.0$ kg·m²
(b) $m = 90.7$ kg, $k_x = 427$ mm
(c) $I_{0x} = 3.66$ kg·m²   (d) $k_{0x} = 201$ mm
18.19   (a) $I_x = 0.0607$ lb·s²·in,
$I_y = 0.0413$ lb·s²·in   (b) $m = 0.00316$ in·s²/in,
$k_x = 4.38$ in   (c) $I_{0x} = 0.0264$ lb·s²/in
(d) $k_{0x} = 2.89$ in
18.21   (a) $I_x = 3.28$ lb·s²·in, $I_y = 8.02$ lb·s²·in
(b) $m = 0.0795$ lb·s²/in, $k_x = 6.42$ in
(c) $I_{0x} = 0.547$ lb·s²·in   (d) $k_{0x} = 2.62$ in
18.23   (a) $I_x = 2.45 \times 10^{-5}$ kg·m²,
$I_y = 1.80 \times 10^{-5}$ kg·m²   (b) $m = 0.0351$ kg,
$k_x = 26.4$ mm   (c) $I_{0x} = 1.29 \times 10^{-5}$ kg·m²
(d) $k_{0x} = 19.2$ mm
18.25 3.97×10^{-5} lb·s²·in
18.33   (a) 0.0228 lb·s²·in   (b) 8.81 lb·in²
18.35   (a) 0.0417 kg·m²   (b) 142 lb·in²
18.37   (a) 0.0160 lb·s²·in   (b) 2.15 in
18.39 0.000109 lb·s²·in
18.41 1.79×10^{-6} kg·m²
18.43 $I_x = 6.33 \times 10^{-5}$ kg·m², $k_x = 16.1$ mm
18.45   (a) $I_x = 7.46 \times 10^{-7}$ kg·m²,
$I_y = 1.25 \times 10^{-6}$ kg·m²   (b) $k_x = 5.54$ mm,
$k_y = 7.17$ mm
18.47 0.496 percent
18.49 $I_x = 0.0108$ kg·m², $I_y = 0.0943$ kg·m²,
$I_z = 0.00243$ kg·m²
18.51 $I_x = 0.0106$ kg·m², $I_y = 0.0932$ kg·m²,
$I_z = 0.00231$ kg·m²
18.53 $I_x = 0.00737$ lb·s²·in, $I_y = 0.0324$ lb·s²·in,
$I_z = 0.0294$ lb·s²·in
18.55 $I_x = 0.00649$ lb·s²·in, $I_y = 0.0272$ lb·s²·in,
$I_z = 0.0246$ lb·s²·in
18.57 $I_x = 0.00171$ kg·m², $I_y = 0.00249$ kg·m²,
$I_z = 0.000963$ kg·m²
18.59 0.893 lb·s²·in (centroid is 5.184 in from end
with large hole)
18.61 $I_x = 0.00559$ kg·m², $I_{x_1} = 0.00450$ kg·m²,
$I_y = 0.000544$ kg·m²
18.63 $I_x = 0.00578$ kg·m², $I_{x_1} = 0.0102$ kg·m²,
$I_y = 0.00721$
18.65 0.00340 lb·s²·in
18.69 $l/d \geq 3.77$
18.71   (a) $a/d \leq 0.199$ (b) $a/d \leq 0.289$
18.73   (a) $I_y = 0.0318$ lb·s²·in
(b) $I_{y_1} = 0.0618$ lb·s²·in   (c) $I_{0y} = 0.0313$ lb·s²·in
18.75   (a) $I_{0z} = 0.000223$ kg·m²   (b) 79.9 mm

Chapter 19

19.1   (a) 178 rad/s²   (b) 66.9 rad/s
19.3   (a) 19.6 s   (b) 24.5 r
19.5 0.235 s
19.7 -3.13 in·lb
19.9 0.08 kg·m²

19.11   (a) 278 rad/s²   (b) $1,110$ rad/s,
$2,220$ rad   (c) 118 rad/s
19.13   (a) 154 rad/s²   (b) 616 rad/s,
$1,230$ rad   (c) 87.9 rad/s
19.15   (a) 1.27 lb   (b) no
19.17 61.3 rad/s²
19.19 5.7 in·lb
19.21   (a) 0.0119 in·lb   (b) $F = 0$
19.23 3.80 N at each bearing
19.25   (a) 46.0 rad/s²   (b) No change
19.27 24.1 N
19.29   (a) $P_{max} = (mg\mu_s)/\{[\cos\theta/(1 + mr^2/I_0)] + \mu_s \sin\theta\}$ (b) $\theta = 15°$: $P_{max} = 11.1$ N; $\theta = 30°$:
$P_{max} = 11.7$ N; $\theta = 45°$: $P_{max} = 13.4$ N
19.31   (a) 28.2 N   (b) 7.37 rad/s²
19.33 $\mu_s \geq 0.29$
19.35   (a) $35.8°$ (b) 0.857 s
19.37 $l = 3.17$ in
19.39   (a) $\beta = \tan^{-1}(3.5\mu_s)$ (b) $38.8°$
19.41   (a) $T_A = 575$ N, $T_B = 586$ N,
$a_y = 1.67$ m/s²   (b) $1,260$ N   (c) 1.83 m/s
19.43   (a) 1.73 m/s², $T = 162$ N, $R_{ax} = 162$ N,
$R_{ay} = 174$ N, $R_{bx} = 162$ N, $R_{by} = 190$ N
(b) 1.76 m/s   (c) 1.67 m/s², $T_{AC} = 163$ N,
$T_{CD} = 162$ N, $T_{BD} = 161$ N, $R_{ax} = 162$ N,
$R_{ay} = 175$ N, $R_{bx} = 162$ N, $R_{by} = 189$ N
(d) 1.73 m/s
19.45 6.46×10^{-4} lb
19.47   (a) 155 in/s²   (b) 0.254 s
(c) 39.4 in/s   (d) $t = 0.161$ s, $v_B = 62.1$ in/s
19.49   (a) $\alpha_1 = 112$ rad/s², $\alpha_2 = 44.8$ rad/s²
(b) $\alpha_1 = 44.9$ rad/s², $\alpha_2 = 18.0$ rad/s²
19.51 $\alpha_1 = 126$ rad/s², $\alpha_2 = 54$ rad/s²,
$\alpha_3 = 189$ rad/s²
19.53 $\alpha_1 = 188$ rad/s², $\alpha_2 = 81$ rad/s²,
$\alpha_3 = 282$ rad/s²
19.55   (a) 4.23 in/s², 7.91 lb   (b) 13.0 in/s
19.57   (a) $a_x = \mu_s bg/(l - \mu_s c)$ (c) 14.8 ft/s²
19.59   (a) $a_x = \{[\mu_s a \cos\beta/(l - \mu_s c)] - \sin\beta\}g$
(c) 1.61 ft/s²
19.61   (a) $a_x = (\mu_s \cos\beta - \sin\beta)g$, 12.8 ft/s²
(b) Stationary: $N_F = 1,560$ lb $N_R = 1,340$ lb,
maximum acceleration: $N_F = 1,340$ lb, $N_R = 1,560$ lb
19.63   (a) $a_x = \{[\mu_s b \cos\beta/(l - \mu_s c)] + \sin\beta\}g$
(c) 22.7 ft/s²
19.65   (a) $a_x = \{[\mu_s a \cos\beta/(l - \mu_s c)] + \sin\beta\}g$
(c) 18.3 ft/s²
19.67   (a) $a_x = (\mu_s \cos\beta + \sin\beta)g$, 29.5 ft/s²
(b) Stationary: $N_F = 1,860$ lb, $N_R = 1,040$ lb,
maximum acceleration: $N_F = 1,340$ lb, $N_R = 1,560$ lb
19.69   (a) $a_x = \{[\mu_s b \cos\beta/(l - \mu_s c)] - \sin\beta\}g$
(c) 6.03 ft/s²
19.71 $N_a = 389$ N, $F_a = 70.0$ N, $N_b = 120$ N,
$F_b = 21.6$ N
19.73 $h \leq 273$ mm
19.75   (a) 5.66 m/s²   (b) 906 N
19.77 25.8 ft/s²

19.79 22.0 ft/s^2

19.81 (a) Slides, if $a_x > (\mu_s \cos \beta - \sin \beta)g$ and $\mu_s < b/a$; Tips, if $a_x > (b/a \cos \beta - \sin \beta)g$ and $\mu_s > b/a$ (b) Slides, if $a_x > (\mu_s \cos \beta + \sin \beta)g$ and $\mu_s < b/a$; Tips, if $a_x > (b/a \cos \beta + \sin \beta)g$ and $\mu_s > b/a$ (c) Acceleration: $a_x = 3.15$ m/s^2 for sliding, $a_x = 3.64$ m/s^2 for tipping, sliding occurs first; deceleration: $a_x = 8.22$ m/s^2 for sliding, $a_x = 8.72$ m/s^2 for tipping, sliding occurs first

19.83 (a) 29.3 ft/s   (b) 37.6 mi/h   (c) 80.4°

19.85 Sliding:
$$v = \sqrt{[(\mu_s + \tan \beta)\rho g]/(1 - \mu_s \tan \beta)} = 69.4 \text{ mi/h}$$
tipping:
$$v = \sqrt{[(d + 2c \tan \beta)\rho g]/(2c - d \tan \beta)} = 91.2 \text{ mi/h}$$

19.87 $x = l$

19.89 $x = 66.3$ mm

Chapter 20

20.1 (a) 7.86 ft·lb   (b) 7.96 ft/s   (c) 0

20.3 (a) 15.9 ft·lb   (b) 11.3 ft/s   (c) −8 ft·lb

20.5 (a) −22.6 J   (b) −4.75 m/s   (c) 0

20.7 (a) 84,400 ft·lb   (b) 108,000 ft·lb

20.9 (a) 24.5 r

20.11 (a) 14.0 r/s

20.13 (a) $T = mgl/2 \sin \theta$
(b) $\omega = \sqrt{3g \sin \theta/l}$ (c) $\omega = 4.95 \sqrt{\sin \theta}$ rad/s, $T = 14.1 \sin \theta$ J   (d) 4.95 rad/s

20.15 87.5 ft/s

20.17 (a) 17.3 m   (b) 14.9 m/s   (c) 18.4 m/s

20.21 6.53 in

20.23 4.73 m/s

20.25 87.3 N

20.27 (a) 0.76   (b) 1.68 m/s

20.29 4.97 in

20.31 (a) $k = 1$ lb/in   (b) 4.17 ft·lb

20.33 Outer springs: 3.25 in; inner springs: 3.00 in

20.35 3.48 ft

20.37 (a) 67.5 J   (b) 3.87 m/s, 19.4 rad/s

20.39 (a) 67.5 J   (b) 4.01 m/s, 20.0 rad/s

20.41 (a) $v = \sqrt{(4g/3)(R - r)(1 \cos \beta)}$, $\omega = v/r$ (b) $v = \sqrt{2g(R - r)(1 - \cos \beta)}$, $\omega = 0$ (c) $a_n = (4g/3)(1 - \cos \beta)$ (rolling), $a_n = 2g(1 - \cos \beta)$ (sliding)   (d) Rolling: $\omega = 25.7$ rad/s, $v_c = 0.643$ m/s, $a_n = 2.37$ m/s^2; sliding: $v_c = 0.788$ m/s, $a_n = 3.55$ m/s^2

20.43 988 mm

20.45 618 mm

20.47 (a) 1.77 m/s   (b) 1.73 m/s

20.49 (a) 51.8 rad/s

20.51 1.08 ft/s

20.53 (a) 2.75 ft/s   (b) 4.34 ft/s

20.55 7.64 rad/s

20.57 (a) 2.46 m/s

20.59 2.62 ft

20.61 3.66 ft/s

20.63 2.5 ft

20.65 (a) 1,250 in/s^2 (b) 1,490 in/s^2

20.67 2.53 ft/s

20.69 (a) 448 hp   (b) 655,000 ft·lb

20.71 (a) 1,370 W   (b) 1,440 W

20.73 AB: 15.7 kW: BC: 33.0 kW; CD: 20.4 kW

20.75 75,400 W

20.77 (a) 4.65 ft   (b) 1.25 hp

Chapter 21

21.1 31.7 ft/s

21.3 328 lb

21.5 35.7 ft/s, down the plane

21.7 (a) $t = 1$ s: $v = 9.33$ ft/s, to the right; $t = 3$ s: $v = 6.12$ ft/s, to the left   (b) $t = 1$ s, $v = 4.5$ ft/s, to the right; $t = 3$ s: $v = 3.64$ ft/s, to the left

21.9 (a) $t = 1$ s: $v = 5.47$ ft/s; $t = 3$ s: $v = 20.4$ ft/s   (b) $t = 1$ s: $v = 0.714$ ft/s; $t = 3$ s: $v = 5.38$ ft/s   (c) 0.387 s

21.11 (a) $t = 1$ s: $v = 21.6$ ft/s; $t = 3$ s: $v = 36.5$ ft/s   (b) $t = 1$ s: $v = 17.2$ ft/s; $t = 3$ s: $v = 31.5$ ft/s   (c) $t = 0$ s

21.13 (a) 2.09 s   (b) 1.07 s

21.15 (a) 984 mm   (b) 3.03 J   (c) 5.89 N·s

21.17 (a) 0.916   (b) 1.14 J   (c) 1,270 mm
(d) First impulse: 4.55 N·s; second impulse: 4.17 N·s

21.19 (a) 7.57 ft, 5.73 ft, 4.34 ft   (b) 0.243 ft·lb, 0.184 ft·lb, 0.139 ft·lb

21.21 (a) 0.978 s   (b) $v'_A = 0$, $v'_B = 5.11$ ft/s

21.23 (a) 0.97 s   (b) $v'_A = 2.04$ ft/s, $v'_B = 3.07$ ft/s

21.25 (a) 0.286 s   (b) $v'_A = 6.1$ m/s, to the right; $v'_B = 4.4$ m/s, to the left   (c) $I' = 25.2$ N·s   (d) 0.571 s

21.27 (a) $t = 0.299$ s, $v'_A = 7.98$ m/s, to the right; $v'_B = 1.64$ m/s, to the left; $I' = 23.1$ N·s, $t = 0.698$ s   (b) 22.6 m

21.29 (a) 0.299 s, $v'_A = 6.83$ m/s, to the right: $v'_B = 0.866$ m/s, to the left, $I' = 20.8$ N·s   (b) 16.1 m   (c) 20 J

21.31 (a) $v'_A = 75.9$ in/s, $v'_B = 52.5$ in/s, both downward   (b) 3.63 lb·s

21.33 (a) $v'_A = 19.8$ in/s, $v'_B = 5.84$ in/s, both downward, $I' = 2.18$ lb·s   (b) 95.2 percent

21.35 (a) $v_B = 6.09$ m/s (using $e = 0.773$)
(b) $v'_A = 6.25$ m/s, to the left

21.37 $v_A = 9.18$ ft/s

21.39 $v_A = 7.02$ ft/s

21.41 16.6 ft/s

21.43 (a) 6.77 in   (b) 4.37 in   (c) 6.13 in
(d) 4.37 in

21.45 (a) 10.1 m/s   (b) $T_1 = 5.49$ J, $T_2 = 5.11$ J

21.47 (a) 9.46 m/s   (b) $T_1 = 5.49$ J, $T_2 = 4.48$ J

21.49 (a) $v_B = [(1 + e)/2]\sqrt{2gl(1 - \sin\theta)}$
21.51 (a) $\theta_1 = \sin^{-1}\{[(1 + e)^2/4](l/l_1)(1 - \sin\theta)\}$
(b) $53.4°$ (c) $87.3°$ (d) 7.8 percent
21.53 (b) $25.8°$ (c) $36.0°, 52.4°$
21.55 (a) $70.6\,\mu s$, 600 lb   (b) $71.8\,\mu s$, 309 lb
(c) $82.3\,\mu s$, 548 lb
21.57 (a) $v'_{Ax} = -0.403$ m/s, $v'_{Ay} = 2.04$ m/s,
$v'_{Bx} = 2.04$ m/s, $v'_{By} = 0.403$ m/s
(b) $v'_{Ax} = 0.403$ m/s, $v'_{Ay} = 2.04$ m/s, $v'_{Bx} = 2.04$ m/s,
$v'_{By} = -0.403$ m/s
21.59 (a) (Using $v_A = 1.64$ m/s, $v_B = 2.44$ m/s)
$v'_{Ax} = -304$ m/s, $v'_{Ay} = 1.94$ m/s, $v'_{Bx} = 1.94$ m/s,
$v'_{By} = 0.502$ m/s   (b) 8.8 percent (using
$v_A = 2.44$ m/s, $v_B = 1.64$ m/s) $v'_{Ax} = 0.502$ m/s,
$v'_{Ay} = 1.94$ m/s, $v'_{Bx} = 1.94$ m/s, $v'_{By} = 0.304$ m/s
(c) 8.8 percent
21.61 (a) $v'_{Ax} = -4.70$ ft/s, $v'_{Ay} = -3.16$ ft/s,
$v'_{Bx} = 4.7$ ft/s, $v'_{By} = -8.14$ ft/s   (b) 0.292 lb·s
(c) 6.5 percent
21.63 $v'_A = 4.08$ in/s downward, $v'_B = 13.9$ in/s
$60°\,\searrow$, $v'_C = 13.9$ in/s $\measuredangle\,60°$
21.65 $v'_A = 1.35$ in/s upward, $v'_B = 14.1$ in/s
$41.4°\,\searrow$, $v'_C = 14.1$ in/s $\measuredangle\,41.4°$
21.67 (a) 7,330 lb   (b) 1.50×10^7 ft·lb
21.69 (a) 1,110 rad/s
21.71 (a) 617 rad/s
21.73 (a) $v' = 13.9$ ft/s, $\omega' = 63.8$ rad/s
(b) 51.6 ft·lb   (c) 4.89 ft
21.75 (a) $v' = 3.79$ m/s, $\omega' = 10.1$ rad/s
(b) 29.4 J   (c) 1.29 m
21.77 $\mu_S = 2h\,[7d\sqrt{(h/d)(1 - h/d)}]$
21.79 (a) $v'_x = v_c\,[\cos\beta + \mu_S\,(1 + e)\sin\beta]$,
$v'_y = ev_c\sin\beta$, $\omega' = \omega - [\mu_S mrv_c\,(1 + e)\sin\beta]/I_0$
(b) $\mu_S = [I_0\,\omega - (v_cI_0\cos\beta)/r/[(1 + e)v_c(rm + I_0/r)$
$\sin\beta]$ (c) $v'_x = 8.29$ m/s, $v'_y = 4.10$ m/s, $\omega' =$
51.8 rad/s   (d) $v'_x = 8.29$ m/s, $v'_y = 2.73$ m/s,
$\omega' = 51.8$ rad/s
21.81 (a) $v'_x = 2.08$ m/s, $v'_y = 7.67$ m/s,
$\omega' = 41.6$ rad/s   (b) Same as part a
(c) $v'_x = 2.08$ m/s, $v'_y = 3.84$ m/s, $\omega' = 41.6$ rad/s
(d) $v'_x = 1.73$ m/s, $v'_y = 3.84$ m/s, $\omega' = 56.0$ rad/s
21.83 $v'_x = 8.33$ m/s, $v'_y = 3.42$ m/s,
$\omega' = 52.1$ rad/s
21.85 $a = [2(l^2 - 3bl + 3b^2)]/3(l - 2b)]$

Chapter 22

22.1 (a) $R_{ay} = R_{by} = 23.6$ lb
(b) $R_{by_0} = -11.8$ lb, $R_{bz_0} = 20.4$ lb, $R_{ay_0} = 11.8$ lb,
$R_{az_0} = -20.4$ lb   (c) 47.2 in·lb
22.3 23.2 lb
22.5 5,330 r/min
22.7 (a) $R_a = -4$ lb, $R_b = 66.5$ lb
(b) $R_a = -79.5$ lb, $R_b = 94.5$ lb
(c) $R_a = -120$ lb, $R_b = 17$ lb
22.11 $R_a = 0.00119\,\omega^2$, $R_b = 0.00169\,\omega^2$
22.15 (a) $T = 1,210$ N, $R = 1,140$ N
(b) 5.17 rad/s

22.17 (a) $\omega_0 = \sqrt{2g/r}$ (b) $\omega_0 = 265$ r/min
(c) $N = 0.0654$ lb, $R = 0.0371$ lb
22.21 387 r/min
22.23 (a) $R_a = R_b = 1.12$ N   (b) R_a,
$R_b = 0.633$ N, 1.76 N
22.25 204 r/min
22.27 $R_a = 218$ N, $R_b = 58$ N
22.29 $R_a = R_b = 5.42$ lb
22.31 (a) $R_a = 2,650$ N, $R_b = 754$ N
(b) Center line displaced towards A: $R_a = 3,730$ N,
$R_b = 1,830$ N; center line displaced towards B:
$R_a = 1,560$ N, $R_b = 320$ N
22.33 6,650 r/min
22.35 (a) 321 N   (b) 396 N
22.37 $R_a = 278$ lb, $R_b = 420$ lb
22.39 $d_A = 13.9$ mm, $\beta_A = 250°$, $d_D = 25.8$ mm,
$\beta_D = 326°$
22.41 (a) 4,950 r/min   (b) 0.0279 in
(c) 0.103 in   (d) 3,200 r/min: $R_a = 204$ lb,
$R_b = 102$ lb; 5,800 r/min: $R_a = 1,060$ lb, $R_b = 525$ lb
22.43 (a) 5,450 r/min   (b) 0.0962 mm,
$R_a = 73$ N, $R_b = 513$ N   (c) 0.210 mm,
$R_a = 158$ N, $R_b = 1,120$ N   (d) 2.13 mm,
$R_a = 1,620$ N, $R_b = 11,300$ N
22.45 $R_{ay} = 3.55$ lb, $R_{by} = -3.55$ lb
22.47 $R_{an,\,max} = 61.8$ N, $R_{an,\,min} = 23.8$ N,
$R_{bn,\,max} = 182$ N, $R_{bn,\,min} = 144$ N, $R_{bx} = 7.2$ N
22.49 $R_{an,\,max} = 101$ N, $R_{an,\,min} = 88$ N,
$R_{bn,\,max} = 32$ N, $R_{bn,\,min} = 19$ N, $R_{bx} = 7.2$ N

Chapter 23

23.1 (a) 5,050 N/m   (b) 3.58 Hz, 0.280 s
23.3 (a) 1,100 N/m   (b) Initial
deflection = 2.23 m
23.5 3.36 Hz
23.7 (a) 0.554 s   (b) $\dot{x}_m = 45.2$ in/s,
$t = 0.139 + n(0.554)$ s, $t = 0.416 + n(0.554)$ s,
$n = 0, 1, 2, \ldots$ (c) $\ddot{x}_m = 510$ in/s^2, $t = n(0.554)$ s,
$t = 0.277 + n(0.554)$ s, $n = 0, 1, 2, \ldots$ (d) 8 lb
(e) 14 lb
23.9 (a) 5 lb/in   (b) 1.75 Hz
(c) $\dot{x}_m = 22$ in/s, $\ddot{x}_m = 242$ in/s^2
23.11 (a) $x_m = 0.75v/\omega_n$ (b) $\dot{x}_m = 0.75v$,
$\ddot{x}_m = 0.75v\omega_n$ (c) $F_m = 0.75\,kv/\omega_n$
(d) $x_m = 1.45$ in, $\dot{x}_m = 45$ in/s, $\ddot{x}_m = 1,400$ in/s^2,
$F_m = 65.3$ lb
23.13 (a) 0.81 m/s   (b) 13.1 m/s^2 (c) 340 N
23.17 (a) 1,170 N/m   (b) 12.3 N
23.19 33.5 N·m
23.21 (a) $\omega_n = \sqrt{[(m_Bb - m_Aa)g]/(m_Aa^2 + m_Bb^2)}$
(b) $(m_Bb - m_Aa)g$ (c) Stable if $m_Bb > m_Aa$
(d) 1.96 kg
23.23 (a) $\omega_n = a/l\sqrt{3k/m}$ (b) 7.50 Hz
23.25 (a) $\omega_n = \sqrt{(ka^2 + m_Agl_1)/(m_Al_1^2 + m_Bl_2^2)}$
(b) 4.65 Hz   (c) No

23.27 (*a*) 2.78 in (*b*) 11.1 lb (*c*) 19.1 lb
(*d*) 0.995 in, 3.98 lb, 12.0 lb
23.29 $\omega/\omega_n \geq 1.83$
23.31 $k \leq 12{,}000$ N/m $k \geq 13{,}000$ N/m
23.33 $w \geq 28.0$ N
23.35 0.0422 in
23.37 $k < 1.01 \times 10^6$ N/m
23.39 (*a*) 28 kg/s (*b*) 3.15 Hz
23.41 (*a*) 3,510 kg/s (*b*) 0.639
23.43 (*a*) 0.241 (*b*) 11.1 mm (*c*) 0.0383
(*d*) 41.8 kg/s
23.47 (*a*) 0.984 in (*b*) 170° (*c*) 7.15 in, 31°
23.49 All values of k
23.51 (*a*) 164 N (*b*) 73.9 N (*c*) 180 N
23.53 0.395 s
23.55 (*a*) 0.632 (*b*) 5.44 lb
23.57 (*a*) $\omega/\omega_n \leq 0.551$, $\omega/\omega_n \geq 1.22$
(*b*) $\phi \leq 28.3°$, $\phi \geq 120°$
23.59 (*a*) 188 N (*b*) 93.1 N (*c*) 122 N
23.61 0.180

Chapter 24

24.1 (*a*) $F_A = 1.04$ N, $F_B = 1.51$ N
(*b*) $P = 1.37$ N, $R_a = 1.18$ N

24.3 (*a*) 1,160 mm (*b*) $F_A = 163$ N, $F_B = 237$ N
24.5 (*a*) $v = 49.8$ in/s, $x = 73.9$ in
(*b*) 16.1 in (*c*) 0.0996 lb (*d*) 7.39 in·lb
24.7 (*a*) 43 ft/s (*b*) $v = 21.8$ ft/s,
$x = 40.2$ ft (*c*) 20.1 ft·lb (*d*) 1.29 lb, at terminal
velocity (*e*) 19.2 s
24.9 (*a*) 0.260 ft/s (*b*) $v = 0.260$ ft/s,
$x = 0.258$ ft (*c*) $t = 19.2$ s, $v = 0.260$ ft/s
24.11 (*a*) 0.393 ft/s (*b*) $v = 0.393$ ft/s,
$x = 0.388$ ft (*c*) $t = 12.7$ s, $v = 0.393$ ft/s
24.13 3,280 N
24.15 (*a*) 150 r/min (*b*) 268 N
24.17 (*a*) 1,430 N (*b*) 18,100 N
(*c*) 21.5 kW (*d*) 272 kW
24.19 (*a*) 0.703° (*b*) 1.70 hp
24.21 (*a*) $v_1 = v_2 = 3.75$ m/s, $v_3 = 0$,
$x_1 = 2.67$ m, $x_2 = 6.49$ m, $x_3 = 10$ m (*b*) 2.92 s
(*c*) 214 N
24.23 (*a*) 63,300 lb (*b*) 0.57 lb (*c*) 19.2 hp
24.25 63,300 lb
24.27 0.029 s
24.29 (*a*) $v_1 = v_2 = v_3 = 2.23$ ft/s
(*b*) $x_1 = 2.23$ ft, $x_2 = 4.46$ ft, $x_3 = 6.69$ ft
(*c*) 0.1416

TABLE 18.6: CENTROIDS, AND MOMENTS OF INERTIA, FOR SEVEN ELEMENTARY PLANE AREAS

Case	Shape	A	X_c	Y_c	I_{0x}	I_{0y}	I_{0z}
1	Square	a^2	$\dfrac{a}{2}$	$\dfrac{a}{2}$	$\dfrac{a^4}{12}$	$\dfrac{a^4}{12}$	$\dfrac{a^4}{6}$
2	Rectangle	ab	$\dfrac{a}{2}$	$\dfrac{b}{2}$	$\dfrac{ab^3}{12}$	$\dfrac{ba^3}{12}$	$\dfrac{ab}{12}(a^2+b^2)$
3	Right triangle	$\dfrac{ab}{2}$			$\dfrac{ab^3}{36}$	$\dfrac{ba^3}{36}$	$\dfrac{ab}{36}(a^2+b^2)$
4	General triangle*	$\dfrac{ab}{2}$	$\ldots$	$\dfrac{b}{3}$	$\dfrac{ab^3}{36}$		
5	Circle	$\pi a^2 = \dfrac{\pi d^2}{4}$	$a=\dfrac{d}{2}$	$a=\dfrac{d}{2}$	$\dfrac{\pi a^4}{4}=\dfrac{\pi d^4}{64}$	$\dfrac{\pi a^4}{4}=\dfrac{\pi d^4}{64}$	$\dfrac{\pi a^4}{4}=\dfrac{\pi d^4}{32}$
6	Semicircle	$\dfrac{\pi a^2}{2}$	a	$\dfrac{4a}{3\pi}$	$a^4\left(\dfrac{\pi}{8}-\dfrac{8}{9\pi}\right)$	$\dfrac{\pi a^4}{8}$	$a^4\left(\dfrac{\pi}{4}-\dfrac{8}{9\pi}\right)$
7	Ellipse	$\dfrac{\pi ab}{4}$	$\dfrac{a}{2}$	$\dfrac{b}{2}$	$\dfrac{\pi ab^3}{64}$	$\dfrac{\pi a^3b}{64}$	$\dfrac{\pi ab}{64}(a^2+b^2)$

*The area centroid of any triangle is at the common intersection of the three angle bisectors, at a height above each base of $\frac{1}{3}$ of the altitude.

$$\frac{-b \pm \sqrt{b^2-4ac}}{2a}$$

law of sines $\Rightarrow \dfrac{A}{\sin a} = \dfrac{B}{\sin b} = \dfrac{C}{\sin c}$